# THE SCOTS MUSICAL MUSEUM

ORIGINALLY PUBLISHED BY

JAMES JOHNSON

WITH

ILLUSTRATIONS OF THE LYRIC POETRY AND MUSIC OF SCOTLAND

BY

WILLIAM STENHOUSE

VOLUME ONE

FOREWORD BY

HENRY GEORGE FARMER



FOLKLORE ASSOCIATES
HATBORO, PENNSYLVANIA
1962

This edition of James Johnson's **Scots Musical Museum** has been reprinted in facsimile reproduction from the four volume edition of 1853. The new Foreword by Henry George Farmer is copyright, 1962.

Printed in the United States of America by
PHILIP KARBEN ENTERPRISES, Inc.

# FOREWORD

*'This land, classic in song and history.'*

—Henry Ward Beecher:
Oration at Glasgow City Hall, October, 1863.

1.

It is not at all strange that the great American preacher and reformer should have hit on these two significant words in reference to Scotland. Such things are to the Scots almost as phylacteries; since the history of their land teems with the profound influence of the national song on its people from the days of that simple *cantus* that girded them so strongly after Bannockburn down to the more modern 'Scots wha hae'. Indeed the 'song' itself, in its themes, is often an actual index to Scottish history as in 'Sir Patrick Spens' or 'The Bonny Earl of Murray.' The geographical or topographical appeal, as in the 'Braes of Ballochmyle' or 'The Bush aboun Traquair,' has made a deep impression on the people. Burns himself confessed that he made 'a pilgrimage to the spot from which every individual song took its rise, "Lochaber" and "The Braes o' Ballenden" excepted.' Scottish song has so spacious a spiritual *gamut* that it stands almost alone in that respect. The chief plaint may be love, nature, patriotism, humour, but the individual themes are as varied as the radiant colours of the spectrum. To realize its abounding scope one must take the pages of John Stuart Blackie's *Scottish Song: Its Wealth, Wisdom, and Social Significance* (1889) as a sure and certain guide, for as he insisted, the jingle of their verse and the lilt of their melody had been passed on to most Scots as croonings with their mother's milk. The social significance of the national songs is of paramount importance, since all music is primarily a phase of social life, however much aesthetes may think otherwise. That was why I showed in my *History of Music in Scotland* (1947) that the national song and dance was an integral part of the general social structure. For over two centuries—from the days of William Thomson, Oswald, McGibbon and Bremner in the 18th century down to the more recent Mackenzie, MacCunn, Drysdale and Moffat—hundreds of collections of Scottish music have appeared at the hands of native editors; but the most famous of all was *The Scots Musical Museum* because of the magic hand of Burns. What was the origin of all this?

As Robert Chambers (*Songs of Scotland Prior to Burns, 1862*), so rightly guessed, the renascence of the national song was concommitant with the country's emancipation from the religious struggle. A glance at the *Cantus* (1662, 1666, 1682) of Forbes produces absolute certainty that the national song was not on the lips of the upper classes, and so we may take it for granted that it was with the common people that the 'auld Scots sangs' found their repository, just as it was in the days of *Cockelbie's Sow* and *Peblis to the Play,* both of the 15th century. Chambers was indubitably correct when he claimed that Scottish poets of the 15th century—William Dunbar and Gavin Douglas—did not write anything 'strictly of the nature of songs. Such men never thought of composing songs, that is, lyrical compositions to be sung to music by the people.' When the Reformation came in the 16th century the secular song and the dance became *anathema.* * Yet *The Gude and Godlie Ballatis* (1567), the Bannatyne MS. (1568), and *Newes from Scotland* (1591) reveal the existence of the songs of the people.† It was not until the late 17th century that the Scots song was taking a hold of all and sundry, in such a spate even to over-

*Farmer, *A History of Music in Scotland* (1947), pp. 81-87.
†Ibid, pp. 129-141.

flowing its banks so far south as London. Here 'Katherine Ogie,' 'Thro' the wood laddie,' 'The Bush aboun Traquair,' and 'Tweedside' became prime favourites. John Playford had 'borrowed' many a Scotch tune, and Henry Playford found that it was a profitable venture to issue his *Collection of Original Scotch-Tunes* (1700).

In Scotland, the *Musick for Allan Ramsay's Collection of Scots Songs* (*ca.* 1725), set by Alexander Stuart, was the first of its kind to be printed in that land, and it contained melodies to match the songs in Ramsay's *Tea-Table Miscellany* (1724). That became the very Bible of authority for the melodic outline of the songs of Scotland, although Burns almost completely ignored it as a source book. The reason for that is not so manifest as one might suppose. It is obvious that so far as those dance melodies—which he used for his songs—are concerned, he was impressed both orally and visually by the decorative adornments which had smothered the melody at the hands of 'brither fiddlers.' An example of that may be seen in 'Wae is my heart,' which is definitely a fiddler's editing. The snap, trills, and grace notes prove that. James C. Dick said,—'I have not found it [the air] earlier than the *Museum,*' That is true enough—note for note—but there are phrases here and there in Ramsay's unsophisticated, and Oswald's more decorative examples of it, which show the stirp of that air. On the other hand, John Glen is dubious that it belongs to Burns at all. More palpable is 'The mill, mill O,' in which Burns follows the fiddler's idiosyncrasies in what is popularly termed the 'twiddle-i-bits,' such as we see in Oswald and Bremner. Before leaving the dance tunes which were vocalised by Burns and often used in their pristine *tempi,* one must confess that he was always at his best when he adopted a syllabic setting of the melody, as exemplified in 'O Tibbie, I hae seen the day.' Better still was—I use the past tense deliberately—'Lassie wi the lint-white locks,' a delightful setting of 'Rothiemurche's Rant.' Burns once confessed to George Thomson that 'the air puts me in raptures.' He found that melody in Bremner's *Collection of Scots Reels.* Alas! modern editors of Burns have played havoc with that setting, and have laid vandal hands on the actual notation and rhythm. It was bad enough that Burns should have had to chide Pleyel for altering notes in the Scots songs, but when a Scot like George Farquhar Graham does the same there can be no defence. Burns knew the 'sweeping, kindling, bauld strathspey' not only by its music but by its steps, and was so intrigued by the former that he was compelled to put a brake on the *tempo* and conceive it '*lento, largo,* in the play,' to use his own words, when he wished to use it for some of his sentimental and plaintive verses. That is what he did with the melody of 'Loch Erroch Side' when he fashioned the words of 'Young Peggy Blooms' to that enchanting air.

We must not imagine that all the songs of Burns were garnered from song and dance collections. Many were copied from singers he heard in the Highlands and Lowlands, both rich and poor. 'Craigieburn Wood' came from a humble lassie at a farmhouse door, whilst that incomparable 'Ca the yowes' was gifted by a friendly minister. It was a melody that he heard in the Gaelic Highlands—*Bhanarach dhon na chruidh*—that inspired him to pen those charming verses in 'How pleasant the banks of the clear winding Devon,' and that is another of his purely syllabic settings. Unfortunately, those words are now sung to the tune of 'The maids of Arrochar.' Nor is that the only change that has been made in the songs of Burns. 'Flow gently, sweet Afton,' was the opening sentence of those heart-easing verses which the poet set to an air—otherwise unknown—called 'Afton Water.' Within fifty years of the death of the poet, Alexander Hume set the words to a melody of his own, and that which had inspired Burns has been forgotten. It may be true that

Hume's melody is vastly superior to that which attracted Burns, but today many people imagine that it is the original song to which they are listening. Most Burnsians are aware how deeply the poet was indebted not only to the Scottish airs collected by James Oswald but to the latter's own music. Yet hardly one of Oswald's compositions to which Burns set verses have remained in the Burnsian repertory. The reason for that is their wide compass, which is beyond the larynx of the generality of singers. How was it that Burns was not cognizant of that obstacle to popularity? He spoke of 'humming every now and then the air,' in a letter to George Thomson (1793), and earlier in the *Commonplace Book* he admitted that 'to sough [hum] the tune... is the readiest way to catch the inspiration.' In humming, Burns may have been mislead as to the compass of ordinary laryngeal production. Four examples of such deterrents to popular acceptance may be seen in Burns' settings of Oswald's airs, viz.,—'O, were I on Parnassus' hill,' 'O, leeze me on my spinnin-wheel,' 'The lovely lass of Inverness' (all three *b.* or *b*♭. to $g.^2$), and 'It is na, Jean, thy bonie face' (*c.* to $g^2$.).

Out of well over 200 songs in the *Museum* in which Burns had a hand one way or another, only one-half can be said to have survived, and certainly only a quarter are on the lips of Burnsians. In some cases only the words of 'the Bard' have been spared to us, since other melodies have been chosen for them by captious editors, often to their detriment. Some of the latter have imagined that the addition of a quaver or two is a real 'improvement.' George Farquhar Graham has so changed the rhythm of 'Lassie wi' the lint-white locks'—one of Burns' gems—that its whole character is lost. The Gaelic air 'Oran Gaoil,' to which Burns set 'Behold the hour,' has changed its initial pulse—a slow triple time—to a lilting *barcarolle* swing in 6/8 time which alters its rhythmic character. Worse still is changed notation which has spoiled its modal character. One of the most notorious pieces of vandalism is to be seen in John Wilson's new air for 'Go *fetch* to me a pint of wine.' Wilson, who featured this fresh melody in his concert tours, changed the words to 'Gae *bring* to be a pint of wine,' the obvious reason being that he could not sing the word 'fetch' because of its four consonants and a weak vowel, and so substituted the more vocable 'bring.' Yet there was no reason for him to intone the word 'fetch.' To Burns, the word was a command! It meant 'go and bring.' Sadder still is the pernicious alteration of the stress in 'O *my* luve's like a red, red rose,' which the poet set to an old strathspey called 'Major Graham.' That stood firm in popularity for fifty years, until George Farquhar Graham adopted another melody for those words called 'Low down in the broom.' That preference may be simply a matter of taste and can be absolved. But when the whole meaning of the words is changed there can be no excuse. Because Graham's new tune began with *two* quavers instead of *one*—as in Burns—Graham had to change the opening words to accommodate those preliminary quavers, and thus produced 'O my *luve* is like a red, red rose,' a sentiment utterly alien to the thoughts of Burns. Graham stressed '*love*' in the abstract, whereas Burns—in his own personal ecstacy—was voicing '*my* love,' and even repeated that accentuation in another setting of 'Red, red, rose' in the *Museum.* Even so careful an editor as James C. Dick, repeated that vandalism, giving the *Museum,* No. 402, as his authority, for which there is not the slightest justification; and further it was in the key of F and not E flat. It is such occurrences as the above which reveal the true value of the *Scots Musical Museum* as a textbook of the 'auld Scots sangs,' the collecting of which was the heart's desire of Burns when he wrote:

'That I, for poor auld Scotland's sake,
Some useful plan, or book could make,
Or sing a sang at least.'

## 2.

*'Facts are chiels that winna ding,*
*And downa be disputed.'*

— Robert Burns.

Whatever else Scotland may be lacking, there is certainly no dearth in collections of its national melodies. In that respect Scotland stands pre-eminent above her neighbours in the British Isles. Whether this abundance is due to the nation's artistic longing—as Ruskin would have us believe, or merely the outcome of a perfervid nationalism—as Blackie would persuade us, is of little import for the nonce. What does matter is that this urge is part and parcel of national life, and has been for the past two hundred years and more. Such a boon naturally gave birth to editors and annotators who essayed to probe the historic past of such songs and melodies, and the first real delving was actually done by 'The Immortal Bard' himself in his notes to Johnson's *Scots Musical Museum* (1787-1803), in the production of which Burns played so important a part. Yet in those days there was no institution in Scotland at which one might pursue a leisured survey of accumulated material on the subject, nor could the researcher look for much assistance elsewhere. The result was that anyone so minded had to begin *de novo* in his quest, and often had to accept verity from the shadow rather than from the substance which cast it.

One such early worker in this field was William Stenhouse (1793-1827), who became so enamoured by Johnson's *Scots Musical Museum* that—like Burns—he began collecting historic material as annotations for the songs. To a considerable extent Stenhouse was a pioneer, and in consequence made all sorts of assumptions which, had he been able to make a closer scrutiny, he could have avoided. Yet let us remember that he did not have the treasures of the British Museum, nor those of the National Library of Scotland, in which to check his statements, as later researchers have had the benefit. Because of that one has to be tolerant of his slips, and to remember that although his work was printed in 1820 it was not published until 1839, whilst he himself died in 1827. A later musicologist—George Farquhar Graham (1789-1867)—was able to correct some of the errors of Stenhouse in his *Songs of Scotland* (1848-49), whilst further adjustments were made by David Laing (1790-1878) in his additional notes to Stenhouse's *Illustrations* (1853). Many of Stenhouse's blunders were actually careless slips, and it did not need wide erudition to detect them, but they gave a handle to an English musicographer named William Chappell (1809-88) to make an arrogant and mischievous onslaught on Stenhouse and on Scottish music in general. That appeared in the Chappell's *Popular Music in the Olden Time* (1855-59), a work which became the textbook of its day, and still holds considerable sway in that particular sphere, more especially in its later dress as *Old English Popular Music* (1893) as revised and edited by H. Ellis Wooldridge.

Chappell was a rabid anti-Scot of the brew that boiled up as far back as the days of *Roderick Random,* and he chose Stenhouse as his stalking horse, firstly because he was dead, and secondly because he was an easy target. One is compelled to observe Chappell's milder tone towards George Farquhar Graham and David Laing who were living. He made a noisy fanfare in correcting the dates of Stenhouse, although both Graham and Laing had already made that monitoring unnecessary two or three years earlier. Yet when Chappell accuses Stenhouse of deliberate falsification of evidence, and without the slightest proof, it makes one rather anxious to examine whether all that Chappell tells us is *bona fide.* He speaks of the notes of Stenhouse as being 'like historic novels,—i.e. when facts do not chime in with the plan of the tale, imagination supplies the deficiency.' In other words, Stenhouse manufactured his evidence. According to Chappell,—

> Stenhouse's plan was 'to claim every good tune as Scotch. . . . All this he accomplished in a way peculiar to himself. Invention supplied authors and dates, and fancy inscribed the tunes in sundry old manuscripts, where the chances were greatly against anyone's searching to find them. If the search should be made, would it not be made by Scotchmen? Englishmen only care for foreign music, and do not trouble themselves about the matter; and will Scotchmen expose what has been done from such patriotic motives?'

That passage is quoted out of many other churlish and malevolent utterances of Chappell, so that his malignancy can be fully appreciated, and also as an explanation why poor Stenhouse was chosen as an 'Aunt Sally' for Chappell's brickbats. It was not only that his missiles should hit his dummy, but that one or two should reach some patriotic Scots who were lookers-on, especially those who had the impertinence—so he thought—to harbour the notion that Scotland actually possessed national songs.

Strange to say, that brazen effrontery was allowed to pass unchallenged for forty-five years, although the late Professor H. Ellis Wooldridge (1845-1917) did try to soften some of Chappell's scurrilities, and check his inaccuracies—if not falsifications—in his re-issue of Chappell in 1893. Yet from the most unlikely of places there came a man who thought it worth while to re-examine the claims of the notorious Chappell that the music which the Scots had for so long cherished as their own was actually—for a considerable part—of *English origin!* The name of the new researcher was John Glen (*c.* 1833-1904), the son of Thomas Macbean Glen of Edinburgh, famed as a musical instrument maker. John became a keen student of old Scottish music, amassing a library of its treasures which was considered the finest in the land. This latter, thanks to the generosity of the late Lady

Dorothea Ruggles-Brise, was acquired for the National Library of Scotland.

It took John Glen many years to build up his material for a critical survey of what was considered by the Scots to be their own national music. Eventually he made bold to challenge the invidious claims of William Chappell that some of the best of Scotland's traditional music were not only 'borrowings' from English sources, but knavish 'thievings.' John Glen was not a trained research worker nor was he an academic historian. He was not even what some refined folk would call a skilled musician. His chief possession was an extremely logical mind. That, coupled with a thorough knowledge of the music of the folk of the Scottish past, *plus* a spirit that could not be intimidated nor side-tracked by the bluster and thimble-rigging of a William Chappell. In his first books,—*The Glen Collection of Scottish Dance Music* (1891, 1895)—John Glen revealed his ability to give a 'Roland for an Oliver' with the utmost complacency, of which we give two examples:

> 'Mr Chappell... accuses Stenhouse of misleading Dauney as to the original of *Katherine Ogie* and, to prove his position, he quotes an Appendix (1688) to John Playford's *Dancing-Master,* published in 1686, as having the earliest known copy of the tune under the title of *Lady Catherine Ogle,* a new Dance,... Mr. Chappell, however, has overlooked the fact that Playford, in his *Apollo's Banquet,* published in 1687, calls it "A Scotch tune."'

The 'know-all' Englishman Chappell had also accused Stephen Clarke—who had harmonized the airs in the *Museum*—of transforming the English *Polly put the kettle on* into *Jenny's Bawbee* for Johnson's *Museum* of 1797 [December 1796]. To that squib John Glen replied:

> 'Now, while it is quite true that *Jenny's Baubee* appears in *The Scots Musical Museum* for 1797, and that three years previously the same tune, under the title of *Polly put the kettle on* had become very popular, it is equally true that if Mr. Chappell had extended his researches a

little further, he would have found *Jenny's Baubee* in Scots collections of 1794, 1788, and 1778.'‡

These, and many other corrections of Chappell, make interesting reading in view of the latter's stock parading of English 'priority' of date in publication. Apart from John Glen's straightening of the meanderings of Chappell, his contributions to the history of the national music of Scotland, together with much fresh light thrown on its early musicians and music sellers, are of great value.

More important, to the general student of Scottish music, is John Glen's *Early Scottish Melodies* (1900), which is not only a complete *exposé* of the fallacies of William Chappell, but a veritable mine of information on the subject of the old songs and melodies of Scotland. Still, it is Chappell and his futile attacks on Scottish claims which concern us at the moment, and Glen devotes a chapter of eleven pages to repelling them. Not content with flaying Stenhouse, who had been dead for thirty years, Chappell attacked two other defunct Scots,—Allan Ramsay and William Dauney. He complained that 'Allen Ramsay entitled his *Tea-Table Miscellany* a "Collection of Scots Songs."' That title, he said, could undoubtedly cover the first two volumes, but not the third which, he claimed, was made up of songs that were 'entirely English.' Yet, what are the facts? Only one copy of the original volume I (1724) of the *Tea-Table Miscellany* exists, and that is in the United States of America, but it does *not* contain the complementary 'Scots Sangs' tag. The original volume II (1726?) and volume III (1727?) are not extant. How then can Ramsay be fathered with initiating the offending sub-title? It is true that the pirated Dublin edition of volume I (1729), and the complete London issue

‡See Archibald Duff, *A Collection of Strathspeys, Reels, . . .*, Edinburgh, 1794: James Aird, *A Selection of Scotch, English, Irish, and Foreign Airs . . .*, Glasgow, 1788: and Joshua Campbell, *A Collection of the Newest and Best Reels . . .*, Glasgow, 1778.

(1730) do certainly contain that sub-title, but surely that is not the responsibility of Ramsay? In any case, there is an edition of 1734 in which volume III is specifically labelled 'A Collection of Celebrated Songs,' and one may safely assume that this was not done merely to placate some irate forerunner of Chappell. One recalls that John Playford called his first terpsichorean musical volume *The British Dancing Master* (1651); but when he issued a second edition, 'Enlarged and Corrected from many grosse Errors,' which included a Scottish air or two, he called it *The Dancing Master* (1652), but if he had not, one can be fairly certain that there would have been no rabid Scot anxious to 'thraw his neck' for not recognizing Scotland.

John Glen's next chapter is entitled 'English Claims,' and therein he discusses minutely the arguments of Chappell anent many of Scotland's best known airs—twenty-six in all—giving the variants in the melodic outline over the centuries from both Scottish and English sources in a synoptic fashion, so that one can judge at a glance their original fount for himself. After that, Glen takes a wider *gamut* in Chapter VI, wherein he traverses anew the ground covered by his predecessors who had annotated the *Scots Musical Museum,* but even with greater skill and thoroughness than Dauney, Graham, Laing, or Wood.

The contribution of John Glen to the literature of Scottish song will long remain a monument to his memory for he performed 'a fine piece of work, thoroughly critical and substantial' of which we should be proud. Glen, in his claims, did not want a solitary item retained for Scotland which was not hers by a moral right. Indeed he insisted that his mission was to retrieve 'melodies which primarily belong to Scotland,' and to renounce all others 'erroneously supposed to be Scottish productions.' John Glen saw the Scottish melodies admired elsewhere, as in

Germany, where Adolf Marx, in his *Kunst des Gesanges,* had given examples of them saying,—'They are invaluable, and no musician, and especially no singer, should be unaquainted with them.' Is it any wonder that Glen should evince pride in Scotland's music and defend it from jealous mediocrities who would try to rob her of treasures which are the heritage of the nation.

3

> 'I see every day, a new musical publication advertised; but what are they? Gaudy, hunted butterflies of a day, and then vanish for ever: but your work will well outlive the momentary neglect of idle fashion, and defy the teeth of time.'
>
> —*Letter of Burns to James Johnson,* 15-11-1788.

Although the hallowed pages of the *Scots Musical Museum* entrance the devoted music lover, they are a bane to the meticulous book collector. Because of that casualty it is a prerequisite that we should know precisely what this 'thorn in the flesh' amounts to. The trouble is that—like Topsy in *Uncle Tom's Cabin*—the *Scots Musical Museum* 'growed.' It was conceived by a humble music engraver in Edinburgh named James Johnson, who had been plying his trade since 1772. His name does not occur in any *Edinburgh Directory* before 1775-76, and even then he is dubbed 'Johnstone,' and that misnomer continued in the directories until 1805, a circumstance that would seem to indicate the relative unimportance of Johnson, the originator of the *Scots Musical Museum.* The truth is that the latter was a mere accident. Originally Johnson had resolved on a general collection of sentimental ballads, but as that scheme did not secure any backing from likely subscribers, he turned to the songs of his own country. Yet there was already a surfeit of that commodity. William Thomson, a London Scot, had published his *Orpheus Caledonius* (1725, 1733), and Robert Bremner of Edinburgh had issued his *Thirty Scots Songs* (1757), only to be followed by similar ventures as seen in the collections of Neil Stewart (1772) and Domenico Corri (1783). On the face of that it looks as though Johnson was taking some risk in that plunge. Yet with the national 'ca canny' outlook, he saw that it was only the cost of the pewter plates and the paper that meant the outlay of 'siller,' whereas others had greater overhead charges. Thus Johnson visualized merely a couple of volumes of the old Scottish songs of no more than two hundred in all, as the prefatory note—May 1787—of the first volume indicates. Incidentally, the joke is that having already 'punched' two or three airs on pewter plates that were 'not of Scots composition,' he actually included them in his first volume rather than waste good pewter, although he did apologize—with tongue in cheek—in his second volume for having 'inadvertently inserted' them!

One need not be clairvoyant to guess the reason for the expansion of Johnson's two volumes to six. It was the entry of Burns into the pages of the *Museum* which augured its immediate extension and ultimate success, despite the fact that Johnson advertised the information that his venture was under 'the Patronage, direction, and Review of a number of Gentleman of an undisputed taste, who had been pleased to encourage, enrich, and adorn the whole literary part of the Performance.' He failed to name any of those benefactors, although Dr. Thomas Blacklock was undoubtedly one of them, as was Dr. James Beattie, the author of *Essays on Poetry and Music* (1776). The fascination of Burns for the 'auld Scots sangs' had been kindled long before the genesis of the *Museum*. When he was but fifteen years old (1774) the lovely voice of Nellie Kilpatrick lured him to set words to a tune—as yet untraced—called 'I am a man unmarried.' He said in a letter to Dr. Moore,—'Among her love-inspiring qualities she sang sweetly; and it was her favorite reel to which I attempted giving an embodied vehicle in rhyme.' The *Commonplace Book* shows that by 1784 he possessed books of songs—without the music—and we know how deeply they affected him, especially 'a select collection of English songs.' That same collection—said Burns—'was my *vade mecum.*' 'I pored over them, driving my cart or walking to labour, song by song, verse by verse.' All sorts of guesses have been made in attempts to identify that collection. George Farquhar Graham suggested it was *The Scots Nightingale* (*ca.* 1776), whilst William E. Henley imagined that it was *The Lark* (1765). Against those assumptions is the fact that Burns distinctly mentions a collection of 'English songs.' Therefore it may be far more likely that it was Ritson's *A Selection of English Songs* (1783), although he had been writing poems long before that year.

In September 1785 we find the bard with fixed ideas about Scottish songs and their airs.

> 'There is a great irregularity in the old Scottish songs, a redundancy of syllables with respect to the exactness of accent and measure that the English poetry requires, but which glides in, most melodiously, with the respective tunes to which they are set.... There is a degree of wild irregularity in many of the compositions and fragments which are daily sung to them by my compeers... This had made me sometimes imagine that, perhaps, it might be possible for a Scottish poet, with a nice judicious ear, to set compositions to many of our most favourite airs, particularly that class of them mentioned above, independent of rhyme altogether.'

By the next year the poet was well into his stride. Four songs set to old Scots airs—'Corn Riggs,' 'I had a horse,' 'Gilderoy,' and 'Goodnight and joy be wi' you a''—are to be found in the Kilmarnock edition of his poems (1787), with five more songs set to the Scots airs—'Gilliekrankie,' 'My Nanny O', 'Jockey's gray breeks,' 'Roslin Castle,' and 'Prepare my dear brethren,' in the Edinburgh edition of his poems (1787), although neither of those books contained the music. After that came Burns' first letter to the engraver James Johnson—May 1787—in which he refers to one of the tunes of William McGibbon, which may mean that he was already acquainted with the latter's book *A Collection of Scots Tunes* (1742-1755), and we can be fairly certain that he was *au fait* with Oswald's well known volumes, *The Caledonian Pocket Companion* (*ca.* 1743-59), as well as Bremner's *Collection of Scots Reels*... (*ca.* 1758).

Burns seems to have first met Johnson at that more than convivial 'Crochallan Club'; and we know that the poet soon began to feel a sincere regard for the publisher of the *Scots Musical Museum.* In Burns' letter to Johnson in May 1787—the very month of the birth of the *Museum*—we are able to judge his appreciation of his new friend. We read,—'I have met with few people whose company and conversation are so congenial to my own.' That was the opinion of the man who was then being sought by the very *élite* of Scottish 'society.' He did not come in contact with Johnson again until the autumn; and taking everything into consideration, the statement of James C. Dick that it was Burns who suggested the title of the *Scots Musical Museum,* cannot be accepted. No sooner had the first volume appeared than Burns began to take a fatherly interest in the next volume, and started writing to his correspondents about Johnson who—as he explained to Mr. Hoy in October 1787—was a man who—'not from mercenary views but from an honest Scotch enthusiasm set about collecting all our native songs and setting them to music.' To the Rev. John Skinner—of 'Tullochgorum' fame—he wrote in similar enthusiastic terms about the *Museum* saying,—'there is a certain something in the old Scots songs, a wild happiness of thought and expression, which peculiarly marks them, not only from English songs, but also from the modern efforts of song-wrights.' To Clarinda also he pours out his boyant and optimistic views of the future of the *Museum,* and especially of the important part that he himself was playing for its success. 'This, you will guess,' he writes, 'is an undertaking exactly to my taste. I have collected, begged, borrowed and stolen all the songs I could meet with.' He pleads for her patronage of that first volume. Strangely enough the pages of the first printing only allows but one song to Burns, whereas he actually contributed four.

The second volume is dated March 1788, and the Preface itself was from the hand of Burns. The same can be said of the third and fourth volumes. The index of the second volume, according to James C. Dick, shows but one song of Burns, although we know from his correspondence that he contributed more; and in the reissue of that volume his name is attached to sixteen songs. Actually, some forty-one songs are from his hand, either original or adaptations. The third volume carries the date February 1790, and in the original issue only six songs are allocated to 'the Bard'; yet later reprints show eight under his name, whilst some critics believe that at least forty-nine are of his facture. The fourth volume—the last which Burns was to see published—carried the date of August 1792. The original issue mentions Burns being responsible for six songs, but in the reissues no less than twenty-seven are named as his, and careful students say that some sixty-five at least came from his pen. As for the fifth volume, Burns had written to Johnson saying,— 'I send you...forty-one songs for your fifth volume.' That appeared in December 1796, the original issue making Burns responsible for only fifteen songs, whereas the reprint allots nineteen to him. In solemn fact, his hand is recognized in some fifty-four songs. The sixth and last volume of the Museum is dated June 1803, with a title page considerably altered because it was the complementary volume to the set: it was worded thus:—*The Scots / Musical Museum / in Six volumes. / Consisting of Six Hundred Scots Songs / with proper Bases for the / Piano Forte &c. / Humbly Dedicated / To the Society / of / Antiquaries of Scotland / By James Johnson. / In this publication the original simplicity of our / Ancient National Airs is retained unincumbered / with useless Accompaniments & graces depriving the / hearers of the sweet simplicity of their native melodies.* The latter sentences were lusty lunges at George Thomson's *Select Collection of original Scottish Airs for the voice, to which are added... accompaniments for the piano forte, violin and violoncello* (1793 *et seq.*), this being the work of Pleyel, Kozeluch, Haydn, and Beethoven. Burns was in high dudgeon that those composers had dared to alter the melody of Scottish national songs, simply to satisfy their own harmonic preferences. The poet could not stomach such liberties and promptly wrote George Thomson:—'Whatever Mr. Pleyel does, let him not alter one iota of the original Scots airs. Let our national airs preserve their native features.' But to return to the sixth volume and its contents. The original volume, according to James C. Dick, shows twenty-six songs accredited to Burns, but the latter actually ignores 'Scenes of woe' and 'Sweetest May' in his *Songs of Robert Burns* (1903) which, on his own showing, should bring the total down to twenty-five, although the copy on my desk at this moment contains twenty-seven songs with the name of Burns attached to them. However, what is of greater consequence is Johnson's preface to this last volume. He says:

> 'Without wishing to over rate this publication, the Editor may be permitted to observe, that it unquestionably contains the greatest Collection of Scotish Vocal Music ever published, including many excellent Songs written for it by BURNS. He therefore flatters himself with the hope

> that the prediction of our celebrated BARD respecting it will be verified: and that "To future ages the *Scots Musical Museum* will be the Text Book and Standard of Scotish Song and Music."'

To procure nowadays a complete set of the original *Museum* is almost as difficult as 'for a camel to go through the eye of a needle,' as St. Matthew assures us. For the complete wording of the title page of each volume as issued at its original nativity, one must consult James C. Dick's *The Songs of Robert Burns* (1903, p. xxxvi). But even that *desideratum* will not solve the many *differencia* which the various reissues present. As each volume was sold out, the plates were reprinted bearing a different title page—that of the booksellers of the last published volume. That is not all. Indices and page headings vary, especially in the acknowledgement of the Burns contributions. The upshot is that one is in a perfect maze in trying to complete a set of any precise period of the re-issues of the *Museum*. In the *Memorial Catalogue of the Burns Exhibition, 1896* (Glasgow, 1898), there were displayed a varied assortment of original issues and re-issues. No. 1405 had this title—presumably *verbatim—The Scots Musical Museum. Humbly dedicated to The Catch Club instituted at Edinr., June 1771. By James Johnson. In six volumes. Edinburgh: printed and sold by James Johnson.* 1787 [1803]. Yet in view of the mention of 'six volumes' that title could not have been the first or second volume of 1787 and 1788. No. 1406, is called 're-issue, with different imprint,' whilst No. 1407 is dubbed 'Another issue.' The whole question is a veritable *arcanum,* and it is only of volume 6 (1803) that one can speak with anything like certitude, and on that occasion all the previous volumes were reprinted with the 1803 title page, but they contained the latest acknowledgements of Burns, which Johnson had added to the original plates on both the page headings and indices.

After the death of James Johnson in 1811, his widow was left in straightened circumstances, just as Jean Armour the wife of Burns had been left. About 1815, Johnson's original pewter plates were acquired by the well known Edinburgh publisher William Blackwood, together with many of Burns' manuscripts. The possession of those valuable relics of 'the Bard' led Blackwood to conceive the re-issue of the *Museum* accompanied by critical and historical notes, and it will be remembered that Burns himself had drawn up something of the sort—which had not been published—for an interleaved copy of the *Museum* belonging to Riddell of Glenriddell. This latter, together with other material, was used by R. H. Cromek in his *Reliques of Robert Burns* (1808) and the *Select Scottish Songs* which were so fatuously attacked by James C. Dick in his *Songs of Robert Burns* (1903). Fortunately, the publisher Blackwood managed to contact a man who, 'along with more than ordinary antiquarian research, and much general information, possessed a thorough practical knowledge of music, and who, moreover, had been personally acquainted with [James] Johnson, ... and with [Stephen] Clarke by whom the airs [in the *Museum*] had been chiefly harmonized.'

The name of this new annotator was William Stenhouse (1773-1827), whose reputation has been viciously assailed by William Chappell, as the previous pages have demonstrated. It is to Stenhouse that we owe that massive production known as *Illustration of the lyric poetry and music of Scotland,* which eventually came to serve as an introduction to Blackwood's re-issue and the *Scots Musical Museum.* Stenhouse had begun his researches for Blackwood quite early, since we find his notes on that question in *Blackwood's Magazine* of 1817, and Blackwood soon began the printing of Stenhouse's researches which appear to have been completed towards the close of 1820. Yet Blackwood's plan to re-issue the *Scots Musi-*

*cal Museum* with Stenhouse's *Illustrations* was—for some latent reason—held up, and the death of Stenhouse in 1827, followed by that of Blackwood in 1834, put a further brake on the scheme, until David Laing took the matter in hand and brought it to finality.

David Laing was known as the editor of the *Select remains of the ancient poetry of Scotland* (1822) and *Early metrical tales* (1826). He was librarian of the Signet Library, Edinburgh, and honorary secretary of the Bannatyne Club, whilst his knowledge of music lent an added import to his new undertaking, in which he was assisted by George Farquhar Graham, William Dauney, and Charles Kirkpatrick Sharpe; by the last named to a considerable extent as the pages of the 'Additional Illustrations' to Stenhouse give ample evidence. In this first issue of the *Illustrations of the lyric poetry and music of Scotland* in 1839, one has to discriminate between the 'Illustrations' of Stenhouse, and the 'Additional Illustrations' of Laing. For example,—the 'Introduction' of Stenhouse covers pages xxi to lxxx, whereas the 'Appendix to the Introduction' by Laing is contained with pages lxxxi to cxxxii, *plus* the Index. Then follow the 'Illustrations' to each of the volumes or parts of the *Scots Musical Museum* by Stenhouse. For example, the 'Illustrations' to Volume I or Part I take up pages 1 to 104, which are succeeded by Laing's 'Additional Illustrations,' which are pages * 105 to 144. * Each succeeding volume follows the same pattern, Laing's contributions being distinguished by an asterisk-marked pagination, except for Volume VI or Part VI, in which the pagination of the 'Additional Illustrations' follows in regular numerical sequence. Here it should be stated that the 1839 issue of this historical work was entitled *The Scottish Musical Museum*, and the 'Illustrations' and 'Additional Illustrations' appeared *in their relative place in each volume.*

For some unknown reason this 1839 issue stopped publication, only a few copies having survived, which is an added enigma to the previous obscurities which have clouded the *Museum* from the birth. The stoppage may have been due to an objection to the title *Scottish* instead of *Scots,* which would certainly have displeased the Burns enthusiasts. In 1853, however, it was on the market once more, but again with an incomprehensible plan to issue it in three distinct forms:

1) *The Scots / Musical Museum: / consisting of / Upwards of six hundred songs, / with proper basses for the pianoforte / originally published by / James Johnson: / and now accompanied with copious notes and illustrations of / the lyric poetry and music of Scotland, / by the late / William Stenhouse. / With additional notes and illustrations. / New edition—in four volumes. / ... William Blackwood and Sons / Edinburgh and London /* MDCCCLIII. The *Museum* itself was printed from the plates used for the issue of the six volumes in 1803. Volume I contained a letter *en facsimile* of Burns.

2) *Illustrations / of / the lyric poetry and music / of / Scotland. / By the late / William Stenhouse. / Originally compiled to accompany the "Scots Musical Museum," / and now published separately, with / additional notes and illustrations. / William Blackwood and Sons / Edinburgh and London /* MDCCCLIII. One volume. It contained the letter *en facsimile* of Burns.

3) *Illustrations / of the / lyric poetry and music / of / Scotland / by the late / William Stenhouse / in six parts / William Blackwood and Sons / Edinburgh and London /* MDCCCLIII (.). This does not contain the 'additional notes and illustrations,' nor does it contain the letter *en facsimile* of Burns.

These were the last of the baffling and inscrutable problems which have beset the *Scots Musical Museum* since it first appeared in 1787. God forbid that anyone should devote a lifetime—it could not be done in less—in attempting to collect and collate a complete *corpus* of every issue of the *Museum*. Although the letters of Laing and Stenhouse to Blackwood, or Laing to Stenhouse, or Sharpe to Blackwood and Laing, if rooted out, would make interesting *addenda*. Meanwhile let us be content that the present edition serves all that we need to know of the *Scots Musical Museum* itself, and especially the emergence of Burns to its pages. On the other hand the fascination of Burns for the *Museum* actually created a debit balance in the higher forms of Scottish literature, because it was Burns' passion for the 'auld sangs' that distracted him from producing further masterpieces like the transcending 'Tam o' Shanter,' 'The Jolly Beggars,' and 'The Holy Fair.' Yet we must be grateful for his songs. Despite the idiom, his language is direct in its implication, and winsome in its fancy. Sometime brimful of jest and humour as in 'Tibbie I hae seen the day;' at other times delightfully ribald and profane as in 'Guid-e'en to you, kimmer.' On the sentimental side, the pleading cadences of 'Wae is my heart' lighten the souls of the weary; just as 'Scots wa hae' will rouse the patriot to an intensity unpredictable. If Burns the *poet* is acclaimed by the classes, it is Burns the '*song-wright*' who is revered by the masses.

P. S. I desire to acknowledge the advice offered to me by my colleague Major John L. Weir, Keeper of Manuscripts, Glasgow University Library.

HENRY GEORGE FARMER

# ADVERTISEMENT.

In preparing a limited number of copies of the Notes and Illustrations in a separate form, to accommodate such persons or libraries as possess the earlier editions of *The Scots Musical Museum*, it has been considered advisable to alter the mode of arrangement which was adopted in 1839. Instead of keeping the work in its original form as six volumes, or parts, with the Notes at the end of each, the Musical portion is now comprised in three volumes, each containing Two Hundred Songs, and the Notes and Illustrations form the fourth or concluding volume. In all other respects the copies are alike.

I gladly, however, avail myself of this apportunity to add a few additional pages to the Introduction, with the view of rendering the Catalogue of the older collections of Scottish Music somewhat more complete.

This Catalogue exhibits the only attempt that has hitherto been made to give a minute and detailed list of such publications. The number of later works has been considerably increased by notices obligingly communicated by Mr A. J. Wighton, Dundee; and I have also to express my best thanks to the very eminent musical antiquary Dr E. F. Rimbault, for information more especially in reference to Playford's various publications. Had it been a matter of any great importance, these aditions might no doubt have been further enlarged.

Separate copies of these additional pages, with the new title-pages, are provided for the purchasers of the Work as it appeared in 1839.

DAVID LAING.

EDINBURGH, *May* 1853.

# CONTENTS

## VOLUME ONE

## VOLUME TWO

# PREFACE.

In bringing before the Public a new edition of Johnson's collection of Scotish Songs, entitled The Scots Musical Museum, a few words of preface may be required, both in regard to the history of the work itself, and to the nature of the Notes or Illustrations with which it is now accompanied.

The original publisher and the ostensible editor of the work, was James Johnson, a Musicseller and Engraver in Edinburgh. His object, as first announced, was, "in a portable form, to unite the Songs and Music of Scotland in one general collection;" and it was commenced in May 1787, by the publication of the First Part, or volume, containing One Hundred Songs, which appeared "under the patronage, direction, and review of a number of gentlemen of undisputed taste, who have been pleased to encourage, enrich, and adorn the whole literary part of the performance." Johnson has nowhere stated who these gentlemen were, nor does it appear that any one of them took a prominent share in the publication.[1] Dr Blacklock was an occasional contributor both of songs and airs; Dr Beattie has also been mentioned, along with Mr Tytler of Woodhouselee, as persons who interested themselves in the progress of the work; but, whatever aid Johnson might have derived from these or other gentlemen "of undisputed taste," it may be confidently asserted, that, unless for one fortunate circumstance, "The Scots Musical Museum" might never have extended beyond a couple of parts or volumes; or, at least, might never have acquired the reputation which it has enjoyed for half a century, and which it still promises to retain.

The circumstance to which we allude was the visit of BURNS the Poet to Edinburgh, in November 1786. Having become acquainted with the publisher before the first part was completed, he furnished Johnson with two original Songs, Nos. 77 and 78, *Green grow the Rashes*, and *Young Peggy blooms*, to the tune of *Loch Eroch Side;* and probably also rendered him other assistance. The Musical Museum was a work so congenial to the Poet's mind, that it evidently had a decided effect in directing his efforts more exclusively to Song-writing. The early associations connected with his love of ballad-poetry, and the rustic strains familiar to the peasantry, were thus awakened, and his intimate

[1] The volumes of the Musical Museum, as originally published, were "Humbly dedicated to the Catch Club, instituted at Edinburgh June 1771." On the completion of the Sixth and last volume, in 1803, Johnson substituted a new set of title-pages, dedicating the work "To the Society of Antiquaries of Scotland."

acquaintance with the older and more popular melodies with which such strains had long been happily united, enabled him, with a rare degree of felicity, thus to give vent to his feelings, by which he has attained the first rank as a Lyric Poet. The interest, or rather enthusiasm, which he felt in contributing to the success of Johnson's undertaking, appears very manifest in his correspondence; and Burns, from this period, ought to be considered not simply as a contributor, but as the proper and efficient editor of the work. He not only contributed a large number of original songs, expressly written for it, but he applied to every person likely to render assistance; and, while visiting different parts of the country, he diligently gleaned fragments of old songs, hitherto unpublished, which he completed with additional lines or stanzas, as might be required; and, at the same time, he frequently determined the airs to which the words should be set, besides writing the prefatory notices to the several parts or volumes of what he esteemed to be a national work.

The following are the terms in which Burns writes to some of his friends respecting Johnson's collection. To Mr Candlish, then at Glasgow, in June 1787, he says, "I am engaged in assisting an honest Scotch enthusiast, a friend of mine, who is an engraver, and has taken it into his head to publish a collection of all our Songs set to Music, of which the words and music are done by Scotsmen. This, you will easily guess, is an undertaking exactly to my taste. I have collected, begged, borrowed, and stolen, all the songs I could meet with." To the Rev. John Skinner, author of Tullochgorum, in October 1787, he says, in reference to the Museum, "I have been absolutely crazed about it, collecting old stanzas, and any information remaining respecting their origin, authors, &c." In the same month, he informs another correspondent in the North, that "an engraver, James Johnson, in Edinburgh, has, not from mercenary views, but from an honest Scotch enthusiasm, set about collecting all our native songs, and setting them to music, particularly those that have never been set before. Clarke, the well-known musician, presides over the musical arrangement; and Drs Beattie and Blacklock, Mr Tytler of Woodhouselee, and your humble servant, to the utmost of his small power, assist in collecting the old poetry, or sometimes, for a fine air, make a stanza when it has no words." To Johnson himself, in November 1788, he remarks, "I can easily see, my dear friend, that you will very probably have four volumes. Perhaps you may not find your account lucratively in this business; but you are a patriot for the music of your country, and I am certain posterity will look on themselves as highly indebted to your public spirit. Be not in a hurry; let us go on correctly, and your name shall be immortal." Johnson appears most wisely to have followed Burns's directions, and with such aid, he was enabled to give his collection a distinct original character, as well as greatly to extend his original plan; a Second, Third, and Fourth Part, each containing One Hundred Songs, having successively appeared in the months of March 1788, February 1790, and August 1792.

Shortly after the appearance of the Fourth Part, Burns had engaged with a like congenial spirit to assist Mr George Thomson in his projected collection of Scotish Songs. His correspondence with that gentleman, extending from September 1792, to July 1796 (the month in which the Poet died), has now been nearly forty years before the public. This correspondence included upwards of sixty songs, written expressly for Mr Thomson's select and elegant publication. That the progress of the Musical Museum was retarded in consequence of this engagement, need scarcely be remarked. Hitherto, an average interval of two years had intervened between the publication of each part; but five years elapsed, and the Poet himself died before the Fifth Part was completed, to which he had, however, furnished the chief portion of the contents; and the Sixth Part, with which the work terminates, did not appear till June 1803, or eight years after the death of the Ayrshire bard.

Although Burns's attention had been thus diverted into another channel for a space of nearly four years, while giving form and vitality to that collection, his original predilection in favour of the Musical Museum was unchanged, as appears from his letters addressed to Johnson while the Fifth Part was in progress; and more particularly from his last letter, which has no date, but which both Johnson and Cromek fix as having been written on the 4th of July 1796, or seventeen days before the Poet died. An accurate facsimile of that interesting and affecting letter is given at the end of this Preface, as a suitable accompaniment to a work which the publisher might well acknowledge was indebted to him "for almost all of those excellent pieces which it contains." In this letter, Burns says, "You may probably think, that for some time past I have neglected you and your work; but, alas! the hand of pain, and sorrow, and care, has these many months lain heavy on me! Personal and domestic afflictions have almost entirely banished that alacrity and life with which I used to woo the rural Muse of Scotia." And, in another part, he adds, "Your work is a great one; and now that it is near finished, I see, if we were to begin again, two or three things that might be mended; yet, I WILL VENTURE TO PROPHESY, THAT TO FUTURE AGES YOUR PUBLICATION WILL BE THE TEXT-BOOK AND STANDARD OF SCOTTISH SONG AND MUSIC."

To enlarge, in this place, on the services which BURNS rendered to the Lyric Poetry of Scotland, might well be regarded as superfluous. It is but proper, however, to consider, in how far such services were influenced by his connexion with the present work. It has often been asserted, that all his best songs were expressly written for Mr Thomson's collection, thus virtually claiming for it a distinction to which it is in no respect entitled, that of having directed his mind to the subject of song-writing. It is with no wish to lessen the importance of that work, the merits of which rest on somewhat different grounds from that of Johnson's, that I conceive it necessary in this place to remark, that for six years previous to its commencement, Burns had exclusively contributed songs to Johnson's Museum, written too in his happiest moods, when nothing had occurred permanently to depress his spirits; and that the original songs which it contains, not only exceed in number, but may fairly be put in competition in regard to merit, with those that were written for the later publication. In considering his contributions to these respective collections, there is likewise this marked difference, that while for the one the airs and subjects were generally suggested to the poet, for the other his fancy was altogether uncontrolled; and although he was frequently led to write with a degree of carelessness, and with less delicacy, than if such effusions had to undergo the ordeal of criticism, and to bear his name as the author, this want of polish is amply compensated by the greater freshness, spirit, and vivacity of his compositions. But, on this point, I cannot do better than quote Dr Currie's words, prefixed to his selection of the Songs by Burns contained in the Museum. "In his communications to Mr Johnson, to which his name was not in general affixed, our Bard was less careful than in his compositions for the greater work of Mr Thomson. Several of them he never intended to acknowledge, and others, printed in the Museum, were found somewhat altered afterwards among his manuscripts. In the selection [consisting of 47 Songs] which follows, attention has been paid to the wishes of the Author as far as they are known. The printed songs have been compared with the MSS., and the last corrections have been uniformly inserted. The reader will probably think many of the Songs which follow, among the finest productions of his Muse."[2]

Nor was it alone by his original productions that Burns enriched the Musical Museum and the literature of his country. The diligence which he used in collecting, from all quarters, the remains of old unpublished ballads and songs, and snatches of popular melodies, has been emulated by persons without one spark of genius, and possessed of more zeal than judgment; but the skill and happiness with which, as with a master-hand, he imparted spirit and life to mutilated fragments, or remodelled those effusions unfit for ordinary society, attributed to the Scotish Muse as she went "high-kilted o'er the lea," have never been surpassed. "Burns, who, of all poets that ever breathed (to use the fine words of a kindred spirit), possessed the most happy tact of pouring his genius through all the meanderings of music, was unrivalled in the skill of brooding over the rude conceptions of our old poets, and in warming them into grace and life. He could glide like dew into the fading bloom of departing song, and refresh it into beauty and fragrance."[3] He himself says, "The songs marked Z in the Museum, I have given to the world as old verses to their respective tunes; but, in fact, of a good many of them little more than the chorus is ancient, though there is no reason for telling every body this piece of intelligence."[4] In regard to this skill, Sir Walter Scott remarks: "The Scotish

[2] Burns's Works, by Currie, vol. iv. p. 269.

[3] Cunningham's Songs of Scotland, vol. i. p. 66.

[4] Letter quoted in Cromek's Select Scotish Songs, vol. ii. p. 194.

Songs and Tunes preserved for Burns that inexpressible charm which they have ever afforded to his countrymen. He entered into the idea of collecting their fragments with all the zeal of an enthusiast; and few, whether serious or humorous, past through his hands without receiving some of those magic touches, which, without greatly altering the song, restored its original spirit, or gave it more than it ever possessed. So dexterously are these touches combined with the ancient structure, that the *rifacciamento,* in many instances, could scarcely have been detected, without the avowal of the Bard himself."[5] It has indeed been questioned, by the same high authority, whether it were fortunate, or otherwise, that Burns, during the latter period of his life, should have exclusively confined himself to Song-writing. "Notwithstanding the spirit of many of the lyrics of Burns, and the exquisite sweetness and simplicity of others, we cannot but deeply regret that so much of his time and talents was frittered away in compiling and composing for musical collections. . . . . Let no one suppose that we undervalue the songs of Burns. When his soul was intent on suiting a favourite air with words humorous or tender, as the subject demanded, no poet of our tongue ever displayed higher skill in marrying melody to immortal verse. But the writing of a series of songs for large musical collections, degenerated into a slavish labour, which no talents could support, led to negligence, and above all, diverted the Poet from his grand plan of Dramatic composition."[6]

[5] Quarterly Review, vol. i. p. 30. [6] *Ib.* p. 32.

That Burns in many instances overtasked himself while complying with continuous requests to furnish songs to suit particular airs, is undeniable, but that the proper bent of his genius tended more especially to lyric poetry, is equally certain. The instantaneous and lasting popularity of his songs can be ascribed to no fortuitous circumstance, but solely to the mode in which he expressed those feelings, so true to nature, which could be appreciated alike by all classes. How many collections of Songs before and since his time have appeared and been forgotten; and in the two works which owe their chief distinction to his aid, how immeasurably superior are the songs of Burns to the united contributions of the many distinguished names which are found standing in juxtaposition with his own. May we not therefore be justified in expressing a doubt, whether, if Burns had succeeded in writing one or two successful dramas, this would in any way have been comparable to the advantage which our literature has gained by his Songs, or would have outweighed the almost unequalled influence which they have exercised not among his countrymen only. Happy, indeed, had it been, could the mention of Burns's name only call up the vision suggested by the words of our great English poet, when he speaks of

> Him who walked in glory and in joy,
> Following his plough upon the mountain side.

But it is impossible to forget the depressing circumstances in which Burns was placed; his scanty annual income, which "was for some time as low as fifty, and never rose to above seventy pounds a-year;" his increasing cares, and his unremitting attention to the vexatious and harassing duties of his official situation, appointed "to guard ale-firkins;" all these conjoined, left him neither time nor disposition for any such sustained literary efforts. It must always be a humiliating consideration to think, that some suitable occupation or place had not been found, which might have left him unharassed by pecuniary difficulties. From the date of publication of the subscription edition of his Poems at Edinburgh, to that of his decease, being a period of nine years, he may be said absolutely to have received no pecuniary advantage from his writings. This doubtless was in some degree owing to his own lofty but mistaken notions, which led him to reject any stipulated recompense, as if this implied a mere sordid or speculating inducement to literary enterprise. There is no distinct proof that he ever received any acknowledgment for his contributions to the present work,[7] beyond the occasional donation of copies to be presented to his friends. All the world likewise, unfortunately knows the extent of benefit which he derived from his connexion with its more costly and ambitious rival collection. With no prospect of amended circumstances, need we wonder, therefore, (as Dr Currie remarks,) "that as his health decayed, his proud and feeling heart sunk under the secret conscious-

[7] In a printed paper, dated 15th of March 1819, soliciting Subscriptions in favour of Johnson's widow, it is stated, that her husband had "on more than one occasion befriended our favourite Scottish Poet in *his* pecuniary distresses;" but I am not aware of any thing to justify such a statement.

ness of indigence and the apprehensions of absolute want. Yet poverty never bent the spirit of Burns to any pecuniary meanness;"[8] and the character of the Poet stands only the more nobly in having thus, in midst of poverty and personal distress, and the increasing cares of a rising family, earned such an enduring fame. All the lamented and unfortunate circumstances connected with his literary career are indeed long since past, and cannot be recalled; but the recollection of them will remain indelible, as such incidents in the lives and fortunes of men of genius retain a peculiar and lasting degree of interest; and these Songs, the fruits of his genius in matured life, for which he gained neither fee nor reward, "are likely to transmit the name of Burns to all future generations."[9]—He died on the 21st of July 1796, in the thirty-eighth year of his age.

James Johnson, the original publisher of the Musical Museum, survived the completion of the work nearly eight years. Of his personal history not much is known. From the few letters still preserved, or that have been published, it appears that Burns entertained for him a sincere personal regard. In his first letter, 3d of May 1787, before setting out on his Border Tour, he sends him a song received from Dr Blacklock, and says, "Farewell, my dear Sir! I wished to have seen you, but I have been dreadfully throng [busy], as I march to-morrow. Had my acquaintance with you been a little older,

8 Burns's Works, by Currie, vol. i. p. 229.
9 Edinburgh Review, vol. xiii. p. 263.

I would have asked the favour of your correspondence, as I have met with few people whose company and conversation gave me so much pleasure, because I have met with few whose sentiments are so congenial to my own." In a letter written in 1794, he says, "As to our Musical Museum, I have better than a dozen songs by me for the fifth volume to send with Mr Clarke when he comes. . . . If we cannot finish the fifth volume any other way, what would you think of Scots words to some beautiful Irish airs? In the mean time, at your leisure, give a copy of the Museum to my worthy friend Mr Peter Hill, bookseller, to bind for me, interleaved with blank leaves, exactly as he did the Laird of Glenriddell's, that [I may insert every anecdote I can learn, together with my own criticisms and remarks on the songs. A copy of this kind I shall leave with you, the editor, to publish at some after period, by way of making the Museum a book famous to the end of time, and you renowned for ever]."[1] In another letter, about the same time, but without date, he says, "My dear Sir, I send by my friend Mr Wallace, forty-one songs for your fifth volume. Mr Clarke has also a good many, if he have not, with his usual indolence, *cast them at the cocks*. I have still a good parcel among my hands, in scraps and fragments, so that I hope we will make a shift for our last volume. You should

[1] The words within brackets, in consequence of the original letter being mutilated, have been supplied from Cromek's Reliques. He, however, has formed strange compounds, by gleaning sentences out of three distinct communications to Johnson, and printing them as one letter.

have heard from me long ago; but over and above some vexatious share in the pecuniary losses of these accursed times, I have all this winter been plagued with low spirits and blue devils, so that I have almost hung my harp on the willow-trees." And in his last letter, already quoted (of which an exact fac-simile is afterwards given), he says to Johnson, "I am extremely anxious for your work, as indeed I am for every thing concerning your or you welfare. You are a good, worthy, honest fellow, and have a good right to live in this world—because you deserve it. Many a merry meeting this publication has given us, and possibly it may give us more, though, alas! I fear it."

Although numerous collections of Scotish Songs, with or without music, and in every possible form, have appeared during the last fifty years, the Musical Museum still keeps its ground. Such collections as those of Mr George Thomson, of the late R. A. Smith, and of Messrs John Thomson and Finlay Dun, possess each of them strong and individual claims; but the present work far exceeds these, or any others that have appeared, in the number of the genuine old melodies of Scotland. When the publication was first projected, Johnson's chief advisers, Dr Blacklock and Mr Tytler of Woodhouselee, it has been remarked, "were of opinion that these wild yet pathetic and melodious strains, these fine breathings and heartfelt touches in our songs, which true genius can alone express, were bewildered and utterly lost in a noisy accompaniment of instruments. In their opinion, the full chords of a thorough bass ought to be used sparingly and with judgment, not to overpower, but to support and strengthen the voice at proper pauses: that the air itself should be first played over, by way of symphony or introduction to the song; and at the close of every stanza, a few bars of the last part of the melody should be repeated, as a relief to the voice, which it gracefully sets off;" &c. . . . "The plan of publishing our Scottish songs in this simple, elegant, and chaste manner, was highly approved of by the late MR STEPHEN CLARKE. This celebrated organist and musician readily agreed to select, arrange, and harmonize the whole of the melodies; a task which, from his brilliant genius, fine taste, and profound scientific knowledge, he was eminently qualified to perform."[2] This want of every thing like florid accompaniments, has been held as a peculiar recommendation. In regard also to the Songs, the collection is unrivalled for the extent of the good old standard productions of the Lyric Muse, including so many of Burns's finest compositions.

Johnson died at Edinburgh on the 26th of February 1811.[3] He left a widow in such indigent circumstances, that at a subsequent period, it has been

[2] Blackwood's Edinburgh Magazine, July 1817, p. 377.

[3] "Died at Edinburgh [26th of February 1811], much regretted, Mr James Johnson, Engraver, Musicseller, and Copperplate Printer;—being the first who attempted to *strike* music upon pewter, whereby a great saving is made in the charge of that article. Mr Johnson will long be remembered in the musical world. He published several interesting pieces of late; and in none was more successful than in his elegant work, 'The Scots Musical Museum,' in six volumes, &c."—(Scots Magazine, 1811, p. 318.)

stated, she had nothing more to subsist on than "the occasional donations of a few of her husband's old friends and acquaintance;" and, after remaining for some time as an out-pensioner, she at length found shelter as an inmate of the Edinburgh Charity Workhouse.[4]

Three or four years after Mr Johnson's death, the original pewter plates and remaining copies of "The Scots Musical Museum," including the copyright, and such of Burns's manuscript communications[5] as had been preserved, were exposed to sale, and became the property of the late MR WILLIAM BLACKWOOD, bookseller. In the view of bringing out the work in a new and improved form, he was desirous to have it accompanied with notes or illustrations. This was indeed part of the scheme originally contemplated by Burns, as appears from passages in other letters, besides the one above quoted. Mr Thomson having informed him that he expected to receive from Dr Beattie, "an Essay upon the subject of our National music," to illustrate his own collection, Burns in his letter, dated 26th of January 1793, immediately replied: "Dr Beattie's essay will, of itself, be a treasure. On my part, I

4 This appears from a printed paper entitled "Notice respecting Mrs Johnson, widow of the late Mr James Johnson, Engraver in Edinburgh," dated March 15, 1819.

5 When Cromek was in Edinburgh collecting materials for his "Reliques of Burns," in the year 1808, he mentions having seen 180 Songs and Poems in Burns's autograph, which he had transmitted to Johnson for the Musical Museum. The greater portion of these interesting transcripts are still preserved.

mean to draw up an appendix to the Doctor's essay, containing my stock of anecdotes, &c., of our Scots Songs. All the late Mr Tytler's[6] anecdotes I have by me, taken down in the course of my acquaintance with him, from his own mouth. I am such an enthusiast, that in the course of my several peregrinations through Scotland, I made a pilgrimage to the individual spot from which every song took its rise, 'Lochaber' and the 'Braes of Ballenden' excepted. So far as the locality, either from the title of the air or the tenor of the song, could be ascertained, I have paid my devotions at the particular shrine of every Scots Muse." Neither the Essay nor the Appendix was undertaken; but Burns, in an interleaved copy of the first four volumes of the Musical Museum, which belonged to Riddell of Glenriddell, had inserted a number of occasional notes and remarks regarding the songs. Mr Cromek[7] having obtained the use of this copy, transcribed and published them in his volume of Burns's Reliques, 1808, and again in his collection of "Select Scotish Songs," 1810; and these notes usually form an integral part in the modern editions of the Poet's works.

In preparing, therefore, to publish an ...on of the Musical Museum, with notes, illust... of the

[6] William Tytler of Woodhouselee, Esq. ... the signet, and author of a Dissertation on Scott... a Vindication of Mary Queen of Scots, and other ... died on the 12th of September 1792, in the eighty...is age.

[7] R. H. Cromek was an ...ondon. He died in 1812. See note respecting ... p. 456*.

Lyric Poetry and Music of Scotland, Mr Blackwood applied, according to my recollection, to more than one individual supposed to be most competent, for such a task. It was finally intrusted to the late WILLIAM STENHOUSE, Esq., Accountant in Edinburgh, who, along with more than ordinary antiquarian research, and much general information, possessed a thorough practical knowledge of music, and who, moreover, had been personally acquainted with Johnson, the publisher of the work, and with Clarke,[8] by whom the airs had been chiefly harmonized. To one of the earliest numbers of "Blackwood's Edinburgh Magazine," Mr Stenhouse, under the signature of "Scotus," communicated a notice of the projected edition, accompanied with two specimens of his illustrations to Songs 37 and 66; which shows that at the time, in July 1817, he must have made considerable progress in his undertaking. Having completed his series of Illustrations, the printing was commenced towards the close of 1820, and in the course of a few months was completed, extending in all to 512 pages. Some delay unfortunately occurred in regard to a general preface for the work, which eventually occasioned the publication to be laid aside. Whether this preface was intended to

8 S.
Episco CLARKE was a teacher of music, and organist of the
Burns lit pel in the Cowgate, Edinburgh. He survived
on the 6th than twelve months, having died at Edinburgh
cal pieces of t 1797. "He was composer of many musi-
successor, Wi le merit;" and after his death, his son and
like service in Mus, appears to have rendered Johnson the
the Musical he airs for the concluding volume of
died about the year 1820.

embrace a detailed historical essay on Scotish Song, and Mr Stenhouse's declining health or other avocations prevented its being completed, or whether such a preface was actually written, I cannot distinctly remember; but this point cannot now be ascertained, as no traces of such a preface were found among his papers; and in the lapse of time both the Editor[9] and the Proprietor died, and the copies of the printed sheets remained in the printer's warehouse neglected as an imperfect work.

[9] Although I knew Mr Stenhouse personally for many years, I regret my inability to furnish any particular details of his history. He was, I believe, a native of Roxburghshire, and was born in the year 1773. He was brought up as an accountant in Edinburgh, in the office of Charles Selkrig, Esq. His chief work was published under the title of "Tables of Simple Interest, and of Commission, Brokerage, or Exchange, at all the usual rates per cent, constructed on a plan entirely new, easy, and mathematically accurate. By William Stenhouse, accountant." Edinburgh, 1806, large 8vo. These Tables have always been highly esteemed.

In a MS. tour, written in 1816, by Mr Alexander Campbell (see the present work, vol iv. p. 373*), he thus describes, while waiting for the Jedburgh coach, his meeting with Mr Stenhouse's father: "Mr Scott of Maxpoffle (he says) accompanied me to New Elden, where, on entering the smithy, he kindly took a[n] old gentleman by the hand, and calling him Mr Stenhouse, who turned out to be the father of my acquaintance Mr William Stenhouse, the accountant in Edinburgh. The old gentleman is above eighty, is still pretty active, has all his faculties, his sight excepted (being a little impaired), is sensible, [conve]rsable, and cheerful. He told me many entertaining anecdo[tes o]f my friend, his son William, who showed a very early turn [for m]ental acquirements. The Blucher (a diligence coach) cor[ning u]p, we nodding, parted."

Mr William Stenhouse died at Edi[nburgh] on the 10th of November 1827, at the age of fifty-f[our, and] was interred in St Cuthbert's churchyard.

At this time, when the new edition of the Musical Museum appears after such a protracted interval, it may be stated, that the Publishers have brought it out in compliance with the request of several persons interested in such works, or who knew Mr Stenhouse, and were aware that his Illustrations contained a mass of curious matter regarding the poetry and music of the last century. In regard to this edition, therefore, I have only to remark, that the Work itself remains substantially the same as when originally published by Johnson, retaining the old title-pages and prefaces, most of which were written by Burns, as showing the progressive advancement of the work, and the information obtained or communicated regarding the names of the authors of the Songs; but the whole has been printed off, by a new process, in a superior style as to external appearance. To each volume is now added the portion of Mr Stenhouse's Illustrations that relates to the songs which it contains; and these are accompanied with a series of additions and corrections, distinguishing those which have been obligingly ontributed by C. K. Sharpe, Esq., by having his in ials subjoined. Mr Stenhouse's Notes, it will be obse ed, remain precisely as they were thrown off nearly en y years ago. Had they been reprinted, I should ave presumed to make various changes, by omissi or correction. It will be remarked, that many our old favourite Songs are the composition of ns who never appeared as professed authors; an ough most of them flourished at so late a period ring the last century, the information to be obtained respecting their personal history is far less satisfactory than could have been desired. In the Additional Illustrations, therefore, without entering too much into detail, our chief endeavour has been to ascertain some particulars respecting the history of the less known Song-writers, whose names appear in the pages of the Musical Museum, and more especially of those Ladies who have enriched our Lyric poetry with some of its finest compositions. If this attempt has not been successful, it was not from any want of research or direct application, where it could be made, to the relations or personal friends of the several authors; and I have availed myself of many obliging communications, which are duly acknowledged, as the surest mode of giving authenticity to the information thus recorded.

I cannot conclude this Preface without expressing my best thanks to JAMES CHALMERS, Esq., for the loan of Sir Robert Gordon of Straloch's MS. Lute-book, written in 1627; to GEORGE FARQUHAR GRAHAM, Esq., for the very obliging manner in which he deciphered a variety of ancient airs from tha
manuscript, some of which, rendered into m ern
notation, have been introduced in the tional
Illustrations; to WILLIAM DAUNEY, E dvocate,
for frequent advice and assistance rd to these
old airs; and above all, to C KIRKPATRICK
SHARPE, Esq., my coadjut t may be truly
described as a labour of

DAVID LAING.

SIGNET LIBRAR

M.DC

mation to be obtained respecting their personal history is far less satisfactory than could have been desired. In these Additional Illustrations, therefore, without entering too much into detail, my chief endeavour has been to ascertain some particulars respecting the history of the less known Song-writers, whose names appear in the pages of the Musical Museum, and more especially of those Ladies who have enriched our Lyric poetry with some of our finest compositions. If this attempt has not been successful, it was not from any want of research, or direct application, where it could be made, to the relations or personal friends of the several authors; and I have availed myself of many obliging communications, which are duly acknowledged, as the surest mode of giving authenticity to the information thus recorded.

I cannot conclude this Preface without expressing my best thanks to James Chalmers, Esq., for the loan of [illegible] of Scottish [illegible] books, [illegible] Esq., for the very obliging manner in which he dispensed a variety of particulars [illegible] [illegible] some of which, rendered into modern notation, have been introduced in the [illegible] Illustrations; to William Dauney, Esq., for the frequent advice and assistance in reading old music; and above all, to Charles [illegible] Sharpe, Esq., [illegible] my [illegible] described as a Labour of love [illegible]

[illegible]

mation to be obtained respecting their personal history is far less satisfactory than could have been desired. In the Additional Illustrations, therefore, without entering too much into detail, our chief endeavour has been to ascertain some particulars respecting the history of the less known Song-writers, whose names appear in the pages of the Musical Museum, and more especially of those Ladies who have enriched our Lyric poetry with some of its finest compositions. If this attempt has not been successful, it was not from any want of research or direct application, where it could be made, to the relations or personal friends of the several authors; and I have availed myself of many obliging communications, which are duly acknowledged, as the surest mode of giving authenticity to the information thus recorded.

I cannot conclude this Preface without expressing my best thanks to JAMES CHALMERS, Esq., for the loan of Sir Robert Gordon of Straloch's MS. Lute-book, written in 1627; to GEORGE FARQUHAR GRAHAM, Esq., for the very obliging manner in which he deciphered a variety of ancient airs from that manuscript, some of which, rendered into modern notation, have been introduced in the Additional Illustrations; to WILLIAM DAUNEY, Esq., Advocate, for frequent advice and assistance in regard to these old airs; and above all, to CHARLES KIRKPATRICK SHARPE, Esq., my coadjutor in what may be truly described as a labour of love.

DAVID LAING.

SIGNET LIBRARY, EDINBURGH,
M.DCCC.XXXIX.

How are you, my dear Friend? & how comes on yr. fifth volume? — You may probably think that for some time past I have neglected you & your work; but, Alas, the hand of pain, & sorrow, & care has these many months lain heavy on me! — Personal & domestic affliction have almost entirely banished that alacrity & life with which I used to woo the rural Muse of Scotia. — In the mean time, let us finish what we have so well begun. — The gentleman, Mr. Lewars, a particular friend of mine, will bring out any proofs (if they are ready) or any message you may have. —

Farewel!

R Burns

turn over

You should have had this when Mr Lewars called on you, but his saddle-bags miscarried.— I am extremely anxious for your work, as indeed I am for every thing concerning you & your welfare.— You are a good worthy, honest fellow, & have a good right to live in this world— because you deserve it.— Many a merry meeting this Publication has given us, & possibly it may give us more, though, alas! I fear it — This protracting, slow, consuming illness which hangs over me, will, I doubt much, my ever dear friend, arrest my sun before he has well reached his middle career, & will turn over the Poet to far other & more important concerns than studying the brilliancy of Wit, or the pathos of Sentiment — However, Hope is the cordial of the human heart, & I endeavour to cherish it as well as I can — Let me hear from you as soon as convenient.— Your Work is a great one; & though, now that it is near finished, I see if we were to begin

begin again, two or three things that might be mended, yet I will venture to prophesy, that to future ages your Publication will be the text-book & standard of Scotish Song & Music. —— I am ashamed to ask another favor of you because you have been so very good already, but my wife has a very particular friend of hers, a young lady who sings well, to whom she wishes to present The Scots Musical Museum. If you have a spare copy, will you be obliging as to send it by the very first Fly, as I am anxious to have it soon.

Yours ever

R Burns

Mr James Johnson
Engraver
Lawn-market
Edinr

# INTRODUCTION.

THE high estimation in which the National Music of Scotland has always been held, renders it a theme of more than ordinary interest. There is indeed so much beauty and unaffected simplicity in the modulation and general character of our native melodies, that they seldom fail to convey delight to persons of all classes, although uninfluenced by early or local associations. These melodies have likewise been long inseparably connected, or identified with the singularly varied effusions of the Lyric Muse of Scotland; and it is scarcely necessary to remark, how happily the words and airs are usually adapted to each other, whether it be in strains of tender passion and refined sentiment, or of comic humour and rustic festivity. It would have been singular, therefore, had there been no attempts made to ascertain the origin of such a style of national music; yet, notwithstanding the ingenious speculations of several learned writers, it must be confessed that the subject remains as obscure and uncertain as ever. What is it, at best, but idle conjecture, whatever view may be adopted? It has been imagined, for instance, that our native melodies, in their structure and succession of intervals, have preserved an affinity to the old Enharmonic scale of the Greek Music; or assuming for Scotish Melody an Oriental origin, that it found a resting-place in this remote and barren clime, in the Westward progress of civilisation. While some persons have, in general terms, deduced the history of Scotish Music from the time of the Romans; others, without ascending to so remote a period, discover in our popular airs, what they consider a striking resemblance to the ecclesiastical modes, or the Canto-fermo of the Romish Church-service. The invention or improvement of our Melody has likewise been assigned to particular individuals,—to James the First, King of Scotland, (1424—1437;) or to David Rizzio, (1563—1566.) Such a distinction has also been claimed for certain nameless shepherds and shepherdesses, inhabiting at some undefined period (called a pastoral age) the secluded pastoral vales of the South of Scotland. Unfortunately, the absence of all historical evidence of any considerable antiquity, and the inability to produce any proofs, in a written form, of the existence of our present popular tunes of an older date than the close of the sixteenth century, is but poorly compensated for by uncertain traditions or conjectures, however ingenious and plausible.

It would be altogether foreign to the purpose of the present work, to attempt any thing like an Historical Inquiry into the origin and progress of Scotish Music. An eminent English antiquary, Joseph Ritson, whose accuracy and research deserve unqualified praise, suggested, that the previous step to any such inquiry would be, "to determine which of the airs now extant are to be considered as the original or most ancient;" and he himself, with great care, embodied in his "Historical Essay on Scotish Song," the various dispersed and incidental notices that he was able to glean from authentic writers. He was led, however, to conclude, that no direct evidence could be produced of the existence of scarcely any Scotish tunes now known, prior to the year 1660; and that not so much as one of these could be "found noted, either in print or manuscript, before that period."

Since Ritson's time, more extensive research has thrown additional light on this head; and the subject has been resumed in the Preliminary Dissertation to a volume recently published under the title of "Ancient Scotish Melodies," from the Skene MS. The author, Mr Dauney, has, with great zeal and diligence, retraced Ritson's steps, and brought to light much new and interesting information, both respecting the history of music, and the musical instruments commonly used in Scotland prior to the seventeenth century; and this work bears ample evidence, that to an accurate and enlightened acquaintance with musical science, he unites an enthusiastic antiquarian zeal, so requisite for the proper investigation of such a subject. This volume is further enriched by a valuable addition contributed by Mr Finlay Dun, an eminent professional musician, in the form of an Analysis of several of our old popular Melodies, which cannot fail to be highly esteemed by competent judges.—Still, it may be asserted, that the history of Scotish Music is yet in its infancy of illustration; and although there is little probability that it ever can be completely elucidated, it may be suggested, whether it might not be the most effectual mode to remove in part the obscurity that surrounds the origin of our music, to institute a more profound and comprehensive inquiry into the affinities of the National music of other countries.

In this place, it occurred to the Editor, that however

humble the attempt, and but of limited interest, it might not be unsuitable to present a Chronological List of the various publications of Scotish Music, of a date prior to the completion of Johnson's Museum. The following list cannot pretend to be either complete, or the arrangement correct. The common absurd practice in all kinds of music, of omitting the dates of publication, and the frequent alteration of publishers' names on the title-pages, renders accuracy in such details a matter of some difficulty. Occasional biographical notices of the Composers or Collectors during the last century, are also added, to relieve a dry catalogue of title-pages.

Of the works described, the Editor possesses several of the earlier ones, but by far the greater number of those printed during the last century are in the possession of Charles Kirkpatrick Sharpe, Esq.

---

## CHURCH MUSIC OF THE REFORMERS.—1565.

THE work commonly but improperly known under the name of "Knox's Liturgy and Psalms," is here noticed from the circumstance, that the first edition of it, in 1565, is the earliest book printed in Scotland that contains musical notation. It is so extremely rare, that perhaps not two perfect copies are in existence. It has the following title:—"THE FORME OF PRAYERS AND MINISTRATION OF THE SACRAMENTS, &c., vsed in the English Church at Geneua, approued and receiued by the Churche of Scotland. whereunto besydes that was in the former bokes, are also added sondrie other prayers, with the whole Psalmes of Dauid in English meter. PRINTED AT EDINBVRGH, BY ROBERT LEKPREVIK. M.D.LXV." Small 8vo.

The several Psalms are set to particular tunes, which are printed with music types, at the head of each; or a reference is made when the same tune was appropriated to more than one Psalm. It may be added, that nearly all the subsequent editions of this old version of the Psalms, previous to 1650 when its use in Scotland was superseded by the present version, also contain the tunes. This seems to show, that some knowledge of sacred music must have been very general; which may be easily accounted for, as music schools existed in different parts of the country. The following anecdote confirms such a supposition:—James Melvill, in his Diary, in 1582, noticing the return of John Durie, one of the ministers of Edinburgh, who had incurred the displeasure of the Court, says, "Within few days thereafter, Ihone Durie gat leiue to ga hame to his awin flok of Edinbruche; at whase retourning thair was a great concours of the haill town, wha met him at the Nather Bow; and, going up the streit, with bare heads and loud voices, sang to the praise of God, and testifeing of grait joy and consolation, the 124th Psalm, '*Now Israel may say, and that trulie,*' &c., till heauin and earth resoundit. This noyes, when the Duc [of Lennox] being in the town heard, and ludgit in the Hiegat [High street], luiked out and saw, he raue his barde for anger, and hasted him af the town." (Diary, p. 95.) Such a procession, consisting probably of some thousand persons singing this tune, (still used in our churches as the 'Old 124th,') is characteristic enough of the good old Scotish Presbyterians.

## WOOD'S MANUSCRIPTS—1566–1578.

The oldest Manuscripts written in Scotland that have yet been discovered containing any specimens of secular music, are two volumes out of four, written and noted by

Thomas Wood, who styles himself Vicar of St Andrews, in 1566. It is, however, at the end of these volumes, and evidently written at a subsequent date, that the airs alluded to are contained.

In making an exception by noticing Wood's Manuscripts, it is partly because Mr Stenhouse, in his Notes, has more than once referred to these volumes, and has fallen into a mistake regarding their exact date; and also, because they have not elsewhere been described. It appears that Wood, in the year 1566, employed himself in writing four different volumes, each containing a distinct part of the music for the Psalms, Canticles, and Hymns of the Church used in this country after the Reformation. Wood himself records, that this task occupied him four years, and it seems to have been a laborious employment, from the care which he took to adorn the volumes with rude designs and ornamented capitals. One of the set, containing the Contra-tenor, is preserved in the University Library of Edinburgh, having been presented to the Library by Mr James Browne, in the year 1672. Another, the "Bassus," was purchased by the late Mr Blackwood, some twenty years ago, and, after his death, when part of his stock was disposed off by auction, the present Editor was lucky enough to secure it. The fate of the two other parts has not been ascertained.

On the blank leaves of the latter volume, some subsequent possessor has inserted the Basses of a number of secular airs, with the first words of the songs. The handwriting is evidently not earlier than 1620; yet Mr Stenhouse refers to this portion of the volume, as if written by Wood in 1566. Most of these airs are apparently English, and were no doubt taken from some of the printed collections of the time. The Christmas Carol, and the Medley which Mr S. quotes, must be considered as inserted in this

MS. nearly half a century after Wood's time; and they are also contained in the second edition of "Cantus, Songs, and Fancies," Aberdeen, 1666, 4to.

Being well acquainted with Wood's volumes, the Editor was surprised (in the autumn of 1835), while having the privilege of examining the manuscripts preserved in Trinity College Library, Dublin, to meet with a small volume in 4to (F. 5. 13,) lettered "Airs and Sonnets," and bearing the following title:—"This is the fyft Buke addit to the four Psalme Bukkis, for Songis of four or fyve pairtis, meit and apt for musitians to recreat their spirittis, when as they shall be overcum with hevines or any kynd of sadnes; not only musitians, but also euin to the ingnorant (sic) of a gentle nature hearing shal be comforted, and be mirry with us. 1569." 4to. pp. 112.

Wood's portion of this volume, however, extends only to page 33. This is followed by a great variety of "Airs and Sonnets"—"which are all notted heir with the Tennor or common pairt they ar sung with." The handwriting of this portion corresponds with the additional pages at the end of the "Bassus," and, indeed, presents the same airs, with the advantage of having, in most instances, the words of the songs added.

Wood, who uniformly styles himself Vicar of St Andrews, survived probably till the close of the sixteenth century. Some additions, at least, in his hand occur, as late as 1584, and 1592. It was not an uncommon name, and therefore we cannot be certain that he was the same person with Thomas Wood, who was admitted minister or rather vicar of Carnbee, in Fife, November 7th, 1576. That he was only vicar, is probable, for William Laing, in 1582, and Andro Huntar, in 1585, appear successively as ministers; while Thomas Wood is specially named as vicar of Carnbee, in 1585. Another Thomas Wood was admitted first minister of Dysart, in November 1584.

These manuscripts contain a few notices of persons distinguished during the sixteenth century as musical composers. It may not be uninteresting to collect such notices under one point of view.

Angus, John, in Dunfermline. In Wood's MS. he is usually styled 'gude Angus,' or 'gude and meike Johne Angus.' The editor of the Psalms, in 1635, calls him Dean John Angus; and in one place, Wood says, "quod Angus in Dumfermling."

Blackhall, Mr Andrew. According to Wood's authority, he was a canon in the Abbey of Holyroodhouse, before the Reformation. He afterwards became one of the Protestant ministers; and in 1567, and again in 1569, his name occurs as minister of Ormiston. He was translated before 1576, to the parish of Inveresk or Musselburgh, and here he spent the remainder of his life. In October 1592, the Synod of Lothian and Tweeddale, having inquired if any of their brethren were "greifit with the greit charge of their flock?" Mr Andro Blackhall declared, that he was "greifit with his greit congregation;" and in October 1593, the following entry occurs in the Minutes of the Synod:—"Anent the desyre of thair brother, Mr Andro Blackhall, minister of Mussilburgh, crauing, in respect of his adge [age] and greitnes of his flock, That the Assemblie wald causs the presbytery of Dalkeyth deall with the parochinaris of Mussilburgh for a secund minister to serwe in the cure of that kirk, and for sum prouisioun for him. The Assemblie, considering the greitnes of the said congregatioun, as also the adge of thair brother, Ordanis the presbytrie of Dalkeyth to trawell with the town."

In reference to the above commission, the Presbytery of Dalkeith, in October 1594, reported, that "they have bene deilling in that matter; Quhais declaratioun being considerit, the Assemblie ordanis, That thai insist in the samin." The subsequent minutes have not been preserved; but it appears from the Books of the Thirds of Benefices, in 1601, in 1607, and 1608, that Adam Colt was Blackhall's colleague, and that Edward Leyn was reidar at Inveresk or Musselburgh, at the same time. Blackhall probably died about 1610, when he must have attained a very advanced age.

Futhy, Sir John. The title of *Sir* denotes that he was a priest. A moral song, beginning, 'O God abufe,' in four parts, was composed by him, 'baith letter and not,' —that is, both the words and notation. "This man (says Wood, in the Dublin MS.) was the first organeist that ever brought in Scotland the curious new fingering and playing on organs; and zit is mair nor threscore zeiris since he com hame: this is wreatin in I$^{m}$ v$^{c}$ fourscore & xij. (1592.)" He must thus have attained a very advanced age; for, according to Wood's statement, he had returned before the year 1532, and, we may presume, that he was then upwards of twenty. In Bannatyne's MS., written in 1568, there are two poems, signed 'Fethy,' and 'Fethe,' which no doubt were by the same person. (Memorials of Geo. Bannatyne, pp. 74 and 76. Edinb. 1830, 4to.)

Heggie, Francis. See under Peblis, David.

Johnson, Robert. Wood calls him "Ane Scottis preist, borne in Dunse, his name Robert Johnson; fled for accusation of heresy: Thomas Hutson's [Hudson's] father knew him weill." In another volume, Wood had added to the hymn, '*Dominus in virtute tua letabitur Rex,*' in five parts, "quod ane Inglishe man; and, as I have heard, he was blind quhen he set it." This he has erased, and says, "This was set in Ingland be ane Scottis preist baneist." Ben Jonson, when at Hawthornden, informed Drummond that he understood his grandfather had come from Annandale to Carlisle; and that his father was a minister, and had fled or was imprisoned for heresy during the reign of Queen Mary, he himself being a posthumous son. Query, could this Robert Johnson have been related to the great Dramatic Poet?

Kemp, Andrew. Wood styles him a minister; but this probably was an error, as no such name occurs in the Registers of Scotish Ministers at that period; while it appears that Andrew Kemp was appointed by the Magistrates of Aberdeen, Master of their Music School, in the year 1570. (Kennedy's Annals of Aberdeen, vol. ii. p. 135.) One of the airs contains this memorandum by Wood:—"Quod Kemp, and noted (or written) be his awin hand, and not myne."

Lauder, James, was Chaplain of St Catharine's Altar in the Collegiate Church of St Giles, Edinburgh, before the Reformation. This appears from the following entry in the Council Register, January 26th, 1552-3:—"The quhilk day the Provest, Baillies, Counsale, and Dekynes, sittand in jugement anent the Supplicatioun given in be James Lawder, Prebendar of thair queir, grantis license to the said James to pas furth of the realme to the partis of Ingland and France, thair to remaine for the space of ane year nixt efter the dait hereof, to the effect that he mon have and get better eruditioun in musik and playing nor he hes; provyding always that the said James caus ane Chaiplain to keep his foundatioun of Sanct Kathyranis altar be ane preist quhill the said year be done." In 1567, we find a James Lauder holding the office of Exhorter in the Church of Logybryde, in Stratherne; but whether he was the same person must be left to conjecture.—In one of Wood's volumes is inserted a tune, entitled " My Lord Marche Pauen. Set be Jamis Lauder, 1584."

Peblis, David, styled an " honourable man," and one of the Canons of St Andrews before the Reformation, set the Canticle, '*Si quis diliget me*,' in five parts. In the MS. Bassus, Wood says, this was " Set be David Pablis in four pairtis, in the zeir of God 1530 or thairby; ane noueice Francy Heagy, and wes this Dauid Pablis awin dissyple, set the Fyft [part] a lytill before Pinky—[1546], and that verray weill." In the Dublin MS., we find, " Quod David Pablis, sumtyme ane chanone in the Abbay of Sanctandrous, ane of the principal musitians in all this land, in his tyme. This sang was set about the zeir of God I$^{m}$. v$^{c}$. xxx zeiris." Wood elsewhere mentions that David Peblis set in four parts the Psalm, '*Quam multi, Domine, sunt*,' at the desire of my Lord of March, in 1576.

The Editor of the edition of the Psalms, with the music, " Printed at Edinburgh by the Heires of Andrew Hart, 1635," 8vo, in a prefatory notice, after mentioning the pains he had taken to give the Psalm Tunes correctly, in all the four parts, has thus mentioned the names of some of the composers of Sacred Music in Scotland at the time of the Reformation, which corroborates Wood's notices. The Editor signs his name E. M. I regret that we should be so ignorant respecting this enthusiastic lover of sacred melody, as even not to know his name:—

" I acknowledge sincerely the whole compositions of the parts to belong to the primest Musicians that ever this kingdome had, as Deane John Angus, Blackhall, Smith, Peebles, Sharp, Black, Buchan, and others, famous for their skill in this kind. I would bee most unwilling to wrong such Shyning-lights of this Art, by obscuring their Names, and arrogating any thing to myselfe, which any wayes might derogate from them: For (God is my witnes) I affect not popular applause, knowing how little soliditie there is in that shadow-like seeming substance, studying to approve myself to God in a good conscience; which testimonie finding in my soul, I contemne all worldly approbation, or opprobration. The first copies of these parts were doubtlesly right set down by these skilfull Authors, but have been wronged and vitiat by unskilfull copiers thereof, as all things are injured by tyme: And heerein consisted a part of my paines, that, collecting all the sets I could find on the Psalmes, after painfull tryal thereof, I selected the best for this work, according to my simple judgement."

## PLAYFORD'S DANCING-MASTER—1657.

Mr Stenhouse, in the course of his Illustrations to the Musical Museum, has repeatedly mentioned this work, and has copied from it several Scotish airs. See, in particular, pages 129, 316, and 318. At the end of Playford's "Catch that catch can; or the Musical Companion," 1667, it is thus described in "A Catalogue of late printed Musick-books,"—"The Dancing-Master; or a Book of Rules for Dancing Country Dances, with the Tunes to each Dance; and other New Dancing Tunes for the Treble-Violin."—It passed through several editions, but the first, of 1657, is very rare, and is interesting, as perhaps the earliest printed work that exhibits several genuine Scotish airs.

## THE ABERDEEN CANTUS—1662.

"Cantus, Songs and Fancies. To Thre, Foure, or Five partes, both apt for voices and viols. With a briefe Introduction of Musick, as is taught in the Musick-Schole of Aberdene, by T. D. Mr. of Musick. Aberdene, printed by Iohn Forbes, and are to be sold at his Shop. Anno Dom. M,DC,LXII." Small oblong 4to—leaves.

This collection, the earliest printed in Scotland, is unfortunately a set of English tunes, or of tunes composed in an English style, rather than of genuine Scotish melodies. The above title is printed within a rude wood-cut border, representing a lady with a lute on one side, and a gentleman with a music-book on the other. This cut is repeated in the two subsequent impressions. It usually passes under the printer's name, as "Forbes's Cantus;" although Mr T. D., or Thomas Davidson, may have been the editor; and it may be objected that the word "Cantus" is improperly used, as applied to a collection of airs, instead of to only one of the Parts.

THOMAS DAVIDSON succeeded his father Patrick Davidson, as Teacher of the Music-School at Aberdeen, in the year 1640. (Kennedy's Annals, vol. ii. p. 135.)—The first edition of the "Cantus" is of very great rarity, and contains sixty-one songs. The dedication, by Forbes, is in such a singular style of bombast, that it may amuse the reader to hear of the heavenly melody and the nightingales of Bon-Accord, or Aberdeen.

"Unto the Right Honourable William Gray, *L. Provest;* Alexander Alexander, Iohn Scot, Iohn Duncan, Charles Robertson, *Bailies;* Thomas Mitchell, *Dean of Gild;* Iohn Ross, *Theasurer;* and the rest of the Honourable Councell of the City of Aberdene.

"*Right Honourable,—*

SEEING it hath been the chief Honor and singular Praise of this famous CITY, to have been the Sanctuary of Sciences, the Manse of the MUSES, and Nurserie of all Artes; So that under you, and your Honors' Predecessors prudent patrocinie, vigilant care, and fatherly inspection, so little a Plate of Ground hath yeelded many Plants of renowne, who hath flowrished as Trees of delight, both in Church and State, through out all the corners of Great BRITTAINE: Notwithstanding of many strange Stormes, dismall Disasters, and malicious Designes; endeavouring to blast the Beautie of BON-ACCORD, to spoile HER of all HER Decorements; and amongst the rest to rob Her of that famous Ornament of Vocall and Instrumentall MUSICK, which allwayes SHE could have claimed, as the proper native and heritable Iewell of the PLACE; In which HER Excellency hath been so eminent, that to have been Borne or Bred in ABERDENE, hath been sufficient Argument, and Testimony, to advance any to the Profession of that Science elsewhere. Yea, How many have come of purpose from the outmost partes of this ILAND, to hear the cheerfull PSALMS and heavenly melody of BON-ACCORD? till of late, some who had monopolized Crotchets to their own Pates, dauncing to the Pype of these tratarous times, contrare to the express Command of the ALMIGHTY, and laudable practise of all Christian Churches in the world, that their Vocal-Worship might be consonant to the harsh howling of their Hell-hatched Common-wealths, would levell and astrict the Praises of the MOST HIGH at all times to a Common-Tune. But now, seeing it hath pleased the grand Ruler of Heaven and Earth, with the greatest of Blessings, Our Dread SOVERAIGNE, CHARLES, by the Grace of GOD, KING OF GREAT BRITTAINE, FRANCE, AND IRELAND, Defender of the True Apostolicke Faith, &c.; to bring all things to their ancient Order, put an end to these dismall Discords, string the Hearts of BRITTAINE with true Loyalty; and turne them to their proper Tunes: Elevating and Rousing all loyall Spirits to see the royall Harpe blase in the royall Scutcheon: I who hath made it my resolute purpose and constant resolution, to saile all winds, and serve up the weake partes which GOD and Nature hath bestowed on me: that so, at least with the *Ephesian*-BEE, I might contribute my little Wax, and sillie Bumb, to the Hyve of BON-ACCORD'S Common-well, that the paines of your Children in attaining the first elements of MUSICK may be lesned, and the Scarrcraw of difficultie taken off the Hinges of the School-doore, hath endeavoured with all the clearnesse I can, to make the entry so patent, that the feeblest be not afrighted to step in. I shall not weary your patience with the commendation of this heasty embrio, seeing it must owe its Life and Beeing to Your Honors. It's wealing in the Craddle; holding out its Hand for your assistance, suffer it not to perish, shine on it with a beninge Aspect; let it appeare to the World that the meanest Schrub in BON-ACCORD, can share of your Influence aswell as the talest Cedar; who knowes? but this humble creeping Ivy, if suffered to lay hold on your Favour, and lean on your Goodness, may flowrish and winter its greenness with its growth, as the Summer Bowre, and Winter Bush of many sweet singing Nightingales: while either it answer the expectation of many, or get its stature and perfect period, from your Hs. ever acceptable commands. Accept of it as an Interlude to your more serious Effaires, and measure not the minde of the offerer, by the Leannesse and Leamness of the offering, whose Honor and Dignity depends on your gratious acceptance; which is onely able to cover its escapes, attonne its presumption, and shield it from all the poysoned Dartes of back-byting envy: So posterity shall sing your Praises, and you shall be the soul of that, to which (if we shall beleeve divine *Plato* and his followers) the Vniverse doth owe that heavenly soule, by which it is animate, and you and your children may make that your recreation in time, which most be the worke of all Saints throughout all Eternity: and that BON-ACCORD may resemble Heaven in an harmonious-Concord, and your Honors meet with the out-bearing and best blessings of the ALMIGHTY, on all your Designes and Enterprises, shall be the daily Prayer of

"Your Honors' most engaged Servant,

"IOHN FORBES."

THE ABERDEEN CANTUS, 2d edit.—1666.

"Cantus, Songs and Fancies, to three, four, or five Parts, both apt for voices and viols. With a brief Introduction to Musick, as is taught by Thomas Davidson, in the Musick-School of Aberdene. Second Edition, corrected and enlarged. Aberdene, printed by John Forbes, and are to be sold at his shop, Anno Domini, M.DC.LXVI." Small oblong 4to. 50 leaves.

A perfect copy of this edition is very rare. It has on the title the same rude wood-cut border as in the first edition. The dedication to the Magistrates of 1666 is changed, but it is also in a similar strain of bombast. It contains only 55 songs; the six following songs, for some reason, not easily to be divined, having been omitted.

37th. The time of Youth sore I repent.
42d. Yee Gods of Love looke downe in pity.
47th. Now, O now, I needs must part.
55th. Martine said to his Man.
56th. A Shepherd in a shade.
60th. Come againe, sweet Love doth thee invite.

There are added, however, at the end of the volume, the

celebrated medley, entitled a "Pleugh-Song. Cantus. Three voices," beginning—

My heartly service to you, my Lord,
I recommend, as should accord;
There is an Ox into your Pleugh, &c.

And two Carols, or Songs, for three voices, viz.—

All sons of Adam, &c.,
Trip and go, hey, &c.

The following is a portion of the dedication to this second edition.

"Unto the Right Honble. Gilbert Gray, Lord Provest, &c. &c., and to the rest of the Honorable Counsel of the City of Aberdene.

*Right Honorable,—*

A FEW years ago, that I might approve myself no less an observant Citizen then a provident Parent, being invited by the desires of some, allured by the kindness of others, and encouraged by the expectation and good hopes of the usefullness of the thing itself to the Place, I did lay down my First-born as a fondling, at the feet of your Honorable Bench; solemnly engaging that, as it received its being from BON-ACCORD, and its growth from your goodness, so it should period its stature with your pleasure. This promise hath pressed me, that my Press might always bear the impress of your vertues; and express (though in a small type) my thankfulness, according to the laudable custom of votaries, in all ages, after a few years' growth, to represent the same to your Sanctuary, that it may be confirmed in your favour. . . . . . . . . . . . . . . . . . . . . . . And now, seeing it hath pleased Providence, in your Wisdom's Persons, to bless the Bench of Bon-Accord with such an harmonious Consort, of as many Musitians as Magistrats, that all under your Magistracie may descant on your labors, and posteritie sing your praises to coming ages; admit this poor present to your acceptance, its breath and being depends on your brow, being willing to receive its sentence from the same, whether it shall be smothered in the birth, or view the public under your patrocinie. However, that the best blessings and out-bearing of the Almighty may accompany your Wisdoms in all your honorable designs, shall be the daily prayer of your Honors' own servant,

"IOHN FORBES."

THE ABERDEEN CANTUS, 3d edit.—1682.

"Cantus, Songs, and Fancies, to three, four, or five Parts," &c., ornamented title like the preceding editions—and a second title as follows:

"Cantus, Songs, and Fancies, to severall Musicall Parts, both apt for voices and viols. With a brief Introduction to Musick, as is taught into the Musick-School of Aberdeen. The Third Edition, exactly corrected and enlarged. Together also, with severall of the choisest Italian-Songs, and New English-Ayres, all in three parts, (viz.) Two Treebles and a Bass: most pleasant and delightfull for all humours. Aberdeen, printed by John Forbes, Printer to the Ancient City of Bon-Accord, Anno Dom. 1682." Small oblong 4to, 58 leaves.

This edition is not uncommon. It contains only fifty-five Songs, like the second edition; but the Plough Song and the two Cantus are omitted, to make room for "Severall of the choisest Italian Songs, composed by Giovanni Giacomo Castoldi da Carravaggio: together also, with some of the best new English-Ayres, collected from their chiefest authors, all in three parts."

As the Printer still preserved his peculiar style of complimenting the Aberdeen Magistrates, a portion of his dedication, and his address to all true lovers of Musick, may be quoted. But, in taking leave of this collection, we cannot but regret that the publisher should have substituted 'Choice Italian-Songs and new English-Ayres,' instead of a series of the popular Scotish melodies of his time.

"Unto the Right Honorable Sir George Skene of Fintray, Lord Provest, &c. &c. &c., and to the rest of the Honorable Counsell of the City of Aberdeen.

*Right Honorable,—*

YOUR Honors' servant having had the good opportunity some years ago, at two severall occasions, to present your Honors' worthy predecessors with the patronage of this Musick Book, of which two impressions there are few extant; and he being again (of new) invited by the earnest desires of some, yea allured by the kindness of others, and encouraged by the expectation and good hopes of the usefulness and profitableness of the book itself, not onely to this famous city, but also to all lovers of musick within this nation, hath (according to his very bound duty) presented your Honors with the patronage of this third edition; especially seeing it hath ever been the chief honor and singular praise of this famous city, to be the sanctuary of sciences, the manse of the muses, and nurserie of all arts; so that under your (and your Honors' worthy predecessors) prudent patrocinie, vigilant care, and fatherly inspection, so little a plate of ground hath yielded very many plants of renown, who have always flourished, as trees of delight, both in church and state, throughout all the corners of Great Brittain; yea, whose excellency hath ever been so eminent, that to have been born or bred in Aberdeen, hath been a great argument and ground to procure promotion for any, to places of any profession elsewhere: yea, the fame of this city for its admirable knowledge in this divine science, and many other fine enduements, hath almost overspread whole Europe, witness the great confluence of all sorts of persons from each part of the same, who, of design have come (much like that of the Queen of Sheba) to hear the sweet chearful Psalms, and heavenly melody of famous Bon-Accord, whose hearts have been ravished with the harmonious concord thereof. If then the Almighty hath bestowed such a grand blessing upon the same, sure the heavenly and divine use will much more redound to our eternall comfort, if with our voices we joyn our hearts, when we sing in His holy place. . . . . .

. . . . . . . . . . .

*Courteous Reader,—*

"To all Ingenuous and True Lovers of Musick.—The two former Impressions of this Musick-Book, finding so generall acceptance, hath encouraged me to adventure upon the printing of this Third Edition, in which I have not only made it my care to amend some defects which were into the former impressions, but indeed to new modell the whole, by adding a considerable number of choise Italian-Songs and English-Ayres, all in three parts, (viz.) two trebles and a bass, which were never printed with the former Impressions, and that for the severall humour of all persons, male and female, old and young; wherefore (I may truly say) this Musick-Book, (as it is now published,) for such sweet harmonious songs, hath never been extant in this nation. You have also herewith printed, for the encouragement of young beginners in vocall musick, the print of the hand, for teaching the Gam thereon, with the scale of the Gam, and parts thereof; as also a full exposition of the Gam, and cliefs, moods, degrees, concords, and discords, &c., and that into a plain and brief manner, for every one's capacity. I must confess, the work as to the musick is not mine, but for printing and publishing hereof, I am still ready, and most willing in my generation to improve my talent and parts (which the Almighty of his infinite goodness hath been pleased to bestow upon me,) both for the good of this City and of my Countrey; therefore, if these my labours prove pleasant and delightfull by your favorable acceptance, the same shall incite me very shortly to publish abroad, severall other Musicall Songs and Ayres of various kinds, both Catches, and Parts-Songs, which are not readily to be found within this kingdom, with a brieff and plain introduction to musick, conform to each severall book, all very pleasant for every humour, yea harmful to none: and that all my painfull labors may tend for this City and my Countrey's good, shall be the hearty prayer and earnest desire of

"JOHN FORBES."

## D'URFEY'S COLLECTION—1720.

"There are many fine Scots airs in the Collection of Songs by the well known Tom D'Urfey, intitled 'Pills to purge Melancholy,' published in the year 1720, which seem to have suffered very little by their passing through the hands of those English Masters who were concerned in the correction of that book; but in the multiplicity of Tunes in the Scots style that have been published in subsequent collections, it is very difficult to distinguish between the ancient and modern." (Hawkins' Hist. vol. iv. p. 6.)—The earlier volumes of this well-known collection passed through several editions, which was enlarged in 1720, by the publication of a sixth volume.

## THOMSON'S ORPHEUS CALEDONIUS—1725.

"Orpheus Caledonius, or a collection of the best Scotch Songs, set to musick, by W Thomson. London; engraved and printed for the Author, at his house, in Leicester Fields.

Enter'd at Stationers' Hall, according to Act of Parliament." Folio.

This volume is dedicated to Her Royal Highness the Princess of Wales, afterwards Queen Caroline, and contains fifty songs, engraved on separate folios, followed by eight leaves, containing the airs of the songs "for the flute." This work may be considered as entitled to the distinction of being the first professed collection of Scotish Tunes. Although it bears no date, the year usually given to it is correct, as the Editor appeared, and entered his work in the books at the Stationers' Hall, 5th of January 1725.

In the index, Thomson affixes a (*) to the seven following Songs, as having been "composed by David Rezzio." "The Lass of Patie's Mill."—"Bessie Bell."—"The Bush aboon Traquair."—"The Bonny Boatman."—"An' thou wert my ain thing."—"Auld Rob Morris"—and "Down the Burn, Davie." In republishing this work, as the first volume of his Orpheus, in 1733, no such marks are affixed.

### THOMSON'S ORPHEUS—1733.

"Orpheus Caledonius: or a Collection of Scots Songs, set to musick, by W. Thomson. London; printed for the author, at his house in Leicester-Fields, 1733," 2 vols. 8vo.

The license granted by George I. for printing this work, to "our trusty and well-beloved William Thomson, of our City of London, Gent.," for the term of fourteen years, is dated 11th May 1733. Each volume contains fifty Songs. The 1st vol., as in the folio edition, is dedicated "To the Queen;" the 2d vol. "To her Grace the Dutchess of Hamilton."

William Thomson was the son of Daniel Thomson,

one of the King's Trumpeters, and when a boy made his appearance at the grand concert on St Cecilia's day, at Edinburgh, in November 1695.—" Daniel Thomson (says Mr Tytler in his account of that concert) was one of the King's trumpeters, and was said to have understood music, and to have been a good performer of the obligato, or solo parts, in the trumpet songs of Purcell's Opera of Dioclesian, Bonduca, and other theatrical pieces then exhibited on the stage. . . . His son, William Thomson, was early distinguished for the sweetness of his voice, and the agreeable manner in which he sung a Scots song. He went to London; and at the time when the Opera, and the compositions of Handel, were at their height, the sweet pathetic manner of Thomson's singing a Scots song, which he accompanied with a thorough bass, became a fashionable entertainment at Court, where he often performed."

" In February 1722, there was a benefit concert for Mr Thomson, the first editor of a collection of Scots tunes in England. To this collection, for which there was a very large subscription, may be ascribed the subsequent favour of these national melodies south of the Tweed. After this concert, ' at the desire of several persons of quality,' was performed a *Scottish Song*."—(Burney's Hist. vol. iv. p. 647.)

Hawkins (vol. iv. p. 7) says of Thomson—" The editor was not a musician, *but a tradesman*, and the collection is accordingly injudicious, and very incorrect." I should think he must have been misinformed in making such a statement.

### TEA-TABLE MISCELLANY—circa 1726.

" Musick for Allan Ramsay's collection of Scots Songs: Set by Alexander Stuart, and engraved by R. Cooper, Vol. First. Edinburgh; printed and sold by Allan Ramsay."

This is a small oblong volume of pp. 156, divided into six parts, and contains the music of seventy-one Songs, selected from the first volume of the Tea-Table Miscellany, printed in 1724. It is very scarce, and no second volume ever appeared. There is a frontispiece to the volume, of a lady touching a harpsichord (on which is the name of the maker, Fenton), and a gentleman with a violin in his hand. Each part has a separate title,—" Musick for the Scots Songs in the Tea-Table Miscellany. Part First," &c.

" Part First—inscrib'd to the Right Honourable Countess of Eglintoun,"—(Susanna Kennedy. To this lady Ramsay dedicated his Gentle Shepherd.)

" Part Second—inscrib'd to the Right Honourable Lady Somerville,"—(Anne Bayntun, grand-daughter of the witty Earl of Rochester.)

" Part Third—inscrib'd to the Honourable Lady Murray of Stanhope,"—(Grizzel Baillie, the lady who was the authoress of Memoirs of her Parents. See vol. ii. p. *100 of the present work.)

" Part Fourth—inscrib'd to the Honourable Lady Weir" (of Blackwood—Christian Anstruther, afterwards Countess of Traquair.)

" Part Fifth—inscrib'd to Miss Christian Campbell."

" Part Sixth—inscrib'd to Mrs Young."

## BOCCHI'S SONATAS—1726.

" Signor LORENZO BOCCHI has published an Opera of his own composition, by Subscription, containing 12 Sonatas, or Solos, for different instruments, viz. a Violin, Flute, Violoncello, Viola de Gamba, and Scots Cantate; with instrumental parts, after the Italian manner, the words by Mr Ramsay; with a thorow Bass for the Harpsichord. Subscribers may have their copies at Mr John Steill's any time before the first of March ensuing. Any person that has not subscribed, may likewise be furnished, there being more copies cast off than will serve the Subscribers."—*Caledonian Mercury*, February 22, 1726.

In Allan Ramsay's Poems, vol. ii. p. 271, is inserted "A Scots Cantata,—Music by L. Bocchi." It begins, "*Blate Johny faintly tald.*" Whether Mr John Steill was a Music-seller, is uncertain; but there was advertised for the 26th of February 1729, a "Sale by Auction, of the haill Pictures, Prints, Musick-books, and Musical Instruments belonging to Mr John Steill."—(*Caled. Mercury.*)

## WATTS'S MUSICAL MISCELLANY—1729–1731.

"The Musical Miscellany; being a Collection of Choice Songs, set to the Violin and Flute, by the most eminent Masters.

> The man that hath no musick in himself,
> And is not mov'd with concord of sweet sounds,
> Is fit for treasons, stratagems, and spoils.
>
> SHAKESPEAR.

Volume First. London, printed by and for John Watts, at the Printing-office in Wild Court, near Lincoln's-Inn Fields, 1729." 2 vols. small 8vo.

"The Musical Miscellany; being a Collection of Choice Songs and Lyrick Poems; with the Basses to each Tune, and transpos'd for the Flute, by the most eminent masters. Vols. 3 and 4, London, &c., 1730: Vols. 5 and 6, London, &c., 1731, small 8vo.

This collection, forming six volumes, includes several Scotish airs and songs, evidently derived from Thomson's Orpheus, 1725, or the Tea-Table Miscellany.

## CRAIG'S COLLECTION—1730.

"A Collection of the choicest Scots Tunes, adapted for the Harpsichord or Spinnet, and within the compass of the Voice, Violin, or German Flute. By Adam Craig. Edinburgh, 1730. R. Cooper, fecit. Entered in Stationer's Hall." Oblong folio, pp. 45, besides the titles and dedication. It is thus dedicated "To the Honourable Lords and Gentlemen of the Musical Society of Mary's Chappell:" "As you are generous encouragers and great promoters of Musick, it is natural for me, on this occasion, to beg your patronage, which is my highest ambition. The following collection, being the first of the kind, and the nature and genuine product of the country, I flatter myself that the countenance and protection of so noble a Society will make it generally acceptable, and contribute much to the benefit of, my Lords and Gentlemen,

"Your most dutiful and most obedient servant,

"ADAM CRAIG."

ADAM CRAIG was a leading performer at the Concert on St Cecilia's Day, in 1695, at Edinburgh. Mr Tytler, in the Transactions of the Antiquarian Society, vol. i. 1792, published an interesting paper, containing a programme, "The Order of the Instrumental Music for the Feast of St Cecilia, 22d November 1695;" and giving the names of the performers. Mr T. says, "Adam Craig was reckoned a good orchestra player on the violin, and teacher of music. I remember him as the second violin to M'Gibbon, in the Gentleman's Concert." In the "Catalogue of Musick, being the complete and curious Collection of the late Lord Colville, to be sold by auction, on the 26th day of November 1728," 4to, pp. 70, are several manuscript articles, as well as printed works, some of which are noted as "brought from Italy," or "brought from Rome," by Mr Michael Kinkaid. One article in the Catalogue is "Mr Adam Craig's Works, in one book, folio MS." Robert Lord Colville of Ochiltree, it may be added, was a celebrated musical amateur, as well as collector. Lord Colville succeeded his father in February 1671, and died unmarried 26th of March 1728. He is said to have been "a thorough master of Music, and to have understood counterpoint well." He played on the Harpsichord and Organ; and he was one of the performers at "the Feast of St Cecilia," in 1695.

> The God of Musick joins when Colvil plays,
> And all the Muses dance to Haddington's Essays;
> The charms are mutual, peircing, and compleat—
> This in his art excells, and that in wit."
>
> *De Foe's Caledonia,* 1706.

According to Professor Mackie's MS. Obituary, (see vol. iv. p. *384,) "Adam Craig, musician," died in October 1741.

### MUNRO'S COLLECTION—1730.

ALEXANDER MUNRO'S Collection, is thus quoted by Hawkins (Hist. of Music, vol. iv. p. 7) :—

"About the year 1730, one Alexander Munroe, a native of Scotland, then residing at Paris, published a collection of the best Scotch Tunes fitted to the German Flute, with several divisions and variations; but the simplicity of the airs is lost in the attempts of the author to accommodate them to the style of Italian music."

Riddell, in the preface to his Border Tunes, also mentions that this collection was printed at Paris; and that its chief excellency is the fine basses that accompany the tunes. I regret not having had an opportunity to see this collection.

## AIRS FOR THE FLUTE—1735.

"Airs for the Flute, with a thorough Bass for the Harpsichord." Small oblong 4to, pp. 27. Dedication.—"To the Right Honourable the Lady Gairlies (Lady Catharine Cochrane.) Madam,—The following airs having been composed by a Gentleman for your Ladyship's use when you began to practice the Flute à Beque, I thought I could not chuse a better subject for my First Essay, as an engraver of musick, than these airs; as well because they were made for beginners on the Flute and Harpsichord, as that they were composed by a gentleman who first put a pencil in my hand, and then an engraver; but chiefly because they were originally made for your ladyship's use, which gives me so fair a handle to send them into the world under the protection of your Ladyship's name. I am, with the greatest respect, Madam,

Your Ladyship's most obedient and most humble servant,

"ALEX. BAILLIE.

"*Edinburgh, December* 1735."

Who the gentleman was that composed these Airs has not been stated.

## JAMES OSWALD—1735-1742.

The earliest notices of this eminent collector and composer of Scotish Melodies, which I have been able to meet with, are the following advertisements in the Caledonian Mercury. From these it appears that Oswald was originally a dancing-master in Dunfermline, and that he afterwards came to Edinburgh, where he taught both dancing and music.

"There is to be published by subscription, a Collection of Minuets, adapted for the Violin and Bass Viol, with a thorough Bass for the Harpsichord or Spinnet—most of them within the compass of the Hautboy or German Flute. Composed by JAMES OSWALD, Dancing-master. Each subscriber to give in two shillings at subscribing, and three shillings on receipt of the book. Subscriptions will be taken in at Edinburgh, by Mr Cooper, engraver; and at Dunfermline, by the author. 'Tis expected that such as do not incline their names should be prefixed, will signify it. The author desires they who have taken the trouble to get subscriptions will send the lists to him at Dunfermline, with first occasion.—*N. B.* The author has by him several Sonatas and Solos, one of which is to be published along with this collection: if it is well received, the rest, with some other pieces of Musick, may in time be published."—(August 12th, 1734.)

"MR OSWALD is to publish his book of Musick, against Friday the 16th of January inst. Therefore, all subscribers for said book, are desired to call at Mr Andrew Martin, Bookseller, at his Shop, in the Parliament Close; or at the Author's Lodgings in Skinner's Close (where he teaches Dancing, in company with Mr Jones), to receive their Copies, upon paying the full Subscription, being three shillings to those who have paid the first moiety, and five shillings to those who have not."—(January 6th, 1736.)

"Whereas MR OSWALD, musician in Edinburgh, is, at the request of several ladies and gentlemen, publishing by subscription a Collection of Scots Tunes before he sets out for Italy, which will consist of above 50 Tunes, many of which were never before printed, and all within the compass of the Hautboy and German Flute, with Thorough Bass for the Harpsichord and Spinnet; and amongst which there are several new Mason Songs, with words for three voices. Subscriptions taken in at his lodgings in Carrubber's Close; at Messrs A. Kincaid, G. Hamilton & Co., A. Martin, W. Miller, Booksellers; and at the Exchange Coffee-House, Edinburgh.—*N. B.* The Subscribers will please send in their names, as also those who have Subscription Papers, before the 1st of June next, by which time the book will be published. The Price to Subscribers is 5s., on delivery of the Book, and to others 6s."—(May 8th, 1740; repeated on the 15th, 19th, and 22d of the same month.)

Whether Oswald visited Italy, and how long he remained are uncertain; but London appearing a wider field for his exertions than the Scotish Metropolis, he settled there in 1741 or 1742. See the Epistle in verse, addressed to him on his leaving Edinburgh, in vol. iv. p. 405, of the present work; where some further notices respecting him are given.

OSWALD'S SCOTS TUNES—1740.

"A Curious Collection of Scots Tunes, for a Violin, Bass Viol, or German Flute, with a thorough Bass for the Harpsichord; as also a Sonata of Scots Tunes, in three parts, and some Mason's Songs, with the Words, for three voices; to which is added a number of the most celebrated Scots Tunes, set for a Violin or German Flute. By James Oswald, Musician in Edinburgh." No date; oblong folio, pp. 42.

This work is dedicated "To His Grace James Duke of Perth;" and it might be inferred, from the name of James Colquhoun, Esq., as "Lord Provost of Edinburgh," appearing in a numerous list of subscribers, that it was published either in the year 1738 or 1739. The above advertisement proves that it did not appear till June 1740.

"A Collection of curious Scots Tunes, for a Violin, German Flute, or Harpsichord. By Mr James Oswald. London; printed for Charles and Samuel Thompson in St Paul's Churchyard." The name of some former publisher has been erased. Folio, pp. 46. At the end, "Philips, Sculp."

"A Second Collection of curious Scots Tunes for a Violin and German Flute, with a thorough Bass for the Harpsichord. By Mr James Oswald. London, &c. (as above.)" Folio, pp. 47.

These two collections originally appeared in 1742; they are included in the list of new publications in the Scots Magazine, November 1742.—The following tunes in the first part—"The Cock Laird"—"The Black Eagle"—

"Peggy, I must love thee"—"The Lowlands of Holland" —"William's Ghost"—and "The last time I came o'er the moor," are ascribed to "David Rizo." The following MS. note, however, inserted in a copy of the work, contradicts this, and claims them as Oswald's compositions.

"The airs in this volume, with the name of David "Rizo affixed, are all Oswald's. I state this on the autho-"rity of Mrs Alexander Cumming and my mother—his "daughter and sister. (signed) H. O. Weatherley."—"Died at Chester le Street, in the county of Durham, in her 80th year, Nov. 13, 1821, Mrs Weatherley, relict of the late Mr Edward Weatherley of Garden House in the same county, and sister of the late James Oswald, Esq., Chamber Composer to his late Majesty, and justly celebrated as the author of 'Roslin Castle,' 'Tweedside,' and numerous compositions of lasting eminence."

## MACFARLANE'S COLLECTIONS—1740.

"A Collection of Scotch Airs, with the latest Variations, written for the use of Walter M'Farlan of that ilk. By David Young, W. M. in Edinburgh, 1740." MS. 3 vols. folio.

The Laird of Macfarlane, for whom this collection was compiled, was an eminent antiquary, who died in 17 . His manuscripts having been disposed of after his death, the chief portions were acquired for the Advocates' Library. The above collection is chiefly curious from the number of tunes it contains. They are written with all the care of a person, who, from the initials W. M. added to his name, we may conclude, was a writing-master: The volumes were presented by the Honourable Henry Erskine (brother of the Earl of Buchan), to the Society of the Antiquaries of Scotland, 23d of July 1782. Unfortunately, the first volume was borrowed from the Society many years ago, and has never been recovered. The second volume, dated 1740, contains pp. 288, and 250 airs. In the third volume, the date of which is torn off, there are pp. 288, and 292 airs. None of the airs have basses; and to some of them the names of the composers are given, viz., Oswald, M'Gibbon, [——Forbes of?] Disblair, and M'Lean. A few also have the initials of the compiler, D. Y[oung].

### WALSH'S COLLECTION—circa 1740.

"A Collection of original Scotch Songs, with a thorough Bass to each Song, for the Harpsichord. London; printed for and sold by I. Walsh, servant to his Majesty, at the Harp and Hoboy, in Katharine Street, in the Strand." Folio.

This is merely a collection of Songs which had been engraved and sold as single leaves, without any order or arrangement, and including English imitations of Scotish Songs, sung at Vauxhall Gardens, and other places of public amusement.

### WALSH'S COUNTRY DANCES.

"Caledonian Country Dances, being a Collection of all the celebrated Scotch Country Dances now in vogue, with the proper Directions to each Dance, as they are performed at Court and public entertainments. For the Violin, Hoboy, or German Flute, with their Basses for the Bass Violin or Harpsichord. Engraven in a fair character, and carefully corrected. London, printed for, and sold by J. Walsh, music printer and instrument maker to His Majesty, at the Harp and Hoboy in Catherine Street in the Strand." Small oblong 8vo. Eight vols. Many of the dances are not Scotish.—There are later impressions of this work.

## BARSANTI'S COLLECTION—1742.

" A Collection of Old Scots Tunes, with the Bass for Violoncello or Harpsichord, set, and most humbly dedicated to the Right Honourable the Lady Erskine, (Lady Charlotte Hope,) by Francis Barsanti. Edinburgh, printed by Alexander Baillie, and sold by Messrs Hamilton and Kincaid; price 2s. 6d." Folio, pp. 15.

This collection was published 14th of January 1742, (Caledonian Mercury, and Scots Magazine for January 1742.)

Barsanti, a native of Lucca, was born about the year 1690. He commenced his studies of civil law at Padua, but afterwards chose music for his profession, and came to England in the year 1714. He continued many years a performer at the Opera house; but at length, with some favourable prospects, he settled in Scotland; "and, with greater truth than the same is asserted of David Rizzio, he may be said to have meliorated the music of that country, by collecting and making basses to a great number of the most popular Scots Tunes." About the year 1750, Barsanti returned to England, (Hawkins, History of Music, vol. iv. p. 37.)—Barsanti had a daughter who made a considerable figure on the stage. Her portrait is prefixed to Bell's edition of Shakspeare's Midsummer Night's Dream.

## MACGIBBON'S COLLECTIONS—1746-1755.

" Six Sonatos or Solos for a German flute or violin, composed by Willm. M'Gibbon. Edinburgh; printed by R. Cooper for the author. 1740." Oblong folio.

" A Collection of Scots Tunes, some with Variations for a Violin, Hautboy, or German Flute, with a bass for a Violoncello or Harpsichord. By William M'Gibbon. Book 1st.

—*N. B.* Where there is double notes, the highest is for the flute, and the lowest for the violin. Edinburgh; printed by Richard Cooper. 1742." Oblong folio, pp. 36.

"A Second Collection, &c. Edinburgh; printed by Richard Cooper, 1746." Oblong folio, pp. 36.

"A (Third) Collection, &c. Edinburgh; printed by Richard Cooper. 1755. Oblong folio, pp. 36.

A second edition of the first two collections, (in 1755 or 1756) bears on the title, "Edinburgh; printed and sold by R. Bremner, at the Harp and Hautboy."

Another edition in 8vo, of the three books, bears "London; printed for D. Rutherford, in St Martin's Lane," &c.

An edition of M'Gibbon's Collection, in three books, with some additions, by Bremner, is advertised in the Scots Magazine, February 1762. There is also an edition, "With some additions, by Robert Bremner. London, printed and sold at the Music-shop of Robert Bremner, opposite Somerset-house." Oblong 4to, pp. 120. It contains 4 books.

William Macgibbon, was "well known and celebrated in his time for his great execution on the violin." His father, Matthew Macgibbon, was esteemed a good performer on the Hautboy; and was one of the performers at St Cecilia's Concert, in 1695. His son William (according to Mr Tytler) "was sent early to London, and studied many years under Corbet, then reckoned a great master and composer. Corbet's sonatas for two Violins and a Bass were esteemed good, and often played as act-tunes in the play-house. His scholar William M'Gibbon was for many years leader of the orchestra of the Gentlemen's Concert at Edinburgh, and was thought to play the music of Corelli, Geminiani, and Handel, with great execution and judgment. His sets of Scots tunes, with variations and basses, are well known." This eminent composer, and editor of the above collections of Scotish tunes, between 1740 and 1755, died at Edinburgh the 3d of October 1756. According to the obituary notice in the Scots Magazine, 1756, p. 470, he bequeathed the whole of his estate and effects to the Royal Infirmary.

Fergusson the poet, in his "Elegy on Scots Music," pays the following compliment to Macgibbon. He was too young, however, to have had any personal recollection of the musician.

Macgibbon's gane: ah! wae's my heart!
The man in music maist expert,
Wha could sweet melody impart,
And tune the reed,
Wi' sic a slee and pawky art;
But now he's dead.

Ilk carline now may grunt and grane,
Ilk bonny lassie make great mane,
Since he's awa', I trow there's nane
Can fill his stead;
The blythest sangster on the plain!
Alake, he's dead.

There is a miniature portrait of Macgibbon introduced, as a vignette, in the title-page of "Flores Musicæ, or the Scots Musician," published by J. Clark, at Edinburgh, in 1773.

### BREMNER'S COLLECTIONS, &c.—1749.

"Thirty Scots Songs for a Voice and Harpsichord. The music taken from the most genuine sets extant; the words from Allan Ramsay. Price 2s. 6d. Edinburgh; printed for, and sold by R. Bremner, at the Harp and Hoboy." Folio, pp. 33. "Circa 1749. This is a genuine copy of the first impression before Bremner went to London; it is extremely rare. The title page was afterwards altered."—(MS. note by Mr Stenhouse.)

"A Second Set of Scots Songs for a Voice or Harpsichord. Price 2s. 6d. Edinburgh, printed, &c. (as above.)" Folio, pp. 33.

"Twelve Scots Songs, for a Voice or Guitar, with a thorough Bass adapted for that instrument. By Robert Bremner. Price 1s. 6d. Edinburgh, printed and sold at his music-shop," &c. [1760.] Oblong 4to, pp. 18; advertised in Scots Magazine, May 1760.

"A Collection of Scots Reels or Country Dances, with a Bass for the Violoncello or Harpsichord. Price 6s. London, printed and sold by Robert Bremner, at the Harp and Hautboy, in the Strand." [1764?] Oblong 4to.

"A curious Collection of Scots Tunes, with Variations for the Violin, and a Bass for the Violoncello or Harpsichord. Music, 2s. 6d. Bremner." Advertised in Scots Magazine, Aug. 1759.

"The Songs in the Gentle Shepherd, adapted to the Guitar. Music 1s. 6d. Bremner." Scots Magazine, December 1759.

"Thirty Scots Songs, by Robert Bremner. The words by Allan Ramsay. London, printed and sold by R. Bremner, opposite Somerset House, in the Strand."

"The Freemason's Songs, with Choruses, in three and four parts, and a Bass for the Organ or Violoncello. Music 1s. Bremner." Scots Magazine, June, 1759.

Bremner, as above stated, settled in London. This probably was about 1764, and he continued for a number of years to carry on an extensive business as a music-seller. "Mr Robert Bremner, Music-Printer in the Strand, died at Kensington, 12th of May, 1789."

## OSWALD'S POCKET COMPANION—1759.

"The Caledonian Pocket Companion, containing a favourite Collection of Scotch Tunes, with Variations for the German Flute or Violin. By James Oswald."

This work was originally published in successive books or parts, at "London; printed for the Author, and sold at his musick shop in St Martin's Churchyard in the Strand." This imprint was afterwards altered to "London; printed for J. Simpson in Sweeting's Alley," &c. Later copies bear "London; printed for Straight and Skillern, St Martin's Lane;" but all of them without dates. Oswald himself, on completing the 7th part, published them with the general title, "The Caledonian Pocket Companion, in seven volumes;" but the entire work extends to 12 parts, usually bound in two volumes.

Among Oswald's miscellaneous compositions are the following:—

"Colin's Kisses, set to musick by Mr Oswald. Printed in the year 1743." (The Kisses, as appears from a MS. note, were written by Robert Dodsley). 4to.

"Six pastoral Solos for a Violin and Violoncello, with a thorough Bass for the Organ or Harpsichord, composed by James Oswald. Printed for the author, and sold at his music shop in St Martin's Churchyard. Price 5s." Oblong folio, pp. 16.

"Airs for the Spring, Summer, Autumn, and Winter. By James Oswald. Printed for the author, and sold at his music shop, St Martin's Churchyard." 4 parts, folio, The same engraved frontispiece serves for all the Seasons, which were published separately.

At the end of "The Comic Tunes in Queen Mab, as they are performed at the Theatre-Royal in Drury Lane; set for the Violin, German Flute, or Hoboy, with a thorough

Bass for the Harpsichord, composed by James Oswald," is the following notice of an edition of Oswald's works. It has no date; but what publication was here meant is uncertain:—

"Some time before Mr Oswald's death, he had fitted for the press a correct edition of his works, as well those that were known and acknowledged to be his, as those that were really such, but had formerly been published under the names of others, for reasons not difficult to guess. There are many excellent composers whose circumstances will not permit them to please themselves, by addressing their compositions to the heart, instead of the ear only. His fine taste, his elegant compositions, his pathetic performance, were well known and justly admired.

"In compliance with his own intentions, a genuine edition of his works is now presented to the public. For such a publication no apology is necessary. That they are his, is sufficient to justify their appearance, and recommend them to all good judges and true lovers of musick."

### BURK HUMOTH'S AIRS—circa 1760.

"Twelve Scotch and twelve Irish Airs, with Variations, set for the German Flute, Violin, or Harpsichord, by Mr Burk Humoth. London; printed for, and sold by John Simpson, at the Bass Viol and Flute, in Sweeting's Alley," &c. Royal 8vo, pp. 49.

### GENERAL REID'S MINUETS, &c.—1770.

"A Sett of Minuets and Marches, inscribed to the Right Hon. Lady Catharine Murray, by J[ohn] R[eid], Esq. London; printed and sold by R. Bremner, in the Strand." Price 5s. Oblong 4to, pp. 31. This contains, at the end of the minuets, three marches, and Athole House, ditto.

"Six Solos for a German Flute or Violin, with a thorough Bass for the Harpsichord, by J[ohn] R[eid], Esq., a member of the Temple of Apollo. London; printed for J. Oswald, and sold at all the musick shops." Oblong folio. "A Second Sett of Six Solos," &c.

"Captain Reid's Solos." Sold also by Bremner, as appears from his catalogue of music.

The name of GENERAL REID, in regard to the "Musical Museum," is only connected with one air, (according to the note at page 202;) but as it is likely he will be long and gratefully remembered in this country, a more than casual notice in this place may be excused. In his Will, dated at London 19th of April 1803, he styles himself "JOHN REID of Woodstock Street, Oxford Street, in the county of Middlesex, Esquire, General in His Majesty's Army, and Colonel of the 88th regiment of foot;" and states, that he was "the last representative of an old family in Perthshire, which on my death will be extinct in the male line."

General Reid was the son of Robertson, alias Reid of Straloch, a property near Strathardel, in Perthshire—a family whose head was anciently designated as Baron Reid.

He mentions that his birthday was the 13th of February, but he omits to say in what year. It must have been about 1720, or 1721. He was sent to the University of Edinburgh, and we find his name in the list of Professor Stevenson's Classes, in 1734 and 1735. How long he continued at the University, where he says, "I had my education, and passed the pleasantest part of my youth," or what other classes he attended is uncertain, as the lists of students at that time have only been partially preserved. But this recollection of his earlier days had no doubt its influence, when he bequeathed the reversion of his property to the University. Having embraced a military profession, he himself mentions his having been a lieutenant in the Earl of Loudon's regiment, raised in the year 1745.

By his will, General Reid bequeathed the bulk of his fortune to the Principal and Professors of the University of Edinburgh, with the special provision for endowing a Professorship of Music; and as his property (to the amount of nearly L.80,000) has now become available by the death of his relations, who had a liferent of the property, we may speedily expect this part of his will carried into effect; and there can be no doubt that the appointment of a gentleman thoroughly acquainted with the history, theory, and practice of music, may be the means of raising the character, and giving an impetus to the progress, of that science in this country, that will tend to perpetuate the name and liberality of the founder. General Reid died at his house in the Haymarket, London, 6th of February 1807, aged 87. He directs in his will, that annually on his birthday, the 13th of February, there shall be a concert of music, including a full military band, and to perform some specimens of his own compositions, to show the style of music that prevailed about the middle of the last century.

## CLARK'S FLORES MUSICÆ—1773.

"Flores Musicæ, or the Scots Musician, being a general Collection of the most celebrated Scots Tunes, Reels, Minuets, and Marches. Adapted for the Violin, Hautboy, or German Flute, with a Bass for the Violincello or Harpsichord. Published the 1st June, 1773, by J. Clark, plate and seal engraver, printer, &c., first fore stair below the head of Forrester's Wynd, Edinburgh." Folio, pp. viii. 8vo.

From an advertisement in the Scots Magazine, May 1773, this collection was to be published in twenty numbers; but probably no second part ever appeared. The editor's name is not mentioned. A small vignette portrait of "W. Macgibbon," is engraved in the centre of the title page. In the preface, it is stated that "David Rizzio is now generally fixed upon as the composer of the best of those delicate songs; but how so gross a falsehood comes to be so universally believed, is not easy to determine. That the Scots music is of no older a date than two centuries ago, no one, we hope, will venture to assert, who is in the least acquainted with the history of the kingdom," &c. The editor professes to have "examined a great variety of old manuscripts, and endeavoured with the utmost accuracy to trace out the errors that have of late but too frequently appeared in the editions of Scots tunes," and to have "adhered as closely as possible to their primitive simplicity." The number of tunes given is 22.

### LORD KELLY'S MINUETS, &c.—1774.

"The favourite Minuets, perform'd at the Fete Champetre, given by Lord Stanley at the Oaks, and composed by the Right Honourable the Earl of Kelly. Price 2s. London; printed for and sold by William Napier, the corner of Lancaster Court, Strand." Oblong 4to, published 1774 or 5. Lady Betty Hamilton, daughter of the Duke of Hamilton, was married to Lord Stanley, afterwards Earl of Derby, in 1774. This fete was given on occasion of their nuptials.

Some notice of Lord Kelly is given in a subsequent part of this work. (See vol. vi. pp. 529 and 532.) He died at Brussels, 9th of October 1781, in the fifty-first year of his age.

### FRAZER'S COUNTRY DANCES—1774.

"The Dancer's Pocket Companion, being a Collection of Forty Scots and English figures of Country Dances, with two elegant copperplates, showing all the different figures made use of in Scots or English Country Dancing. Properly explained, by William Frazer, Dancing-master. Edinburgh, printed in the year 1774." 12mo., pp. 16.

There is, however, no music to the figures.

### NEILL STEWART'S COLLECTION, circa 1775.

"Thirty Scots Songs, adapted for a Voice or Harpsichord. The words of Allan Ramsay. Edinburgh. Book 1st, price 3s. 6d. Printed and sold by N. Stewart and Co., No. 37, South Bridge Street. J. Johnson, sculpt." Folio, pp. 31.—The same, book second, price 3s., pp. 33. Book third. Printed and sold by Neil Stewart, at his Shop, No. 37, South Bridge Street. J. Johnson, sculpt. Edinburgh, pp. 28.

"A New Collection of Scots and English Tunes, adapted to the Guitar, with some of the best Songs out of the Beggar's Opera, and other curious Ballads, most of them within the compass of the common flute. Price 1s. 6d. Printed and sold by Neil Steuart, at the music-shop opposite the head of Blackfryers Wynd, Edinburgh." Oblong 4to, circa 1760.

"A Collection of the newest and best Minuets, adapted for the Violin or German Flute, with a Bass for the Violoncello or Harpsichord. Edinburgh; printed for and sold by Neil Steuart, at his music-shop, opposite to the Tron Church." Oblong 4to, pp. 94, circa 1770.

This collection, which is almost entirely Scotish, contains some of Lord Kelly's compositions.

"A Second Collection of Airs and Marches for Two Violins, German Flutes, and Hautboys, all of which have Basses for the Violoncello or Harpsicord. Edinburgh; printed and Sold by N. Stewart, at his shop, Parliament

Closs. Where may be had, The first Collection of Marches and Airs. Price 6s."

"A Collection of Scots Songs, adapted for a Voice or Harpsichord. Edinburgh; printed and sold by Neil Stewart, at his shop, Parliament Square." Folio, circa 1790, pp. 28.

### DOW'S MINUETS—circa 1775.

"Twenty Minuets, and sixteen Reels or Country Dances, for the Violin, Harpsichord, or German Flute. Composed by Daniel Dow. Edinburgh; printed for the author, and sold at the music-shops, in town and country. Entered at Stationers' Hall. Price 2s. 6d." Oblong 4to, pp. 36. Mr Sharpe mentions, that his mother told him that Dow was a teacher of music, particularly the guitar, when she was a young girl.

Collection of Ancient Scots Music, (Highland Airs,) by Daniel Dow, (title-page wanting,) about 1778. Oblong folio, pp. 44.

### PEACOCK'S AIRS—circa 1776.

"Fifty favourite Scotch Airs, for a Violin, German Flute, and Violoncello, with a thorough Bass for the Harpsichord. Dedicated to the Right Honourable James Earl of Erroll, Lord High Constable of Scotland, &c., by Francis Peacock. London; printed for the publisher in Aberdeen, and sold by Mrs Johnson in Cheapside; Thompson & Sons, St Paul's Churchyard; R. Bremner, N. Stewart, in Edinburgh; and A. Angus in Aberdeen." Folio, pp. 35, with Lord Errol's arms engraved on the title page. His Lordship died 3d of July 1778.

The preface contains this silly passage—"No species of

pastoral music is more distinguished by the applause and admiration of all good judges than the songs of David Rizzio. We cannot, indeed, certainly distinguish his compositions from those of his imitators, nor can we determine whether he formed the musical taste of the Scots, or only adapted himself to the musical taste established before his time; but if we may believe tradition, it is to him that the Scots are indebted for many of their finest airs; and custom has now affixed his name to this particular mode of musical composition."—The book was published by subscription.

Francis Peacock died on the 26th June 1807, aged eighty-four years, as is stated on a marble tablet, erected to his memory on the wall of Collison's Aisle, on the north side of St Nicholas Church, at Aberdeen. The aisle has been lately taken down. There is a notice of him in The History of Aberdeen, by Walter Thom, vol. ii. p. 192. Aberdeen, 1811. 2 vols. 12mo. Mr Peacock died in pretty easy circumstances, leaving a considerable sum to the charitable institutions of the town. A lane on the north side of the Castlegate is called after him Peacock's Close. His dancing-school was in an old house called Pitfoddell's lodging, in the Castlegate, which was taken down about the year 1800, to make way for the office of the Aberdeen Banking Company.

I am indebted for the above information to Joseph Robertson, Esq., F.S.A. Scot.; and for the following communication to William Dauney, Esq., advocate.

Francis Peacock, the author of the Collection of Scottish Tunes published at Aberdeen, was a dancing-master in that place, where he died about the year 1806. He was well versed in the science of music, and an excellent player on the violin and violoncello, upon both of which instruments he used to perform at the concerts of the Aberdeen Musical Society, an institution on the model of the St Cecilia Hall, and supported by the nobility and gentry of that part of the country, among whom were the father of the late Duke of Gordon, the grandfather of the present Earl of Kintore, Dr Beattie, &c. Dr Beattie himself was a tolerable performer on the violoncello. Another gentleman who distinguished himself as an amateur of this Society was Mr Littleton, a brother of Sir George Littleton, who lived for many years in Aberdeen. He had been a barrister, but had retired from public life, and selected Aberdeen for his residence, as a comparatively secluded part of the world, where he might enjoy the amusements of shooting, fishing, and music, free from the cares and bustle of society; and, to disconnect himself the more completely from his family, he changed his patronymic to Smith, and was usually known in that quarter under the name of 'Fishing Smith.' Some account of him will be found in Mr Pryse Gordon's very amusing Memoirs, published a few years ago."

### FOULIS'S SOLOS—circa 1776.

"Six Solos for the Violin, with a Bass for a Violoncello or Harpsichord. Composed by a Gentleman." Inscribed to the Honourable Francis Charteris, Esq. of Amisfield, (afterwards Earl of Wemyss.) In a copy that belonged to the late Charles Sharpe of Hoddam, Esq., the author's name is given as "Foulis." Folio, pp. 26.—The above date 1776, is perhaps a few years too recent.

### MACLEAN'S COLLECTION—circa 1776.

"A Collection of favourite Scots Tunes, with Variations for the Violin, and a Bass for the Violoncello or Harpsichord. By the late Mr Charles M'Lean and other eminent masters.

Edinburgh; printed for, and sold by N. Stewart, at his music-shop, Parliament Square." Oblong folio, pp. 37.

### M'GLASHAN'S COLLECTION—circa 1778.

"A Collection of Strathspey Reels, with a Bass for the Violoncello or Harpsichord. By Alexander M'Glashan. Edinburgh; printed for A. M'Glashan, and sold by Neil Stewart, at his music-shop, Parliament Square." Oblong folio, pp. 34.

"A Collection of Scots Measures, Hornpipes, Jigs, Allemands, Cotillons, and the fashionable Country Dances, with a Bass for the Violoncello or Harpsichord. By Alexander M'Glashan. Edinburgh; printed for the publisher, and sold by Neil Stewart, Parliament Square." Price 5s. Oblong folio, pp. 36.

ALEXANDER M'GLASHAN, "better known by the appellation of King M'Glashan, which he acquired from his tall stately appearance, and the showy style in which he dressed; and who, besides, was in high estimation as an excellent composer of Scottish airs, and an able and spirited leader of the fashionable bands."—(Chambers's Dict. vol. ii. p. 477.)

### CUMMING'S COLLECTION—1780.

"A Collection of Strathspey or old Highland Reels. By Angus Cumming, at Grantown in Strathspey.

> Come and trip it, as you go
> On the light fantastic toe,
> And in thy right hand lead with thee
> The mountain nymph, sweet Liberty.
>
> MILT.

Edinburgh, 1780." Oblong folio, pp. 20.

## M'DONALD'S HIGHLAND AIRS—1781.

"A Collection of Highland Vocal Airs, never hitherto published. To which are added a few of the most lively Country Dances, or Reels, of the North Highlands and Western Isles; and some specimens of Bagpipe Music. By Patrick M'Donald, Minister of Kilmore in Argyleshire. Edinburgh; printed for the publisher, and to be had at the Music-shops of Corri and Sutherland, Bridge Street, and N. Stewart, Parliament Square." [1781.] Folio, pp. 22 and 43. Dedicated "To the Noblemen and Gentlemen who compose the Highland Society in London."

The preface states, that "this is the largest collection of the Vocal music of the Highlands of Scotland that has ever been offered to the public." "Almost the whole of the North Highland airs, which form the first and the largest division of the following work, were collected by the late Mr Joseph M'Donald, the publisher's brother; whose musical genius and attainments, as well as the enthusiastic attachment which he had to the peculiar music of his native country, are still remembered by many. He was born in Strathnaver, the most northerly district of Scotland, and passed the first years of his life under the tuition of his father, who was a minister in that part of the country." He afterwards completed his studies at Haddington and Edinburgh, where he had the benefit of professional musical instruction. Previous to his going to the East Indies, in 1760, "he wrote out a copy of a number of the vocal airs which he had collected, and left it with a sister as a token of affection. All his other collections and papers relating to Highland music and poetry, he carried along with him. He did not live to accomplish his plan (of completing his collection of Highland airs.) A malignant fever cut him off, in the prime of life, before he had been much more than a twelvemonth in the country. His premature death will be considered, by the lovers of Highland music, as a public misfortune; as, from the collection which he had made, from his abilities and zeal, there was reason to expect from him a large and correct publication."

His brother, the Rev. Patrick M'Donald, was settled as minister of Kilmore, Presbytery of Lorn, Argyleshire, 12th of May 1757; and, after holding the incumbency for the very lengthened period of sixty-eight years, he died 25th of September 1824.

Prefixed to this volume is a Dissertation "On the influence of Poetry and Music upon the Highlanders." It is anonymous, but was written by the Rev. Walter Young (afterwards D.D.), who composed the basses. Dr Young, who was profoundly skilled in the theory of music, was settled as minister of Erskine in Renfrewshire, in 1772, and died at an advanced age, 6th of August 1814.

### NEIL GOW'S REELS—1784.

"A Collection of Strathspey Reels, with a Bass for the Violoncello or Harpsichord. By Neil Gow, at Dunkeld, 5s. N. Stewart, Edinburgh."—(Scots Magazine, August 1784.)

Neil Gow, so celebrated as a performer on the violin, and also as a composer of Scotish airs, was born in Perthshire on the 22d of March 1727. In the Scots Magazine for January 1809, appeared "A brief Biographical Account of Neil Gow," which has been attributed to the late Rev. Dr Macknight. A fuller account of Neil Gow, with a memoir of his son, Nathaniel Gow, and notices of their several publications, contributed by Joseph Macgregor, Esq., will be found in Chambers's Scottish Biography. Without attempting to give any analysis of these accounts, it may be sufficient to add, that Neil Gow died at Inver, near Dunkeld, on the 1st of March 1807; and his son at Edinburgh, 17th of January 1831.

AIRD'S COLLECTION—circa 1784.

" Selection of Scots, &c. Airs, adapted to the Fife, Violin, or German Flute. 3 vols.—each containing 200 airs. Price of each vol. 3s. 6d." Advertised in the title-page of Malcolm Macdonald's Strathspey Reels.

James Aird appears to have been settled in Glasgow, and to have carried on an extensive business as a Music-seller, during the latter half of the last century.

JOHN RIDDELL'S COLLECTION—circa 1786.

" A Collection of Scots Reels, Minuets, &c., for the Violin, Harpsichord, or German Flute. Composed by John Riddell, in Ayr. The second edition, greatly improved. Entered in Stationers' Hall. Glasgow; printed and sold by James Aird, at his music-shop in New Street." Oblong 4to, pp. 60.

Riddell's Scots Reels for Violin or Pianoforte. Published by J. Aird, Glasgow, price 5s. Advertised in the title-page of Macdonald's Strathspey Reels.

Burns, referring to the Air, No. CCLXXI. in the present collection, considered it to be " the happiest composition of that bard-born genius, John Riddell, of the family of Glencarnock, at Ayr."

MACDONALD'S REELS—circa 1786.

" A Collection of Strathspey Reels, with a Bass for the Violoncello or Harpsichord, dedicated to Mrs Baird of Newbyth. Composed by Malcolm Macdonald, Glasgow.

Printed and sold by J. Aird, and by the Author," &c. No date. Oblong 4to, pp. 24.

CORRI'S COLLECTION—circa 1788.

"A New and Complete Collection of the most favourite Scots Songs, including a few English and Irish, with proper Graces and Ornaments peculiar to their character; likewise the New Method of Accompaniment of thorough Bass. By Sig. Corri. Edinburgh, printed for, and sold by Corri and Sutherland." Two thin vols. folio. The title-page was probably from a design by D. Allan, and contains a portrait of Neil Gow. Folio.

Domenico Corri, in 1810, published "The Singer's Preceptor, or Corri's Treatise on Vocal Music," in 2 vols. folio. To this he prefixed a "Life" of himself, from which we learn, that he was born at Rome, 4th of October 1746. He early showed an inclination for Music, and was benefited by the instructions of several eminent masters. The Cardinal Portocaro, in whose establishment Corri's father was confectioner, in his zeal for the religious orders, used all his endeavours to persuade young Corri to study for the priesthood; but, after a few years, the Cardinal's death left him at liberty to follow the natural bent of his genius, to which his father was in no way disinclined.

"At Naples (he says) I lived and boarded with Porpora for five years, attended with great expense to my parents, and at his death returned again to Rome. The name of my preceptor, Porpora, was of great weight and service in my introduction to the first society in Rome, among whom were then residing many English noblemen and gentlemen, to whom I had soon the honour of becoming known; namely, the Dukes of Leeds and Dorset, Messrs Harley, Jones,

Lighton, Hanbury, Sir William Parsons, &c., &c., and particularly my highly esteemed friend Dr Burney. These fortunate connexions contributed to place me in a situation consonant to my wishes and interest, being appointed to conduct the concert parties which then took place among the Roman and English nobility. This period was the pontificate of Ganganelli, who was the friend of Prince Charles, the Pretender, brother of Cardinal York. That prince frequently gave entertainments and concerts to the nobility, the conducting of which was also assigned to me. With Prince Charles I had, previously to this period, lived two years, during which time he had kept entirely private, not seeing any one whatever, it being in the reign of the preceding Pope, who had refused to acknowledge the title he assumed. In his retired life Prince Charles employed his hours in exercise and music, of which he was remarkably fond. I usually remained alone with him every evening, the Prince playing the violoncello and I the harpsichord, also composing together little pieces of music; yet these *tête à tête's* were of a sombre cast. The apartment in which we sat was hung with old red damask, with two candles only, and on the table a pair of loaded pistols, (instruments not at all congenial to my fancy,) which he would often take up, examine, and again replace on the table; yet the manners of this prince were always mild, affable, and pleasing."

Before leaving his native country he married Miss Bacchelli; and he gives the following account of his coming to Edinburgh:—

"About this time (in 1780) the Musical Society of Edinburgh, wanting a singer and conductor for their concerts, wrote to l'Abbé Grant at Rome, desiring him to obtain for them, if possible, either of the two persons mentioned by Dr Burney. At the arrival of this letter, l'Abbé

Grant found these two persons, namely Miss Bacchelli and myself, united in marriage. This circumstance being no impediment to the proposal from Edinburgh, on the contrary a favourable occurrence, he immediately concluded for us an engagement for three years, at Edinburgh, with a handsome provision for our journey. We accordingly left Italy about three months after, and arrived at Edinburgh, August 1781 ; and here I beg leave to make my most sincere and grateful acknowledgements for the liberal favour and support we received from the noble families of Buccleuch, Gordon, Hamilton, Lauderdale, Argyle, Athol, Elphinstone, Kelly, Elgin, Errol, Haddo, Hopetoun, Melville, Haddington, Selkirk, Breadalbane, and Lothian, also the Gentlemen Directors of the Musical Society, and the Scotch nation in general. The second year of our Edinburgh engagement, proposals were made to me from London by Mr Yates, to compose for the Opera House, and by Messrs Bach and Abel to Mrs Corri, to sing at the first opening of the Hanover Square Rooms. These proposals we were enabled to accept through the kind indulgence of the directors of the Edinburgh society. After this season in London we again returned to Edinburgh, which engagement we continued eighteen years."

During that period, he lived alternately at London and Edinburgh; but, unfortunately, he involved himself in diffilties by the multiplicity of his affairs, in his management of the Theatre, his Pianoforte manufactory, his Musicselling, &c. At length, finding it necessary on account of his family to settle in London, he thus concludes the sketch of his life.

" I now conclude this short sketch of my professional life, adding, that at the age of sixty-four, still blessed with good health, I am enabled to pursue my musical career, and accustomed avocations of instructing in Vocal Music, the Pianoforte, thorough Bass, and Composition. I also continue to take young persons as apprentices, to qualify them as public professors, or private tutors.—N.B. Mrs Corri also instructs in Vocal and Instrumental Music."

Domenico Corri, died at Hampstead, 22d of May 1825. His younger brother, Natale Corri, as early as the year 1790, had also settled at Edinburgh as a Teacher of Music and Musicseller. He died at Weisbaden, 24th of June 1822, in the 57th year of his age.

SHIRREFFS'S AIRS, &c.—1788.

"The Overture, Airs, Songs, and Duets, in Jamie and Bess, by Andrew Shirreffs, A.M., 4s."—(Advertised along with the following in the Scots Magazine, May 1788.)

"Forty Pieces of Original Music, by Andrew Shirreffs, A.M., containing his Address to his Crutch, &c., 6s. Sold by the Author at Aberdeen: Stewart and Co. Edinburgh."

For some notice of Shirreffs, see vol. vi. pp. 479 and 525.

CLARKE'S SONATAS—circa 1790.

"Two Sonatas for the Piano-Forte or Harpsichord, in which are introduced favourite Scotch Airs, composed and respectfully dedicated to Mrs Erskine, junr. of Mar, by Stephen Clarke, Organist of the Episcopal Chapel, Edinburgh. Price 5s. Printed for and sold by the author," &c. Oblong folio, pp. 16.

Some account of STEPHEN CLARKE, who harmonized the airs in the present collection, is given in the Preface, p. xviii.

NAPIER'S COLLECTION—1790.

"A Selection of the most favourite Scots Songs, chiefly Pastoral, adapted for the Harpsichord, with an accompaniment for a Violin. By eminent Masters. Respectfully inscribed to Her Grace the Duchess of Gordon. Price L.1, 6s. London; printed for William Napier, Musicseller to their Majesties, No. 474, Strand." [1790.] Folio.

This was published by subscription, and contains Mr Tytler's dissertation at the beginning. The sets are excellent. Napier printed a second volume, "A Selection of original Scots Songs, in three Parts, the harmony by Haydn. Dedicated to H. R. H. the Duchess of York. London," &c. [1792.] Folio, pp. 101.—A Third volume was entered at Stationers' Hall in 1794.

CAMPBELL'S COUNTRY DANCES—circa 1790.

"Campbell's First Book of new and favourite Country Dances and Strathspey Reels, for the Harp, Piano-forte, and Violin. Printed and sold by Wm. Campbell, No. 8, Dean Street, Soho." This collection, in oblong 4to, was continued to Book 12th. Price each, 2s. 6d. Some of the tunes are marked as composed by W. Campbell.

BRYSON'S COLLECTION—1791.

"A curious selection of favourite tunes, with variations. To which are added upwards of fifty favourite Irish airs, for the German Flute or Violin; with a Bass for the Harpsichord or Violoncello, 5s. J. Bryson."—(Scots Magazine, June 1791.)

THE MUSICAL MISCELLANY—1792.

"The Edinburgh Musical Miscellany: a Collection of the most approved Scotch, English, and Irish Songs, set to Music. Selected by D. Sime, Edinburgh. Edinburgh, printed for W. Gordon, &c. 1792." The same, "Vol. II. Edinburgh, printed for John Elder, &c. 1793," 2 vols. 12mo.

The Editor speaks of "the professional abilities of the Compiler."—David Sime also selected the Songs in

Haydn's Collection, published by Mr Whyte; see page lxxx. He was a teacher of Music in Edinburgh, and died many years ago.

GEORGE THOMSON'S COLLECTION—1793, &c.

"A Select Collection of original Scottish Airs for the voice, to each of which are added introductory and concluding Symphonies, and accompanyments for the Violin and Pianoforte, by Pleyel, with select and characteristic verses, by the most admired Scotish Poets, adapted to each air; many of them entirely new. Also suitable English verses to such of the Songs as are written in the Scotish dialect. Entered at Stationers' Hall. London, printed and sold by Preston and Son, at their wholesale warehouse, No. 97, Strand, for the Proprietor. First set, price 10s. 6d." Folio. The preface dated "Blair Street, Edinburgh, 1st May 1793."

This well-known collection was originally published at considerable intervals, in books, or half-volumes, each containing twenty-five Songs; and has passed through many editions. An edition, in 6 volumes, royal 8vo, was published in 1822; and another in five volumes folio, has appeared while this sheet is at press.

MACKINTOSH'S REELS, &c.—1793.

"Sixty-eight new Reels, Strathspeys, and Quick Steps; also some slow Pieces, with variations, for the Violin or Pianoforte, with a Bass for the Violoncello or Harpsichord. Composed by Robert Mackintosh, and dedicated by permission to the Hon. Mrs Campbell of Lochnell. Price to subscribers, 5s.; non-subscribers, 6s. Printed for the Author." (Scots Magazine, April 1793.)

Mr Stenhouse, in his note at page 479, has given a short notice of Mackintosh, who, he says, died at London, in February 1807.

## DALE'S COLLECTION, 1794.

Collection of Scotish Songs, quoted by Mr Stenhouse. Three books of this Collection were entered at Stationers' Hall in 1794.

## RIDDELL'S COLLECTION.—1794.

" A Collection of Scotch, Galwegian, and Border Tunes, for the Violin and Piano-Forte, with a Bass for the Violoncello or Harpsichord. Selected by Robert Riddell of Glenriddell, Esq. Price 7s. Edinburgh; printed and sold by Johnson & Co., Musicsellers, Lawnmarket." Folio, pp. 37. Published in 1794, (Scots Magazine, 1st May 1794.)

" New Music for the Piano-forte or Harpsichord, composed by a gentleman, (R. Riddell of Glenriddell;) consisting of a Collection of Reels, Minuets, Hornpipes, Marches, and two Songs in the old Scotch taste, with variations to five favourite tunes. Published by James Johnson, engraver, Bell's Wynd, Edinburgh." Folio.

Robert Riddell of Glenriddell, Esq., was much respected, and obtained some celebrity as an antiquarian, although his researches were not very profound, and some of his theories fanciful.

" Mr Riddell was an excellent man, but no musician; as I have been assured by a competent judge, whose partiality to the author would have made him very sensible of any merit his compositions might possess." Mr Sharpe, in addition to this note, says in reference to a poem, " The Bedesman of Nithside," 1792, 4to, with a vignette, by Captain Grose,—" Sir Walter Scott told me that this production puzzled him—it was much too good for the one and much too bad for the other."

Mr Riddell was member of several learned societies, and communicated various papers which were inserted in their

Transactions. He was a particular friend of Captain Grose; and was likewise a neighbour and friend of Burns, who honoured his memory by writing a Sonnet on his death, which took place at his house at Friar's Carse, near Dumfries, 21st of April 1794.

### RITSON'S COLLECTION—1794.

" Scotish Songs, in two volumes. London; printed for J. Johnston in St Paul's Churchyard; and J. Egerton, Whitehall, 1794." 2 vols. 12mo.

An excellent collection, edited by JOSEPH RITSON, an eminent English antiquary, who has prefixed a very elaborate " Historical Essay on Scotish Song." The music consists of the simple airs, without basses, and is chiefly taken from the collections already mentioned, with the assistance of William Shield, the well-known English Composer, who supplied some original airs. Ritson died in September 1803, and Shield in January 1828.

### URBANI'S COLLECTION—circa 1794.

" A Selection of Scots Songs, harmonised and improved, with simple and adapted graces. Most respectfully dedicated to the Right Honourable [Elizabeth Dalrymple] the Countess of Balcarras, by Peter Urbani, professor of music. Book I. Entered at Stationers' Hall. Price 12s. Printed for the author, and sold at his house, foot of Carrubber's Close, and at all the music-shops, Edinburgh; M'Gown's, Glasgow; Longman and Brodrip, London; Mrs Rhimes and Mr Lee, Dublin." Folio, pp. 51. Book II. is dedicated to Lady Katharine Douglas, daughter of the Earl of Selkirk.—Of this Collection, vol. i. (perhaps a new edition,) was entered at Stationers' Hall in 1797; vol. ii. in 1794; and vol. iii. in 1799.

In vol. iv. p. 318–19, of the present work, Mr Stenhouse has given a short notice of Urbani. The following extract is from the Obituary in the Scots Magazine, December 1816.

"Died lately, in South Cumberland Street, Dublin, aged 67, after a painful and tedious illness, which he bore with Christian resignation, PETER URBANI, professor of music, a native of Milan, in Italy, where he obtained the degree of Doctor of Music. The celebrated Rontzini and Urbani were the only remaining two of that great school of science. They finished their studies nearly about the same time, quitted their native home together, and arrived in London. After some years, Rontzini went to Bath, Urbani to Edinburgh, where he resided for many years with distinguished eclat. He has left an aged widow behind, a foreigner, now deprived of every thing, even the means of subsistence."

## THE VOCAL MAGAZINE—1797.

"The Vocal Magazine, containing a Selection of the most esteemed English, Scots, and Irish Songs, ancient and modern, adapted for the Harpsichord or Violin. Edinburgh; printed by C. Stewart & Co., 1797;" Vol. II. 1798; and Vol. III. 1799; royal 8vo. Each volume price 10s. 6d. bound.

The editor of this collection is said to have been James Sibbald, bookseller in Edinburgh. It was published in Nos. every second month, at 1s. 6d. After it had reached No. 19, being the first No. of vol. IV., it terminated, without any cause being assigned.

A new series of the Vocal Magazine was afterwards commenced, including a number of foreign airs. It is also in large 8vo. but only a few numbers appeared, containing 79 airs; the publication apparently terminating abruptly, when its publisher, James Sibbald, died, in the year 1803.

## ROSS'S COLLECTION.

"A Select Collection of Ancient and Modern Scottish Airs, adapted for the Voice, with introductory and concluding Symphonies and Accompaniments for the Pianoforte, composed by John Ross, Organist, St Paul's, Aberdeen. Vol. I. Price 12s. Edinburgh; printed and sold by John Hamilton, No. 24, North Bridge Street, &c." Folio pp. 62.

"Mr John Ross, late organist of St Paul's Chapel, Aberdeen, was born in the town of Newcastle, Northumberland, on the 12th of October 1763. He was called to St Paul's when very young; and arrived in Aberdeen on the 18th of November 1783. He studied under Mr Handen seven years, who recommended him to the managers of St Paul's Chapel. He continued to do the duty of organist in the above chapel for 53 years. He died at Craigie Park, near Aberdeen, on the 28th July 1837, in his 74th year. He was married to Miss Tait, eldest daughter of Mr Tait, who was 44 years organist of St Paul's, and Mr Barber's predecessor when Mr Ross succeeded. On his retiring from the duties of St Paul's, he was presented with an elegant piece of plate, in testimony of esteem, by the congregation, and also with a splendid edition of Bagster's large Bible, by the Rev. John Brown, senior clergyman of St Paul's Chapel. Two notices of him appeared in the Aberdeen Journal of the 9th August 1837, bearing testimony to his private virtues. In the one it is said, 'He possessed eminent talents both as a performer and as a composer of music;' and in the other that he was 'celebrated as a musical composer, at once chaste and original in his style.' The last was written by the Rev. John Brown of St Paul's."—(MS. communication by Joseph Robertson, Esq.)

## HAYDN'S COLLECTION.

"A Collection of Scottish Airs, harmonized for the

Voice or Pianoforte, with introductory and concluding Symphonies; and accompaniments for a Violin and Violoncello. By Joseph Haydn, Mus. Doct. (Vol. I. and II.) Edinburgh, published by the proprietor, William Whyte, No. 1, South St Andrew's Street; and sold by Clementi and Co. 26 Cheapside." Folio, two thin volumes, pp. 67; the first containing 40, the second 25 Airs.

In the advertisement to this Collection, dated 1st March 1806, the Publisher says, "The Harmonies of the Songs, in all existing editions of Scottish Airs, are the productions of Composers of various descriptions and degrees of genius and talent. The Harmonies of the present are composed exclusively by HAYDN; confessedly the first of modern masters. From this circumstance it is, that while the genius of the composer, indulging in all the varieties of its luxuriance, has accommodated itself to the specific characteristics of each different air, there yet arises a general uniformity, which can hardly fail to give pleasure to the classical ear.

"The selection of the melodies, it is hoped, will be found to comprise the most beautiful of the different classes to which they belong. The proprietor has, in this respect, to acknowledge his obligations to the taste and professional abilities of Mr Sime, by whom the selection was made, and who has exerted himself to conduct the work to its completion, with so much industry and care, as must, in a great measure, be considered as a pledge for its accuracy."

## JOHNSON'S SCOTS MUSICAL MUSEUM.

The present work, extending to six parts or volumes, was commenced in 1787, and completed in 1803. See the Preface to this new edition.

# APPENDIX TO THE INTRODUCTION.

---

## THOMAS WOOD'S MANUSCRIPTS—1566–1578.

(See page xxvii.)

ON the 21st March 1575–6, Thomas Wod, having obtained from "my Lord Regent's Grace, a presentation to the vicarage of Sanctandrois, Mr John Wynrame, Superintendent of Fyfe, was charged to admit him to the said vicarage."—(Registrum Secreti Sigilli.)

After the paragraph at p. xxviii., ending "the fate of the two other parts has not been ascertained," I might have added, that one of these, which belonged to the late Archibald Constable, Esq., afterwards came into my possession; but having, several years ago, given the loan of it to a friend, it was unfortunately lost. The following note was written at the foot of one of the pages:—"*Thir four bukkis was only pennit be me, Thomas Wod, Vicar of Sanctandrois,* [*after*] *four yeiris labours.*" Like the other volumes, we may presume it had also secular airs added at a subsequent period; but the volume happened to be imperfect both at the beginning and end.

Of the Composers of Sacred Music at the period of the Reformation, whose names occur in Wood's Manuscripts, as detailed at pp. xxx.–xxxiii., some additional particulars have since been discovered.

Angus, John. He was one of the Conventual brethren of the Monastery of Dunfermline. Besides some similar deeds of a later date, I have one in which his name, "Et ego Johannes Anguss," occurs, in a discharge granted by George, Commendator of Dunfermline, "with assent and consent of the Convent of the samyn chaptourlie convenit," to Master Hew Rig and his spouse, "of our landis of Carberry," dated at "our said Abbey, May 22, 1543." After the Reformation, Angus, having joined the Protestants, was appointed to one of the livings attached to the Chapel-Royal of Stirling. On the 24th December 1584, he received the Confirmation "of the preceptorie and eleemozinarie of St Leonardis in Dunfermling,"—"as he has bene thir dyvers yeiris bypast preceptor and eleemosinar of the Hospitalle of St Leonardis besyd Dunfermling."—(Register of Presentations to Benefices). Pensions of £10 each were assigned out of the Abbey of Dunfermline, "to his lovit daylie oratouris, John Angus (and seven others), Conventual brether of the said Abbay of Dunfermling," 22d December 1584, and were confirmed 27th May 1587.—(*Ib.*) He died probably in 1596, as, on the 2d March 1596–7, Mr David Drummond, Minister of Crieff, was presented "to the personage of Creif, callit *Creif Secundo,* vacand be deceis of umquhile Deane John Angus, last person and possessor thereof."—(*Ib.*) This presentation, it seems, was not confirmed, as the same living was granted, on the 9th March 1598–9, to Mr Thomas Gray, "to use and exerce of ane musician in His Hienes Chappell-Royall of Stirling;" and on the 4th of January 1602, the parsonage and vicarage of Kirkcowen (one of the livings attached to the Chapel-Royal) was granted to Mr Andrew Lamb, Minister of the King's House; both livings being said to be vacant "be deceis of umquhile Deane John Angus, ane of the Conventuall brether of the Abbacie of Dunfermling."

Blackhall, Mr Andrew. In Wood's Manuscripts, the CI. Psalm, set in five parts, is said to have been composed "by Maister Andro Blakehall in Halyrudehous, 1569 (now minister of Musselburgh), and giffin in propyne to the Kyng."

On the 22d July 1582, James the Sixth granted a confirmation "of a pension to Mr. Andro Blackhall, Minister, ane of the Conventuall brether of the Abbay of Halyrudhous, and to Andro Blackhall his son." In October, 1593, he applied to the Synod of Lothian, craving, in respect of his advanced age, and the greatness of the congregation, that a Second Minister be provided for the parish. According to the following inscription, he was born in 1536, became minister of Inveresk or Musselburgh in 1574, and died in 1609. When Inveresk church was rebuilt in 1805, a large slab was built into the wall near the south porch of the church, with this inscription:—

"Here lyes Mr Andrew Blackhall, Pastor of this Church 35 years. Who dyed 31 January 1609, aged 73." His son, of the same name, became minister of Aberlady.

Buchan, Andrew. The editor of the Psalms, in 1635, has named him among "the prime musicians" of his age connected with the Chapel-Royal. He was probably related to Alexander Buchane, clerk and singer in the King's College within the Castle of Stirling, who obtained a grant of £20 yearly, 11th November 1500.—(Privy Seal Register). He died before 1584, as "Our Soverane Lord ordanis ane letter disponand to Johne Buchane, Maister of the Sang Scule of Hadington, all and haill the prebendarie of the Chapell Royall of Striveling callit the Parsonage of Dalmellingtoun, in Kingis Kyle, with all the ruites, &c., vaikand be deceis of umquhile Andro Buchan, last possessour thairof."—Register of Presentations to Benefices, 13 March

1583–4.) This presentation was superseded by another grant of the same parsonage, "vaikand be deceis of umquhile Andro Buchan," to John Gib, "ane of the vallettis of his Majesteis chalmer," which was confirmed 4th January 1585–6.—(*Ib.*)

Hagie, Andrew. On the 29th January 1582–3, the vicarage of Martoun was "vacant be deceis of umquhile Sir Andro Hagie."—(Register of Presentations to Benefices).

Henryson, Edward, "Maister of the Sang Schole of Edinburgh, and Prebendare of St Geilis Queir," died on the 15th of August 1579.—(Register of Confirmed Testaments).

Peblis, David, "sumtyme ane of the Conventuall brether of the Abbay of Sanctandrois," died in December 1579.—(Register of Confirmed Testaments).

At page xxxiii., in mentioning "E. M." the editor of the Psalms in Four Parts, published in 1635, I expressed regret "that we should be so ignorant respecting this enthusiastic lover of Sacred Melody, as even not to know his name." It is some satisfaction, therefore, now to be able to identify him with Mr Edward Millar, a Prebendary of the Chapel-Royal, who resided in Edinburgh as a teacher of music.

This appears from the "Register of Presentations to Benefices," in which we find that "Mr Edward Millar, musitiane, indwellar in Edinburgh," was presented, in 1634, to the parsonage and vicarage of St Mary Kirk of the Lowis. The presentation is in the following terms:—

"Charles R.—Oure Soverane Lord ordaines ane letter to be maid under His Hienes Privie Seal in dew forme, makand mentioun, That His Maiestie being crediblie informed of the qualificatioune and abilitie of Mr Edward Millar, musitiane, indwellar in Edinburgh, to undergoe the functioune and charge of ane prebendar within His Hienes Chappell Royall of Stirling, and of the said Mr Edward his experience and skill in the airt of Musick, Thairfoir nominating and presenting, likeas be the tennour hereof nominatis and presentis the said Mr Edward Millar, during all the dayes of his lyftyme, in and to the personage and viccarage of the kirk and parochine of Sanct Marie Kirk of the Lowis, lyand in Atrik Forrest, the whole fruittis, rentis, emolumentis, and deuties of the same as being ane of the kirkes belonging to His Hienes said Chappell Royall of Strivieling and prebendaries of samyn, now vacant in his Majesties handis, and at His Hienes presentatioune be deprivatioune of Edward Kellie, last prebendar thairof, &c. Requyring heirby ane Reverend father in God, Adame Bishope of Dunblane, and Deane of the said Chappell Royall, to tak tryall of the literature, qualificatioune, lyfe, and conversatioune of the said Mr Edward Millar ; and he being fund meitt and abill to use and exerce the chairge and functioune of ane prebendare within the said Chappell Royall, to admit him thairto ; to tak his aith for acknowledging of his Hienes authoritie and prerogative royall, and dew obedience to the said Bishope his Ordinar, &c. Gevin at Quhythall, the 15th day of February 1634."—Vol. vii. f. 24.)

The reference by " E. M." to his brethren of the Chapel-Royal leaves no doubt in regard to his identity. It may therefore be added, that Millar pursued his studies at the University of Edinburgh, where he took the degree of A.M. in August 1624. Previously, however, to the above presentation, he had been connected with the Chapel-Royal. In some MS. lists, dated in 1627, the name occurs of " Mr Edward Millar, in Blackfriars Wynd, [who] teaches bairns."

Also of "James Crichtone, blind: Mr Edward Millar stayes with him."—(Balcarres Papers, vol. vii.) But how long he survived has not been ascertained.

THE SKENE MANUSCRIPT—circa 1620.

The original proprietor or compiler of this manuscript was probably "Mr John Skene of Halyairds, ane of the Ordinar Clerks of Session," who died in 1640, and whose testament was confirmed 1st June 1650. See the additional note, p. 110. The MS. bears internal evidence of having been written between the years 1614 and 1620; and the publication by Mr Dauney, referred to, in which his zeal and research—aided by his learned friend George Farquhar Graham, Esq.—was so signally displayed, appeared in a handsome volume, 4to, in 1838. The Editor, WILLIAM DAUNEY, Esq., was born in Aberdeen in the year 1800. He received his early education under Dr Glennie, at Dulwich, near London; and having completed his studies at the University of Edinburgh, he was called to the Scottish Bar in 1823. Soon after the publication of his volume of "Ancient Scottish Melodies," from the Skene MS., he went to Demerara, where he practised successfully as a Barrister, and rose to be Solicitor-General in British Guiana, but died at Demerara on the 28th of July 1843.

SIR WILLIAM MURE'S LUTE-BOOK, MS.—circa 1625.

This manuscript is now in my possession. It was given to me by Mr Lyle, surgeon in Airth, in place of another volume of Mure's, which I happened to purchase at the sale of Mr Motherwell's library, but which Mr Lyle was desirous to have restored to Mr Andrew Blaikie of Paisley, from whom, it appeared, he obtained it, and having lent it to Mr Motherwell, it had remained in his possession at the time of his lamented decease. I do not know who is now the possessor of Mr Blaikie's manuscripts.

## PLAYFORD'S DANCING-MASTER—1651.

Although Mr Stenhouse quotes this work as first published in 1657, it is by no means certain that he actually made use of that, which is the second edition; and being a very popular work, the successive editions were constantly altered, and numerous additions made, so that scarcely any two of the editions are found to correspond. In the third edition, as announced in "Playford's Musick's Delight," 1666, there were "an 100 new Tunes added, to be played on the Treble Violin."

The first edition bears the following title: "The English Dancing Master: or, Plaine and easie Rules for the Dancing of Country Dances, with the Tune to each Dance (small engraving, W. Hollar, fecit). London: printed by Thomas Harper, and are to be sold by John Playford, at his Shop in the Inner Temple near the Church doore." Oblong 4to, pp. 104, containing a separate tune on each page.

Of this volume a copy is preserved in the British Museum; and another, marked as a Museum duplicate for sale, was bought for a small sum at Heber's sale, and is now in the Britwell Library. The second edition of "The Dancing Master, containing 132 New and choice Country Dances," was printed in 1657. There is a copy of this edition in the Pepysian Library, Cambridge. According to a list of editions kindly furnished by Dr E. F. Rimbault, the 3d edition appeared in 1665, the 4th in 1670, the 5th in 1675, the 6th in 1680, the 7th in 1686, the 8th in 1690, and the 9th in 1695. In the 10th edition, 1698, and five subsequent editions, bearing the respective dates 1700, 1703, 1706, 1711, and 1713, a Second Part was added. The 16th, 17th, and 18th editions, in the years 1716, 1721, and [1725], consist of two volumes; and in 1728, Young printed a third volume of the "Dancing Master."

The 17th edition, containing 358 Tunes, the whole revised, &c., was published at London, printed by W. Pearson, 1721, in oblong 8vo. The 18th edition has no date. Of this work. William Chappell, Esq., editor of the valuable "Collection of Ancient English Melodies, with illustrations," possesses the 5th edition, 1675; the 7th, 8th, 9th, and 10th; also the 15th, 16th, and 17th, with the above dates, and the 18th, without date, but printed in the year 1725.

### JOHN PLAYFORD'S MUSICK'S DELIGHT—1666.

"Musick's Delight on the Cithren, restored and refined to a more easie and pleasant Manner of Playing than formerly; And set forth with Lessons *A la Mode*, being the choicest of our late new Ayres, Corants, Sarabands, Tunes, and Jiggs. To which is added several New Songs and Ayres to Sing to the Cithren. By John Playford, *Philo-Musicæ*. London, printed by W. G., and are sold by J. Playford, at his shop in the Temple, 1666." Small oblong volume, with an engraved frontispiece, "R. Gaywood, fecit." In this volume there are some tunes, with at least Scottish titles, such as "Gen. Leshley's March," p. 31; "Highlander's March," p. 66; "Montrosses March," p. 67.

In a note to the Hon. Roger North's interesting "Memoirs of Musick," Dr Rimbault has given a notice of the editions of Playford's popular collections of Catches, Songs, and Glees, under the title of the "Musical Companion," (p. 109, Lond. 1846, small 4to.)

"Apollo's Banquet, or the Violin Book, containing New Ayres, Theater Tunes, Horn-pipes, Jiggs, and *Scotch Tunes.* The Second part of this Book contains a collection of French

Dance Tunes, used at Court, and in Dancing-Schools; as several new Brawls, Corants, Bores, Minuets, Gavots, Sarabands, &c., most of which are proper to play on the Recorder or Flute, as well as on the Violin. Newly printed, with large additions, price 1s. 6d." The same is advertised in Vol. 2d of the Theater of Music, published 1685.

As Playford's name is connected with so many curious works on music, it may be noticed that he was born in the year 1623. This appears from one of his engraved portraits, marked "A.D. 1663, ætat. 40." According to the Ashmole MS., quoted in Busby's "History of Music" (vol. ii. p. 206), Playford was Clerk of the Temple Church, near the door of which his music-shop was situated. His dwelling-house was in Arundel Street, in the Strand. In 1659, he styles himself "A faithfull servant to all Lovers of Musick;" and was highly esteemed by most persons of distinction in his time. His "Introduction to the Skill of Music" was a very popular work. It was first published in 1655, and he lived to superintend the 10th edition in 1683, which is enlarged with An Introduction to the Art of Descent, in place of Campion's treatise under a similar title. Sir John Hawkins, in mentioning Playford, is mistaken when he says, "he lived to near the age of fourscore, dying, as it is conjectured, about the year 1693."—(Hist. of Music, vol. iv. p. 473.) The 11th edition of the "Introduction to the Skill of Music" was printed for his son and successor, Henry Playford, 1687; and in this volume there is "An Ode on the Death of Mr John Playford."

### HENRY PLAYFORD'S SCOTTISH TUNES—1700.

"A Collection of Original Scotch-Tunes (full of the Highland Humours) for the Violin: Being the first of this kind yet Printed: most of them being in the compass of the Flute. London: Printed by William Pearson, in Red-

Cross Alley in Jewin-street, for Henry Playford, at his shop in the Temple-Change, Fleet-street, 1700." Oblong 4to, pp. 16.

Henry Playford, the publisher of this Collection, as above mentioned, was the second son of John Playford. The eldest son, John Playford, also was a music-seller, "at his shop near the Temple Church, 1699."

As Henry Playford's seems to be the earliest collection in a substantial form of Scottish Tunes, and is so rare that no second copy is known, a list of the Tunes may be added :—

ORIGINAL SCOTCH TUNES.

Mr Mc. Laine's Scotch-measure.
Mr Mc. Clauklaine's Scotch-measure.
I love my Love in seacreit.
Madam Mc. Keeny's Scotch-measure.
Cronstoune.
Keele Cranke.
The Berkes of Plunketty.
Good night, and God be with you.
The Laird of Cockpen's Scotch-measure.
My Lord Sefoth's Scotch-measure.
Ginleing Georde.
The Collier's Lass.
Sir William Hope's Scotch-measure.
Stir her up, and hold her ganging.
Oreck's Scotch-measure.
My Lady Hope's Scotch-measure.
Peggy was the pretiest Lass in aw the Town.
Bride next.
The comers of Largo, A reell.
Bess-Bell.
Dick a Dollis.
A new Scotch-measure.
Wappat the Widow my Lady.
If Love is the cause of my mourning.
The Berks of Abergelde.
For old long Gine my Joe.
Allen Water.
Madam Sefoth's Scotch-measure.
Wallis' Humour in Tapping the Ale.
The Lard of Cockpen's Scotch-measure.
A New Scotch-measure.
Widow, gin thou be waking.
Aways my Heart that we mun sunder.
The Lass of Leving-Stone.
I fix my Fancy on her, a Round O.
Quoth the Master to the Man.
Cosen Cole's Delight.
Holy Even, a Scotch-measure.
The Deal stick the Minster.
Finis.

ADAM CRAIG.—(Page xlvi.)

From the Confirmed Testaments, we find that Adam Craig, Music Master in Edinburgh, and Ann Montire his relict, both died at Boroughmuirhead, near Edinburgh, the said Adam in [the date blank, but in October 1741, see p. xlvii.], and the said Ann Montire 3d February 1763, leaving a daughter, Helen Craig, married to James Craighead,

Teacher of English in Leith.—(Conf. Test. Commiss. of Edinb. 6th March 1766.)

### WALSH'S MUSICAL MISCELLANY.

"The British Musical Miscellany; or, the Delightful Grove: Being a Collection of Celebrated English and Scotch Songs. By the best Masters. Set for the Violin, German Flute, the Common Flute, and Harpsicord. Vol. 1. Engraven in a fair Character, and Carefully Corrected. London: Printed for and sold by J. Walsh, Musick printer and Instrument Maker to his Majesty, at the Harp and Hoboy in Cathrine Street in the Strand." In 6 volumes small 4to, 145 pages in each volume, and nearly one-sixth of the collection are Scotch airs.

### MUNRO'S COLLECTION—1732.

This collection, noticed at p. xlvii., is curious on account of its having been published in France. It is of importance only for its scarcity. Mr A. J. Wighton, Dundee, possesses a copy, from which the following note was taken. It has two title-pages, viz.: (1.) "A Collection of the best Scots Tunes, fited to the German Flute, with several Divisions, and Variations, by A. Munro. Dumont, sculpsit. At Paris." (2.) "Recueil des Meilleurs Airs Ecossois, pour la Flûte Traversière, et la Basse. Avec plusieurs Divisions, et Variations, par Mr Munro. Gravé par Dumont. A Paris, avec Permission," folio, pp. 45; besides the royal warrant for printing, dated at Paris, 18th July 1732. It contains only the following twelve tunes:—Wallace March, Mary Scott, The Bush aboon Traquair, The Boatman, Bonny Christy, Nancy's to the Greenwood gane, Bonny Jean, Tweedside, Galla Sheils, The Souters of Selkirk, Corn Riggs, Fy gar rub her o'er wi' strae.

## THOMSON'S ORPHEUS CALEDONIUS—1733.

Among the MS. collections of George Chalmers, I find it stated, from Dodsley's Receipt Books, that, on the 3d of March 1753, Thomson received from Dodsley, the well-known London bookseller, the sum of £52, 10s. for the copyright, with the plates of his *Orpheus Caledonius.* The booksellers, Hicks, Millar, and Rivington, it is added, were equally concerned in this purchase. Copies of the work itself remained in quires, till a comparatively recent period, in the warehouse of the Messrs Rivington.

## AIRS FOR THE FLUTE—1735.

There was a small treatise, on Thorough Bass, "by A. B.," printed in 1717; whether it should be ascribed to Alexander Baillie can only be conjectured. The title is, "An Introduction to the Knowledge and Practice of the Thoro' Bass. Humbly Inscrib'd to the Right Honourable the Lord Colvill. By A. B. Edinburgh: Printed in the year M.DCC.XVII." Folio, pp. 11. The dedication copy, having an inscription on the title-page, "To my Lord Colvill," is in the possession of James Maidment, Esq., advocate. In the same volume there is a neatly-written MS., "Institutions of Musick, wherein are sett forth the Practicall Principles of Musicall Composition, in Two Parts," pp. 22.

## MACLEAN'S COLLECTION—1737.

"Twelve Solos or Sonatas for a Violin and Violoncello, with a Thorough Bass for the Harpsicord. Dedicated to the Honourable the Governour and Members of the Musical Society. Composed by Charles Macklean. Opera Prima. N.B.—The four last Solos are adapted for the German

Flute. Edinburgh, printed by R. Cooper for the Author, and sold by him and Mr And. Martin, bookseller in the Parliament Closs, 1737." This title, within a narrow engraved border, is followed by a list of Subscribers. Folio, pp. 46.

"A Collection of Favourite Scots Tunes, with Variations for the Violin, &c. And a Bass for the Violoncella and Harpsichord, by the late Mr Chs. M'Lean, and other Eminent Masters. Edinburgh, printed for and sold by N. Stewart, at his music shop, opposite the Tron Church. J. Johnson, sculpt. Edinr." Oblong folio, pp. 37. Another edition, with the imprint slightly varied, is noticed at page lxv.

MACFARLANE'S COLLECTION—(See page li.)

Walter Macfarlane, of Macfarlane, in Dumbartonshire, was "descended in a direct male line from the old Earls of Lennox." An account of the family is contained in Douglas's Baronage of Scotland, pp. 93–97. He was esteemed the best genealogist of his time; and his collections, made at great expense, have proved highly useful to antiquaries and other persons engaged in historical investigations. He married Lady Elizabeth Erskine, daughter of Alexander, sixth Earl of Kelly, and died at his house in Canongate, Edinburgh, on the 5th of June 1767.

OSWALD'S COLLECTIONS.

"A Collection of Scots Tunes, with Variations, particularly adapted for the Violin and Harpsicord: Most humbly Dedicated to the Right Hon$^{ble}$. the Earl of Bute (arms of Lord Bute). By James Oswald. London, printed for the Author, at his music shop on the pavement in St Martin's Churchyard; of whom may be had, the Caledonian Pocket Companion, in seven volumes, for the German Flute, with variety of new musick printed abroad." Folio, pp. 37.

In a later edition, the number of Tunes, 43, is added on the title; and the imprint is thus altered, "London, printed and sold by J. Bland, at his music warehouse, No. 45 Holborn."

"A Collection of the best Old Scotch and English Songs set for the Voice, with accompaniments and Thorough Bass for the Harpsichord: Most humbly Dedicated to Her Royal Highness the Princess Dowager of Wales, by James Oswald, Church Composer to his Majesty. London, printed for J. Oswald, and sold at his music shop on the pavement in St Martin's Churchyard, where may be had a variety of New Music, &c. J. Phillips, sculpt." Folio, pp. 36. Oswald's appointment as Church Composer to George the Third is dated 31st January 1761; the Princess Dowager (mother of George the Third) died in 1772.

It may be noticed, that after the imprint is added, "*Where may be had*, Two Collections of all the most favourite old and new Scotch Tunes, several of them with Variations entirely in the Scotch taste, set for the German Flute, Violin, or Harpsichord; in two Books, the First Book now engrav'd the size of the Second Book, with addition of several new Airs, with Variations. Dedicated to his Royal Highness the Prince of Wales, by Mr James Oswald."

A Collection of Scottish Airs, &c., wanting the title-page, in royal 8vo. This was probably by Oswald, and published before the year 1760. It begins on page 1 with Mary Scott and the Broom of Cowdenknows; ending, on page 48, with Pattie and Peggy. The music consists of the Air and the Bass; and may be the First Book above mentioned.

Sir Walter Scott, in "Redgauntlet," mentioning "the favourite air," Roslin Castle (No. viii.), introduces the blind fiddler Willie Steenson, who says of it, "Here's another;

it's no a Scots tune, but it passes for ane. Oswald made it himsell, I reckon—he has cheated mony a ane, but he canna cheat Wandering Willie." It is proper, however, to add, that Oswald has not claimed this air as his own composition, whilst, as Mr Stenhouse has pointed out, it occurs in M'Gibbon's Collection under the name of "The House of Glams."

## M'GIBBON'S COLLECTIONS—1746–1762.

The following is a note of the titles of two of the editions mentioned at p. liv. :—"A Collection of Scots Tunes, some with Variations for a Violin, Hautboy, or German Flute: With a Bass for a Violoncello or Harpsichord. By William M'Gibbon. Book First. London; printed for D. Rutherford, at the Violin and German Flute, in St Martin's Court, near Leicester Fields, where may be had all the most favourite Minuets and Country Dances, likewise Books of Instructions for all Instruments," pp. 21. Book II., same title, pp. 21. Book III., same title, pp. 21.

TUNES IN BOOK FIRST.

Sae merry as we have been.
The bonniest Lass in a' the World, and 2 variations.
The Bush aboon Traquair.
I love my Love in secret.
Steer her up, and haud her gaun.
Polwart on the Green.
Mary Scott.
An thou were my ain thing.
Tweedside.
The Highland Laddie.
Love is the cause of my moaning.
Mucking of Geordy's Byer.
The Lass of Patie's Mill.
I wish my Love were in a myre.
Peggie, I must love thee.
Alloa House.
Leith Wynd.
If e'er you do well, it's a wonder.
Green grows the rashes.
Robin Cushie.
I'll never leave thee.

"A Collection of Scots Tunes for the Violin, or German Flute, and a Bass for the Violoncello or Harpsichord. By William M'Gibbon. With some additions by Robert Bremner. Book I., price 1s. 6d. London; printed and sold at the Music shop of Robt. Bremner, opposite Somerset House." Oblong 4to. Along with Books II., III., and IV., pp. 120.

The First Book contains 32 Tunes ; the Second, 36 ; the Third, 44 ; and the Fourth, 41—in all, 153 Tunes or Airs.

Six Sonatas for two German Flutes, compos'd by Mr Wm. M'Gibbon of Edinburgh. London ; printed for J. Simpson, in Sweeting's Alley, opposite the East door of the Royal Exchange. Royal 8vo, pp. 22.

### BARSANTI'S COLLECTION—1742.

Before leaving Scotland, Barsanti dedicated a set of Six Anthems to the Right Hon. Lady Catharine Charteris, expressing the obligations he was under to her Ladyship and her Noble Family. The title bears, "Sei Antifone composte, da Francesco Barsanti. Opera Quinta." No date. Folio, pp. 32.

### BREMNER'S COLLECTION—1749–1789.

Additions to M'Gibbon's Collection. See pp. liv. and xcv.

The later impressions of the "Thirty Scots Songs," and "A Second Set of Scots Songs," with a portrait of Allan Ramsay, were published at London. "Printed and sold by Preston and Son, at their warehouses, 97 Strand, and Exeter Change," price 3s. each.

"A curious Collection of Scots Tunes, &c. (see p. lvi.) Edinburgh ; printed and sold by R. Bremner, price 2s. 6d. James Read, sculpt., Edinburgh." Oblong folio, pp. 20.

"Twelve Scots Songs, for a Voice or Guitar, &c. By Robert Bremner. London, printed and sold at his Music Shop in the Strand." (Circa 1785). Oblong 4to, pp. 18. This is a later edition of the small work, published in 1760. See p. lvi.

"A Collection of Scots Reels, &c." (See p. lvi.) This work is an oblong 4to, pp. 96.

"A Second Collection of Scots Reels or Country Dances,

with a Bass for the Violoncello or Harpsichord, and proper Directions to each Dance. London: Printed by R. Bremner in the Strand, and at his Music shop in Edinburgh, &c." Oblong 4to, from page 97 to page 112 inclusive. This Collection is advertised in the Scots Magazine for April 1761. He also published a Collection of Minuets in numbers; and No. 4 is advertised along with the above 11th and 12th No. of Reels.

"A Collection of Catches, for Three and Four Voices, by different Authors. Price 6 pence. Edinburgh; printed for R. Bremner, at his Music shop," &c. Oblong 4to, pp. 8.

"Miscellany for the Harpsichord or Spinnet, by R. Bremner, London." 3s., and advertised in Scots Magazine for August 1761. Oblong folio, pp. 26.

"Instructions for the Guitar, with a Collection of Airs, Songs, and Duets, fitted for that Instrument. By Robert Bremner, London. Printed for the Author, and sold at his Music-shop, facing Somerset-House in the Strand." Oblong 4to, pp. 28. Price 1s. 6d.

"A Collection of Airs and Marches, for Two Violins or German Flutes. Printed for, and sold by Robt. Bremner, at the sign of the Harp and Hautboy, Edinburgh. Where may be had, the Rudiments of Music, price, bound and gilt, 3s. As also all Sorts of Music and Musical Instruments, at the London price." Oblong 4to, pp. 8. Bremner's "Rudiments of Music" is a small volume, Edinburgh, 1756; a second edition, "with considerable additions, printed for the Author, and sold at his Music shop," appeared in 1762; and a third edition, London, 1763, 12mo.

## ANONYMOUS COLLECTION—circa 1760.

"The Land of Cakes. Book the first, containing Six Songs set to Musick in the True Scots Taste. To which is added, The Tears of Scotland. London; printed for R. Williams, price 1s. T. Kitchen, sculpt." Folio, 8 leaves.

### BURK THUMOTH'S AIRS—circa 1760.

By a typographical mistake, his name, at p. lviii., is printed "Humoth."

### GENERAL REID'S SOLOS.

"Six Solos for a German Flute or Violin, with a thorough Bass for the Harpsichord. Inscribed to the Countess of Aielsbury, by J. R., Esq., a Member of the Temple of Apollo. London, printed for William Randall, successor to the late Mr Walsh, in Catharine Street, Strand. Price 3 sh. J. Shuter, Sculp. John Shuter." Oblong folio, pp. 17.

"Three Grand Marches, and Three Quick-steps, for a full Military Band, by an Eminent Master [query, General Reid?] Price 6s. London, printed for William Napier, Musician in Ordinary to his Majesty, &c. Lisle Street, Leicester Square." Oblong 4to, in separate sheets for the different instruments.

### GILSON'S COLLECTION—1769.

"Twelve Songs for the Voice and Harpsichord, composed by Cornforth Gilson. Edinburgh; printed for, and sold at Mr Gilson's lodgings, and at Mr Bremner's music-shop, Edinburgh and London. 1769." Folio, pp. 14.

Gilson was a teacher of music, and had previously published "Lessons on the Practice of Singing, with an Addition of the Church Tunes, in four Parts, and a Collection of Hymns, Canons, Airs, and Catches, for the improvement of beginners. By Cornforth Gilson, Teacher of Music in Edinburgh. Edinburgh, 1759." 4to, pp. vi. 40. In the Scots Magazine, May 1759, it is advertised as published, price 2s. 6d. In his Introduction he says, "I need not trouble the Public with any Preface to a performance of this kind. The utility of such performances is now well known; especially since the introduction of the late improvement in Church Music, which now so happily prevails in this country."

In the Scots Magazine for May 1755, April and December 1756, various notices are given of the improvement which took place in singing in the different Edinburgh congregations. Bremner, in the second edition of his "Rudiments of Music," 1762, also makes special reference to such improvement in congregational singing. By an Act of the Town Council, "for improving the Church Music in this City," candidates for the office of "Master of Music" were invited to come forward, among whom was Gilson from Durham, who, being tried and approved by the Musical Society, was elected to the said office in 1756.

### CLARK'S FLORES MUSICÆ—1773.

Clark republished, or rather completed, this work, under the same title, containing 126 Tunes, on 82 pages, folio. The 22 Tunes in the separate Number, mentioned at pp. lx. lxi., are interspersed.

### EARL OF KELLY'S MINUETS, &c.—1774.

Robert Bremner, musician and musicseller in Edinburgh, obtained a Royal license for the sole printing and publishing of the Earl of Kelly's compositions in music, for the space of nineteen years, on the 17th of July 1761. He accordingly published at that time "Six Overtures in eight parts, and a thorough Bass for the Harpsichord, composed by the Right Hon. the Earl of Kelly." A list of other compositions of this very eminent musical genius, with a biographical notice, is given in the Introduction of a volume of "Minuets, &c., composed by the Right Hon. Thomas Earl of Kelly." Edinburgh, 1836. 4to. Edited by the late Charles Kirkpatrick Sharpe, Esq., and embellished with an engraved title and vignette, and a portrait of Lord Kelly.

In mentioning this volume, which was printed for private distribution, it will not be considered out of place to add, that Mr SHARPE, who with a singular amount of antiquarian taste, skill, and knowledge joined the accomplishments of a musical amateur, and who so cheerfully contributed to the Notes and Illustrations in the present collection in 1839, was the second son of Charles Sharpe, Esq. of Hoddam, Dumfries-shire. He was educated at Christ's Church, Oxford, but spent the latter period of his life at Edinburgh, where he died, October 1851, aged 71, and was interred in the family burying-vault, in the churchyard of Hoddam.

The chief portion of Mr Sharpe's musical collections was purchased, after his death, by the Right Hon. Lady John Scott.

## ANGUS CUMMING.

The original copies have no printer or publisher's name, but the title is followed by two leaves of letterpress, containing a long list of upwards of 340 subscribers (of whom the half were of the name of Grant), several of them subscribing for two and four copies of the work. In the Preface Cumming says, " The Publisher follows the profession of his forefathers, who have been for many generations Musicians in Strathspey;" and states that he had spent several years in forming this collection.

In another edition, bearing the following title, the list of subscribers and preface are suppressed:—

" A Collection of Strathspeys, or Old Highland Reels. By Angus Cumming, at Grantown in Strathspey. With a Bass for the Violoncello, Harpsichord, or Piano Forte. Glasgow, printed and sold by James Aird, at his music shop in New

Street. Where may be had, a Collection of Scots Reels, Minuets, &c. by John Riddell, Musician in Ayr, price 5s. A Selection of Favourite Scots, English, Irish, and Foreign Airs, Adapted to the Fife, Violin, or German Flute, in a Neat Octavo Voll., price 3s. Clagget's 6 Easy Duets for 2 Ger. Flutes or Violins. Op. 6th, 3 sh. Favourite Scots Medleys, each 6d. With great variety of Music or Musical Instruments at the London prices. Musical Instruments repaired or lent out per month or quarter. Graved by J. Johnson, Edinburgh." Oblong folio, pp. 20.

DANIEL DOW.

"A Collection of Ancient Scots Music, for the Violin, Harpsicord, or German Flute, never before printed, consisting of Ports, Salutations, Marches or Pibrachs, &c. By Daniel Dow. Edinburgh: Printed for and sold by the Publisher, and to be had at the Music shops in Town and Country. Price 10s. 6d." James Johnson, sculpt. Edinr. Oblong folio, pp. 46, with list of subscribers, and dedication to the Duchess of Athole.

"Thirty-seven New Reels and Strathspeys, for the Violin, Harpsichord, Pianoforte, or German Flute. Composed by Daniel Dow. Entd. Stat. Hall. Price 2s. Edinburgh: Printed and sold by N. Stewart, at his music shop, Parliament Square, where may be had, Scots Songs with Symphonies; each Book 2s. 6d." (J. Johnston, sculpt.) Oblong 4to, pp. 26.

JOHN RIDDELL, AYR—circa 1776.

"A Collection of Scots Reels, or Country Dances and Minuets, with two particular Slow Tunes, with a Bass for the Violin, Violincello, or Harpsichord. Composed by John Riddle at Ayr, and Sold by Himself there; likewise by Mr

Rob[t]. Bremner in Edin[r]., also at his shope at the Harp and Hautboy, opposite Sumerset House, in the Strand, London. Price 5s. Enter'd Stationers Hall.

Wm. Edward, Sculp[t]. }
Dun. Cameron Prints it. } Edin[r]."

Oblong 4to, pp. 45. This is the first edition of the Collection described at page lxix.

According to a note by the Editor of the Ballads and Songs of Ayrshire, "old John Riddell" had a small salary from some gentlemen of note in the county, and had several pupils who obtained local celebrity. In stating that "Riddell was blind, it is believed, from infancy," (p. v.), this probably is not correct.

### ANONYMOUS COLLECTION—circa 1776.

"A Collection of Airs, &c. for the Violin or German Flute, with a Bass for the Violoncello or Harpsichord, taken from the best Masters, and published in Six numbers. Each number consists of sixteen pages, price One Shilling. To be had at the shop of Tho[s]. Phinn, Engraver, Luckenbooths.

"N.B.—As the Person who has collected the above Numbers has avoided inserting any one Air found in other Collections of the kind, and has been carefull of his choice, only adding a few Scots tunes in his own taste, with some Airs of his Composition, it is hoped this Collection will meet with a favourable reception."

Oblong 4to. Query, by General Reid? The copy I have extends only to page 48, or equal to three numbers; and I cannot ascertain whether it was ever completed.

### STEWART'S COLLECTION OF CATCHES—1780.

"A Collection of Catches, Canons, Glees, Duettos, &c. Selected from the works of the most eminent Composers, antient and modern. Edinburgh; printed for N. Stewart, and sold at his music shop, Parliament Close. Where may be had,

3 books of Scots Songs, with Symphonies, each 2s. 6d.

A New Collection of Strathspey Reels, 5s.

M'Lean's Scots Tunes, with Variations, 5s."

In oblong 4to, pp. 112. The dedication, "To the Catch Club, instituted at Edinburgh June 1771," by the publisher, N. Stewart, is dated Edinburgh, June 1780.

### NIEL GOW'S COLLECTIONS—1782–1809.

"A Collection of Strathspey Reels, with a Bass for the Violoncello or Harpsichord, most humbly dedicated to her grace, the Dutchess of Athole. By Niel Gow, at Dunkeld. Edinburgh, printed for the Author, and sold by Corri and Co., Music sellers to Her Majesty." Folio, pp. 36.

"A Second Collection, &c. Dedicated (by permission) to the Noblemen and Gentlemen of the Caledonian Hunt." Edinburgh, printed for Corri and Sutherland, &c. Pp. 36.

"A Third Collection of Strathspey Reels, &c., for the Pianoforte, Violin, and Violoncello. Dedicated to the Most Noble, the Marchioness of Tweeddale. By Niel Gow, at Dunkeld. Price 6s. Edinburgh, printed for the Author, and to be had of him, at Dunkeld; Nath. Gow, Baillie Fyffe's Close, Edinburgh; John and Andrew Gow, No. 60 King's Street, Golden Square, London." Pp. 36.

William, John, and Andrew Gow, all sons of Niel Gow, gave early indications of musical talent, but were eclipsed by their younger brother Nathaniel, who was born at Inver, 28th May 1766. John and Andrew, it appears from the above title, had settled in London as music-sellers; and it will be seen, from some of these publications, that Nathaniel also carried on business in Edinburgh for some years. Another edition of this Third Collection has "Edinburgh, printed and sold by N. and M. Stewart, Music sellers, 37 South Bridge, &c. Where may be had M'Glashan's First and Third Collection of Strathspey Reels, &c."

"A Fourth Collection of Strathspey Reels, &c., for the Pianoforte, Violin, and Violoncello, dedicated to the Right Honourable the Earl of Eglintown, by Niel Gow, at Dunkeld. Entered at Stationers' Hall. Price 6s. Edinburgh, printed by Gow and Shepherd, Music sellers, No. 41 North Bridge Street; to be had of the author at Dunkeld, and John Gow, No. 31 Carnaby Street, Golden Square, London, where all the author's Reels may be had. J. Johnson, sculpt., Edinburgh." Folio, pp. 36. On the last page is this intimation, "And [I] add, for the information of those who wish to possess themselves of my Reels, or what is called GOW'S REELS, that the books I have published are five in number, and are as follows:—

A Collection (my first) of Strathspey Reels, dedicated to the Dutchess of Athole. Price 6s.

A Second Collection of Strathspey Reels, dedicated to the Caledonian Hunt. 6s.

A Third Collection of Strathspey Reels, dedicated to the Marchioness of Tweeddale. 6s.

A Complete Repository of the Original Scotch Slow Strathspeys and Dances, dedicated to the Dutchess of Gordon. 7s. 6d.

And the Fourth Collection, dedicated to the Earl of Eglintown. 6s."

Another edition of this Fourth Collection has on the title, "Edinburgh, printed by Gow and Sutherland, 16 Princes Street."

A Fifth Collection, by Neil Gow and Sons, "Edinburgh, printed for Gow and Sutherland," appeared subsequently to 1808. The date is ascertained by the reference on the title-page to CROMEK'S *Reliques of Burns,* which was published in the year 1808.

"Sixth Collection of Strathspeys, Reels, &c. Dedicated

to the Marchioness of Huntly." Price 8s. Published 1822. Pp. 36.

"Part Second of the Complete Repository of Original Scots Slow Tunes, Strathspeys, and Dances. Dedicated to the Duchess of Buccleuch." Price 8s. Pp. 38.

"Part Third of Ditto. Dedicated to the Countess of Loudoun and Moira." Price 8s. Pp. 38.

"Part Fourth of Ditto. Dedicated to the Nobility and Gentry of Scotland." Price 8s. Pp. 38.

Being in all Six Collections and Four Repositories, published by Neil Gow & Sons.

"The Beauties of Neil Gow, being a Selection of the most favourite Tunes from his First, Second, and Third Collections of Strathspeys, Reels, and Jigs, chiefly comprising the Compositions of Neil Gow & Sons. (The Dances arranged as Medleys). All of which are adapted for the Harp, Pianoforte, Violin, and Violoncello. Respectfully dedicated to the Noblemen and Gentlemen of the Caledonian Hunt, by Nathaniel Gow. Entd. Stat. Hall. Price 6s. Edinburgh: Published and sold by Alex. Robertson, 39 Princes Street," &c. Part 1st, pp. 38; part 2d, pp. 38; part 3d, pp. 38—all folio.

"The Vocal Melodies of Scotland. Dedicated to his Grace the Duke of Buccleugh and Queensberry. Arranged for the Pianoforte, or Harp, Violin, and Violoncello, by Nathaniel Gow. Entd. Stat. Hall. Edinburgh: Printed and sold by A. Robertson, 39 Princes Street." In three parts, at 8s. each, and 36 pages each.

"The Ancient Curious Collection of Scotland, consisting of Genuine Scotch Tunes, with their Original Variations, with Basses throughout for the Pianoforte, or Harp, Violin, and Violoncello. Dedicated to Sir Walter Scott, Bart., by Nathaniel Gow. Entd. Stat. Hall. Price 8s. Edinburgh:

Published by Robertsons, 39 Princes Street." 1823. Folio, pp. 36.

"A Select Collection of Original Dances, Waltzes, Marches, Minuets, and Airs. Respectfully dedicated to the Most Noble the Marchioness of Queensberry. Many of which are composed, and the whole arranged for the Pianoforte and Harp, by Nath. Gow. Entd. Stat. Hall. Price 8s. Edinburgh: Published by Alexander Robertson & Co., 39 Princes Street." Folio, pp. 36.

"A Collection of Airs, Reels, and Strathspeys, being the Posthumous Compositions of the Late Neil Gow, Junr. Arranged for the Pianoforte, Harp, Violin, and Violoncello. Gratefully dedicated to the Right Honourable the Earl of Dalhousie, by his much obliged servant, Nathaniel Gow. Entd. Stat. Hall. Price 6s. Edinburgh: Published and sold by Alex. Robertson & Co., 39 Princes Street." Folio, pp. 22. Published 1849. There is a Memoir of Neil and Nathaniel that accompanies the work.

The Works of Neil Gow and Sons, and Nathaniel Gow, consist of—

6 Collections of Reels, &c.
4 Parts of the Repositories.
3 Parts of the Beauties of Neil Gow.
3 Parts of the Vocal Melodies of Scotland.
1 Ancient Curious Collection of Scotland.
1 Select Collection of Original Dances.
1 The Posthumous Compositions of Neil Gow, jun.

In all 19 Parts, goes under the name of Neil Gow & Sons Works.

The following Collections were published by Nathaniel Gow towards the close of last century:—

"A Collection of Strathspey Reels, with a Bass for the Violoncello or Harpsichord, containing the most approved

Old and the most fashionable New Reels, some of which are composed, and others with additions, by Nathl. Gow. To which are added, a few favourite Irish Airs. Price 6s. Printed by Corri Dussek & Co., Music-sellers to the Royal Family, No. 69 Dean Street, Soho, No. 28 Haymarket, London; No. 8 South St Andrew Street, and 37 North Bridge, Edinburgh. N.B.—All the original tunes in this Collection are entered in Stationers' Hall, according to act of Parliament. J. Johnson, sculpt." Folio, pp. 36.

"New Strathspey Reels for the Pianoforte, Violin, and Violoncello. Composed by a Gentleman, and given with permission to be published by Nathl. Gow. Price 5s. Edinburgh: Printed and sold by N. Stewart & Co." Folio, pp. 24. (On Mr Wighton's copy is written "Composed by the Earl of Eglintoun.")

"A Collection of much-admired Marches, Quick-steps, Airs, &c. Composed by a Lady, and very generously given (with permission to be published) to her much obliged and very humble servant, Nath. Gow. Price 2s. 6d. Entd. Stat. Hall. Edinburgh: Printed and sold by N. Stewart & Co., Music-sellers, No. 37 South Bridge, where may be had all the different Collections of Reels, by Gow, M'Glashan, &c." Johnson, sculpt. Folio.

"A Collection of entirely Original Strathspey Reels, Marches, Quick-steps, &c. for the Pianoforte, Violin, German Flute, &c. &c., by Ladies resident in a remote part of the Highlands of Scotland. N.B.—Corrected by Nath. Gow. Pr. 5s. To be had of Gow & Shepherd, and of the principal Music-sellers in Town and Country." Johnson, sculpt. Folio, pp. 24.

"A Complete Collection, of Originall German Valtz, for the Pianoforte or Violin and Violoncello, with a Second Violin Accompaniment. Dedicated to Lady Charlotte Campbell, by Nath. Gow. Price 6s. Entered at Stationers' Hall. Edinr., printed for Gow & Shepherd, No. 16 Princes Street. Where may be had, Petrie's New Reels, Miss Sitwell's Reel, and every Foreign and London publication, &c. &c. J. Johnson, sculpt. N.B.—A Second Collection will be published soon." Folio, pp. 24.

"A Complete Repository of Old and New Scotch Strathspey's, Reels, and Jigs, adapted for the German Flute. Edinburgh: Printed and sold by Gow & Shepherd, No. 40 Princes Street." Oblong 4to, pp. 48, including two pages with Index. Price 5s.

Book Second, same title-page, pp. 50. 5s.

### MALCOLM M'DONALD'S REELS.

The Collection, mentioned at the foot of page lxix., in other copies has this imprint: "Edinburgh, printed for the Author, and sold by all the Music shops in Town and Country. Price 2s. 6d." It was followed by three others, viz.:—

"A Second Collection of Strathspey Reels, &c. With a Bass, &c. Dedicated to the Right Hon. the Earl of Breadalbane. By Malcolm M'Donald, corrected by Neil Gow, at Dunkeld. Edinburgh, printed by Corri and Sutherland, where may be had Gow's First and Second Set of Reels." Folio, pp. 13.

"A Third Collection of Strathspey Reels, &c. (same as first and second collections). Dedicated by permission to Miss Drummond of Perth, by Malcolm McDonald, at Dunkeld. Price 2s. 6d. Edinburgh, printed for the author, and sold by Corri and Co., Johnson and Co., R. Bryson, and all the Music sellers in Town and Country. J. Johnson, sculpt." Some copies have in the title, "Edinburgh, printed for J. Brysson, &c. Price 3s." Folio, pp. 12.

"A Fourth Collection of Strathspey Reels, &c. (same as above). Dedicated to the Right Honble. the Countess of Breadalbane, by Malcolm M'Donald, at Dunkeld. Price 3s. Edinburgh, printed for the Author, and to be had at Gow & Shepherd's." Folio, pp. 13.

### CORRI'S COLLECTIONS.

One of Corri's most important publications is, "A Select Collection of the most admired Songs, Duets, &c., from Operas of the highest esteem, and from other works, in Italian, English, French, Scotch, Irish, &c. In Three Books. By Dominico Corri. Edinburgh, printed for John Corri, sold by him, and by C. Elliot, Parliament Square." 3 vols. folio.

"A Select Collection of Forty of the most favorite Scots Songs. With introductory and concluding symphonies, proper graces peculiar to their character, and accompaniments for the Pianoforte. By D. & N. Corri. The fourth Edition, with additions and improvements, price 7s. 6d., folio. Edinr., printed and sold by N. Corri, &c., at his Concert Room, head of Leith Walk."

### M'INTOSH'S REELS, &c.—1793.

The Collection, described at page lxxv., folio, pp. 39, was continued by the publication of "A Second Book of Sixty-eight new Reels and Strathspeys."

And by "A Third Book of Sixty-eight new Reels and Strathspeys, &c., compiled and composed by Robert M'Intosh, and dedicated to Mrs Oswald of Auchincruive. Price 7s." Folio, pp. 39.

"Airs, Minuetts, Gavotts, and Reels. Mostly for two Violins, and a Bass for the Violoncello or Harpsichord. Composed by Robert Macintosh. Opera first. Price 7s. 6d. To which is added a Solo, intended as a Specimen of a set of Solos for the Violin, which the Author purposes to publish afterwards. Edinburgh; printed for the Author, and sold at his house in Advocate's Close, and at Corri & Sutherland's, and the other Music shops. J. Johnson, sculpt., Edinburgh." Folio, pp. 40.

"Sixty-eight New Reels, Strathspeys, and Quick Steps; also some Slow Pieces, with Variations, for the Violin and Pianoforte, with a Bass for the Violoncello or Harpsichord. Composed by Robert Mackintosh, and Dedicated, by permission, to the Honourable Mrs Campbell of Lochnell. Entd. in Stationers' Hall. Price 6s. Where may be had, at the undermentioned places, the Author's first Book of Airs, Minuets, Reels, &c. Printed for the Author, and to be had at his house, Skinner's Close, & of all the Music sellers in Edinburgh; A. Macgowan, Glasgow; & Longman & Brodrip, London." Folio, pp. 39.

"A 3rd Book of Sixty-Eight New Reels and Strathspeys, also above forty old Famous Reels. For the Violin and Pianoforte, with a Bass for the Violoncello or Harpsichord. Compiled & Composed by Robert Mackintosh. Dedicated, by permission, to Mrs Oswald of Auchincruive. Entd. in Stationers' Hall. Price 7s. May be had at the undermentioned places the Author's 1st & 2nd Book of Airs, Minuets, Reels, &c. Printed for the Author, and to be had at his house, Skinner's Close, & of all the Music sellers in Edinburgh; A. Macgowan, Glasgow; & Longman & Brodrip, London." Folio, pp. 39.

"A Fourth Book of New Strathspey Reels, also some Famous old Reels, for the Pianoforte or Harp. Dedicated, by permission, to her Grace the Dutchess of Manchester. Compiled and Composed by Robert Mackintosh. Entd. at Stationers' Hall. Price 8s. London; printed for the Author, 3 Little Vine Street, Piccadilly, by Lovenu and Mitchell,

Music Sellers to his Royal Highness the Prince of Wales, No. 29 New Bond Street."

Robert M'Intosh, or "Red Rob," as he was familiarly called, settled in London, where he died in 1807.

## NAPIER'S COLLECTIONS—1790–1792.

It may be added, that the first volume of this Collection, published in February 1790 by William Napier, music-seller in the Strand, contains 81 Songs, the Airs harmonised by four professional Musicians—Dr S. Arnold, William Shield, Thomas Carter, and F. H. Barthelemon. The Harmony consists of a figured bass for the Harpsichord, with a Violin Accompaniment. The second volume contains 100 Songs, the whole of the Airs harmonised by Joseph Hadyn; but in neither volume are there any Symphonies. This Second volume, "Printed for William Napier, Music seller to their Majesties, No. 9 Great Queen Street, Lincoln's Inn Fields," [1792], has an engraved frontispiece by Bartolozzi, from a design by W. Hamilton, R.A.

"A Selection of Original Scots Songs, in Three Parts. The Harmony by Hadyn. Dedicated by permission to Her Majesty. Vol. III., price 26s. London; printed for Willm. Napier, Music seller to their Majesties, No. 49 Great Queen Street, Lincoln's Inn Fields. Neele, sc. Strand. The above vol. may be had, in four separate Numbers, at 7s. each. Entered at Stationers' Hall."

"Napier's Selection of Dances and Strathspeys, with new and appropriate Basses, adapted for the Pianoforte, Harp, &c., price 10s. 6d. Entd. Stationers' Hall. Printed for Wm. Napier, Music Seller, and Musician in Ordinary to his Majesty, Lisle Street, Leicester Square. Where may be had, Napier's Three Volumes of Scots Songs. The Harmony by Hadyn and other eminent Composers." Folio, pp. 36.

"Died lately at Somerston, Mr William Napier, in the 72d year of his age. He was distinguished for his musical skill, and for the beautiful selections of Scotch Ballads which he edited. For many years he belonged to his Majesty's Band, and to the professional concert, but was obliged to retire on account of the gout in his hands, to which he became a victim."—See Scots Magazine, August 1812, pp. 648.

URBANI'S COLLECTIONS—1792, &c.

The notice of Urbani's works, at page lxxvii., is by no means complete; and the publication of Book I. should be referred to 1792, or the beginning of 1793. In a letter, dated 2d May 1793, a request is made to a lady, by a friend of the writer, to purchase for her "a copy of Urbani's new publication of Songs, at Corri's or any other Music shop." Book II., dedicated to Lady Catherine Douglas, has a portrait of Allan Ramsay and the same imprint as the first, and contains pp. 50. Book III. is dedicated to the Hon. Lady Carnegie. Edinburgh, printed and sold by Urbani and Liston, 10 Princes Street, pp. 54. Book IV. is entitled "A Selection of Scots Songs," &c., and is dedicated to the Right Hon. Lady Lucy Ramsay, with the same imprint as Book III. Books V. and VI., completing the work, were published together, as "A Select Collection of Original Scotch Airs; with Verses, the most part of which were written by the celebrated Robert Burns." The imprint is the same; and the dedication, to the Duchess of Bedford, is dated from Edinburgh, February 1, 1804. The Words and the Music are printed on opposite pages, and each extend to pp. 59.

A new edition of this Collection bears "Edinburgh, printed and sold by John Sutherland," as four volumes in three, the first corresponding with Books I. and II.; the second with Books III. and IV.; the third and fourth in one, with Books V. and VI., retaining, in this volume, the original dedication to the Duchess of Bedford. In this Collection, as Mr Graham remarks, "The Melodies were harmonised by Urbani, with an accompaniment for the Pianoforte, the Harmony filled up in notes for the right hand; and the first four volumes have, besides, Accompaniments for Two Violins and a Viola, all printed in score, along with the Voice part. Each song has introductory and concluding Symphonies. Urbani's Selection is remarkable in three respects—the novelty of the number and kind of instruments used in the Accompaniments; the filling up of the Pianoforte Harmony; and the use, for the first time, of introductory and concluding Symphonies to the Melodies."

"A Favourite Selection of Scotch Tunes, properly arranged as Duettos, for Two German Flutes or Two Violins, by P. Urbani. Book 1st, price 5s. N.B.—The first part arranged to play as Solos, price 3s. Edinburgh: Printed and sold by Urbani and Liston. Entd. Stat. Hall." Oblong 4to, pp. 24.

Book Second (same title as above), from page 25 to 48 inclusive.

Books First and Second, for Second Violin or Flute, separately, same size and number of pages.

THE EDINBURGH COLLECTION OF CATCHES.

"A Collection of Catches, Canons, Glees, Duetts, &c. Selected from the Works of the most eminent Composers, Antient and Modern. Vol. I. Edinburgh: Printed for J. Sibbald, Parliament Square, and Messrs Corri and Sutherland, Music sellers to Her Majesty. J. Johnson, sculpt., Edin^r." 4 vols. oblong 4to, each volume containing pp. 112. The first volume of this Collection is a republication of that of Stewart, in 1780, described *supra*, p. xcv. The imprint in some copies was changed to "Edinburgh, printed for J. Sibbald & Co., and sold at their Circulating Library, Parliament Square." A still later edition of the same Collection has this imprint: "Edinburgh, printed and sold by Gow & Shepherd, Music sellers, No. 41 North Bridge, price 8s. 6d." There is also an edition of the first two volumes: "Printed and sold by John Watlen, Music seller, 34 North Bridge. Price 8s. 6d."

### EDINBURGH COLLECTION OF DUETTS.

"A Collection of Duetts for Two German Flutes or two Violins. Selected from the best Authors, and containing many scarce and valuable pieces. By a Society of Gentlemen. Price 4s. 6d. Edinr.: Printed and sold by J. Brysson, Music seller, Cross, where may be had, The Scots Musical Museum in Four Volumes, each Volume consisting of 100 Scots Songs, each Vol. 6s.—24s." In oblong 4to, pp. 60.

### AIRD (JAMES).

"A Selection, &c." See p. lxix. This collection, in place of three, consists of six volumes. It was twice republished by Aird's successor, under the following titles:—

"A Selection of Scotch, English, Irish, and Foreign Airs, adapted for the Fife, Violin, or German Flute. Vol. I. Humbly dedicated to the Volunteer and Defensive Bands of Great Britain and Ireland. (Glasgow Musical Circulating Library.) Printed by J. M'Fadyen, Glasgow. Price 3s. 6d. Where may be had the other Five Volumes."

The same engraved title serves for each of the six volumes, the number of the volume being filled in with the pen. In small oblong 8vo. Vol. I., pp. 74; Vol. II., pp. 80; Vol. III., pp. 155 to 233; Vols. IV., V., and VI., each pp. 80

Except the last volume, which ends with 181, the other volumes have each 200 Airs.

"Aird's Selection of Scotch, English, Irish, and Foreign Airs, adapted to the Fife, Violin, or German Flute. Glasgow, printed and sold by J. M'Fadyen." Volumes First to Fifth, small oblong 8vo.

"Aird's 6th and Last Volume of Scotch, English, Irish, and Foreign Airs, adapted for the Fife, Violin, or German Flute. Glasgow, printed and sold, with the other 5 volumes, by J. M'Fadyen, Music seller and stationer, Willson Street, &c. G. Walker, sclupt." Pp. 80.

ANDERSON (JOHN).

"A Selection of the most approved Highland Strathspeys, Country Dances, English and French Dances, with a Harpsichord & Violoncello Bass. Dedicated to the Gentlemen of the Musical Society of Greenock. By John Anderson. Edinburgh: Printed for the Author, and sold by Corri and Sutherland, Music-sellers to her Majesty, and by all Music and Booksellers in Scotland. Price 6s. J. Johnson, sculp." Folio, pp. 36, and 105 tunes.

BOWIE (JOHN).

"A Collection of Strathspey Reels and Country Dances, with a Bass, &c. Dedicated to the Countess of Kinnoul. By John Bowie, at Perth. Edinburgh, printed for the Author." Folio, pp. 35.

BUTLER (T. H.)

"A Select Collection of Original Scottish Airs, arranged for one and two voices. With Introductory and Concluding Symphonies, for the Flute, Violin, and Pianoforte. By T. H. Butler." (Entd. Stationers' Hall. Folio, price 8s.) Most respectfully Dedicated to the Right Hon$^{ble}$. the Earl of Cassilis. (His Lordship's arms engraved on the title-page.) Printed and sold by Muir, Wood, & Co., Music-sellers, Edinburgh, and A. Macgown, Glasgow. 25 pages with music, 25 with words, 25 Airs, and 49 Songs.

CAMPBELL (ALEXANDER).

"Sangs of the Lowlands of Scotland, carefully compared with the original editions, and embellished with characteristic designs composed and engraved by the late David Allan, Esq., Historical Painter. Edinburgh: printed and sold by Andrew Foulis, Strichens Close, High Street, 1799." 4to, pp. 222.

This collection, which scarcely comes within the scope of the present List, is connected with a work entitled "An Introduction to the History of Poetry in Scotland; together with a Conversation on Scotish Song, by Alexander Campbell." Edinburgh, 1798, 4to. At the end of the volume is advertised "Twelve Songs set to Music," by the same author. He was employed by the Highland Society to collect Highland Airs, and the result of his Tours for that purpose appeared in two volumes in folio, under the title of "Albyn's Anthology," 1816 and 1818.—Campbell was born in 1764, and died at Edinburgh in 1824. A notice of his life is contained in Chambers's Scottish Biography, vol. i. p. 463.

CAMPBELL (JOSHUA).

"A Collection of New Reels and Highland Strathspeys, with a Bass for the Violoncello or Harpsichord, by Joshua Campbell. A number of which are his own Composition. Glasgow, printed for the Author, and sold at the Music shops in Edinburgh and Glasgow. Price 5s. 6d. J. Johnson, sculpt. Edin." Folio, pp. 48.

"A Collection of Favourite Tunes, with New Variations, adapted for the Violin and German Flute, with a Bass for the Violoncello, and Thorough Bass for the Harpsichord, by Joshua Campbell. Glasgow, printed for" (the rest cut off in the binding). Oblong 4to, pp. 81.

CLAGGET (WALTER).

"A New Medly Overture, consisting entirely of Scots Tunes and Thirty-Six of the most favorite Scots Airs, to which is added the favorite air of Chivey Chase, all with Variations for two Violins or two German flutes and a Violoncello, also adapted to the Pianoforte. The Airs selected and the Variations composed by Walter Clagget. Entd. Stat. Hall. Edinburgh, printed for the Author, and to be had at all the Music shops." (Engraved by George Walker.) Folio, pp. 28.

The Part for the Second Violin or Flute is published separately, with title-page same as above; folio, pp. 12.

Clagget's Scots Tunes for the Pianoforte or Flute, price 6s.

In a list of favourite music, sold by J. M'Fadyen, at the Glasgow Musical Circulating Library, we find "Six Solos and Six Scots Airs, with Variations for the Violin or Violoncello, with a Thorough Bass for the Harpsichord. Composed by Walter Clagget. Opera, 2do. London, printed for the Author, and sold by him at the Sedan Chair, Great Hart street, Covent Garden, and Messrs Thompson & Sons in St Paul's Church yard." Folio, pp. 39.

CLARK (JOHN).

"A Collection of New Strathspey Reels and Country Dances, with a Bass for the Violoncello or Harpsichord. Dedicated to the Musical Society of Perth. Composed by John Clark, Perth. Entd. Stat. Hall." Folio, pp. 21.

CLARKSON (JOHN).

"Clarkson's Musical Entertainment, being a Selection of various Tunes and Pieces of Music, adapted for the Pianoforte or Harpsichord. London: Published for the Author; to be had at his House, Carrubber's Close, Edinburgh. Price 3s. 6d." Folio, pp. 20.

Died at St Andrews, 20th January 1812, "Mr John Clarkson, many years an eminent Teacher of Dancing there, and at Kirkaldy, Cupar, and Dunfermline."—(Scots Mag. 1812, p. 158.)

CLARKSON (JOHN), JUNIOR.

"A Complete Collection of much-admired Tunes, as Danced at the Balls & Public's of the late Mr Strange. Purchased and arranged for the Pianoforte, and respectfully Dedicated to his Scholars, by John Clarkson, Junr., Teacher of Dancing, Edinburgh. Edinburgh: Printed and sold by J. Hamilton, 24 North Bridge street, opposite the Post Office." Folio, pp. 50. Price 10s. 6d.

COOPER (ISAAC).

"A Collection of Reels, by Isaac Cooper of Banff." Published about 1783; advertised on the last page of Aird's third Glasgow Collection. Price 3s.

DALE (JOSEPH).

"Dale's Collection of Sixty favourite Scotch Songs, taken from the Original Manuscripts of the most celebrated Scotch Authors and Composers, properly adapted for the German Flute. Book II., price 5s. London; printed for J. Dale, No. 19 Cornhill, and the corner of Holles Street, Oxford Street." Oblong 4to.

"Dale's Collection of Duets for two performers on one Piano Forte, by the most celebrated Composers." Folio, in four books, and containing six tunes. A list of "Music published by Joseph Dale, Piano Forte maker to his Royal Highness the Prince of Wales," prefixed to one of these books, has the date 1809.

DANIEL (JAMES).

"A Collection of Original Music, consisting of Slow Airs, Strathspeys, Reels, Quadrilles, Waltzes, Hornpipes, &c. Adapted for the Pianoforte, or Violin and Violoncello. By a Citizen. Aberdeen: Engraved and printed and published by James Daniel, Engraver, &c." Folio, pp. 39.

DING (LAWRENCE).

"The Anacreontic Museum, or, Thirty Select Catches, Canons, Glees, &c. (from the works of the most eminent Masters). Inscribed to all Catch Clubs and Practitioners of Music; by Lawrence Ding, Φιλο-ἁϛμονια, Editor of the Songster's Favourite and Scholar's Assistant. Edinburgh: printed for and sold by the Editor, at his house, first entry within the Netherbow, north side, and at the Music Shops of Messrs R. Bremner, Stewart and Co., &c." Oblong 8vo, pp. 16.

DUFF (CHARLES).

"A Collection of Strathspey Reels, Jigs, &c., with a Bass for the Violoncello or Harpsichord. To which is added Four Minuets, Four Marches, in 3 Parts. Dedicated (by permission) to his Grace the Duke of Athole. By Charles Duff, Dundee. Price 6s. Edinburgh: N. & M. Stewart & Co., Corri & Co., Johnson & Co., R. Ross, and J. Brysson; and by A. M'Gowan, Glasgow; and Longman & Broderip, London. J. Johnson, sculpt. N.B.—The Tunes marked

J. M'D. are composed by Mr Jno. M'Donald, late Dancing-Master, Dundee." Folio, pp. 36.

ELOUIS (J.)

"First Volume of a Selection of Favorite Scots Songs, with Accompaniments for the Harp or Pianoforte, which may be performed on these Instruments either with the Voice or without it, as Familiar Lessons; to which are added Several Airs, with Variations. Composed and Respectfully Dedicated, by permission, to the Right Honorable Lady Montgomerie, by J. Elouis. Ent[d]. at Sta. Hall. Price each vol. One Guinea. Edinburgh: Sold by Messers Gow & Shepherd; Messers Muir, Wood, & Coy., Music-sellers; and by Robt. Birchall, at his music warehouse, No. 133 New Bond Street, London. The music is engraved by J. Johnson, and the letterpress by Oliver & Co. Every copy is signed by the Author and Proprietor, J. Elouis." Folio. The words and music are printed on opposite pages. The former, pp. 49; the latter, 51; also pp. 11, with 3 Airs (without the words) repeated with Variations, and a Glossary. In the preface it is said,—"There is *not one* Edition of *Scottish Songs* in which lines with two, three, and sometimes four syllables *too much or too little* are not frequently to be met with. The troublesome and ungrateful task of restoring the verses to their proper measure, by retrenching or adding words to the defective lines (without encroaching upon the sense), was undertaken by Mrs Elouis, the author's wife. It can now be safely asserted that there is *no other* selection of *Scottish Songs* but this, in which the verses, from being uniformly correct, *always* suit their respective airs."

"Second" Volume of a selection of Favorite Scots Songs, &c. "Dedicated to the Right Honorable the Earl of Eglinton,"—in other respects the title same as the first vol. Pp.

50 with words, and 50 music; and 7 pp. with 3 tunes with variations. Each vol. contains 50 Airs with the words, besides the Airs with variations. Published by subscription. The Queen and thirteen others of the Royal Family are amongst the subscribers. The advertisement to the second volume is dated 1807.

GOW (JOHN AND ANDREW).

"A Collection of Slow Airs, Strathspeys, and Reels, with a Bass for the Violoncello, Harpsichord, or Pianoforte. Dedicated by permission to the Highland Society of London, by Jno. and Andw. Gow. London; printed and sold by Wm. Campbell, No. 8 Dean Street, Soho; and to be had of the Authors, No. 60 King Street, Golden Square, price 7s. 6d." Folio, pp. 36.

GRANT (DONALD).

"A Collection of Strathspey Reels, Jigs, &c., for the Pianoforte, Violin, and Violoncello. Dedicated to Mrs Col. Grant. By Donald Grant. Price 8s. 6d." (Folio, pp. 38; 121 Tunes, 76 original.) "Edinburgh, printed for the Author at Elgin, and Mr Gow, Edinburgh, and Mr Davie, Aberdeen."

GUNN (JOHN).

"Forty favorite Scotch Airs, adapted for the Violin, German Flute, or Violoncello, with the phrases mark$^{d}$., and proper fingering for the latter instrument; being a Supplement to the Examples in the Theory and Practice of fingering the Violoncello. By John Gunn." Ent. Stat. Hall. Price 7s. 6d. Folio. London.

Gunn was the author of other works—"The Art of playing the German Flute on new principles, price 10s. 6d.;'

also, "The School for the German Flute, Part I., 5s.," are advertised along with his Forty Scotch Airs, on the title-page of "The Theory and Practice of fingering the Violoncello, &c., by John Gunn, Teacher of the Violoncello. The second edition. London, printed for the Author, and sold by him, at No. 1 Bennet Street, Rathbone Place, and by Preston, &c." Folio, pp. 64.

Another work which he published was, an "Historical Enquiry respecting the performance on the Harp in the Highlands of Scotland, from the earliest times until it was discontinued, about the year 1734. Drawn up by desire of the Highland Society of Scotland, and published under its patronage, by John Gunn, F.A.S.E., &c." Edinburgh, 1807, large 4to, pp. 112, with three engravings of Queen Mary's Harp and the Caledonian Harp. The Author announces, in a postscript, his intention of publishing a much more detailed work; but it never appeared.

### HAMILTON (JOHN).

"A Choice Collection of Scots Reels, or Country Dances, and Strathspeys, with a Bass for the Violoncello or Harpsichord. Edinburgh, printed and sold by J. Hamilton, North Bridge. Price 3s." Oblong 4to, pp. 40.

"The Caledonian Museum, containing a favorite Collection of Ancient and Modern Scots Tunes, adapted to the German Flute or Violin. Book III. Price 3s. Edinburgh: J. Hamilton, 24 North Bridge Street." Oblong 4to. From page 52 to 75 inclusive, containing 100 Airs.

Hamilton died in 1814. See note to Song 592, p. 537.

### JENKINS (GEORGE).

"Eighteen Airs for Two Violins and a Bass, dedicated (by permission) to her Grace the Duchess of Athol, by George

Jenkins. Price 3s. N.B.—To render this work useful for Harpsichord performers, the first Violin and Bass are put in Score. Printed for and sold by J. Brysson, at his Music shop, Edinburgh." Oblong folio, pp. 9.

"New Scotch Music, consisting of slow Airs, Strathspeys, quick Reels, Country Dances, and a Medley on a new plan, with a Bass for a Violoncello or Harpsichord. Dedicated by permission to his Royal Highness the Prince of Wales. Composed by George Jenkins, Teacher of Scotch Dancing. Price 10s. 6d. To be had of the Author, No. 125 High Holborn, Bloomsbury." Folio, pp. 70.

In the list of New Music, published by George Goulding, (upon the last page of Sir Adam Gordon's Psalms, with music by Drs Arnold and Calcott, in 1791), we find "Jenkins's Thirty Highland Airs, price 5s."

### LEBURN (ALEXANDER).

"A Collection of Strathspey Reels, &c., with a Bass for the Violoncello or Harpsichord. Dedicated, by permission, to Mrs Moncrieff of Reedie, by Alex. Leburn, Auchtermuchty. Price 2s. 6d. Edinr., Johnson & Co." Folio, pp. 12.

### MACDONALD (JOHN).

"Nine Minuets for the Harpsichord or Pianoforte. Composed by John M'Donald, Teacher of Dancing in Dundee. Dedicated to her Grace the Duchess of Athole." Oblong 4to, pp. 11.—See under Duff (Charles), p. cxix.

### M'FADYEN (JOSEPH).

"The Repository of Scots and Irish Airs, Strathspeys, Reels, &c. Part of the Slow Tunes adapted for two Violins and a Bass, others with variations. The whole with improved

Bass for the Harpsichord or Pianoforte. Most respectfully Dedicated to the Right Hon$^{ble}$. Lady Montstewart. Vol. 1st, price 6s.; bound, 7s. 6d. Glasgow; J. M'Fadyen." Oblong 4to. 64 pages with Slow Airs, and 64 of Strathspey Reels, &c.; in all 128 pages.

MACINTOSH (ABRAHAM).

"Thirty New Strathspey Reels, &c., with a Bass for the Violoncello or Harpsichord. Composed by Abrm. Macintosh. Price 3s. Edinr., printed for and sold by the Author, and by J. Brysson, at late Bremner's. A. Macintosh, sc." Folio, pp. 11. Advertised in the Scots Magazine, December 1792.

MACINTYRE (D.)

"A Collection of Slow Airs, Reels, Strathspeys. Dedicated, by permission, to the Right Hon$^{ble}$. Lady Charlotte Campbell. Composed by D. Macintyre. Price 8s. London, John Gow & Son." Folio, pp. 40, and 79 Tunes.

MACKAY (ALEXANDER).

"A Collection of Reels, Strathspeys, and Slow Tunes, arranged for the Pianoforte. Chiefly composed by Alexr. Mackay, Musician, Islay. (Subscribers, 5s.; non-sub., 6s.) Dedicated, by permission, to the Right Hon$^{ble}$. Lady Elinor Campbell of Islay and Shawfield. Glasgow, published by J. M'Fadyen." Folio, pp. 36.

MACLEOD (H. P.)

"A New Selection of the most approved Pieces, properly arranged as Duetts for two German Flutes, by H. P. Macleod, Teacher of Music. Book I. Edinburgh: Printed by the Author, and sold at all the Music Shops. Price 5s. Book II. Edinburgh: Printed and sold by the Author, at his house, Richmond Court. J. Johnson, Sculp$^{t}$." Oblong 4to, the two books pp. 96, and Index.

MARSHALL (WILLIAM).

"A Collection of Strathspey Reels, with a Bass for the Violoncello or Harpsichord. Composed by Wm. Marshall. Price 2s. 6d. Printed for Neil Stewart, and sold at his Music shop, Parliament Square, Edinburgh. Where may be had—3 Books of Scots Songs, with Symphonies, each 2s. 6d.; M'Glashan's Strathspey Reels, 5s.; M'Lean's Scots Tunes, with Variations, 5s.; M'Gibbon's Scots Tunes, 3 Numbers, each 2s. 6d.; Marches and Airs, 1st and 2d Books, 6s. Johnson, sculpt." Oblong folio, pp. 12, and 36 tunes.

"Marshall's Scottish Airs, Melodies, Strathspeys, Reels, &c., for the Pianoforte, Violin, and Violoncello, with appropriate Basses. Dedicated to the Most Noble the Marchioness of Huntly. Entd. Stat. Hall. Price 12s. 6d.; to non-subscribers, 15s. Edinburgh: Published for the Author, and sold by Alex. Robertson, 47 Prince's Street, &c." Folio, pp. 60, and 176 Tunes. 1822.

"Volume 2d of a Collection of Scottish Melodies, Reels, Strathspeys, Jigs, Slow Airs, &c., for the Pianoforte, Violin, and Violoncello, being the Genuine and Posthumous Works of William Marshall. All the Airs in this Collection are now published for the first time. This work is Copyright. Entd. Stat. Hall. Price 6s. Edinburgh: published by Alex. Robertson, 39 Princes Street," &c., [1847]. Folio, pp. 35, and 81 Tunes.

MORRISON (WILLIAM).

"A Collection of Highland Music, consisting of Strathspeys, Reels, Marches, Waltzes, and Slow Airs, with Variations, original and selected, for the Pianoforte, Violin, and

Violoncello. Dedicated to the Right Hon$^{ble}$. Lady Seaforth, by William Morrison. Price 7s. 6d. Printed for, and sold by J. Young & Co., Inverness, &c. Entd. Stat. Hall." Folio, pp. 36.

PEACOCK (FRANCIS).

To the notices given at page lxiv. it may be added, that he was the author of a volume entitled "Sketches relative to the History and Theory, but more especially to the Practice of Dancing, as a necessary accomplishment to the youth of both Sexes, &c. By Francis Peacock, Aberdeen." Aberdeen: printed by J. Chalmers & Co. Sold by Angus and Son, &c. 1805, 8vo. It is dedicated to the Duchess of Gordon; and in the list of subscribers may be found the names of all the leading persons in Aberdeenshire. It also marks the estimation in which the author was held, to find added to this list, "By order of the Town Council of Aberdeen, 20 copies." In his advertisement, dated April 1805, he refers to "the experience of upwards of sixty years, during which he has been a teacher of dancing;" and states that if any emolument should be derived from the publication, it would be appropriated towards the Lunatic Asylum, then lately established in Aberdeen.

PETRIE (ROBERT).

"A Collection of Strathspey Reels and Country Dances, &c., with a Bass for the Violoncello or Harpsichord, humbly dedicated to Mrs Farquharson of Monaltrie, by Robert Petrie, at Kirkmichael, Perthshire. Price 4s. Edinburgh: Printed for the Author, and sold by Stewart & Co., Johnston & Co., Lawnmarket, and all the Music-sellers in Town and Country. J. Johnson, sculpt." Folio, pp. 22.

"A Second Collection of Strathspey Reels, &c., for the Piano Forte, Violin, and Violoncello, humbly dedicated to Mrs Garden of Troup, by Robert Petrie at Kirkmichael. Edinburgh, Printed for the Author, and sold by all the Music sellers in Town and Country." Later copies have, "Edinburgh, printed for Gow and Shepherd, 41 North Bridge Street. George Walker, sculp^t." Folio.

"A Third Collection of Strathspey Reels, with a Bass for the Violoncello or Pianoforte, humbly dedicated to Francis Garden, Esq., junior, of Troup, by Robert Petrie, at Kirkmichael. Price 6s. London: Printed for the Author, and to be had at all the Music-sellers in Town and Country." Folio, pp. 26.

"A Fourth Collection of Strathspeys, Reels, Jiggs, and Country Dances, for the Pianoforte, Violin, and Violoncello. Composed and respectfully dedicated to Mrs Garden Junr., of Troop and Glenlyon, by Robert Petrie. Price 5s. Edinburgh, printed for the Author, and to be had of him at Kirkmichael, Perthshire, and at all Music shops. Engraved by W. Hutton, High Street, Edin." Folio, pp. 24.

### PORTEUS (JAMES).

A Collection of Reels and Strathspeys, &c. Edinburgh. Folio, pp. 40. Wants title-page, &c.

### PRINGLE (JOHN).

"A Collection of Reels, Strathspeys, and Jigs, with a Bass for the Violoncello or Pianoforte, dedicated by permission to the Hon. Miss Elliot, by John Pringle. Entered at Stationers' Hall. Price 5s. Edinburgh, printed for the author, to be had of him, No. 16 Rose Street, and at all the Music shops." Folio, pp. 19.

ROBERTSON (DANIEL).

"A Collection of Reels, Strathspeys, Jigs, Waltzes, &c., for the Pianoforte, Harpsichord, and Violin, with a Bass for the Violoncello. Composed and dedicated, by permission, to Miss Georgina Scott of Seabank, by Daniel Robertson. Price 6s. Edinr., printed by Muir, Wood, & Co., No. 7 Leith Street. Entd. Stat. Hall." Folio, pp. 26.

ROSS (JOHN).

"A Complete Book of Instructions for beginners on the Harpsichord or Piano-Forte. To which is added, a select set of Airs, Scots Songs, and Lessons, composed by John Ross, Organist of St Paul's Chapel, Aberdeen. Price 8s. 6d. London, printed for the Author, by Broderip & Wilkinson, No. 13 Haymarket." Oblong folio, pp. 67.

A notice of Ross is already given at page lxxix.

SHEPHERD (WILLIAM).

"A Collection of Strathspey Reels, &c., with a Bass for the Violoncello or Harpsichord. Dedicated by permission to Miss Abercromby of Tullibody. Composed by William Shepherd. Edinburgh, printed for the Author, and to be had at all the Music shops in town and country. Price 5s. George Walker, Sculp$^{t}$., Edinburgh." Folio, pp. 26.

"A Second Collection of Strathspey Reels, &c., for the Pianoforte, Violin, and Violoncello. Dedicated to Lady Carmichael of Castlecraig. Composed by William Shepherd. Entd. Stat. Hall. Price 6s. Edinburgh, printed and sold by Gow & Shepherd, Music-sellers, No. 16 Princes Street, (J. Johnson, sculpt.)." Folio, pp. 26.

William Shepherd, musician, in 1793 resided in Hamilton's Close, Bristo; and having entered into partnership with Nathaniel Gow in 1796, they carried on business as music-sellers in Edinburgh, under the firm of Gow and Shepherd, on an extensive scale. Shepherd died at Edinburgh on the 19th of January 1812.

STEWART (CHARLES)

"A Collection of Strathspeys, Reels, Giggs, &c., with a Bass for the Violoncello or Harpsichord. Dedicated (by permission) to the Right Hon$^{ble}$. Lady Mary Hay. By Charles Stewart, Musician to the late Mr Strange. Price 5s. N.B. A few New Hornpipes, Minuets, and Cotilions, by the most esteemed Composers. Edinr., printed for the Author, and to be had at Muir, Wood, & Co. Entd. Stat. Hall." Folio, pp. 25.

"A Collection of a few New Hornpipes, Minuets, Cotillions, Jigs, &c. By Charles Stewart." Folio, pp. 25.

THOMSON (GEORGE)

A list of the dates of publication of the several volumes or books of Thomson's Collection, as entered in Stationers' Hall, was communicated to Mr G. F. Graham, and is printed in "The Songs of Scotland," vol. i. p. vi. Mr Thomson, for many years Principal Clerk of the Board of Trustees, Edinburgh, died at Leith Links, on the 18th February 1851, at the very advanced age of 94.—It may be noticed as a singular fact that he should never have seen Burns, or at least have had any personal intercourse with him, notwithstanding the aid so liberally awarded by the Poet, during the four years of their correspondence. The series of the original letters and songs addressed by Burns to Thomson, arranged and bound in one volume, were exposed to sale by auction in November 1852, at the upset price of £210, and fetched Two Hundred and Sixty Guineas.

WALKER (ARCHIBALD).

"A Collection of the most approved Church Tunes now used in the Church of Scotland. To which is added, a few Catches and Songs, by Archd. Walker. Price 1s. Edinburgh, printed and sold at J. Brysson's Music shop, Southside Cross Well. Third edition, with additions. J. Johnson, sculpt." 12mo, pp. 40.

WALKER (JAMES).

"A Second Collection of Reels, Strathspeys, Jigs, &c., with a Bass for the Violoncello or Harpsichord. Dedicated to Lady St Clair of Sinclair, by James Walker, Dysart. Printed for the Author, and to be had at his house in Dysart. Sold also by Jas. Johnson, Music-seller, Lawnmarket, and at all the other dealers of Music in Edinburgh. J. Johnson, sculpt." Folio, price 4s.

WILSON (WILLIAM).

"Twelve Original Scotch Songs, for the Voice and Harpsichord, with an Accompaniment for the Violin or Flute, dedicated by permission to His Royal Highness the Prince of Wales. Composed and adapted by William Wilson. Entered at Stationers' Hall. Op. III. Price 10s. 6d. London, printed for the author, No. 2 Camden Place, Hampstead Road, by Longman and Broderip, No. 26 Cheapside, and No. 13 Haymarket," &c. Folio, pp. 29, besides title and printed list of Subscribers. One of these "Original Scotch Songs," is "Roy's Wife of Auldy Wallach."

Of the preceding Collections, some are no doubt posterior to the period which this Catalogue was intended to comprise. Others again are purposely omitted, when the dates of publication were well ascertained not to fall within that period—such, for instance, as the later publications of George Thomson; the British Minstrel, by R. A. Smith; the Melodies of Scotland, by Finlay Dun; the Dance Music of Scotland, by J. T. Surenne; the Caledonian Repository, by James Davie, Aberdeen; the Complete Repository, by Malcolm Keith; with many others, of more or less importance.

To this list might be added the principal collections of Highland Airs, such as Albyn's Anthology, by Alexander Campbell; Airs and Melodies peculiar to the Highlands of Scotland and the Isles, by Captain Simon Fraser; the Ancient Martial Music of Caledonia, called Piobaireachd, by Donald Macdonald; and the Ancient Piobaireachd or Highland Pipe Music, by Angus Mackay.

But before concluding these Notices, it may not be out of place to mention a volume entitled "Musical Memoirs of Scotland, with Historical Annotations, and numerous illustrative Plates," by the late Sir John Graham Dalyell, Edinburgh, 1849, 4to. The title of this volume furnishes no very distinct notion of its contents, which exhibit the result of a long-continued and laborious investigation into the History of Music in Scotland, "selected from copious collections on the subject of Scottish history, the accumulation of many years;" and accompanied with plates of the various Musical instruments in use from the earliest times.

Another work, published by Messrs Wood, and edited by Mr Farquhar Graham, may also be mentioned, as the information contained in the Notes to JOHNSON'S MUSICAL MUSEUM has been copiously employed by the Editor, and duly acknowledged in the following terms:—"The kind liberality of the Messrs Blackwood has enabled the publishers of this work to avail themselves of those valuable Notes and Illustrations above referred to; and thus to render this new Collection much more interesting than it could otherwise have been." The work referred to contains an extensive and judicious selection, with interesting notices and remarks by the Editor, under the title of "The Songs of Scotland adapted to their appropriate Melodies, arranged with Pianoforte Accompaniments, by G. F. Graham, T. M. Mudie, J. T. Surenne, H. E. Dibdin, Finlay Dun, &c. Illustrated with Historical, Biographical, and Critical Notices, by G. F. Graham. Wood and Co., 12 Waterloo Place, Edinburgh, 1848." 3 vols. royal 8vo.

As reference is made in the previous Introduction to some of the early composers of Sacred Music, I may also be permitted here to specify a recent publication, containing a very extensive and elaborate Collection of Church Tunes, from the earliest and most authentic editions of the English, Scottish, and German Psalters, skilfully harmonised. The volume is entitled "The Standard Psalm-Tune Book, containing upwards of 600 specimens, comprising all the available Tunes in the English, Scotch, and Geneva Psalters, with many others from the German 'Choral Bucher,' and other authentic sources, many of them rare, the whole faithfully compiled from the original editions, and arranged for 4 Voices, with an Organ accompaniment, by Henry Edward Dibdin, Organist of Trinity Chapel, Edinburgh." 1852. Folio.

# INDEX OF THE COLLECTIONS

## DESCRIBED IN THE PRECEDING CATALOGUE

# THE SCOTS Musical Museum

Consisting of Six hundred Scots Songs

with proper Basses for the

PIANO FORTE &c.

Humbly Dedicated

To the Society

OF

Antiquaries of Scotland

BY JAMES JOHNSON

*In this Publication the original simplicity of our Ancient National Airs is retained unincumbered with useless Accompaniments & graces depriving the hearers of the sweet simplicity of their native melodies.*

Volume I Pr. 7s

Butterworth Scripsit

Printed & Sold by JAMES JOHNSON Music Seller EDINBURGH to be had at T. PRESTON No. 97 Strand LONDON. McFADYEN GLASGOW, & at all the principal Music Sellers.

# TO THE TRUE LOVERS OF CALEDONIAN

## MUSIC AND SONG.

IT has long been a juſt and general Complaint, that among all the Muſic Books of SCOTS SONGS that have been hitherto offered to the Public not one, nor even all of them put together, can be ſaid to have merited the name of what may be called A COMPLETE COLLECTION; having been publiſhed only in detached pieces and parcels; amounting however upon the whole, to more than twice the price of this Publication; attended moreover with this further diſadvantage, that they have been printed in ſuch large unportable Sizes, that they could by no means anſwer the purpoſe of being pocket-companions; which is no ſmall incumbrance, eſpecially to the admirers of ſocial Muſic.

To remedy theſe, and all other complaints and inconveniencies of the kind, this work, now before the public eye, has been undertaken, and carried on, Under the Patronage, direction, and Review of a number of Gentlemen of undiſputed taſte, who have been pleaſed to encourage, enrich, and adorn the whole literary part of the Performance _ The Publiſher begs leave only to ſay that he has ſtrenuouſly endeavoured, and will perſevere to exert his utmoſt ſkill and aſſiduity in executing the mechanical part of the work. And he flatters himſelf, that his laudable unremitted emulation to gain the public eſteem, will meet with the favourable regard of his obliging friends and generous Subſcribers _ The Subſcription will be kept open, at leaſt, to the publication of the Second Volume: which was all originally intended; and which will be publiſhed as ſoon as the work can be executed, which is already in great forwardneſs _ Each Volume contains ONE HUNDRED Songs, with the original Muſic, embelliſhed with Thorough Baſses by one of the ableſt Maſters _ And beſides theſe hundred Songs, under the Muſic and Song inſerted in the reſpective titles at the top of the page, the performer will frequently find two or three additional Sets of appoſite words to the ſame tune; adapted to the VOICE, HARPSICHORD, and PIANO-FORTE, &c.

It was intended, and mentioned in the Propoſals, to have adopted a Conſiderable Variety of the moſt Muſical and Sentimental of the Engliſh and Iriſh Songs; But this Scheme, not happening to meet with general approbation, after ſeveral plates had been engraved for the purpoſe, it was determined, in compliance with what ſeemed to be the almoſt univerſal inclination of the Subſcribers, to poſtpone it for the preſent, with a full intention to reſume it afterwards, if it ſhall yet appear to be deſired and encouraged, in a third, or a fourth Volume.

In the meantime, it is humbly requeſted, if any Lady or Gentleman have any Song of Merit with the Muſic (never hitherto Publiſhed) of the true Ancient Caledonian ſtrain, that they would be pleaſed to tranſmit the ſame to the Publiſher, that it may be ſubmitted to the proper Judges, and ſo be preſerved in this Repoſitory of our National Muſic and Song, by their moſt

Obliged and Humble Servant,

JAMES JOHNSON.

Edin. Bell's Wynd, May 22 1787.

# Index of Authors' names in Vol. first, ſo far as can be aſcertained.

# INDEX.

# INDEX.

# The Highland Queen.

No. 1

No more my Song shall be, ye Swains, of purling streams, or flow_ry
Andante
plains; More pleasing beauties now inspire, And Phœbus tunes the warbling
Lyre: Di_vinely aided thus I mean, To ce_le_brate,
Sym
To
ce_le_brate my Highland Queen.
Sy

In her, sweet innocence you'll find,
With freedom, truth, and beauty join'd;
From pride and affectation free,
Alike she smiles on you and me:
The brightest nymph that trips the green,
I do pronounce my Highland Queen.

No sordid wish, or trifling joy,
Her settled calm of mind destroy;
Strict honour fills her spotless soul,
And adds a lustre to the whole:
A matchless shape, a graceful mien,
All center in my Highland Queen.

How blest that youth, whom gentle fate,
Has destin'd for so fair a mate!
Has all these wondring gifts in store,
And each returning day brings more.
No youth so happy can be seen,
Possessing thee, my Highland Queen

## The Highland King.

YE Muses nine, O lend your aid,
Inspire a tender bashful maid!
That's lately yielded up her heart,
A conquest to Love's pow'rful dart:
And now would fain attempt to sing,
The praises of my Highland King.

Jamie, the pride of all the green,
Is just my age, e'en gay fifteen:
When first I saw him, 'twas the day
That ushers in the sprightly May;
When first I felt Love's pow'rful sting,
And sigh'd for my dear Highland King.

With him for beauty, shape, and air,
No other shepherd can compare;
Good nature, honesty, and truth,
Adorn the dear, the matchless youth:
And graces, more than I can sing
Bedeck my charming Highland King

Would once the dearest boy but say
'Tis you I love; Come, Come away,
Unto the kirk, my Love, let's hy;
Oh me! in rapture, I'd comply!
And I should then have cause to sing
The praises of my Highland King.

## An thou were my ain thing.

2
Slow
An thou were my ain thing, O I wou'd love thee, I wou'd
love thee. An thou were my ain thing, how dearly wou'd I love thee!
Then I wou'd claſp thee in my arms, Then I'd ſecure thee from all
harms, For above mortals thou haſt charms, How dearly do I love thee!

Of race divine thou needs muſt be,
Since nothing earthly equals thee;
For heaven's ſake, then pity me,
Who only lives to love thee.
An thou were &c.

To merit I no claim can make,
But that I love, and for your ſake
What man can do I'll undertake;
So dearly do I love thee.
An thou were &c.

The Pow'rs one thing peculiar have,
To ruin none whom they can ſave;
O for their ſake ſupport a ſlave,
Who ever on ſhall love thee.
An thou were &c.

My paſſion, conſtant as the ſun,
Flames ſtronger ſtill, will ne'er have done,
Till fate my thread of life have ſpun,
Which breathing out I'll love thee.
An thou were &c.

## Peggy, I muſt love thee.

3

As from a rock, paſt all relief, The ſhipwreck'd Co _ lin
Slow
ſpying His native ſoil, o'ercome with grief, Half ſunk in waves, & dying,
With the next morning ſun he ſpies A ſhip which gives un_hop'd ſur_
_priſe; New life ſprings up, he lifts his eyes With joy, & waits her motion.

So when by her, whom long I lov'd,
 I ſcorn'd was and deſerted;
Low with deſpair, my ſpirits mov'd,
 To be forever parted:
Thus droop'd I, till diviner grace
I found in Peggy's mind and face;
Ingratitude appear'd then baſe,
 But virtue more engaging.

Then now, ſince happily I've hit,
 I'll have no more delaying;
Let beauty yield to manly wit,
 We loſe ourſelves in ſtaying;
I'll haſte dull courtſhip to a cloſe,
Since marriage can my fears oppoſe:
Why ſhou'd we happy minutes loſe,
 Since, Peggy, I muſt love thee.

Men may be fooliſh if they pleaſe,
 And deem't a lover's duty
To ſigh, and ſacrifice their eaſe,
 Doating on a proud beauty:
Such was my caſe for many a year,
Still hope ſucceeding to my fear;
Falſe Betty's charms now diſappear,
 Since Peggy's far outſhine them.

# Beſs the Gawkie.

4

Blyth young Beſs to Jean did ſay, will ye gang to yon ſun_ny
Andante Affect^o
brae; where flocks do feed, and Herds do ſtray, and ſport a while wi'
Ja_mie! Ah na. laſs, I'll no gang there, nor about Ja_mie tak' nae
care, nor about Jamie tak' nae care, for he's tane up wi' Maggy!

For hark, and I will tell you, laſs,
Did I not ſee your Jamie paſs,
Wi' meikle gladneſs in his face,
Out o'er the muir to Maggy.
I wat he gae her mony a kiſs,
And Maggy took them ne'er amiſs:
'Tween ilka ſmack---pleas'd her with this,
That Beſs was but a gawkie.

For when a civil kiſs I ſeek,
She turns her head, and thraws her cheek,
And for an hour ſhe'll ſcarcely ſpeak;
Who'd not call her a gawkie?
But ſure my Maggy has mair ſenſe,
She'll gi'e a ſcore without offence;
Now gi'e me ane unto the menſe,
And ye ſhall be my dawtie.

O Jamie, ye ha'e mony tane,
But I will never ſtand for ane,
Or twa when we do meet again;
Sae ne'er think me a gawkie.
Ah na, laſs, that ne'er can be,
Sic thoughts as theſe are far frae me,
Or ony thy ſweet face that ſee,
E'er to think thee a gawkie.

But, whiſht!---nae mair of this we'll ſpeak,
For yonder Jamie does us meet;
Inſtead of Meg he kiſs'd ſae ſweet,
I trow he likes the gawkie.
O dear Beſs, I hardly knew,
When I came by, your gown's ſae new,
I think you've got it wet wi' dew.
Quoth ſhe, That's like a gawkie.

It's wat wi' dew, and 'twill get rain,
And I'll get gowns when it is gane,
Sae you may gang the gate you came,
And tell it to your dawtie.
The guilt appear'd in Jamie's cheek;
He cry'd, O cruel maid, but ſweet,
If I ſhould gang a nither gate,
I ne'er could meet my dawtie!

The laſſes faſt frae him they flew,
And left poor Jamie fair to rue,
That ever Maggy's face he knew,
Or yet ca'd Beſs a Gawkie.
As they went o'er the muir they ſang;
The hills and dales with echoes rang,
The hills and dales with echoes rang,
Gang o'er the muir to Maggy.

## Oh open the door, Lord Gregory.

5
Oh o_pen the door, Lord Gre_go_ry, oh o..pen and
Adagio
let me in; the rain rains on my fcar_let robes, the
dew drops o'er my chin. If you are the lafs that
I lov'd once, as I true you are not fhe, Come give me
fome of the to_kens that paft between you and me.

Ah wae be to you, Gregory!
  An ill death may you die!
You will not be the death of one,
  But you'll be the death of three.
Oh don't you mind, Lord Gregory?
  'Twas down at yon burn fide
We chang'd the ring off our fingers
  And I put mine on thine.

# The Banks of the Tweed.

Recitative
6
As on the Banks of Tweed I lay reclin'd beneath a verdant
ſhade, I heard a ſound more ſweet than pipe or flute, ſure more en_
_chanting was not Orpheus' lute; while liſt'ning & amaz'd I turn'd my eyes, the more I
heard, the greater my ſurprze; I roſe & follow'd guided by my Ear, & in a thickſet
grove I ſaw my Dear. Unſeen, unheard, ſhe thought, thus ſung the Maid.
Air.
To the ſoft murm'ring ſtream I will ſing of my Love, How de_
Andante
_ligh_ted am I when a_broad I can rove, To in_dulge a fond

paſsion for Jockey my dear, When he's ab _ ſent I
ſigh, but how blith when he's near! 'Tis this rural a _ muſement de _
_ lights my ſad Heart: Come a _ way to my arms, love! and ne _ ver de _
_ part. To his Pipe I could ſing, for he's bon _ ny and gay; Did he
know how I lov'd him, no lon _ ger he'd ſtay.

Neither Linnet or Nightingale ſung half ſo ſweet,
And the ſoft melting ſtrain did kind Echo repeat,
It ſo raviſh'd my heart and delighted my ear,
Swift as lightning I flew to the arms of my dear:
She ſurpriz'd, and detected, ſome moments did ſtand,
Like the roſe was her cheek, and the lily her hand,
Which ſhe placed on her breaſt, and ſaid, Jockey, I fear
I have been too imprudent, pray how came you here.

For to viſit my ewes, and to ſee my lambs play,
By the banks of the Tweed and the groves I did ſtray
But my Jenny, dear Jenny, how oft' have I ſigh'd,
And have vow'd endleſs love, if you would be my bride!
To the altar of Hymen, my fair one, repair,
Where a knot of affection ſhall tie the fond pair;
To the pipe's ſprightly notes the gay dance we will lead,
And will bleſs the dear grove, by the banks of the Tweed.

## The beds of ſweet Roſes.

7
Andante
As I was a wal _ king one morning in May, The
little birds were ſing _ ing de _ light _ ful and gay, the
little birds were ſinging de _ light _ ful and gay, where
I and my true love did often ſport and play, down a _
_ mong the beds of ſweet roſ _ es, where I and my true love did
often ſport and play, down a _ mong the beds of ſweet roſ _ es.

My daddy and my mammy I oft have heard them ſay,
That I was a naughty boy, and did often ſport and play;
But I never liked in all my life a maiden that was ſhy
Down among the beds of ſweet roſes.

## Roſlin Caſtle.

8
Slow
'Twas in that ſeaſon of the year, when all things gay and ſweet ap-
-pear, that Colin with the morning ray, a-roſe and ſung his rural lay. Of
Nanny's charms the Shepherd ſung, the hills and dales with Nanny rung; while
Roſlin Caſtle heard the Swain, And echo'd back the chearful ſtrain.

Awake, ſweet muſe! the breathing ſpring
With rapture warms; awake and ſing!
Awake and join the vocal throng,
Who hail the morning with a ſong;
To Nanny raiſe the chearful lay,
O! bid her haſte and come away;
In ſweeteſt ſmiles herſelf adorn,
And add new graces to the morn!

O hark, my love! on ev'ry ſpray,
Each feather'd warbler tunes his lay;
'Tis beauty fires the raviſh'd throng;
And love inſpires the melting ſong:
Then let my raptur'd notes ariſe;
For beauty darts from Nanny's eyes;
And love my riſing boſom warms,
And fills my ſoul with ſweet alarms.

O! come, my love! thy Colin's lay
With rapture calls, O come away!
Come, while the muſe this wreath ſhall twine
Around that modeſt brow of thine;
O! hither haſte, and with thee bring
That beauty blooming like the ſpring,
Thoſe graces that divinely ſhine,
And charm this raviſh'd breaſt of mine!

### Same Tune.

FROM Roſlin Caſtle's echoing walls
Reſound my ſhepherd's ardent calls;
My Colin bids me come away,
And love demands I ſhould obey.
His melting ſtrain, and tuneful lay,
So much the charms of love diſplay,
I yield - nor longer can refrain
To own my love, and bleſs my ſwain.

No longer can my heart conceal
The painful-pleaſing flame I feel;
My ſoul retorts the am'rous ſtrain;
And echoes back in love again.
Where lurks my ſongſter. from what grove
Does Colin pour his notes of love.
O bring me to the happy bow'r,
Where mutual love my bliſs ſecure!

Ye vocal hills, that catch the ſong,
Repeating as it flies along,
To Colin's ears my ſtrain convey,
And ſay, I haſte to come away.
Ye zephyrs ſoft, that fan the gale,
Waft to my love the ſoothing tale;
In whiſpers all my ſoul expreſs,
And tell I haſte his arms to bleſs

## Saw ye Johnnie cummin. quo ſhe.

9

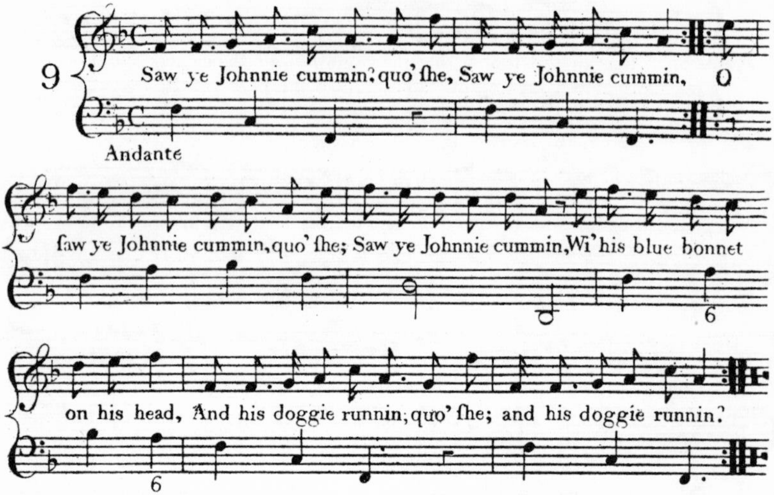
Saw ye Johnnie cummin? quo' ſhe, Saw ye Johnnie cummin, O
Andante
ſaw ye Johnnie cummin, quo' ſhe; Saw ye Johnnie cummin, Wi' his blue bonnet
6
on his head, And his doggie runnin, quo' ſhe; and his doggie runnin?
6

Fee him, father, fee him, quo' ſhe;
Fee him, father, fee him:
For he is a' gallant lad,
And a weel doin;
And a' the wark about the houſe
Gaes wi' me when I ſee him, quo' ſhe;
Wi' me when I ſee him.

What will I do wi' him, huſſy?
What will I do wi' him?
He's ne'er a ſark upon his back,
And I hae nane to gi'e him.

I ha'e twa ſarks into my kiſt,
And ane o' them I'll gi'e him,
And for a mark of mair fee
Dinna ſtand wi' him, quo' ſhe;
Dinna ſtand wi' him.

For well do I lo'e him, quo' ſhe;
Well do I lo'e him:
O fee him, father, fee him, quo' ſhe;
Fee him, father, fee him;
He'll had the pleugh, thraſh in the barn,
And lie wi' me at e'en, quo' ſhe;
Lie wi' me at e'en.

## Woo'd and Married and a'.

10

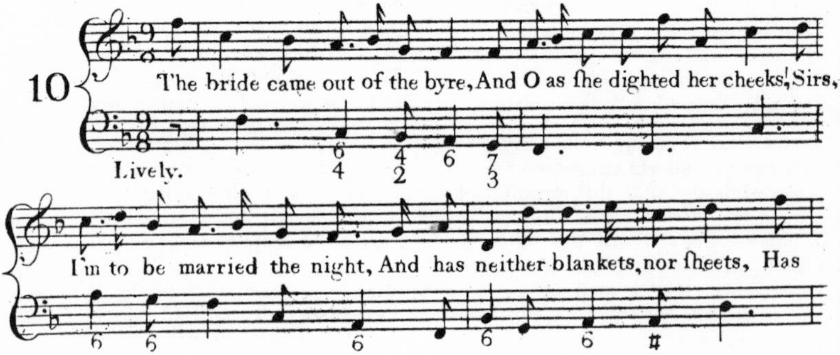
The bride came out of the byre, And O as ſhe dighted her cheeks! Sirs,
Lively.
I'm to be married the night, And has neither blankets, nor ſheets, Has

Continued.

nei_ther blan_kets, nor ſheets, Nor ſcarce a cover_let too. The
bride that has a' thing to borrow, Has e'en right mei_kle a_do.
Chorus.
Woo'd and mar_ried and a', Woo'd and married and a', An
was nae ſhe very weel aff, That was woo'd and married and a.

Out ſpake the bride's father,
As he came in frae the plough,
O had ye're tongue, my doughter,
And ye's get gear enough;
The ſtirk that ſtands i' th' tether,
And our bra' baſin'd yade
Will carry ye hame your corn;
What wad ye be at, ye jade?
Woo'd and married, &c.

Out ſpake the bride's mither,
What d_l needs a' this pride!
I had nae a plack in my pouch
That night I was a bride;
My gown was linſy-woolſy,
And ne'er a ſark ava;
And ye hae ribbons and buſkins,
Mae than ane or twa.
Woo'd and married, &c.

What's the matter, quo' Willie,
Tho' we be ſcant o' claiths,
We'll creep the nearer the gither,
And we'll ſmore a' the fleas:
Simmer is coming on,
And we'll get teats of woo;
And we'll get a laſs o' our ain,
And ſhe'll ſpin claiths anew.
Woo'd and married, &c.

Out ſpake the bride's brither,
As he came in wi' the kie,
Poor Willie had ne'er a tane ye,
Had he kent ye as well as I;
For youre baith proud and ſaucy,
And nae for a poor man's wife;
Gin I canna get a better,
Iſe never tak ane i' my life.
Woo'd and married, &c.

Out ſpake the bride's ſiſter,
As ſhe came in frae the byre,
O gin I were but married!
It's a' that I deſire:
But we poor fo'k maun live ſingle,
And do the beſt we can;
I dinna care what I ſhou'd want,
If I cou'd get but a man.
Woo'd and married, &c.

## Saw ye nae my Peggy.

11

Saw ye nae my Peggy, ſaw ye nae my Peggy, ſaw ye nae my Peggy, coming
Lively
o'er the Lee. Sure, a finer creature, ne'er was formd by nature, ſo compleat each feature,
ſo divine is ſhe. O, how Peggy charms me! ev'ry look ſtill warms me, ev'ry thought alarm
me, leſt ſhe love not me. Peggy doth diſcover nought but charms all over; nature

bids me love her; that's a Law to me.

Who would leave a lover,
To become a rover?
No, I'll ne'er give over,
Till I happy be!
For ſince love inſpires me,
As her beauty fires me,
And her abſence tires me,
Nought can pleaſe but ſhe.
When I hope to gain her,
Fate ſeems to detain her;
Cou'd I but obtain her,
Happy would I be!
I'll ly down before her,
Bleſs, ſigh, and adore her,
With faint looks implore her,
'Till ſhe pity me!

### The Toaſt. Same Tune.

COME let's ha'e mair wine in,
Bacchus hates repining,
Venus loves nae dwining,
Let's be blyth and free.
Away with dull—Here t'ye, Sir;
Ye'er miſtreſs, Robie, gie's her,
We'll drink her health wi' pleaſure,
Wha's belov'd by thee?

Then let Peggy warm ye,
That's a laſs can charm ye,
And to joys alarm ye,
Sweet is ſhe to me.
Some angel ye wad ca' her,
And never wiſh ane brawer,
If ye bare-headed ſaw her
Kilted to the knee.

Peggy a dainty laſs is,
Come lets join our glaſſes,
And refreſh our hauſes
With a health to thee.
Let coofs their caſh be clinking,
Be ſtatesmen tint in thinking,
While we with love and drinking,
Give our cares the lie.

## The Bonny Scot-man.

12
Andante
Ye Gales that gently wave the Sea, and pleaſe the can_ny
Boat-man, bear me frae hence, or bring to me my brave, my bonny
Scot-man! In haly Bands we joyn'd our hands, yet may not this diſ_
_co_ver, while Parents rate a large Eſtate before a faith_fu' Lo_ver.

But I loor chuſe in Highland glens
To herd the kid and goat, man,
E'er I cou'd for ſic little ends
Refuſe my bonny Scot-man.
Wae worth the man
Wha firſt began
The baſe ungenerous faſhion,
Frae greedy views,
Love's art to uſe,
While ſtrangers to its paſsion!

Frae foreign fields, my lovely youth,
Haſte to thy longing laſſie,
Who pants to preſs thy baumy mouth,
And in her boſom hauſe thee.
Love gi'es the word,
Then haſte on board,
Fair winds and tenty Boat-man,
Waft o'er, waft o'er,
Frae yonder ſhore,
My blyth, my bonny Scot-man!

## The Flowers of Edinburgh.

13

My love was once a bonny lad, he was the flower of all his kin; The
Andante
absence of his bon_ny face has rent my tender heart in twain. I
day nor Night find no de_light; in si_lent tears I still complain, and ex_
claim 'gainst thos my rival foes; that ha'e ta'en from me my darling Swain.

Despair and anguish fill my breast,
Since I have lost my blooming rose;
I sigh and moan while others rest,
His absence yields me no repose.
To seek my love I'll range and rove,
Thro' ev'ry grove and distant plain;
Thus I'll ne'er cease, but spend my days,
T' hear tidings from my darling swain,

There's nothing strange in Nature's change,
Since parents shew such cruelty;
They caus'd my love from me to range,
And knows not to what destiny
The pretty kids and tender lambs
May cease to sport upon the plain;
But I'll mourn and lament, in deep discontent,
For the absence of my darling swain.

Kind Neptune, let me thee intreat,
To send a fair and pleasant gale;
Ye dolphins sweet, upon me wait,
And convey me on your tail.
Heavens bless my voyage with success,
While crossing of the raging main,
And send me safe o'er to that distant shore
To meet my lovely darling swain.

All joy and mirth at our return
Shall then abound from Tweed to Tay;
The bells shall ring, and sweet birds sing,
To grace and crown our nuptial day.
Thus bless'd with charms in my love's arm
My heart once more I will regain:
Then I'll range no more to a distant shore
But in love will enjoy my darling swain

## Jamie Gay.

14
Andante
As Jamie Gay gang'd blythe his way-a_long the banks of Tweed,
a bonny lafs, as ever was, came trip_ping o'er-the mead. The
hear_ty Swain, untaught to feign, the buxom Nymph fur_vey'd, and
full of glee, as lad could be, be_fpoke the pretty maid,

Dear laffie tell, why by thy fell
Thou haft'ly wand'reft here.
My ewes, fhe cry'd, are ftraying wide;
Can'ft tell me, Laddie, where.
To town I hy, he made reply,
Some meikle fport to fee;
But thou'rt fo fweet, fo trim and neat,
I'll feek the ewes with thee.

She gave her hand, nor made a ftand,
But lik'd the youth's intent;
O'er hill and dale, o'er plain and vale,
Right merrily they went.

The birds fang fweet, the pair to greet,
And flow'rs bloom'd all around;
And as they walk'd, of love they talk'd,
And joys which lovers crown'd.

And now the fun had rofe to noon,
In. zenith of his power,
When to a fhade their fteps they made,
To pafs the mid-day hour.
The bonny lad row'd in his plaid
The lafs, who fcorn'd to frown;
She foon forgot the ewes fhe fought,
And he to gang to town.

# My Dear Jockey.

15

My laddie is gane far a-way o'er the plain, while in ſorrow behind I am
forc'd to remain; tho' blue bells & violets the hedges adorn, tho' trees are in bloſſom &
ſweet blows the thorn, no pleaſure they give me, in vain they look gay; there's nothing can
pleaſe me now Jockey's away: forlorn I ſit ſinging, and this is my ſtrain, haſte, haſte, my dear
Jockey, haſte, haſte, my dear Jockey, haſte, haſte, my dear Jockey, to me back a-gain.
Andante

When lads and their laſſes are on the green met,
They dance and they ſing, and they laugh, and they chat,
Contented and happy with hearts full of glee,
I can't without envy their merriment ſee.
Thoſe pleaſures offend me, my ſhepherd's not there,
No pleaſure I reliſh that Jockey don't ſhare,
It makes me to ſigh, I from tears ſcarce refrain,
I wiſh my dear Jockey return'd back again.

But hope ſhall ſuſtain me, nor will I deſpair,
He promis'd he would in a fortnight be here;
On fond expectation my wiſhes I'll feaſt,
For love my dear Jockey to Jenny will haſte;
Then farewell each care, and adieu each vain ſigh,
Who'll then be ſo bleſt or ſo happy as I!
I'll ſing on the meadows, and alter my ſtrain,
When Jockey returns to my arms back again.

## Fy gar rub her o'er wi' Strae.

16

Andante
And gin ye meet a bon_ny laſsie, gie'er a kiſs, and let her
gae, But if ye meet a dirty huſsy, Fy gar rub her o'er wi' Strae.
Be ſure ye dinna quit the grip Of il_ka joy, when ye are young, Be_
_fore auld age your vi_tals nip, And lay ye twafald o'er a rung.

Sweet youth's a blyth and heartſome time;
  Then, lads and laſſes, while 'tis May,
Gae pu' the gowan in its prime,
  Before it wither and decay.
Watch the ſaft minutes of delyte,
  When Jenny ſpeaks beneath her breath,
And kiſſes, laying a' the wyte
  On you, if ſhe kepp ony ſkaith.

Haith, ye're ill bred, ſhe'll ſmiling ſay,
  Ye'll worry me, ye greedy rook;
Syne frae your arms ſhe'll rin away,
  And hide herſell in ſome dark nook.
Her laugh will lead you to the place
  Where lies the happineſs ye want,
And plainly tell you to your face,
  Nineteen nayſays are haf a grant.

Now to her heaving boſom cling,
  And ſweetly toolie for a kiſs:
Frae her fair finger whoop a ring,
  As taiken of a future bliſs.
Theſe bennifons, I'm very ſure,
  Are of the gods indulgent grant;
Then, ſurly carles, whiſht, forbear
  To plague us wi' your whining cant.

### Same Tune. Sung by PATIE.

DEAR Roger, if your Jenny geck,
  And anſwer kindneſs wi' a ſlight,
Seem unconcern'd at her neglect,
  For women in a man delight,
But them deſpiſe who're ſoon defeat,
  And with a ſimple face give way
To a repulſe; —then be not blate,
  Puſh bauldly on, and win the day.

When maidens, innocently young,
  Say aften what they never mean,
Ne'er mind their pretty lying tongue,
  But tent the language of their een.
If theſe agree, and ſhe perſiſt
  To anſwer a' your love with hate,
Seek elſewhere to be better bleſs'd;
  And let her ſigh when 'tis too late.

## The Laſs of Livingſton.

17

Pain'd with her ſlighting Jamie's love, Bell dropt a tear - Bell
Slowiſh
dropt a tear; The gods deſcended from a_bove, well pleas'd to hear, well
pleas'd to hear. They heard the praiſes of the youth from her own tongue, from her own
tongue, Who now converted was to truth, and thus ſhe ſung, & thus ſhe ſung.

Bleſs'd days when our ingenious ſex,
More frank and kind - more frank and kind,
Did not their lov'd adorers vex;
But ſpoke their mind - but ſpoke their mind,
Repenting now, ſhe promis'd fair,
Wou'd he return - wou'd he return,
She ne'er again wou'd give him care,
Or cauſe him mourn - or cauſe him mourn,

Why lov'd I the deſerving ſwain,
Yet ſtill thought ſhame - yet ſtill thought ſhame,
When he my yielding heart did gain,
To own my flame - to own my flame!
Why took I pleaſure to torment,
And ſeem too coy - and ſeem too coy.
Which makes me now, alas. lament
My ſlighted joy - my ſlighted joy!

Ye Fair, while beauty's in its ſpring,
Own your deſire - own your deſire,
While love's young pow'r with his ſoft wing
Fans up the fire - fans up the fire;
O do not with a ſilly pride,
Or low deſign - or low deſign,
Refuſe to be a happy bride,
But anſwer plain - but anſwer plain.

Thus the fair mourner wail'd her crime,
With flowing eyes - with flowing eyes.
Glad Jamie heard her all the time,
With ſweet ſurpriſe - with ſweet ſurpriſe.
Some god had led him to the grove,
His mind unchang'd - his mind unchang'd,
Flew to her arms, and cry'd, My love,
I am reveng'd - I am reveng'd.

# The last time I came o'er the Moor.

18
Slow
The laſt time I came o'er the moor, I left my love behind
me, Ye pow'rs, what pain do I endure, When ſoft I de_as mind me!
Soon as the ruddy morn diſplay'd, The beaming day en ſuing, I
met betimes my lovely maid, In fit re_treats for wooing.

Beneath the cooling ſhade we lay,
  Gazing, and chaſtely ſporting;
We kiſs'd and promiſ'd time away,
  Till night ſpread her black curtain.
I pitied all beneath the ſkies,
  Ev'en kings, when ſhe was nigh me,
In raptures I beheld her eyes,
  Which could but ill deny me.

Should I be call'd where cannons roar,
  Where mortal ſteel may wound me,
Or caſt upon ſome foreign ſhore,
  Where dangers may ſurround me;
Yet hopes again to ſee my love,
  To feaſt on glowing kiſſes,
Shall make my cares at diſtance move,
  In proſpect of ſuch bliſſes.

In all my ſoul there's not one place
  To let a rival enter:
Since ſhe excels in every grace,
  In her my love ſhall center:
Sooner the ſeas ſhall ceaſe to flow,
  Their waves the Alps ſhall cover,
On Greenland ice ſhall roſes grow,
  Before I ceaſe to love her.

The next time I go o'er the moor,
  She ſhall a lover find me;
And that my faith is firm and pure,
  Tho' I left her behind me:
Then Hymen's ſacred bonds ſhall chain
  My heart to her fair boſom,
There while my being does remain,
  My love more freſh ſhall bloſſom.

## The Happy Marriage

19

Slow
How bleſt has my time been! what joys have I known, Since wedlock's ſoft
bondage made Jeſsy my own! So joyfull my heart is, ſo ea_ſy my
Sy.
chain, That freedom is taſteleſs, and roving a pain.

Thro' walks grown with woodbines, as often we ſtray,
Around us our boys and girls frolic and play:
How pleaſing their ſport is! the wanton ones ſee,
And borrow their looks from my Jeſsy and me.

To try her ſweet temper, oft-times am I ſeen,
In revels all day with the nymphs on the green:
Tho' painful my abſence, my doubts ſhe beguiles,
And meets me at night with complacence and ſmiles.

What tho' on her cheeks the roſe loſes its hue,
Her wit and good humour bloom all the year thro';
Time ſtill, as he flies, adds increaſe to her truth,
And gives to her mind what he ſteals from her youth.

Ye ſhepherds ſo gay, who make love to enſnare,
And cheat. with falſe vows, the too credulous Fair;
In ſearch of true pleaſure, how vainly you roam!
To hold it for life, you muſt find it at home.

# The Laſs of Peaty's Mill.

20
Slow
The laſs of Peaty's mill, So bon_ny blythe and gay, In
ſpite of all my ſkill, Hath ſtole my heart a _ way. When
tedding of the hay, Bare..head_ed on the green, Love midst her
locks did play, And wan_ton'd in her een.

Her arms, white round and ſmooth,
  Breaſts riſing in their dawn,
To age it would give youth,
  To preſs them with his hand;
Through all my ſpirits ran
  An ecſtacy of bliſs,
When I ſuch ſweetneſs fand,
  Wrapt in a balmy kiſs.

Without the help of art,
  Like flow'rs which grace the wild,
She did her ſweets impart,
  Whene'er ſhe ſpoke, or ſmil'd.

Her looks, they were ſo mild,
  Free from affected pride,
She me to love beguil'd;
  I wiſh'd her for my bride.

O! had I all that wealth
  Hopetoun's high mountains fill,
Inſur'd long life and health,
  And pleaſure at my will;
I'd promiſe and fulfil,
  That none but bonny ſhe,
The laſs of Peaty's mill,
  Shou'd ſhare the ſame with me.

## The Highland Laddie.

21

The Lawland Lads think they are fine; But O they're vain and wondrous
Slowifh
gawdy! how much unlike that gracefu' mien, And manly looks of my Highland
Laddie! O my bonny bonny Highland Laddie, O my handfome Highland Laddie!
when I was fick and like to die, he row'd me in his Highland Plaidie.

## Highland Laddie, New Sett.

22

The Lawland lads think they are fine; Fut O, they're vain and idly
Slow
gawdy! how much unlike that gracefu' mien & manly looks of my Highland
Laddie! O my bonny Highland Laddie, my handfome charming highland laddie! may

## Continued.

Heaven ſtill guard, and love reward Our lawland - laſs & her highland laddie!

If I were free at will to chuſe,
  To be the wealthieſt lawland lady,
I'd take young Donald without trews,
  With bonnet blue, and belted plaidy.
    O my bonny, &c.

The braweſt beau in burrow's-town,
  In a' his airs, with art made ready,
Compar'd to him he's but a clown;
  He's finer far in's tartan plaidy.
    O my bonny, &c.

O'er benty hill with him I'll run,
  And leave my lawland kin and dady,
Frae winter's cauld, and ſummer's ſun,
  He'll ſcreen me with his highland plaidy.
    O my bonny, &c.

A painted room, and ſilken bed,
  May pleaſe a lawland laird and lady;
But I can kiſs, and be as glad,
  Behind a buſh in s highland plaidy.
    O my bonny, &c.

Few compliments between us paſs,
  I ca' him my dear highland laddie,
And he ca's me his lawland laſs,
  Syne rows me in beneath his plaidie.
    O my bonny, &c.

Nae greater joy I'll e'er pretend,
  Than that his love prove true and ſtead
Like mine to him, which ne'er ſhall end,
  While heaven preſerves my highland laddie
    O my bonny, &c.

---

## Same Tune

THE lawland maids gang trig and fine,
  But aft they're ſour and unco ſawcy;
Sae proud, they never can be kind
  Like my good-humour'd highland laſſie.
  O my bonny, bonny highland laſſie,
  My hearty ſmiling highland laſſie,
  May never care make thee leſs fair,
  But bloom of youth ſtill bleſs my laſſie.

Than ony laſs in burrows-town,
  Wha mak their cheeks with patches mottie,
I'd take my Katy but a gown,
  Bare footed in her little coatie.
    O my bonny, &c.

Beneath the brier, or brecken buſh,
  Whene'er I kiſs and court my dawtie;
Happy and blyth as ane wad wiſh,
  My flighteren heart gangs pittie pattie.
    O my bonny, &c.

O'er higheſt heathery hills I'll ſten,
  With cockit gun and ratches tenty,
To drive the deer out of their den,
  To feaſt my laſs on diſhes dainty.
    O my bonny &c.

There's nane ſhall dare by deed or word,
  'Gainſt her to wag a tongue or finger,
While I can wield my truſty ſword,
  Or frae my ſide whiſk out a whinger.
    O my bonny &c.

The mountains clad with purple bloom,
  And berries ripe, invite my treaſure
To range with me; let great fowk gloom,
  While wealth & pride confound their pleaſure
  O my bonny, bonny highland laſſie,
  My lovely ſmiling highland laſſie,
  May never care make thee leſs fair
  But bloom of youth ſtill bleſs my laſſie.

---

## From the Duenna. Same Tune.

Ah ſure a pair was never ſeen
  So juſtly form'd to meet by nature!
The youth excelling ſo in mien,
  The maid in ev'ry graceful feature!
O how happy are ſuch lovers,
  When kindred beauties each diſcovers!
For ſurely ſhe was made for thee,
  And thou to bleſs this charming creature.

So mild your looks, your children thence,
  Will early learn the taſk of duty,
The Boys with all their Father's ſenſe,
  The Girls with all their mother's beauty.
O how charming to inherit,
  At once ſuch graces and ſuch ſpirit,
Thus while you live may fortune give,
  Each bleſsing equal to your merit!

## The Turnimſpike.

Tune Clout the Caldron.

23

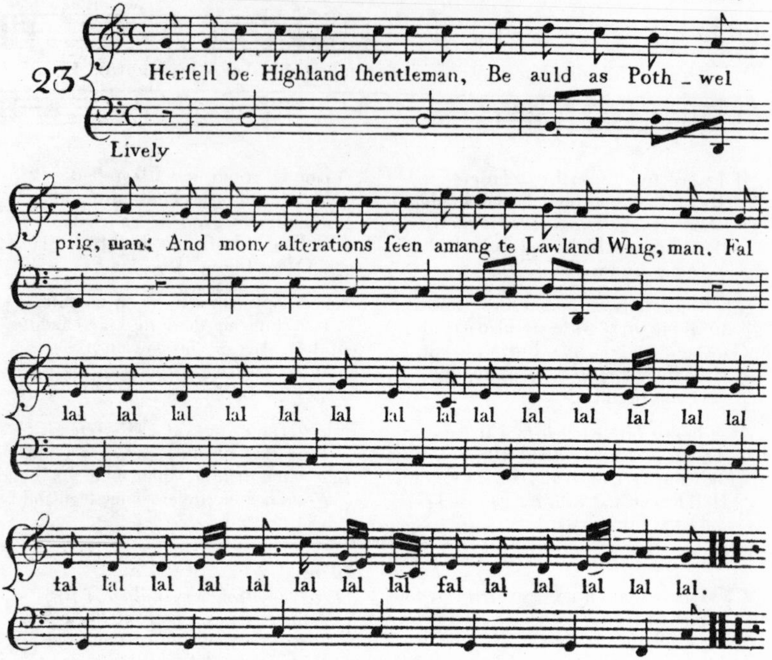
Herſell be Highland ſhentleman, Be auld as Poth _ wel
Lively
prig, man; And mony alterations ſeen amang te Lawland Whig, man. Fal
lal lal lal lal lal lal lal lal lal lal lal lal lal lal
tal lal lal lal lal lal lal lal fal lal lal lal lal lal.

First when her to the Lawlands came,
  Nainſell was driving cows, man:
There was nae laws about him's n —,
  About the preeks or trews, man.

Nainſell did wear the philabeg,
  The plaid prick't on her ſhoulder;
The guid claymore hung pe her pelt,
  The piſtol ſharg'd wi' pouder.

But for wheras theſe curſed preeks,
  Wherewith her n — be lockit,
O hon! that e'er ſhe ſaw the day!
  For a' her houghs be prokit.

Every t'ing in te Highlands now
  Pe turn't to alteration;
The ſodger dwall at our toor-ſheek,
  And tat's te great vexation.

Scotland be turn't a Ningland now,
  An' laws pring on te cadger:
Nainſell wad durk him for her deeds,
  But oh! ſhe fears te ſoger.

Anither law came after that,
  Me never ſaw te like, man;
They mak a lang road on te crund,
  And ca' him Turnimſpike, man.

An'-wow! ſhe pe a ponny road,
  Like Louden corn-rigs, man;
Where twa carts may gang on her,
  An' no preak ithers legs, man.

They ſharge a penny for ilka horſe,
  In troth, ſhe'll no pe ſheaper,
For nought put gaen upo' the crund,
  And they gi'e me a paper.

Nae doubts, Nainſell maun tra her purſe,
  And pay them what hims like, man:
I'll ſee a ſhugement on his toor;
  T'at filthy Turnimſpike, man!

But I'll awa' to te Highland hills,
  Where te'il a ane dare turn her,
And no come near her Turnimſpike,
  Unleſs it pe to purn her.

## Blythe Jockey

24
Andante
My Jockey is the blitheſt Lad, that e_ver Maiden Woo'd; When
he appears my Heart is glad, for he is kind & good. He talks of Love when
e'er we meet, His Words in raptures flow! Then tunes his Pipe, & ſings ſo ſweet, I
have no Pow'r to go, Then tunes his pipe, & ſings ſo ſweet, I have no Pow'r to Go.

All other laſſes he forſakes,
And flies to me alone;
At every fair, and all our walks
To me he makes his moan:
He buys me toys, and ſweetmeats too,
And ribbons for my hair,
No ſwain was ever half ſo good,
Nor half ſo kind and fair.

Where'er I go I nothing fear,
If Jockey is but by;
For I alone am all his care,
When ever danger's nigh.
He vows to wed next Whitſunday,
And make me bleſt for life;
Can I refuſe, ye maidens ſay,
To be young Jockey's wife?

### Same Tune

TO fly, like bird, from grove to grove,
To wander like the bee,
To ſip of ſweets, and taſte of love,
Is not enough for me:
No flattering paſſions wake my breaſt,
I wiſh the place to find
Where fate may give me peace and reſt,
One ſhepherd to my mind.

To every youth I'll not be gay;
Nor try on all my power,
Nor future pleaſures throw away
In toyings for an hour:
I would not reign the general toaſt,
Be prais'd by all the town;
A thouſand tongues on me are loſt;
I'll hear but only one.

For which of all the flattering train
Who ſwarm at beauty's ſhrine,
When youth's gay charms are in the wane
Will court their ſure decline.
Then fops, and wits, and beaux, forbear.
Your arts will never do;
For ſome fond youth ſhall be my care,
Life's chequer'd ſeaſon thro'.

My little heart ſhall have a home,
A warm and ſhelter'd neſt;
No giddy flights shall make me roam
From where I am moſt bleſt:
With love and only that dear ſwain,
What tranquil joys I ſee.
Farewell, ye falſe, inconſtant train;
For one is all to me.

# Auld lang ſyne.

25
Andante
Should auld acquaintance be forgot, Tho' they return with
ſcars? Theſe are the noble hero's lot, Obtain'd in glorious wars:
Welcome, my Varo, to my breaſt, Thy arms a-bout me twine, And
make me once a-gain as bleſt, As I was lang ſyne.

Methinks around us on each bough
A thouſand Cupids play,
Whilſt through the groves I walk with you,
Each object makes me gay:
Since your return, the ſun and moon
With brighter beams do ſhine,
Streams murmur ſoft notes while they run,
As they did lang ſyne.

Deſpiſe the court and din of ſtate;
Let that to their ſhare fall,
Who can eſteem ſuch ſlavery great,
While bounded like a ball:
But ſunk in love, upon my arms
Let your brave head recline;
We'll pleaſe ourſelves with mutual charms,
As we did lang ſyne.

O'er moor and dale with your gay friend
You may purſue the chace,
And, after a blyth bottle, end
All cares in my embrace:
And, in a vacant rainy day,
You ſhall be wholly mine;
We'll make the hours run ſmooth away,
And laugh at lang ſyne.

The hero, pleas'd with the ſweet air,
The ſigns of gen'rous love,
Which had been utter'd by the fair,
Bow'd, to the pow'rs above;
Next day, with glad conſent and haſte,
Th' approach'd the ſacred ſhrine;
Where the good prieſt the couple bleſt,
And put them out of pine.

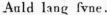

## Leander on the Bay.

26

Leander on the bay Of Helleſpont all naked ſtood, Impatient of de
Slow
6 6 6
-lay, He leap'd into the fatal flood: The raging ſeas, Whom none can
6
pleaſe, 'Gainſt him their malice ſhew, The heavens lour'd, The rain down pour'd,
And loud the winds did blow.

(2)

Then caſting round his eyes,
Thus of his fate he did complain
Ye cruel rocks, and ſkies!
Ye ſtormy winds, and angry main,
What 'tis to miſs
The lovers bliſs,
Alas! ye do not know;
Make me your wreck
As I come back,
But ſpare me as I go.

Lo! yonder ſtands the tower
Where my beloved Hero lies,
And this is the appointed hour
Which ſets to watch her longing eyes.
To his fond ſuit
The gods were mute;
The billows anſwer, No;
Up to the ſkies
The ſurges riſe,
But ſink the youth as low.

Meanwhile the wiſhing maid,
Divided 'twixt her care and love,
Now does his ſtay upbraid;
Now dreads he ſhou'd the paſſage prove:
O fate! ſaid ſhe,
Nor heaven, nor thee,
Our vows ſhall e'er divide.
I'd leap this wall,
Cou'd I but fall
By my Leander's ſide.

At length the riſing ſun
Did to her ſight reveal too late,
That Hero was undone;
Not by Leander's fault, but fate.
Said ſhe, I'll ſhew,
Tho' we are two,
Our loves were ever one;
This proof I'll give,
I will not live,
Nor ſhall he die alone.

Down from the wall ſhe leapt,
Into the raging ſeas to him,
Courting each wave ſhe met,
To teach her weary'd arms to ſwim,
The ſea-gods wept,
Nor longer kept
Her from her lover's ſide,
When join'd at laſt,
She graſp'd him faſt,
Then ſigh'd, embrac'd, and dy'd.

## The Gentle Swain. Tune Johnny's gray Breeks.

27
Slow
Now ſmiling Spring a-gain appears, with all the beauties of her train, Love
ſoon of her arrival hears, & flies to wound the Gentle Swain. How gay does nature
now appear, the lambkins friſking o'er the plain, ſweet featherd ſongſters now we hear, while
Jenny ſeeks her Gentle Swain! How gay does nature now appear, the lambkins friſking
o'er the plain, ſweet featherd Songſters now we hear, while Jenny ſeeks her Gentle Swain.

Ye Nymphs, Oh! lead me thro' the Grove,
Thro' which your ſtreams in ſilence mourn;
There with my Johnny let me rove,
'Till once his fleecy flocks return;
Young Johnny is my Gentle Swain,
That ſweetly pipes along the mead,
So ſoon's the lambkins hear his ſtrain,
With eager ſteps they turn in ſpeed.

The Flocks now all in ſportive play,
Come friſking round the piping ſwain,
Then fearful of too long delay,
Run bleating to their Dams again,
Within the freſh green Myrtle Grove,
The feather'd choir in rapture ſing,
And ſweetly warble forth their love,
To welcome the returning Spring.

### Same Tune

JENNY'S heart was frank and free,
And wooers ſhe had mony yet,
Her ſang was aye,"Of a' I ſee,
Commend me to my Johnie yet.

For air and late, he has ſic a gate
To mak a body cheary, that
I wiſh to be, before I die,
His ain kind deary yet.

Now Jenny's face was fu' o' grace,
Her ſhape was ſma' and genty-like,
And few or nane in a' the place
Had gowd and gear mair plenty yet;
Tho' war's alarms, and Johnie's charms,
Had gart her aft look eerie, yet
She ſung wi' glee,"I hope to be
"My Johnie's ain kind Deary yet:

"What tho' he's now gaen far awa,
"Where guns and cannons rattle, yet,
"Unleſs my Johnie chance to fa'
"In ſome uncanny battle, yet
"Till he return, his breaſt will burn
"Wi' love that will confound me yet,
"For I hope to ſee, before I die,
"His Bairns a' dance around me yet.

## He ſtole my tender Heart away.

28

The fields were green, the hills were gay, And birds were
Andantino Amoroſo
ſinging on each ſpray, When Colin met me in the grove, And
told me ten_der tales of love. Was e _ ver ſwain ſo blythe as he, So
kind ſo faithful and ſo free! In ſpite of all my friends cou'd
ſay, Young Colin ſtole my heart a_way, In ſpite of all my
friends cou'd ſay, Young Col_in ſtole my heart a_way.

When ere he trips the meads along,
He ſweetly joins the woodlark's ſong;
And when he dances on the green,
There's none ſo blithe as Colin ſeen:
If he's but by I nothing fear,
For I alone am all his care;
Then ſpite of all my friends can ſay,
He's ſtole my tender heart away.

My Mother chides when ere I roam,
And ſeems ſurpris'd I quit my home,
But ſhe'd not wonder that I rove,
Did ſhe but feel how much I love.
Full well I know the gen'rous ſwain,
Will never give my boſom pain;
Then ſpite of all my friends can ſay,
He's ſtole my tender heart away.

# Blythe Jocky Young and Gay.

29

Andante
Blythe Joc_ky young and gay, is all my
heart's de_light, He's all my talk by day, and all my
dreams by night. If from the lad, I be,
'Tis win_ter then with me, But when he tar_ries here,
'tis sum_mer all the year.

When I and Jocky met first on the flow'ry dale,
Right sweetly he me tret, and love was a' his tale.
You are the lass, said he, that staw my heart frae me,
O ease me of my pain, and never show disdain,

Well can my Jocky kyth his love and courtesie;
He made my heart fu' blythewhen he first spake to me.
His suit I ill deny'd; he kiss'd, and I comply'd:
Sae Jocky promis'd me, that he wad faithful be.

I'm glad when Jocky comes, sad when he gangs away:
'Tis night when Jocky glooms, but when he smiles 'tis day.
When our eyes meet I pant, I colour, sigh, and faint;
What lass that wad be kind can better tell her mind.

## Bonny Befsy.

Tune Befsey's Haggies.

30

Andante
Bef_ sy's beauties fhine fae bright Were her mony
virtues fewer, She wad e_ver gie de_light, And in tranfport
make me view her. Bonny Bef_ sy, thee a_ _lane
Love I, naething elfe a_bout thee; With thy come_ li
_nefs I'm taen, And langer can_not live without thee

Befsy's bofom's faft and warm,
 Milk-white fingers ftill employ'd,
He who taks her to his arm,
 Of her fweets can ne'er be cloy'd.
My dear Befsy, when the rofes
 Leave thy cheek, as thou grows aulder,
Virtue, which thy mind difclofes,
 Will keep love from growing caulder.

Befsy's-tocher is but fcanty,
 Yet her face and foul difcovers
Thofe enchanting fweets in plenty
 Maun entice a thoufand lovers.
'Tis not money, but a woman
 Of a temper kind and eafy,
That gives happinefs uncommon;
 Petted things can nought but teaze ye.

# Twine weel the Plaiden.

31

O! I hae loſt my ſilken ſnood, That tied my hair ſae yel_low, I've gi'en my heart to the lad I loo'd; he was a gallant fel_low. And twine it weel, my bon_ny dow, And twine it weel, the plaiden; the laſ_ſie loſt her ſilken ſnood, In pu'ing of the bracken.
Slow

He prais'd my een ſae bonny blue,
Sae lily white my ſkin o',
And ſyne he prie'd my bonny mou,
And ſwore it was nae ſin o',
And twine it weel, my bonny dow,
And twine it weel the plaiden;
The laſſie loſt her ſilken ſnood,
In pu'ing of the bracken.

But he has left the laſs he loo'd,
His ain true love forſaken,
Which gars me ſair to greet the ſnood,
I loſt amang the bracken.
And twine it weel, my bonny dow,
And twine it weel, the plaiden;
The laſſie loſt her ſilken ſnood,
In pu'ing of the bracken.

# Faireſt of the Fair.

32
O Nannie, wilt thou gang wi' me, nor ſigh to leave the flaunting
Andante
town; Can ſilent glens have charms for thee, the lowly cot, and ruſſet
gown? Nae langer dreſt in ſilken ſheen, Nae langer deck'd wi' jewels rare. Say,
canſt thou quit each courtly ſcene, Where thou was faireſt of the fair, Where

thou was faireſt of the fair?

(2)

O Nannie, when thou'rt far awa,
 Wilt thou not caſt a wiſh behind.
Say, can'ſt thou face the flaky ſnaw,
 Nor ſhrink before the warping wind.
O can that ſaft and gentleſt mien,
 Severeſt hardſhips learn to bear,
Nor ſad regret each courtly ſcene,
 Where thou waſt faireſt of the fair.

(3)

O Nannie, can'ſt thou love ſo true,
 Thro' perils keen wi' me to gae?
Or when thy ſwain miſhap ſhall rue,
 To ſhare with him the pang of wae.
And when invading pains befal,
 Wilt thou aſſume the Nurſe's care,
Nor wiſhful thoſe gay ſcenes recall,
 Where thou waſt faireſt of the fair.

(4)

And when at laſt thy love ſhall die,
 Wilt thou receive his parting breath.
Wilt thou repreſs each ſtruggling ſigh,
 And chear with ſmiles the bed of death
And wilt thou o'er his much lov'd clay,
 Strew flowers, and drop the tender tear.
Nor then regret thoſe ſcenes ſo gay,
 Where thou waſt faireſt of the fair.

## The Blathrie o't.

33
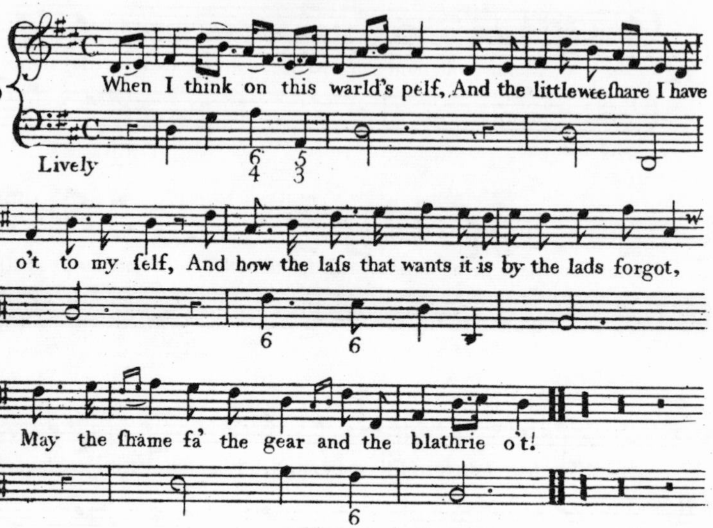

When I think on this warld's pelf, And the little wee ſhare I have
Lively
o't to my ſelf, And how the laſs that wants it is by the lads forgot,
May the ſhame fa' the gear and the blathrie o't!


Jockie was the laddie that held the pleugh,
But now he's got gow'd and gear eneugh;
He thinks nae mair of me that weirs the plaiden coat;
May the ſhame fa' the gear, and the blathrie o't!

Jenny was the laſsie that mucked the byre,
But now ſhe is clad in her ſilken attire,
And Jockie ſays he loes her, and ſwears he's me forgot;
May the ſhame fa' the gear, and the blathrie o't!

But all this ſhall never danton me,
Sae lang as I keep my fancy free:
For the lad that's ſae inconſtant, he's not worth a groat;
May the ſhame fa' the gear, and the blathrie o't!

## Lucky Nancy.

Tune, Dainty Davie.

34

While fops in ſaft I_talian verſe, Ilk fair ane's een & breaſt rehearſe, While
Lively

## Continued.

ſangs abound and ſenſe is ſcarce, theſe lines I have in_dited; But neither darts nor
arrows here, Venus nor Cupid ſhall appear, & yet with theſe fine ſounds, I ſwear, The
Chorus
maidens are de_lighted. I was ay telling you, Lucky Nancy, Lucky
Nancy, Auld ſprings wad ding the new; But ye wad never trow me.

Nor ſnaw with crimſon will I mix,
To ſpread upon my laſſie's cheeks;
And ſyne th' unmeaning name prefix,
Miranda, Chloe, or Phillis.
I'll fetch nae ſimile frae Jove,
My hight of ecſtaſy to prove,
Nor ſighing – thus – preſent my love
With roſes eke and lilies.
I was ay telling you, &c.

But ſtay, – I had amaiſt forgot
My miſtreſs, and my ſang to boot,
And that's an unco' faut, I wot;
But, Nanſy, 'tis nae matter.
Ye ſee I clink my verſe wi' rhyme,
And ken ye, that atones the crime;
Forby, how ſweet my numbers chyme,
And ſlide away like water.
I was ay telling you, &c.

Now ken, my rev'rend ſonſy fair,
Thy runkled cheeks, and lyrat hair,
Thy half ſhut een, and hodling air,
Are a' my paſſion's fuel.
Nae ſkyring gowk, my dear, can ſee,
Or love, or grace, or heaven in thee;
Yet thou haſt charms anew for me;
Then ſmile, and be na cruel.
Leez me on thy ſnawy pow,
Lucky Nancy, Lucky Nancy!
Dryeſt wood will eitheſt low,
And, Nancy, ſae will ye now.

Troth, I have ſung the ſang to you,
Which never anither bard wad do;
Hear then my charitable vow,
Dear venerable Nancy!
But if the warld my paſsion wrang,
And ſay ye only live in ſang,
Ken, I deſpiſe a ſland'ring tongue,
And ſing to pleaſe my fancy.
Leez me on thy &c.

## May-eve, or Kate of Aberdeen.

35

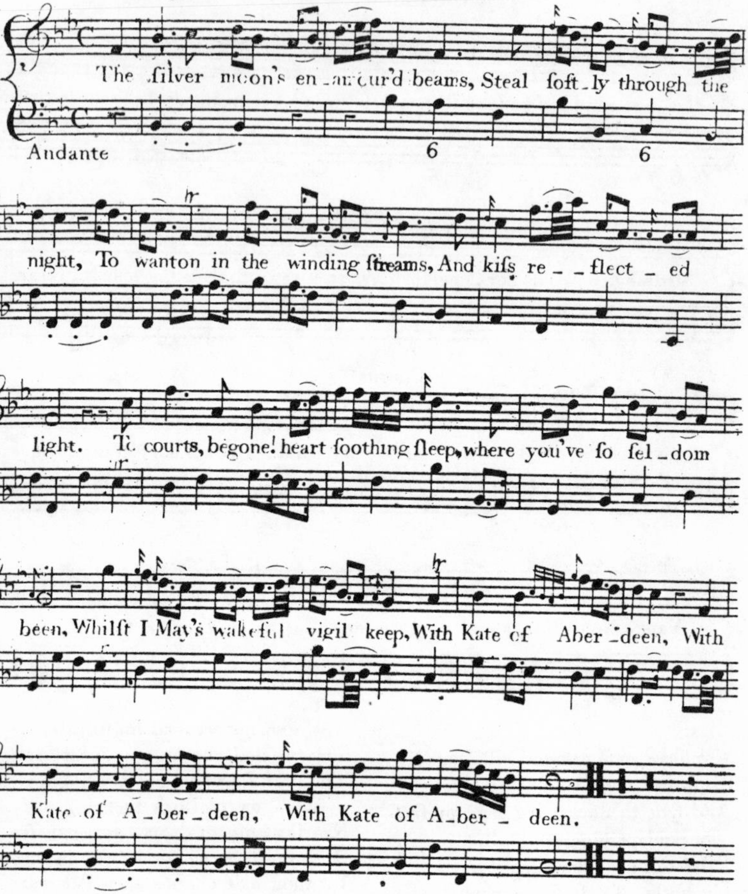
The ſilver moon's en_amour'd beams, Steal ſoft_ly through the
Andante
6
6
night, To wanton in the winding ſtreams, And kiſs re_ _flect_ed
light. To courts, begone! heart ſoothing ſleep, where you've ſo ſel_dom
been, Whilſt I May's wakeful vigil keep, With Kate of Aber_deen, With
Kate of A_ber_deen, With Kate of A_ber_deen.

The Nymphs and Swains, expectant, wait
 In primroſe-chaplets gay,
Till morn unbars her golden gate,
 And gives the promis'd May.
The Nymphs and Swains ſhall all declare
 The promis'd May, when ſeen,
Not half ſo fragrant, half ſo fair,
 As Kate of Aberdeen.

I'll tune my pipe to playful notes,
 And rouſe yon nodding grove,
Till new-wak'd birds diſtend their throats,
 And hail the maid I love.

At her approach, the lark miſtakes,
 And quits the new-dreſs'd green:
Fond bird! 'tis not the morning breaks;
 'Tis Kate of Aberdeen!

Now blithſome o'er the dewy mead,
 Where elves diſportive play,
The feſtal dance young ſhepherds lead,
 Or ſing their love-tun'd lay.
Till May, in morning robe, draws nigh,
 And claims a Virgin Queen;
The Nymphs and Swains, exulting, cry,
 Here's Kate of Aberdeen!

## Tweed Side.

36
What beauties does Flora diſ - cloſe! How ſweet are her
Andante
ſmiles up - on Tweed! Yet Mary's ſtill ſweet - er then thoſe, Both
nature and fancy ex - ceed. No daiſy, nor ſweet bluſh - ing
roſe, Nor all the gay flow'rs of the field, Nor Tweed glid - ing
gently 'thro' thoſe, Such beauty and 'pleaſure does yield.

The warblers are heard in the grove,
The linnet, the lark, and the thruſh,
The blackbird, and ſweet-cooing dove,
With muſic enchant every buſh.
Come, let us go forth to the mead,
Let's ſee how the primroſes ſpring,
We'll lodge in ſome village on Tweed,
And love, while the feather'd folks ſing.

How does my love paſs the long day.
Does Mary not 'tend a few ſheep.
Do they never careleſsly ſtray,
While happilv ſhe lies aſleep.
Tweed's murmurs ſhould lull her to reſt.
Kind Nature indulging my bliſs,
To eaſe the ſoft pains of my breaſt,
I'd ſteal an ambroſial kiſs.

'Tis ſhe does the virgins excel,
No beauty with her may compare;
Love's graces around her do dwell,
She's faireſt, where thouſands are fair,
Say, charmer, where do thy flock ſtray.
Oh! tell me at noon where they feed.
Is it on the ſweet winding Tay,
Or pleaſanter banks of the Tweed.

## Mary's Dream.

37
Slow
The moon had climb'd the higheſt hill, which riſes o'er the ſource of
Dee, And from the eaſtern ſummit ſhed her ſilver light on tow'r and tree:
When Mary laid her down to ſleep, Her thoughts on Sandy far at ſea; When
ſoft and low a voice was heard, Say, Mary weep no more for me.

## New ſet of Mary's Dream.

38
Andante
The moon had climb'd the higheſt hill, Which riſes o'er the ſource of
Dee, And from the eaſtern ſummit ſhed Her ſil-ver light on tow'r and tree:
When Mary laid her down to ſleep, her thoughts on Sandy far at ſea; When
Adag.
ſoft and low a voice was heard, Say, Ma-ry weep no more for me.

She from her pillow gently rais'd
Her head to aſk, who there might be.
She ſaw young Sandy ſhiv'ring ſtand,
With viſage pale and hollow eye;
'O Mary dear, cold is my clay,
'It lies beneath a ſtormy ſea;
'Far, far from thee, I ſleep in death;
'So, Mary, weep no more for me.

3

Three ſtormy nights and ſtormy days
'We toſs'd upon the raging main:
'And long we ſtrove our bark to ſave,
'But all our ſtriving was in vain.
Ev'n then, when horror chill'd my blood,
'My heart was fill'd with love for thee:
'The ſtorm is paſt, and I at reſt
'So, Mary, weep no more for me.

4

'O maiden dear, thyſelf prepare
'We ſoon ſhall meet upon that ſhore,
'Where love is free from doubt and care,
'And thou and I ſhall part no more!
Loud crow'd the cock, the ſhadow fled,
No more of Sandy could ſhe ſee;
But ſoft the paſſing ſpirit ſaid,
"Sweet Mary, weep no more for me!"

## Water Parted from the Sea.

39
Water parted from the Sea _ May increaſe the ri_ver's tide; to the
Andante
bubbling fount may flee or thro' fer_tile valleys glide. Tho' in
ſearch of ſoft repoſe, thro' the land 'tis free to roam, Still it _
murmurs as it flows, Panting for its na _ tive home. Tho' in
ſearch of ſoft re_poſe, thro' the land 'tis free to roam, ſtill it
murmurs as it flows, pan _ ting for its na _ tive home.

## The Maid that tends the Goats. by Mr. Dudgeon.

40

Up amang yon cliffy rocks, Sweetly rings the riſ_ing echo,
Slow
To the maid that tends the goats, Lilting o'er her native notes.
Hark, ſhe ſings, "young Sandy's kind, "An' he's promis'd ay to lo'e me;
"Here's a brotch, I ne'er ſhall tine, "Till he's fairly marri'd to me;
"Drive away, ye drone time, "An' bring about our bridal day.

"Sandy herds a flock o' ſheep,
"Aften does he blaw the whiſtle,
"In a ſtrain ſae ſaftly ſweet,
"Lam'mies liſtning dare nae bleat;
"He's as fleet's the mountain roe,
"Hardy, as the highland heather,
"Wading thro the winter ſnow,
"Keeping ay his flock together;
"But a plai'd, wi' bare houghs,
"He braves the bleakeſt norlin blaſt.

"Brawly he can dance and ſing
"Canty glee or highland cronach;
"Nane can ever match his fling
"At a reel, or round a ring;
"Wightly can he wield a rung
"In a brawl he's ay the bangſter:
"A' his praiſe can ne'er be ſung
"By the langeſt winded ſangſter.
"Sangs that ſing o' Sandy
"Seem ſhort, tho' they were e'er ſae lang.

## I Wish my Love were in a Mire.

41

Slow
Bleſt as th' immortal gods is he, The Youth who fondly
ſits by thee, And hears and ſees thee, all the while, So ſoftly
ſpeak, and ſweetly ſmile. 'Twas this bereav'd my ſoul of reſt, And
rais'd ſuch tumults in my breaſt; For, while I gaz'd, in tranſport
toſs'd, My breath was gone, my voice was loſt.

My boſom glow'd; the ſubtile flame  
Ran quick thro' all my vital frame;  
O'er my dim eyes a darkneſs hung;  
My ears with hollow murmurs rung:  
In dewy damps my limbs were chill'd;  
My blood with gentle horrors thrill'd;  
My feeble pulſe forgot to play:  
I fainted, ſunk, and dy'd away!

## Same Tune.

O Lovely maid, how dear's thy pow'r.
At once I love, at once adore:
With wonder are my thoughts poſſeſt,
While ſofteſt love inſpires my breaſt.
This tender look, theſe eyes of mine,
Confeſs their am'rous maſter thine;
Theſe eyes with Strephon's paſſion play;
Firſt make me love, and then betray.

Yes, Charming Victor, I am thine,
Poor as it is, this heart of mine
Was never in another's pow'r,
Was never pierc'd by love before.

In thee I've treaſur'd up my joy,
Thou can'ſt give bliſs, or bliſs deſtroy:
And thus I've bound myſelf to love,
While bliſs or miſery can move.

O ſhould I ne'er poſſeſs thy charms,
Ne'er meet my comfort in my arms,
Were hopes of dear enjoyment gone,
Still would I love, love thee alone.
But, like ſome diſcontented ſhade,
That wanders where its body's laid,
Mournful I'd roam with hollow glare,
For ever exil'd from my fair.

## Logan Water.

42

For ever, fortune, wilt thou prove, An unrelenting foe to
Slow
love, & when we meet a mutual heart, Come in between, and bid us part;
Bid us ſigh on from day to day, And wiſh & wiſh the ſoul a_way, Till
youth and genial years are flown, And all the life of love is gone?

But buſy, buſy ſtill art thou
To bind the loveleſs, joyleſs vow;
The heart from pleaſure to delude,
And join the gentle to the rude.

For once, O Fortune! hear my prayer,
And I abſolve thy future care;
All other bleſſings I reſign,
Make but the dear Amanda mine

## Allan Water.

43

What numbers shall the muse repeat! What verse be found to
Andante
praise my Annie! O her ten thousand graces wait, Each swain ad -
mires, and owns she's bonny. Since first she trode the hap - py
plain, She set each youthful heart on fire; Each nymph does to her
swain com - plain, That Annie, kin - dles new de - fire.

This lovely darling dearest care,
This new delight, this charming Annie,
Like summer's dawn, she's fresh and fair,
When Flora's fragrant breezes fan ye.
All day the am'rous youths conveen,
Joyous they sport and play before her;
All night, when she no more is seen,
In blissful dreams they still adore her.

Among the croud Amyntor came,
He look'd, he lov'd, he bow'd to Annie;
His rising sighs express his flame,
His words were few, his wishes many.

With smiles the lovely maid reply'd,
Kind shepherd, why should I deceive ye
Alas! your love must be deny'd,
This destin'd breast can ne'er relieve ye.

Young Damon came with Cupid's art,
His wiles, his smiles, his charms beguiling
He stole away my virgin heart;
Cease, poor Amyntor! cease bewailing:
Some brighter beauty you may find:
On yonder plain the nymphs are many;
Then chuse some heart that's unconfin'd,
And leave to Damon his own Annie.

# There's nae luck about the House.

44

And are ye sure the News is true? And are ye sure He's well? Is
Lively
this a time to tawk of wark? Mak haste! set by your wheel! Is this a time to
tawk of wark, when Colin's at the door! Gie me my cloak! I'll to ye Quey, &
see him come ashore. For there's nae luck about the House, there's nae luck a
- wa; There's little pleasure in the House, when our Goodman's a - wa'.

Rise up and, mak a clean fire side,
Put on the mukle Pat;
Gie little Kate her cotton gown,
And Jock his Sunday's coat;
And mak their Shoon as black as Slaes,
Their hose as white as snaw,
It's a' to please my ain Goodman;
For he's been lang awa. Chos.

There is twa Hens upon the Bauk,
S been fed this month and mair;
Mak haste, and thra their necks about,
That Colin well may fare;
And spread the Table neat and clean;
Gar ilka thing look bra;
It's a' for love of my Goodman;
For he's been lang awa. Cho.

O gie me down my bigonets,
My Bishop sattin gown;
For I maun tell the Baillie's wife,
That Colin's come to Town;
My Sunday's shoon they maun gae on,
My hose o' pearl blue,
It's a' to please my ain Goodman;
For he's baith leel and true. Chos.

Sae true's his words, Sae smooth's his
His breath like caller Air, (speech,
His very foot has musick in't,
When he comes up the stair;
And will I see his face again!
And will I hear him speak!
I'm downright dizzy wee the thought
In troth, I'm like to greet. Chos.

The cauld blasts of the winter wind,
That thrilled thro' my heart,
They're a blaun by, I hae him safe,
Till Death we'll never part;
But what puts parting in my head?
It may be far awa;
The present moment is our Ain;
The neist we never saw. Chos.

Since Colin's well, I'm well, content,
I hae nae main to crave;
Could I but live to mak him blest,
I'm blest aboon the lave;
And will I see his face again
And will I hear him speak!
I'm downright dizzy wee the thought:
In troth I'm like to greet. Chos.

## Tarry Woo.

45
Tarry woo, O tarry woo, Tarry woo is ill to ſpin;
Andante
Card it well, oh Card it well, Card it well ere ye be_gin.
When 'tis carded, row'd, and ſpun, Then the work is haſlens done;
But when woven, dreſt, and clean, It may be cleading for a Queen.

Sing, my bonny harmleſs ſheep,
That feed upon the mountains ſteep,
Bleating ſweetly as ye go,
Thro' the winter's froſt and ſnow;
Hart, and hynd, and fallow-deer,
No be ha'f ſo uſeful are:
Frae kings to him that hads the plow,
Are all oblig'd to tarry woo.

Up, ye ſhepherds, dance and ſkip,
O'er the hills and valleys trip,
Sing up the praiſe of tarry woo:
Sing the flocks that bear it too:
Harmleſs creatures, without blame,
That clead the back and cram the wame,
Keep us warm and hearty fou;
Leeſe me on the tarry woo.

How happy is the ſhepher'ds life,
Far frae courts, and free of ſtrife,
While the gimmers bleat and bae,
And the lambkins anſwer mae:
No ſuch muſic to his ear:
Of thief or fox he has no fear;
Sturdy kent, and colly true,
Well defend the tarry woo.

He lives content, and envies none;
Not even a monarch on his throne,
Tho' he the royal ſceptre ſways,
Has not ſweeter holidays,
Who'd be a king, can ony tell?
When a ſhepherd ſings ſae well;
Sings ſae well, and pays his due,
With honeſt heart and tarry woo.

## The Maid in Bedlam.

46

One morning very ear_ly, one morning in the spring, I
Slow
heard a maid in Bedlam, who mourn_ful_ly did sing; Her
chains she rat_tl'd on her hands, while sweetly thus sung she, I
love my love, because I know, my love loves me.

Oh! cruel were his parents, who sent my love to sea;
And cruel, cruel, was the ship that bore my love from me,
Yet I love his parents, since they're his, although they've ruin'd me;
For I love my love, &c.

O! should it please the pitying pow'rs, to call me to the sky,
I'd claim a guardian angel's charge, around my love to fly,
For to guard him from all dangers, how happy should I be!
For I love my love, &c.

I'll make a strawy garland, I'll make it wondrous fine,
With roses, lilies, daisies, I'll mix the eglantine:
And I'll present it to my love, when he returns from sea.
For I love my love, &c.

O if I were a little bird, to build upon his breast;
Or if I were a nightingale, to sing my love to rest;
To gaze upon his lovely eyes, all my reward should be;
For I love my love, &c.

O if I were an eagle, to soar into the sky,
I'd gaze around, with piercing eyes, where I my love might spy:
But ah! unhappy maiden, that love you ne'er shall see;
Yet I love my love, &c.

Whilst thus she sung, lamenting, her love was come on shore,
He heard she was in Bedlam: then did he ask no more;
But straight he flew to find her, while thus replied he:
I love my love, &c.

O Sir, do not affright me: are you my love, or not.
Yes, yes, my dearest Molly; I fear'd I was forgot.
But now I'm come to make amends for all your injury,
And I love my love, &c.

## To the foregoing Tune.

AS down on Banna's banks I stray'd, one evening in May,
The little birds, in blythest notes, made vocal ev'ry spray:
They sung their little notes of love; they sung them o'er and o'er.
Ah! gramachree, mo challeenouge, mo Molly astore.

The daisy pied, and all the sweets the dawn of nature yields;
The primrose pale, the vi'let blue, lay scatter'd o'er the fields;
Such fragrance in the bosom lies of her whom I adore,
Ah! gramachree, &c.

I laid me down upon a bank, bewailing my sad fate,
That doom'd me thus the slave of love, and cruel Molly's hate.
How can she break the honest heart, that wears her in it's core?
Ah! gramachree, &c.

You said, you lov'd me, Molly dear; ah! why did I believe?
Yes, who could think such tender words were meant but to deceive.
That love was all I ask'd on earth; nay Heav'n could give no more.
Ah! gramachree, &c.

Oh! had I all the flocks that graze on yonder yellow hill.
Or low'd for me the num'rous herds, that yon green pastures fill,
With her I love I'd gladly share my kine and fleecy store,
Ah! gramachree, &c.

Two turtle doves, above my head, sat courting on a bough,
I envy'd them their happiness, to see them bill and coo;
Such fondness once for me she shew'd, but now, alas! 'tis o'er.
Ah! gramachree, &c.

Then, fare thee well, my Molly dear. thy loss I still shall moan;
Whilst life remains in Strephon's heart, 'twill beat for thee alone.
Tho' thou art false, may heav'n on thee its choicest blessings pour!
Ah! gramachree, &c.

## To the foregoing Tune.

HAD I a heart for falsehood fram'd, I ne'er could injure you;
For tho' your tongue no promise claim'd, your charms wou'd make me true
To you no soul shall bear deceit, no stranger offer wrong;
But friends in all the ag'd you'll meet, and lovers, in the young.

But when they learn, that you have bless'd another with your heart,
They'll bid aspiring passion rest, and act a brother's part;
Then, lady, dread not their deceit, nor fear to suffer wrong;
For friends in all the ag'd you'll meet, and brothers, in the young.

# The Collier's bonny Laſſie.

47

The collier has a daughter, And O ſhe's wonder bonny! A
Lively
laird he was that ſought her, Rich baith in lands and money.
The tutors watch'd the motion of this young honeſt lover. But
love is like the ocean; Wha can its deeps diſ - cover?

He had the art to pleaſe ye,
And was by a' reſpected,
His airs ſat round him eaſy,
Genteel, but unaffected;
The collier's bonny laſſie,
Fair as the new-blown lillie,
Ay ſweet, and never ſaucy,
Secur'd the heart of Willie.

He lov'd beyond expreſſion
The charms that were about her,
And panted for poſſeſſion,
His life was dull without her,
After mature reſolving,
Cloſe to his breaſt he held her,
In ſafteſt flames diſſolving,
He tenderly thus tell'd her —

My bonny collier's daughter,
Let naething diſcompoſe ye;
'Tis no your ſcanty tocher
Shall ever gar me loſe ye;
For I have gear in plenty,
And love ſays, 'Tis my duty,
To ware what heav'n has lent me
Upon your wit and beauty.

## Within a Mile of Edinburgh.

48
Andante
'Twas within a mile of Edinburgh town, In the ro-fy time of the
year, Sweet flowers bloom'd, and the grafs was down, & each fhepherd
woo'd his dear: Bonny Jockey, blith & gay, Kifs'd fweet Jenny
making hay, The laffie blufh'd, & frowning cry'd, No, no, it will not do, I
cannot, cannot, wonnot, wonnot, mannot buckle too.

Jockey was a wag that never would wed,
Tho' long he had follow'd the lafs,
Contented fhe earn'd and eat her brown bread,
And merrily turn'd up the grafs.
Bonny Jockey, blith and free,
Won her heart right merrily,
Yet ftill fhe blufh'd, and frowning cry'd, No, no, it will not do,
I cannot, cannot, wonnot, wonnot, mannot buckle too.

But when he vow'd, he wou'd make her his Bride,
Tho' his flocks and herds were not few,
She gave him her hand, and a kifs befide,
And vow'd, fhe'd for ever be true.
Bonny Jockey, blith and free,
Won her heart right merrily;
At Church fhe no more frowning cry'd, No, no, it will not do,
I cannot, cannot, wonnot, wonnot, mannot buckle too

## My ain kind Deary-o.

49

Will ye gang o'er the lee-rigg, my ain kind deary-o! And
Andante
cud-dle there fae kind-ly wi' me, my kind deary-o! At
thor-nie dike, and bir-ken-tree, we'll daff, and ne'er be wea-ry-
-o; They'll fcug ill een frae you and me, mine ain kind deary o!

Nae herds wi' kent, or colly there,
Shall ever come to fear ye-o;
But lav'rocks, whiftling in the air,
Shall woo, like me, their deary-o!

While others herd their lambs and ewes,
And toil for warld's gear, my jo,
Upon the lee my pleafure grows,
Wi' you, my kind deary-o!

## Nancy's to the green-wood gane.

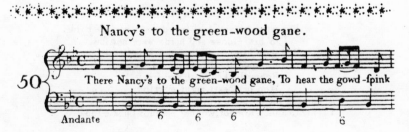

50
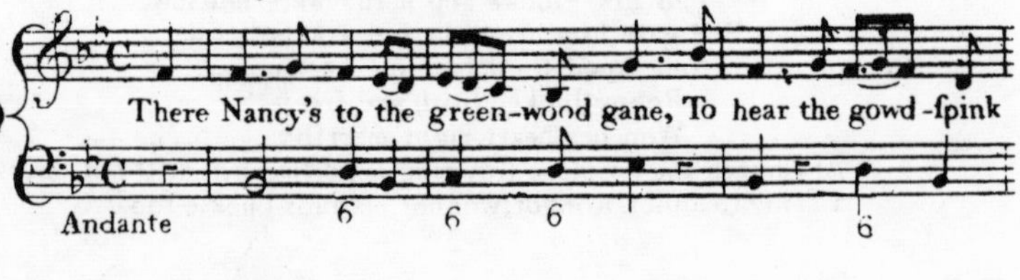
There Nancy's to the green-wood gane, To hear the gowd-fpink
Andante

Continued.

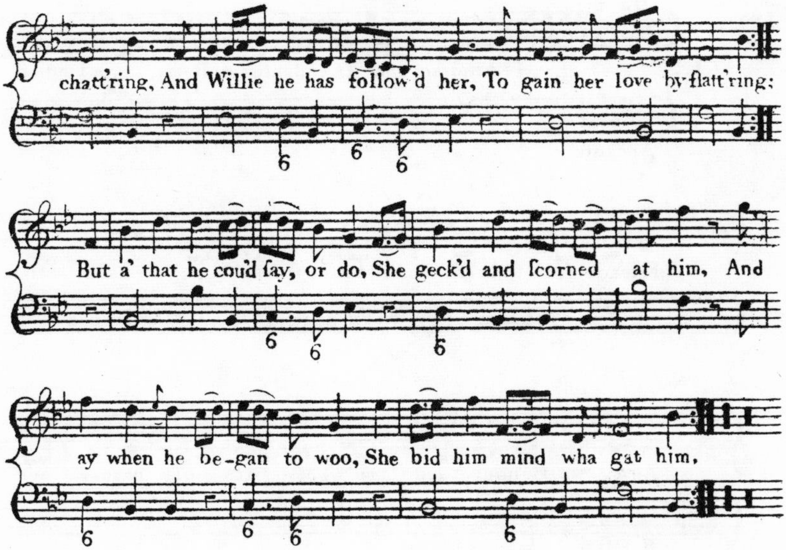
chatt'ring, And Willie he has follow'd her, To gain her love by flatt'ring:
But a' that he cou'd ſay, or do, She geck'd and ſcorned at him, And
ay when he be-gan to woo, She bid him mind wha gat him.

What ails ye at my dad, quoth he,
My minny, or my aunty?
With crowdy-mowdy, they fed me,
Lang-kail, and ranty tanty:
With bannocks of good barley meal,
Of thae there was right plenty,
With chapped ſtocks fou butter'd well;
And was not that right dainty!

Altho' my father was nae laird,
'Tis daffin to be vaunty,
He keepit ay a good kail-yard,
A ha' houſe, and a pantry:
A good blue bonnet on his head,
An owrlay 'bout his cragy,
And ay until the day he died,
He rade on good ſhank's nagy.

Now wae and wander on your ſnout!
Wad ye hae bonny Nanſy.
Wad ye compare ye'rſell to me,
A docken till a tanſie!
I have a wooer of my ain;
They ca' him ſouple Sandy;
And well I wat, his bonny mou'
Is ſweet like ſugar-candy.

Wow, Nanſy! what needs a' this din?
Do I not ken this Sandy
I'm ſure the chief of a' his kin
Was Rab the beggar randy:
His minny, Meg, upo' her back,
Bare baith him and his billy;
Will ye compare a naſty pack
To me your winſome Willy?

My gutcher left a good braid ſword,
Tho' it be auld and ruſty,
Yet ye may tak it on my word,
It is baith ſtout and truſty;
And if I can but get it drawn,
Which will be right uneaſy,
I ſhall lay baith my lugs in pawn,
That he ſhall get a heezy.

Then Nanſy turn'd her round about,
And ſaid, did Sandy hear ye,
Ye wadna miſs to get a clout;
I ken he diſna fear ye:
Sae, had ye'r tongue, and ſay nae mair;
Set ſomewhere elſe your fancy;
For as lang's Sandy's to the fore,
Ye never ſhall get Nanſy.

## Blink o'er the burn, ſweet Bettie.

51
Leave kindred and friends, ſweet Betty, Leave kindred &
Andante
Friends for me! Aſ _ ſur'd thy ſervant is ſted _ dy To
Love, to Honour, and Thee. The gifts of nature and
fortune, May fly by chance as they came, They're grounds the
deſtinies ſport on; But virtue is e _ ver the ſame.

Altho' my fancy were roving,
  Thy charms ſo heav'nly appear,
That other beauties diſproving,
  I'd worſhip thine only, my dear!
And ſhou'd life's ſorrows embitter
  The pleaſure we promis'd our loves,
To ſhare them together is fitter,
  Than moan aſunder, like doves.

Oh! were I but once ſo bleſſed,
  To graſp my love in my arms!
By thee to be graſp'd! and kiſſed!
  And live on thy heaven of charms!
I'd laugh at fortune's caprices,
  Shou'd fortune capricious prove;
Tho' death ſhou'd tear me to pieces,
  I'd die a martyr to love.

## Jenny Nettles.

52

Lively
O Saw ye Jen_ny Nettles; Jenny Nettles, Jenny Nettles!
Saw ye Jen_ny Net_tles', Coming frae-the market; Wi'
Bag and baggage on her back, Her fee and bountith in her lap, wi'
Bag and baggage on her back, And a babie in her oxter.

I met ayont the kairny,
  Jenny Nettles, Jenny Nettles,
Singing till her bairny,
  Robin Rattles baſtard;
To flee the dool upo' the ſtool,
  And ilka ane that mocks her,
She round about ſeeksRobin out,
  To ſtap it in his oxter

Fy, fy! Robin Rattle,
  Robin Rattle, Robin Rattle,
Fy, fy! Robin Rattle,
  Uſe Jenny Nettles kindly;
Score out the blame, and ſhun the ſhame,
  And without mair debate o't,
Tak hame your wean, make Jenny fain
  The leel and leeſome gate o't.

## When absent from the Nymph.

Tune O Jean, I love thee.

53
Slow
When absent from the Nymph I love, I'd fain shake off the
chains I wear; But whilst I strive these to re_move, More
fetters I'm oblig'd to bear. My captiv'd fan_cy, day and
night, Fair_er and fair_er re_pre_sents, Be_linda form'd for
dear delight, But cruel cause of my complaints.

All day I wander through the groves,
And sighing hear from ev'ry tree
The happy birds chirping their loves;
Happy compar'd with lonely me.
When gentle sleep with balmy wings,
To rest fans ev'ry wearied wight,
A thousand fears my fancy brings,
That keep me watching all the night.

Sleep flies, while like the Goddess fair,
And all the graces in her train,
With melting smiles and killing air,
Appears the cause of all my pain.

A while my mind delighted flies
O'er all her sweets with thrilling joy,
Whilst want of worth makes doubts arise,
That all my trembling hopes destroy.

Thus, while my thoughts are fix'd on her,
I'm all o'er transport and desire:
My pulse beats high, my cheeks appear
All roses, and mine eyes all fire.
When to myself I turn my view,
My veins grow chill, my cheeks look wan:
Thus, whilst my fears my pains renew,
I scarcely look or move a man.

## Bonny Jean.

54

Love's goddeſs in a myrtle grove, Said, Cupid, bend thy
Andante
bow with ſpeed, Nor let the ſhaft at random rove; For Jeany's
haughty heart muſt bleed. The ſmiling boy, with divine art, From
Pa_phos ſhot an ar_row keen; Which flew un_err_ing
to the heart, And kill'd the pride of bon_ny Jean.

No more the Nymph, with haughty air,
Refuſes Willy's kind addreſs;
Her yielding bluſhes ſhew no care,
But too much fondneſs to ſuppreſs.
No more the Youth is ſullen now,
But looks the gayeſt on the green,
Whilſt every day he ſpies ſome new
Surpriſing charms in bonny Jean.

A thouſand tranſports crowd his breaſt,
He moves as light as fleeting wind,
His former ſorrows ſeem a jeſt,
Now when his Jenny is turn'd kind;
Riches he looks on with diſdain;
The glorious fields of war look mean;
The chearful hound and horn give pain;
If abſent from his bonny Jean.

The day he ſpends in am'rous gaze,
Which ev'n in ſummer, ſhort'ned ſeems;
When ſunk in downs, with glad amaze,
He wonders at her in his dreams.
All charms diſclos'd ſhe looks more bright,
Than Troy's prize, the Spartan Queen;
With breaking day, he lifts his ſighs,
And pants to be with bonny Jean.

## O'er the Moor to Maggy.

55
And I'll o'er the moor to Maggy; her wit and
Lively
ſweetneſs call me; then to my fair I'll ſhow my mind, What-
_ e _ ver may be_fal me. If ſhe love mirth, I'll
learn to ſing; Or like the Nine to fol_low, I'll lay my
lugs in Pindus' ſpring, And in _ vo_cate' A _ pol _ lo.

If ſhe admire a martial mind,
 I'll ſheath my limbs in armour;
If to the ſofter dance inclin'd,
 With gayeſt airs I'll charm her:
If ſhe love grandeur, day and night,
 I'll plot my nation's glory,
Find favour in my prince's ſight,
 And ſhine in future ſtory.

Beauty can wonders work with eaſe,
 Where wit is correſponding;
And braveſt men know beſt to pleaſe,
 With complaiſance abounding.
My bonny Maggy's love can turn
 Me to what ſhape ſhe pleaſes;
If in her breaſt that flame ſhall burn,
 Which in my boſom blazes.

## Pinky-Houſe.

56
By Pinkie-Houſe oft_let me walk, While circled in my
Andante
arms, I hear my Nel_ly ſweet_ly talk, And gaze o'er
all her charms. O let me, e_ver fond, be_
_hold Thoſe graces void of art, Thoſe chearful ſmiles that
ſweet_ly hold In will_ing chains my heart.

O come, my love! and bring a-new
  That gentle turn of mind;
That gracefulneſs of air, in you,
  By nature's hand deſign'd;
That beauty like the bluſhing roſe,
  Firſt lighted up this flame;
Which, like the ſun, for ever glows
  Within my breaſt the ſame.

Ye Light Coquets! ye Airy Things!
  How vain is all your art!
How ſeldom it a lover brings!
  How rarely keeps a heart!

O gather from my Nelly's charms,
  That ſweet, that graceful eaſe;
That bluſhing modeſty that warms;
  That native art to pleaſe!

Come then, my love! O come along,
  And feed me with thy charms;
Come, fair inſpirer of my ſong,
  O fill my longing arms!
A flame like mine can never die,
  While charms, ſo bright as thine,
So heav'nly fair, both pleaſe the eye,
  And fill the ſoul divine!

## Here awa', there awa'.

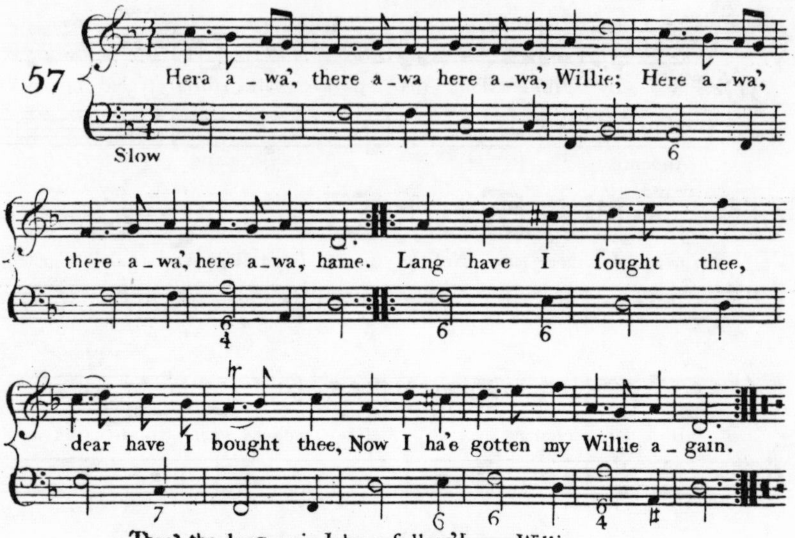
57
Slow
Hera a_wa', there a_wa here a_wa', Willie; Here a_wa', there a_wa', here a_wa, hame. Lang have I fought thee, dear have I bought thee, Now I ha'e gotten my Willie a_gain.

Thro' the lang muir I have follow'd my Willie,
Thro' the lang muir I have follow'd him hame,
Whatever betide us, nought fhall divide us,
Love now rewards all my forrow and pain.
Here awa', there awa', here awa', Willie;
Here awa', there awa', here awa', hame.
Come, Love, believe me nothing can grieve me,
Ilka thing pleafes while Willie's at hame.
Gin ye meet my love, kifs her & clap her;
An gin ye meet my love, dinna think fhame,
Gin ye meet my love, kifs her & clap her,
And fhew her the way to had awa' hame.

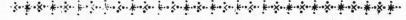

## The Blithfome Bridal.

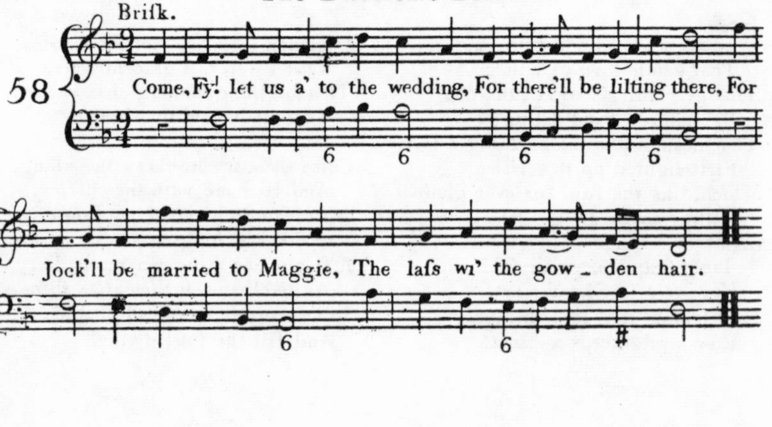
Brifk.
58
Come, Fy! let us a' to the wedding, For there'll be lilting there, For Jock'll be married to Maggie, The lafs wi' the gow_den hair.

Continued.

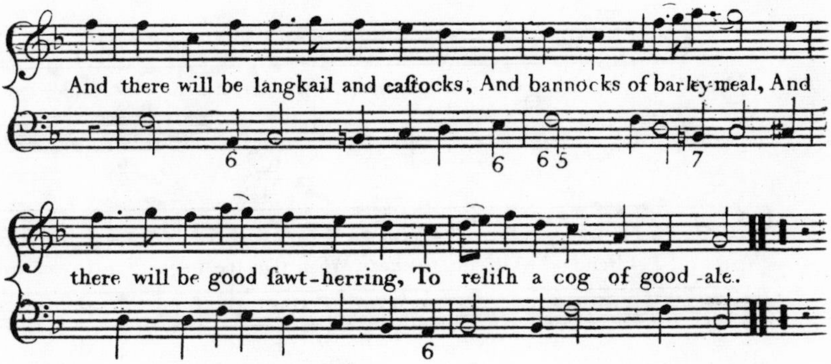
And there will be langkail and caſtocks, And bannocks of barley-meal, And
there will be good ſawt-herring, To reliſh a cog of good-ale.

And there will be Saundy the ſutor,
And Will wi' the meikle mou,
And there will be Tam the blutter,
With Andrew the tinkler, I trow;
And there will be bow'd legged Robie,
With thumbleſs Katie's goodman,
And there will be blew cheeked Dobbie,
And Lawrie the laird of the land.

And there will be ſow-libber Patie,
And plucky fac'd Wat i' the mill,
Capper-nos'd Francie, and Gibbie,
That wins in the how of the hill;
And there will be Alaſter Sibby,
Wha in with black Beſſie did mool,
With ſnivelling Lilly and Tibby,
The laſs that ſtands aft on the ſtool.

And Madge that was buckled to Steenie,
And coft him gray breeks to his a —,
Wha after was hangit for ſtealing,
Great mercy it happen'd nae warſe;
And there will be gleed Geordy Janners,
And Kirſh with the lilly, white-leg,
Wha gade to the ſouth for manners,
And plaid the fool in Mons-meg.

And there will be Judan Maclawrie,
And blinkin.daft Barbara Macleg,
Wi' flea-lugged ſharny fac'd Lawrie,
And ſhangy-mou'd halucket Meg;
And there will be happer a — Nancie,
And fairy-fac'd Flowrie by name,
Muck Madie, and fat-hippit Girſy,
The laſs wi the gowden wame.

And there will be Girn-again Gibby,
With his glakit wife Jeany Bell,
And miſled-ſhinn'd Mungo Macapie,
The lad that was ſkipper himſel.
There lads and laſſes in pearlings,
Will feaſt in the heart of the ha',
On ſybows and riſarts and carlings,
That are baith ſodden and raw.

And there will be fadges and brachan,
With fouth of good gabbocks of ſkate,
Powſowdie, and drammock and crowdie,
And caller nowt-feet in a plate;
And there will be partans and buckies,
And whitens and ſpeldings enew,
With ſingit ſheep-heads and a haggies,
And ſcadlips to ſup till you ſpew.

And there will be lapper'd milk kebbuck
And ſowens, and farles, and baps,
With ſwats and well ſcraped paunches,
And brandy in ſtoups and in caps;
And there will be meal kail and porrage,
With ſkink to ſup till ye rive,
And roaſts to roaſt on a brander,
Of flewks that were taken alive.

Scrapt haddocks, wilks, dulſe and tangle,
And a mill of good ſniſhing to prie,
When weary with eating and drinking,
We'll riſe up and dance till we die;
Then fye let us a' to the bridal,
For there will be lilting there,
For Jock'll be married to Maggie,
The laſs with the gowden hair.

## Sae Merry as we twa hae been.

59
Slow
A Lafs that was laden'd with care, Sat heavily under yon
thorn; I liftend a while for to hear, When thus fhe began for to mourn.
When e'er my dear fhepherd was there, The birds did me-lodioufly fing, And
cold nipping winter did wear, A face that refembled the fpring. Sae
merry as we twa ha'e been, Sae merry as we twa ha'e been, My
heart it is like for to break. When I think on the days we ha'e feen.

Our flocks feeding close by his fide,
  He gently preffing my hand,
I view'd the wide world in its pride,
  And laugh'd at the pomp of command!
My dear, he wou'd oft to me fay,
  What makes you hard hearted to me?
Oh. why do you thus turn away,
  From him who is dying for thee?
    Sae merry, &c.

But now he is far from my fight,
  Perhaps a deceiver may prove,
Which makes me lament day and night,
  That ever I granted my love.
At eve, when the reft of the folk
  Are merrily feated to fpin,
I fet myfelf under an oak,
  And heavily fighed for him.
    Sae merry. &c.

## Bonny Chrifty.

60

How fweetly fmells the fimmer green. fweet tafte the peach & cherry, Paint
Andante
_ ing and order pleafe our een, and claret makes us merry: But fineft
colours, fruits and flowers, and wine, tho' I be thirfty, Lofe a' their
charms, and weaker powers, Compar'd with thefe of Chrifty.

When wand'ring o'er the flow'ry park,
No nat'ral beauty wanting,
How lightfome is't to hear the lark,
And birds in concert chanting!
But if my Chrifty tunes her voice,
I'm rapt in admiration;
My thoughts with ecftafies rejoice,
And drap the haill creation.

Whene'er fhe fmiles a kindly glance,
I take the happy omen,
And aften mint to make advance,
Hoping fhe'll prove a woman:
But, dubious of my ain defert,
My fentiments I fmother;
With fecret fighs I vex my heart,
For fear fhe love another.

Thus fang blate Edie by a burn,
His Chrifty did o'erhear him;
She doughtna let her lover mourn,
But e'er he wift drew near him.
She fpake her favour with a look,
Which left nae room to doubt her;
He wifely this white minute took,
And flang his arms about her.

My Chrifty! _ witnefs, bonny ftream,
Sic joys frae tears arifing,
I wifh this mayna be a dream;
O love the maift furprifing!
Time was too precious now for tauk;
This point of a' his wifhes
He wadna with fet fpeeches bauk,
But war'd it a' on kiffes.

## Jocky ſaid to Jeany.

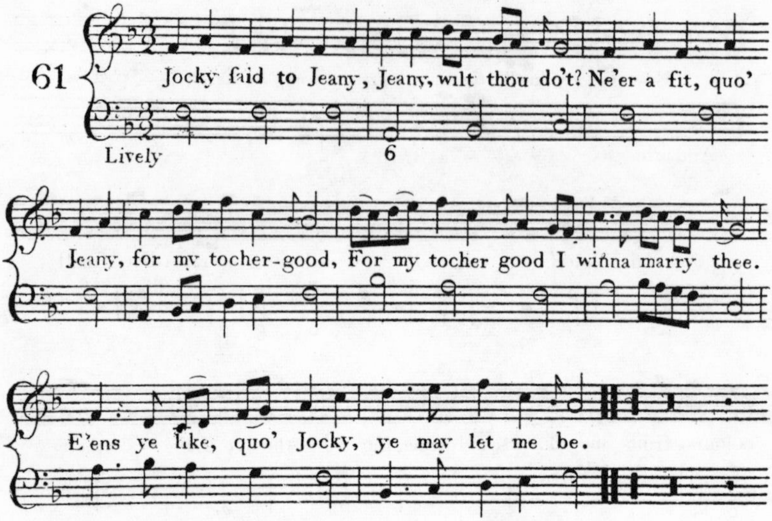
61
Lively
Jocky ſaid to Jeany, Jeany, wilt thou do't? Ne'er a fit, quo'
6
Jeany, for my tocher-good, For my tocher good I winna marry thee.
E'ens ye like, quo' Jocky, ye may let me be.

I hae gowd and gear, and I hae land enough,
I hae ſeven good owſen ganging in a pleugh,
Ganging in a pleugh, and linking o'er the lee;
And gin ye winna tak me, I can let ye be.

I hae a good ha' houſe, a barn, and a byre,
A ſtack afore the door; I'll make a rantin fire,
I'll make a rantin fire, and merry ſhall we be;
And gin ye winna tak me, I can let ye be.

Jeany ſaid to Jocky, Gin ye winna tell,
Ye ſhall be the lad, I'll be the laſs myſell.
Ye're a bonny lad, and I'm a laſſie free,
Ye're welcomer to tak me than to let me be.

## O'er the hills, and far away.

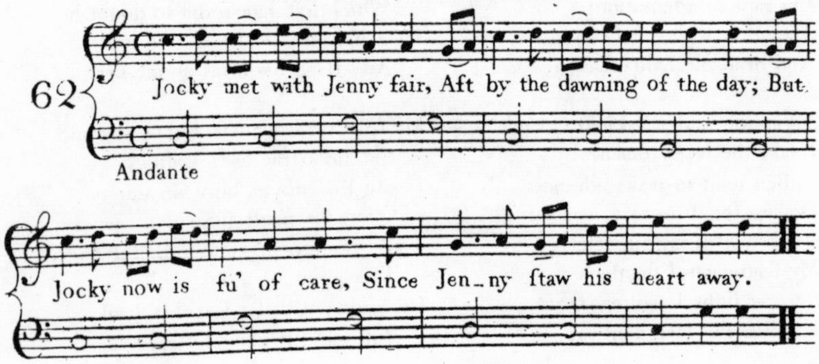
62
Andante
Jocky met with Jenny fair, Aft by the dawning of the day; But
Jocky now is fu' of care, Since Jen-ny ſtaw his heart away.

## Continued.

Al _ tho' ſhe promis'd to be true, She proven has, al _ ake! unkind; which
Chorus
gars poor Jocky often rue, that e'er he lov'd a fickle mind. And it's
over the hills, and far away, over the hills, and far away over the
hills, and far away, The wind has blawn my plaid away.

Now Jocky was a bonny lad
As e'er was born in Scotland fair;
But now poor man! he's e'en gane wood,
Since Jenny has gart him deſpair.
Young Jocky was a piper's ſon,
And fell in love when he was young;
But a' the ſprings that he could play,
Was o'er the hills, and far away.
And it's o'er the hills, &c.

He ſung -When firſt my Jenny's face
I ſaw, ſhe ſeem'd ſae fu' of grace,
With meikle joy my heart was fill'd,
That's now, alas! with ſorrow kill'd.
Oh! was ſhe but as true as fair,
'Twad put an end to my deſpair;
Inſtead of that ſhe is unkind,
And wavers like the winter wind.
And it's o'er the hills, &c.

Ah! cou'd ſhe find the diſmal wae,
That for her ſake I undergae,
She cou'd nae chuſe but grant relief,
And put an end to a' my grief
But oh! ſhe is as fauſe as fair,
Which cauſes a' my ſighs and care;
But ſhe triumphs in proud diſdain,
And takes a pleaſure in my pain.
And it's o'er the hills, &c.

Hard was my hap to fa' in love
With ane that does ſae faithleſs prove;
Hard was my fate to court a maid,
That has my conſtant heart betray'd.
A thouſand times to me ſhe ſwore,
She wad be true for evermore.
But, to my grief, alake, I ſay,
She ſtaw my heart and ran away.
And it's o'er the hills, &c.

Since that ſhe will nae pity take,
I maun gae wander for her ſake,
And, in ilk wood and gloomy grove,
I'll ſighing ſing, Adieu to love;
Since ſhe is fauſe whom I adore,
I'll never truſt a woman more;
Frae a' their charms I'll flee away,
And on my pipe I'll ſweetly play
O'er hills, and dales, and far away, &c.

# The Flowers of the Forest.

63

Slow
Adieu, ye Streams that fmoothly glide, through mazy windings o'er the
plain! I'll in fome lonely cave refide, and ever mourn my faithful fwain.
Flower of the foreft was my Love, Soft as the fighing Summer's gale,
Gentle and conftant as the dove, Blooming as rofes in the vale.
Alas! by Tweed my Love did ftray, for me he fearch'd the banks around, but,
ah! the fad and fa_tal day, my Love the pride of fwains was drown'd.
How droops the willow o'er the ftream, pale ftalks his Ghoft in yonder grove,
dire Fancy paints him in my dream, A_wake I mourn my hopelefs Love.

## Buſk ye, Buſk ye.

64
Slow
Buſk ye, buſk ye, my bonny bride; Buſk ye, buſk ye, my
winſome marrow, Buſk ye, buſk ye, my bonny bride, And let us
to the braes of Yarrow. There will we ſport, and gather dew,
Dancing while lav'rocks ſing in the morning: There learn frae
turtles to prove true; O Bell, ne'er vex me with thy ſcorning.

To weſtlin breezes Flora yields,
And when the beams are kindly warming,
Blythneſs appears o'er all the fields,
And Nature looks more freſh & charming,
Learn frae the burns that trace the mead,
Tho on their banks the roſes bloſſom,
Yet haſtily they flow to Tweed,
And pour their ſweetneſs in his boſom.

Haſte ye, haſte ye, my bonny Bell,
Haſte to my arms, and there I'll guard thee;
Wi' free conſent my fears repel;
I'll wi' my love and care reward thee.
Thus ſang I ſaftly to my fair,
Who rais'd my hopes with kind relenting
O queen of ſmiles, I aſk nae mair,
Since now my bonny Bell's conſenting

## There's my Thumb, I'll ne'er beguile thee.

65

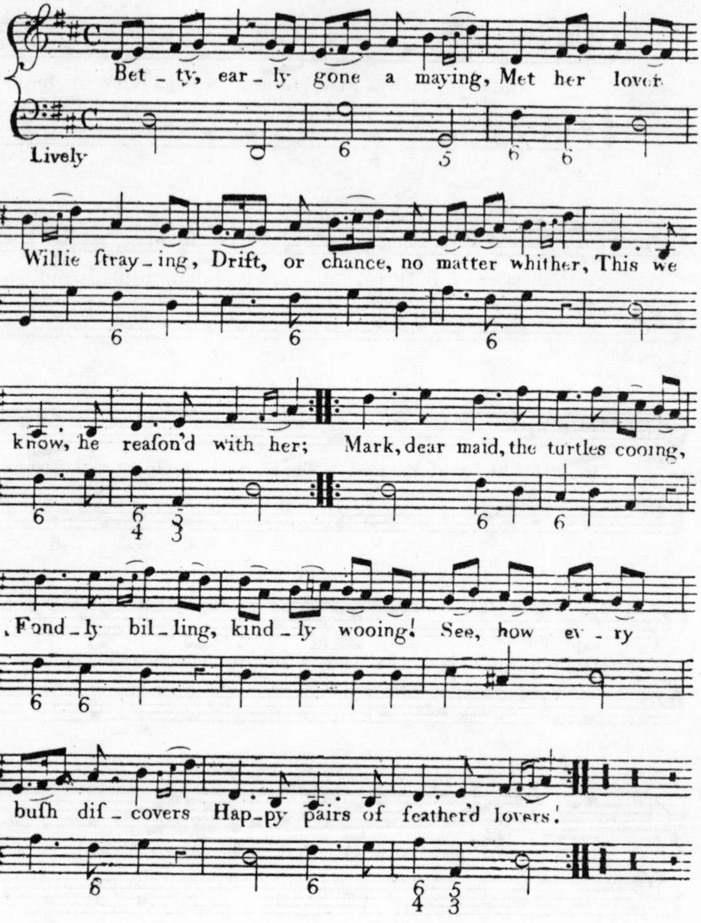
Bet_ty, ear_ly gone a maying, Met her lover
Lively
Willie ſtray_ing, Drift, or chance, no matter whither, This we
know, he reaſon'd with her; Mark, dear maid, the turtles cooing,
Fond_ly bil_ling, kind_ly wooing! See, how ev_ry
buſh diſ_covers Hap_py pairs of feather'd lovers!

See, the op'ning bluſh of roſes
Al' their ſecret charms diſcloſes;
Sweet's the time, ah! ſhort's the meaſure;
O their fleeting haſty pleaſure!
Quickly we muſt ſnatch the favour
Of their ſoft and fragrant flavour;
They bloom to-day, and fade to-morrow,
Droop their heads, and die in ſorrow.

Time, my Beſs, will leave no trace
Of thoſe beauties, of thoſe graces;
Youth and love forbid our ſtaying;
Love and youth abhor delaying;
Deareſt maid, nay, do not fly me;
Let your pride no more deny me;
Never doubt your faithful Willie:
There's my thumb, I'll ne'er beguile thee.

## Gilderoy.

66

Ah! Chloris, cou'd I now but ſit As unconcern'd as
Slow
when Your in_ _fant beau_ty cou'd be_get No
hap_pi_neſs, nor pain! When I thy dawn_ning
did admire, And prais'd the com_ing day I lit_tle
thought that riſe_ing fire Wou'd take my reſt a_way.

Your charms in harmleſs childhood lay,
As metals in the mine;
Age from no face takes more away,
Than youth conceal'd in thine:
But as your charms inſenſibly
To their perfection preſs'd;
So love as unperceiv'd did fly,
And center'd in my breaſt.

My paſſion with your beauty grew,
While Cupid at my heart,
Still, as his mother favour'd you,
Threw a new flaming dart.
Each gloried in their wanton part;
To make a lover, he
Employ'd the utmoſt of his art;
To make a beauty, ſhe.

## John Hay's Bonny Laſſie.

67

Andante
By ſmooth winding Tay a ſwain was reclining; aft cry'd he, oh
hey! maun I ſtill live pining Myſelf thus a - way, & darna diſcover To
my bonny Laſs, that I am her Lover! Nae mair it will hide, the flame
waxes ſtronger, If ſhe's not my bride, my days are nae langer; Then I'll tak a
heart, & try at a venture: May be, e'er we part, my vows may content her.

She's freſh as the ſpring, and ſweet as Aurora,
When birds mount and ſing, bidding day a goodmorrow:
The ſwart of the mead, enamell'd with daiſies,
Look wither'd and dead, when twinn'd of her graces.

But if ſhe appear where verdures invite her,
The fountains run clear, and flow'rs ſmell the ſweeter:
'Tis heaven to be by when her wit is a flowing;
Her ſmiles and bright eye ſet my ſpirits a glowing.

The mair that I gaze, the deeper I'm wounded;
Struck dumb with amaze, my mind is confounded:
I'm all in a fire, dear maid, to careſs ye;
For a' my deſire is John Hay's bonny laſſie.

## The Bonny Brucket Laſsie.

68

Slow
The Bonny Brucket Laſsie, She's blue beneath the e'en; She
was the faireſt Laſsie That danc'd on the green. A
lad he loo'd her dear - ly, She did his love re - turn; But
he his vows has broken, And left her for to mourn.


"My ſhape, ſhe ſays, was handſome,
"My face was fair and clean,
"But now I'm bonny brucket,
"And blue beneath the een,
"My eyes were bright and ſparkling,
"Before that they turn'd blue;
"But now they're dull with weeping,
"And a', My Love, for you.

"My perſon it was comely,
"My ſhape they ſaid was neat;
"But now I am quite changed,
"My Stays they winna' meet.
"A' night I ſleeped ſoundly,
"My mind was never ſad;
"But now my reſt is broken,
"Wi' thinking o' my lad.

"O could I live in darkneſs,
"Or hide me in the ſea,
"Since my love is unfaithful,
"And has forſaken me.
"No other love I ſuffer'd
"Within my breaſt to dwell;
"In nought I have offended
"But loving him too well.

Her lover heard her mourning,
As by he chanc'd to paſs;
And preſs'd unto his boſom
The lovely brucket laſs.
"My dear, he ſaid," ceaſe grieving;
"Since that your love's ſo true,
"My bonny, brucket laſsie,
"I'll faithful prove to you.

## The Broom of Cowdenknows.

69

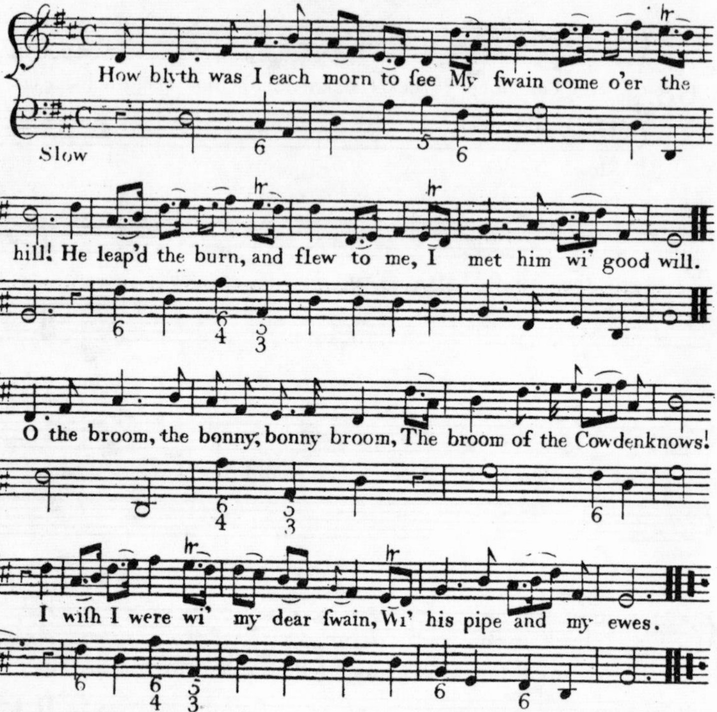
How blyth was I each morn to fee My fwain come o'er the
Slow
hill! He leap'd the burn, and flew to me, I met him wi' good will.
O the broom, the bonny, bonny broom, The broom of the Cowdenknows!
I wifh I were wi' my dear fwain, Wi' his pipe and my ewes.

I neither wanted ewe nor lamb,
While his flock near me lay;
He gather'd in my fheep at night,
And chear'd me a' the day.
O the broom, &c.

He tun'd his pipe and reed fae fweet,
The birds ftood lift'ning by;
Ev'n the dull cattle ftood and gaz'd,
Charm'd wi' his melody.
O the broom, &c.

While thus we fpent our time, by turns
Betwixt our flocks and play,
I envy'd not the faireft dame,
Tho' ne'er fo rich and gay.
O the broom, &c.

Hard fate! that I fhou'd banifh'd be,
Gang heavily and mourn,
Becaufe I lov'd the kindeft fwain
That ever yet was born!
O the broom, &c.

He did oblige me ev'ry hour;
Cou'd I but faithfu' be?
He ftaw my heart; cou'd I refufe
Whate'er he afk'd of me.
O the broom, &c.

My doggie, and my little kit,
That held my wee foup whey,
My plaidy, broach, and crooked ftick,
May now ly ufelefs by.
O the broom, &c.

Adieu, ye Cowdenknows, adieu,
Farewel a' pleafures there;
Ye gods, reftore me to my fwain,
Is a' I crave, or care.
O the broom, &c.

## To the foregoing Tune.

WHEN ſummer comes, the ſwains on
 Sing their ſucceſsful loves, (Tweed
Around the ewes and lambkins feed,
 And muſic fills the groves.

But my lov'd ſong is then the broom
 So fair on Cowdenknows;
For ſure ſo ſweet, ſo ſoft a bloom
 Elſewhere there never grows.

There Colin tun'd his oaten reed,
 And won my yielding heart;
No ſhepherd e'er that dwelt on Tweed
 Cou'd play with half ſuch art.

He ſung of Tay, of Forth, and Clyde,
 The hills and dales all round,
Of Leaderhaughs and Leaderſide,
 Oh! how I bleſs'd the ſound.

Yet more delightful is the broom
 So fair on Cowdenknows;
For ſure, ſo freſh, ſo bright a bloom;
 Elſewhere there never grows.

Not Tiviot braes, ſo green and gay,
 May with this broom compare,
Not Yarrow banks in flow'ry May,
 Nor the buſh aboon Traquair.

More pleaſing far are Cowdenknows,
 My peaceful happy home!
Where I was wont to milk my ewes,
 At ev'n among the broom.

Ye powers that haunt the woods and plain
 Where Tweed with Tiviot flows,
Convey me to the beſt of ſwains,
 And my lov'd Cowdenknows.

## Oſcar's Ghoſt.

70

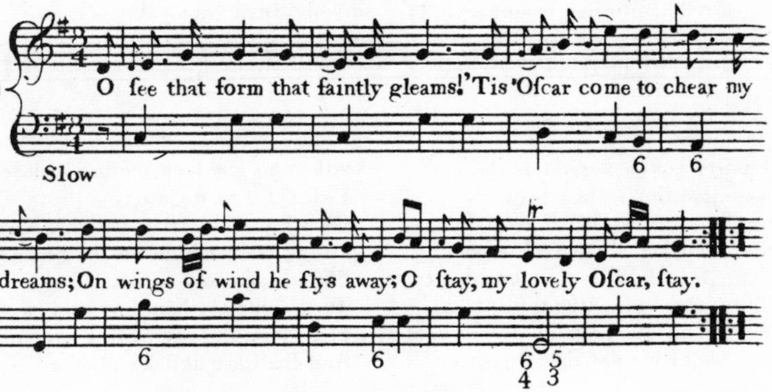
O ſee that form that faintly gleams! 'Tis Oſcar come to chear my
Slow
dreams; On wings of wind he flys away; O ſtay, my lovely Oſcar, ſtay.

Wake Oſsian, laſt of Fingal's line,
And mix thy tears and ſighs with mine;
Awake the harp to doleful lays,
And ſooth my ſoul with Oſcar's praiſe.

The ſhell is ceas'd in Oſcar's hall,
Since gloomy Kerbar wrought his fall;
The Roe on Morven lightly bounds,
Nor hears the cry of Oſcar's hounds.

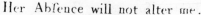

# Her Abſence will not alter me.

71

Though diſtant far from Jeſsy's charms, I ſtretch in vain my longing
Andante
arms, Though parted by the deeps of ſea, Her abſence ſhall not alter me.
Though beauteous nymphs I ſee around, A Chloris, Flora, might be found, Or
Phyllis with her roving eye; Her abſence ſhall not alter me.

A fairer face, a ſweeter ſmile,
Inconſtant lovers may beguile,
But to my laſs I'll conſtant be,
Nor ſhall her abſence alter me.
Though laid on India's burning coaſt,
Or on the wide Atlantic toſt,
My mind from Love no Pow'r could free,
Nor could her abſence alter me.

See how the flow'r that courts the ſun,
Purſues him till his race is run!
See how the needle ſeeks the Pole,
Nor diſtance can its pow'r controul!
Shall lifeleſs flow'rs the ſun purſue,
The needle to the Pole prove true;
Like them ſhall I not faithful be,
Or ſhall her abſence alter me.

Aſk, who has ſeen the turtle dove
Unfaithful to its marrow prove.
Or who the bleating ewe has ſeen
Deſert her lambkin on the green?
Shall beaſts and birds, inferior far
To us, diſplay their love and care?
Shall they in Union ſweet agree,
And ſhall her abſence alter me?

For Conq'ring Love is ſtrong as Death,
Like veh'ment flames his pow'rful breath,
Thro' floods unmov'd his courſe he keeps,
Ev'n thro' the Sea's devouring deeps.
His veh'ment flames my boſom burn,
Unchang'd they blaze till thy return;
My faithful Jeſsy then ſhall ſee,
Her abſence has not alter'd me.

## The Birks of Invermay

72

The smiling morn, the breathing spring, In _ vite the
Andante
tuneful birds to sing, And while they warble from each spray, Love
melts the u _ ni _ ver _ sal lay. Let us, A _ manda, time _ ly
wise, Like them improve the hour that flys, And in soft raptures
waste the day, A _ mong the birks of In _ ver _ may.

For soon the winter of the year,
And age, life's winter, will appear;
At this, thy living bloom will fade,
As that, will strip the verdant shade,
Our taste of pleasure then is o'er,
The feather'd songsters are no more;
And when they droop, and we decay,
Adieu the birks of Invermay.

Behold the hills and vales around,
With lowing herds and flocks abound;
The wanton kids, and frisking lambs,
Gambol and dance about their dams;
The busy bees with humming noise,
And all the reptile kind rejoice:
Let us, like them, then sing and play
About the birks of Invermay.

Hark, how the waters, as they fall,
Loudly my love to gladness call;
The wanton waves sport in the beams,
And fishes play throughout the streams,
The circling sun does now advance,
And all the planets round him dance:
Let us as jovial be as they,
Among the birks of Invermay.

## Mary Scot.

73

Happy's the love which meets re_turn, When in soft
Andante
flame souls e _ qual burn; But words are wanting to discover, The
torments of a hopeless lover. Ye regis_ters of heaven, re _
_ late, If looking o'er the rolls of fate, Did you there see me
mark'd to marrow Mary Scot, the flow'r of Yarrow?

Ah no! her form's too heav'nly fair,
Her love the gods above must share;
While mortals with despair explore her,
And at a distance due adore her.
O lovely maid! my doubts beguile,
Revive and bless me with a smile:
Alas. if not, you'll soon debar a
Sighing swain the banks of Yarrow.

Be hush, ye fears, I'll not despair,
My Mary's tender as she's fair;
Then I'll go tell her all mine anguish,
She is too good to let me languish:
With success crown'd, I'll not envy
The folks who dwell above the sky;
When Mary Scot's become my marrow,
We'll make a paradise of Yarrow.

## Down the burn, Davie.

74

Andante
When trees did bud, and fields were green, And
broom bloom'd fair to fee; When Mary was compleat fifteen, And
love laugh'd in her eye, Blythe Da_vie's blinks her
heart did move, To fpeak her mind thus free, Gang down the
burn, Da_vie, love, And I fhall fol_low thee.

Now Davie did each lad furpafs,
  That dwelt on yon burn fide,
And Mary was the bonnieft lafs,
  Juft meet to be a bride;
Her cheeks were rofy, red and white.
  Her een were bonny blue;
Her looks were like Aurora bright,
  Her lips like dropping dew.

As down the burn they took their way,
  What tender tales they faid!
His cheek to her's he aft did lay,
  And with her bofom play'd;

Till baith at length impatient grown
  To be mair fully bleft,
In yonder vale they lean'd them down;
  Love only faw the reft.

What pafs'd, I guefs was harmlefs play,
  And naithing fure unmeet;
For ganging hame, I heard them fay,
  They lik'd a wa'k fae fweet:
And that they aften fhou'd return,
  Sic pleafure to renew,
Quoth Mary, Love, I like the burn;
  And ay fhall follow you.

# The Banks of Forth.

75

Ye fylvan pow'rs that rule the plain, Where fweet_ly
Andante
wind_ing Fortha glides, Conduct me to thefe banks a_gain, Since
there my charming Ma_ry bides. Thefe banks that breathe their
ver_nal fweets, Where ev_ry fmiling beau_ty meets; Where Mary's
charms a_dorn the plain, And chear the heart of ev_ _ ry fwain.

Oft in the thick embow'ring groves,
  Where birds their mufic chirp aloud,
Alternately we fung our loves,
  And Fortha's fair meanders view'd.
The meadows wore a gen'ral fmile,
Love was our banquet all the while;
The lovely profpect charm'd the eye,
To where the ocean met the fky.

Once on the graffy bank reclin'd,
  Where Forth ran by in murmurs deep,
It was my happy chance to find
  The charming Mary lull'd afleep;
My heart then leap'd with inward blifs,
I foftly ftoop'd, and ftole a kifs;
She wak'd, fhe blufh'd, and gently blam'd,
Why, Damon! are you not afham'd?

Ye fylvan powers, ye rural gods,
  To whom we fwains our cares impart,
Reftore me to thefe bleft abodes,
  And eafe, oh! eafe my love-fick heart:
Thefe happy days again reftore,
When Mary and I fhall part no more,
When fhe fhall fill thefe longing arms,
And crown my blifs with all her charms.

## O Saw ye my Father.

76

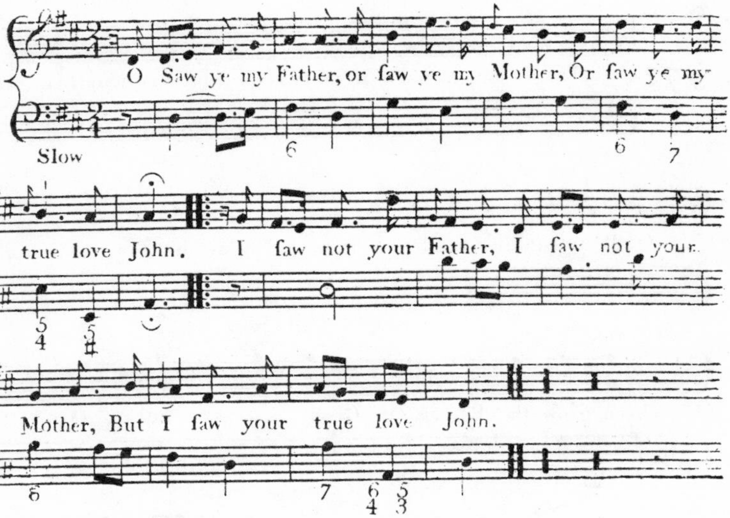
O Saw ye my Father, or ſaw ye my Mother, Or ſaw ye my
Slow
true love John. I ſaw not your Father, I ſaw not your
Mother, But I ſaw your true love John.

It's now ten at night, and the ſtars gi'e nae light,
And the bells they ring,ding dong;
He's met wi' ſome delay, that cauſeth him to ſtay.
But he will be here ere long.

The ſurly auld carl did naething but ſnarl.
And Johny's face it grew red;
Yet tho' he often ſigh'd, he ne'er a word reply'd,
Till all were aſleep in bed.

Up Johny roſe, and to the door he goes,
And gently tirled the pin;
The laſſie taking tent, unto the door ſhe went,
And ſhe open'd, and let him in.

And are you come at laſt, and do I hold ye faſt,
And is my Johny true!
I have nae time to tell, but ſae lang's I like myſell.
Sae lang ſhall I love you.

Flee up, flee up, my bonny gray cock,
And craw when it is day;
Your neck ſhall be like the bonny beaten gold,
And your wings of the ſilver grey.

The cock prov'd falſe, and untrue he was,
For he crew an hour o'er ſoon;
The laſſie thought it day, when ſhe ſent her love away,
And it was but a blink of the moon.

## Green grows the Raſhes.

The words by M! R. Burns.

77
There's nought but care on ev'ry han', In ev'ry hour that paſ_ ſes,
Andante
O: What ſignifies the life o' man, An' twere not for the laſſes, O.
Chorus
Green grow the Raſhes, O; Green grow the raſhes, O; The
ſweeteſt hours that e'er I ſpend, Are ſpent a_mang the laſſes, O.

The warly race may riches chaſe,
An' riches ſtill may fly them, O;
An tho' at laſt they catch them faſt,
Their hearts can ne'er enjoy them, O.
Green grow, &c.

But gie me a canny hour at e'en,
My arms about my Dearie, O;
An' warly cares, an' warly men,
May a' gae tapſalteerie, O!
Green grow, &c.

For you ſae douſe! ye ſneer at this,
Ye'er nought but ſenſeleſs aſſes, O:
The wiſeſt Man the warl' ſaw,
He dearly lov'd the laſſes, O.
Green grow, &c.

Auld Nature ſwears, the lovely Dears
Her nobleſt work ſhe claſſes, O:
Her prentice han' ſhe try'd on man,
An' then ſhe made the laſſes, O.
Green grow, &c.

## Loch Eroch Side.

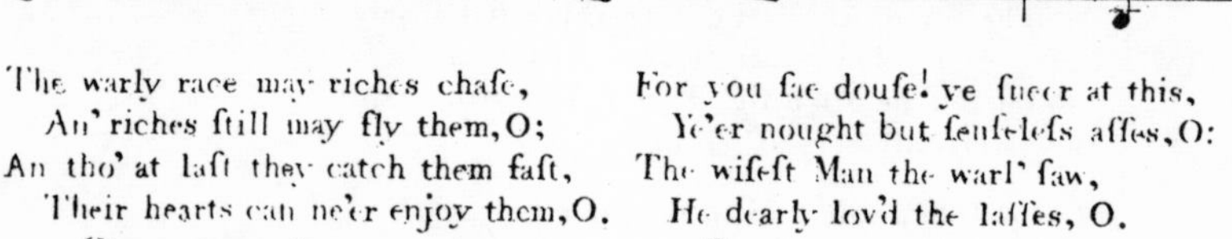
78
As I came by Loch Eroch ſide, The lofty hills ſurveying, The
Andante

Continued.

water clear, The heather blooms Their fragrance ſweet conveying, I met un-
-ſought, my love-ly maid, I found her like May morning; With Graces ſweet, &
1st
2d
tr
Charms ſo rare, Her Perſon all a-dorning, Perſon all a-dorning

How kind her looks, how bleſt was I,
  While in my arms I preſs'd her!
And ſhe her wiſhes ſcarce conceal'd,
  As fondly I careſs'd her.
She ſaid, If that your heart be true,
  If conſtantly you'll love me,
I heed not cares, nor fortune's frowns;
  Nor ought but death ſhall move me.

But faithful, loving, true and kind,
  Forever you ſhall find me;
And of our meeting here ſo ſweet,
  Loch Eroch Side will mind me.
Enraptur'd then, "My Lovely Laſs!
  I cry'd, no more we'll tarry
We'll leave the fair Loch Eroch Side
  For Lovers ſoon ſhould marry."

* * * * * * * * * * * * * * * * * * * * * * * * * * * * * * * * * * * * * * * * * * * * *

## To the foregoing Tune. by Burns

YOUNG Peggy blooms our bonieſt laſs,
  Her bluſh is like the morning,
The roſy dawn, the ſpringing graſs,
  With early gems adorning:
Her eyes outſhine the radiant beams
  That gild the paſſing ſhower,
And glitter o'er the chryſtal ſtreams,
  And chear each freſh'ning flower.

Her lips more than the cherries bright,
  A richer die has grac'd them,
They charm th' admiring gazer's ſight
  And ſweetly tempt to taſte them:
Her ſmile is as the ev'ning mild,
  When feath'red pairs are courting,
And little lambkins wanton wild,
  In playful bands diſporting.

Were Fortune lovely Peggy's foe,
  Such ſweetneſs would relent her.
As blooming ſpring unbends the brow
  Of ſurly, ſavage winter.
Detraction's eye no aim can gain
  Her winning pow'rs to leſsen;
And fretful envy grins in vain,
  The poiſon'd tooth to faſten.

Ye Pow'rs of Honor, Love and Truth,
  From ev'ry ill defend her;
Inſpire the highly favor'd Youth
  The deſtinies intend her;
Still fan the ſweet connubial flame,
  Reſponſive in each boſom;
And bleſs the dear parental name
  With many a filial bloſsom.

## The Bonny grey-ey'd morn.

Sung by Sir William.

79

The bon_ny grey ey'd morning be_gins to peep, And
Andante.
darkneſs flies before the ri_fing ray, The hear_ty hynd ſtarts
from his lazy ſleep, To fol_low healthful la_bours of the day;
With_out a guilty ſting to wrinkle his brow, The lark and the
lin_net tend his le_vee, And he joins their concert driving his
plow, from toil of grimace and pa_gean_try free.

While fluſter'd with wine, or madden'd with loſs
Of half an eſtate, the prey of a main,
The drunkard and gameſter tumble and toſs,
Wiſhing for calmneſs and ſlumber in vain.
Be my portion health, and quietneſs of mind,
Plac'd at due diſtance from parties and ſtate,
Where neither ambition, nor avarice blind,
Reach him who has happineſs link'd to his fate.

## The Buſh aboon Traquair.

80

Hear me, ye nymphs, and ev _ ry ſwain, I'll tell how Peggy
Slow
grieves me; Tho' thus I lan _ guiſh, and com _ _ plain, A
_ las! ſhe ne'er believes me. My vows and ſighs, like ſi _ lent
air, Un _ heed _ ed ne _ ver move her. The bon _ ny buſh a
_ boon Traquair, was where I firſt did love her.

That day ſhe ſmil'd, and made me glad,
No maid ſeem'd ever kinder;
I thought myſelf the luckieſt lad,
So ſweetly there to find her.
I try'd to ſooth my am'rous flame,
In words that I thought tender:
If more there paſs'd, I'm not to blame,
I meant not to offend her.

Yet now ſhe ſcornful flees the plain,
The fields we then frequented;
If e'er we meet, ſhe ſhews diſdain,
She looks as ne'er acquainted.

The bonny buſh bloom'd fair in May,
Its ſweets I'll ay remember;
But now her frowns make it decay;
It fades as in December.

Ye rural pow'rs, who hear my ſtrains,
Why thus ſhould Peggy grieve me.
Oh! make her partner in my pains;
Then let her ſmiles relieve me.
If not, my love will turn deſpair,
My paſſion no more tender;
I'll leave the buſh aboon Traquair,
To lonely wilds I'll wander.

# Etrick Banks.

81

On Etrick banks, ae ſum_mer's night, At gloaming
Andante
when the ſheep came hame, I met my laſ_ſy bra' and tight, While
wand'ring through the miſt her lane. My heart grew light, I,
ran, and flang my arms about her bon_ny neck; I kiſs'd and
clap'd her there fu' lang, My words they were na' mony feck.

I ſaid, my laſſie, will ye go
 To the highland hills the earſe to learn?
I'll baith gi'e thee a cow and ewe,
 When ye come to the Brig of Earn.
At Leith, auld meal comes in, ne'er faſh,
 And herrings at the Broomy-Law;
Chear up your heart, my bonny laſs,
 There's gear to win we never ſaw.

All day when we have wrought enough,
 When winter froſts, and ſnaw begin,
Soon as the ſun gaes weſt the loch,
 At night when you ſit down to ſpin,
I'll ſcrew my pipes, and play a ſpring:
 And thus the weary night will end,
Till the tender kid and lambkin bring
 Our pleaſant ſummer back again.

Syne when the trees are in their bloom,
 And gowans glent o'er ilka field,
I'll meet my laſs among the broom,
 And lead you to my ſummer ſhield.
Then far frae a' their ſcornfu' din,
 That make the kindly hearts their ſport,
We'll laugh and kiſs, and dance and ſing,
 And gar the langeſt day ſeem ſhort.

## My Deary, if thou Die.

82
Love never more shall give me pain, My fan_cy's
Andante
fix'd on thee, Nor e_ver maid my heart shall gain, my
Peg_gy, if thou die. Thy beauty doth such pleasure
give, Thy love's so true to me, With_ _out thee
I can ne_ver live, my deary, if thou die.

If fate shall tear thee from my breast,
How shall I lonely stray!
In dreary dreams the night I'll waste,
In sighs, the silent day.
I ne'er can so much virtue find,
Nor such perfection see:
Then I'll renounce all women kind,
My Peggy, after thee.

No new-blown beauty fires my heart
With Cupid's raving rage;
But thine, which can such sweets impart,
Must all the world engage.

'Twas this that like the morning-sun,
Gave joy and life to me;
And when it's destin'd day is done,
With Peggy let me die.

Ye powers that smile on virtuous love,
And in such pleasure share;
You who its faithful flames approve,
With pity view the fair:
Restore my Peggy's wonted charms,
Those charms so dear to me!
Oh! never rob them from these arms:
I'm lost, if Peggy die.

## She roſe, and let me in.

83

The night her ſi_lent ſa_ble wore, And gloomy
Slow
were the ſkies, Of glitt_ring ſtars ap_pear'd no more, Than
thoſe in Nel_ly's eyes. When to her Fa_ther's
door I came, Where I had of_ten been, I begg'd my
fair my love_ly dame, To riſe, and let me in.

But ſhe, with accents all divine,
Did my fond ſuit reprove;
And while ſhe chid my raſh deſign,
She but inflam'd my love.
Her beauty oft had pleas'd before,
While her bright eyes did roll.
But virtue only had the pow'r
To charm my very ſoul.

Then who wou'd cruelly deceive,
Or from ſuch beauty part!
I lov'd her ſo, I could not leave
The charmer of my heart.

My eager fondneſs I obey'd,
Reſolv'd ſhe ſhould be mine,
Till Hymen to my arms convey'd
My treaſure ſo divine.

Now happy in my Nelly's love,
Tranſporting is my joy,
No greater bleſſing can I prove;
So bleſs'd a man am I.
For beauty may a while retain
The conquer'd flutt'ring heart,
But virtue only is the chain
Holds, never to depart.

# Sweet Anny frae the sea-Beach came.

84
Sweet Anny frae the sea beach came, where Jocky speel'd the Vessel's
Affectuoso
side; Ah! wha can keep their heart at hame, when Jocky's tost a-boon the tide.
Far aff to distant realms he gangs; yet I'll prove true, as he has been, And
when ilk lass a-bout him thrangs, he'll think on Anny, his faithfu ain.

I met our wealthy laird yestreen,
Wi' gou'd in hand he tempted me,
He prais'd my brow, my rolling een,
And made a brag of what he'd gee:
What tho' my Jocky's far away,
Tost up and down the dinsome main,
I'll keep my heart anither day,
Since Jocky may return again.

Nae mair, false Jamie, sing nae mair,
And fairly cast your pipe away;
My Jocky wad be troubled sair,
To see his friend his Love betray:
For a' your songs and verse are vain,
While Jocky's notes do faithful flow:
My heart to him shall true remain,
I'll keep it for my constant Jo.

Bla' saft, ye gales, round Jocky's head,
And gar your waves be calm and still;
His hameward sail with breezes speed,
And dinna a' my pleasure spill!
What tho' my Jocky's far away,
Yet he will bra' in siller shine:
I'll keep my heart anither day,
Since Jocky may again be mine.

# Go to the Ew-Bughts, Marion.

85

Will ye go to the ew - bughts, Ma _ rion, and wear in the
Slow
sheep wi' me! the sun shines sweet, my Ma _ rion, but
nae half sae sweet as thee, the sun shines sweet, my
Ma _ rion, but nae half sae sweet as _ thee.

O Marion's a bonny lass,
And the blyth blink's in her eye;
And fain wad I marry Marion,
Gin Marion wad marry me.

There's gowd in your garters, Marion,
And silk on your white hauss-bane;
Fu' fain wad I marry my Marion,
At ev'n when I come hame.

There's braw lads in Earnslaw, Marion,
Wha gape, and glowr with their eye,
At kirk, when thy see my Marion;
But nane of them lo'es like me.

I've nine milk ews, my Marion,
A cow and a brawny quey,
I'll gi'e them a' to my Marion
Just on her bridal day;

And ye's get a green sey Apron,
And waistcoat of the London brown,
And vow but ye will be vapring,
Whene'er ye gang to the town.

I'm young and stout, my Marion;
Nane dances like me on the green;
And gin ye forsake me, Marion,
I'll e'en gae draw up wi' Jean:

Sae put on your pearlins, Marion,
And kyrtle of the cramasie;
And soon as my chin has nae hair on,
I shall come west and see ye.

## Lewis Gordon.

86
Slow
Oh! fend Lewis Gordon hame, & the Lad I
win_na name; tho' his back be at the wa', Here's to him that's far a_wa',
Chor:
2d
Oh hon! my Highland-man. Oh! my bonny Highland-man, Weel wou'd I my
1st
Oh hon! my Highland-man. Oh! my bonny Highland-man Weel wou'd I my
true love ken amang ten thoufand Highland-men,
true love ken amang' ten thoufand Highland-men,

Oh! to fee his tartan-trews,
Bonnet blue, and laigh-heel'd fhoes,
Philabeg aboon his knee:
That's the Lad that I'll gang wi'.
Oh hon! &c.

The Princely youth that I do mean,
Is fitted for to be a King:
On his breaft he wears a ftar:
You'd tak him for the god of war.
Oh hon! &c.

Oh, to fee this Princely One,
Seated on a royal throne!
Difafters a' wou'd difappear;
Then begins the Jub'lee Year.
Oh hon! &c.

## The Wawking of the Fauld.

87

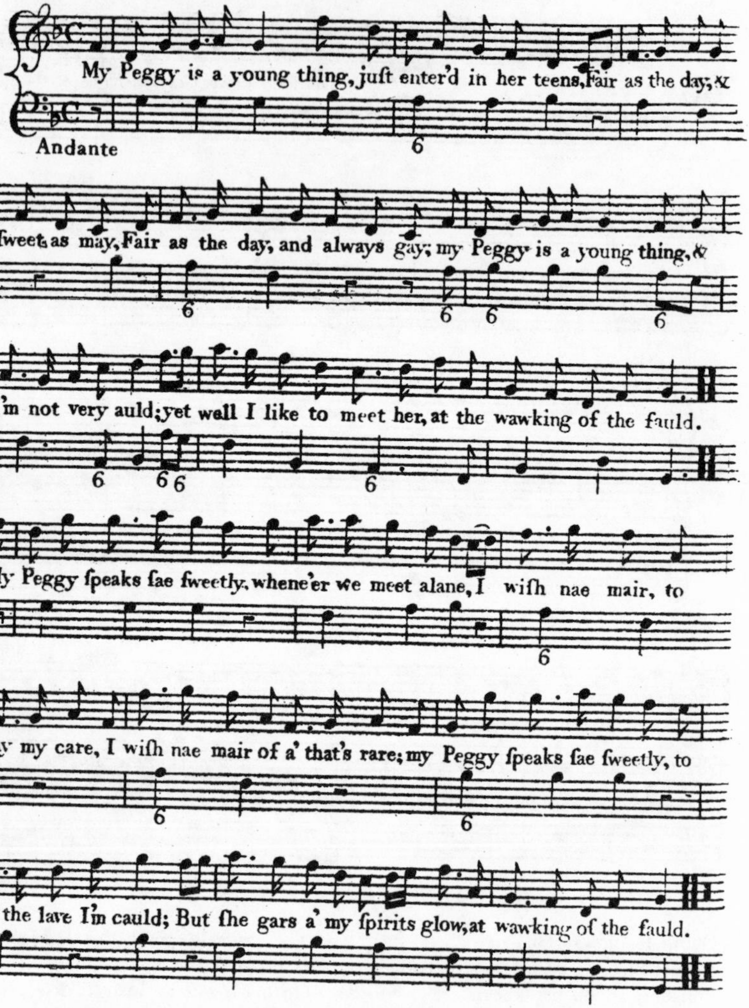
My Peggy is a young thing, juſt enter'd in her teens, Fair as the day, &
Andante
ſweet as may, Fair as the day, and always gay; my Peggy is a young thing, &
I'm not very auld; yet wall I like to meet her, at the wawking of the fauld.
My Peggy ſpeaks ſae ſweetly, whene'er we meet alane, I wiſh nae mair, to
lay my care, I wiſh nae mair of a' that's rare; my Peggy ſpeaks ſae ſweetly, to
a' the lave I'm cauld; But ſhe gars a' my ſpirits glow, at wawking of the fauld.

My Peggy ſmiles ſae kindly,
Whene'er I whiſper love,
That I look down on a' the town,
That I look down upon a crown;
My Peggy ſmiles ſae kindly,
It makes me blyth and bauld;
And naithing gi'es me ſic delight,
As wawking of the fauld.

My Peggy ſings ſae ſaftly,
When on my pipe I play,
By a' the reſt it is confeſt,
By a' the reſt, that ſhe ſings beſt:
My Peggy ſings ſae ſaftly,
And in her ſangs are tauld,
With innocence, the wale of ſenſe,
At wawking of the fauld.

## My Nanny-O.

88

While ſome for pleaſure pawn their health, Twixt Lais and the
Slowiſh
Bagnio, I'll ſave my ſelf, and without ſtealth, Bleſs and careſs my
Nanny-O She bids more fair t'engage a Jove, Than Leda did, or Danae-
-O. Were I to paint the Queen of love, None elſe ſhou'd ſit but Nanny-O.

How Joyfully my ſpirits riſe,
When dancing ſhe moves finely-O
I gueſs what heav'n is by her eyes,
Which ſparkle ſo divinely-O.
Attend my vow, ye gods, while I.
Breathe in the bleſt Britannia,
None's happineſs I ſhall envy,
As long's ye grant me Nanny-O.

My bonny, bonny, Nanny-O!
My lovely charming Nanny-O!
I care not tho' the world know
How dearly I love Nanny-O.

## Oh ono chrio.

89

Slow
Oh was not I a weary wight! oh on_o chri
oh! oh o_no_chri O! Maid, Wife, and Wi_dow,
in one night! oh o_no_chri o_no_chri o_no_chri O!
When in my ſoft and yiel_ding arms, oh o_no_chri
oh o_no_chri O! when moſt I thought him free from
harms, oh o_no_chri o_no_chri o_no_chri oh!

Even at the dead time of the night, &c.
They broke my Bower, and ſlew my Knight, &c.
With ae lock of his jet black hair, &c.
I'll tye my heart for ever mair; &c.
Nae ſly tongued youth, or flattering ſwain, &c.
Shall e'er untye this knott again: &c.
Thine ſtill, dear youth, that heart ſhall be, &c.
Nor pant for aught ſave heaven and thee. &c.

## Low down in the Broom.

90

Andante
My Daddy is a canker'd carle, He'll ne twin wi his gear, My
Minny ſhe's a ſcolding wife, Hads a' the houſe a ſteer; But let them ſay, or
let them do, Its a' ane to me; For he's low down, he's in the broom, that's
waiting on me; Waiting on me, my love, he's waiting on me, For he's
low down, he's in the broom, that's waiting for me.


My aunty Kate ſits at her wheel,
And ſair ſhe lightlies me;
But weel ken I, it's a' envy;
For ne'er a jo has ſhe.
But let them ſay, &c.

My couſin Kate was ſair beguil'd
Wi' Johnnie in the glen;
And aye ſince-ſyne, ſhe cries, Beware
Of falſe deluding men.
But let them ſay, &c.

Glee'd Sandy, he came waſt ae night,
And ſpeer'd when I ſaw Peat.
And aye ſince-ſyne the neighbours round
They jeer me air and late.
But let them ſay, or let them do,
It's a' ane to me;
For I'll gae to the bonny lad
That's waiting on me;
Waiting on me, my love,
He's waiting on me;
For he's low down, he's in the broom,
That's waiting on me.

## I'll never leave thee.

91

One day I heard Mary ſay, How ſhall I leave thee!
Slow
Stay, deareſt A_donis, ſtay; Why wilt thou grieve me! grieve me!
A_las! my fond heart will break, If thou ſhou'd leave me. I'll
live and die for thy ſake, Yet ne_ver leave thee, leave thee.

Say, lovely Adonis, ſay,
  Has Mary deceiv'd thee?
Did e'er her young heart betray
  New love to grieve thee?
My conſtant mind ne'er ſhall ſtray,
  Thou may believe me;
I'll love thee, lad, night and day,
  And never leave thee.

Adonis, my charming youth,
  What can relieve thee?
Can Mary thy anguiſh ſoothe
  This breaſt ſhall receive thee.

My paſſion can ne'er decay,
  Never deceive thee;
Delight ſhall drive pain away,
  Pleaſure revive thee.

But leave thee, leave thee, lad,
  How ſhall I leave thee!
O! that thought makes me ſad;
  I'll never leave thee.
Where would my Adonis fly?
  Why does he grieve me!
Alas! my poor heart will die,
  If I ſhould leave thee.

## Braes of Ballenden.

92

Beneath a green ſhade, a lovely young ſwain one ev'ning re_clin'd, to di
Amoroſo.
_co_ver his pain; So ſad, yet ſo ſweetly he warbled his woe, The
wind ceas'd to breathe, & the fountains to flow: Rude winds with compaſſion could
hear him complain, Yet Chloe, leſs gentle, was deaf to his ſtrain.

How happy, he cry'd, my moments once flew,
Ere Chloe's bright charms firſt flaſh'd in my view!
Theſe eyes then with pleaſure the dawn could ſurvey,
Nor ſmil'd the fair Morning more chearful than they;
Now ſcenes of diſtreſs pleaſe only my ſight,
I'm tortur'd in pleaſure, and languiſh in light.

Thro' changes in vain relief I purſue,
All, all but conſpire my griefs to renew;
From ſunſhine to zephyrs and ſhades we repair,
To ſunſhine we fly from too piercing an air;
But love's ardent fever burns always the ſame,
No winter can cool it, no ſummer inflame.

But ſee the pale moon all clouded retires,
The breezes grow cool; not Strephon's deſires:
I fly from the dangers of tempeſt and wind,
Yet nouriſh the madneſs that preys on my mind!
Ah wretch! How can life this merit thy care,
Since lengthning its moments, but lengthens deſpair.

## Corn-Riggs.

93

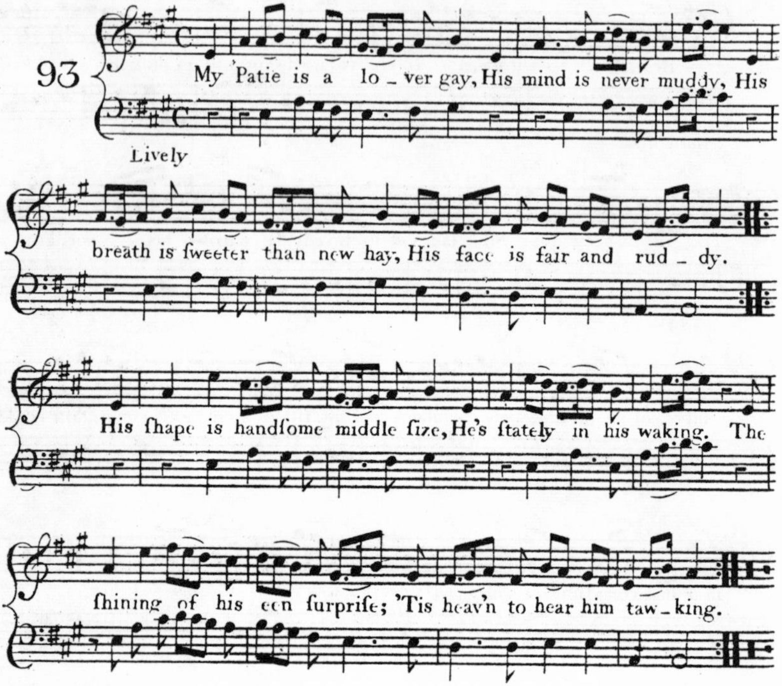
My Patie is a lo _ ver gay, His mind is never muddy, His
Lively
breath is sweeter than new hay, His face is fair and rud _ dy.
His shape is handsome middle size, He's stately in his waking. The
shining of his een surprise; 'Tis heav'n to hear him taw _ king.

Last night I met him on the bawk,
  Where yellow corn was growing,
There mony a kindly word he spake,
  That set my heart a glowing.
He kiss'd, and vow'd he wad be mine,
  And loo'd me best of ony;
That gars me like to sing sinsyne,
  "O corn riggs are bonny."

Let maidens of a silly mind
  Refuse what maist they're wanting;
Since we for yielding are design'd,
  We chastely should be granting;
Then I'll comply, and marry Pate,
  And syne my cokernony,
He's free to touzle, air or late,
  Where corn-riggs are bonny.

**************************************

## My Apron, Dearie.

94

My sheep I've forsaken, and left my sheep hook, And
Slow
6
6
6
5
6
5
3

Continued.

all the gay haunts of my youth I've for-sook, No more for A-
mynta fresh garlands I wove, For ambition, I said, wou'd soon cure me of
love. O what had my youth, with ambition to do! Why left I A-
mynta! why broke I my vow! O give me my sheep, And my
sheep hook restore, And I'll wander from love and Amynta no more.

Through regions remote, in vain do I rove,
And bid the wide ocean secure me from love;
O fool, to imagine that ought can subdue
A love so well founded, a passion so true!
O what had my youth with ambition to do!
Why left I Amynta! why broke I my vow!
O give me my sheep, and my sheep hook restore,
And I'll wander from love and Amynta no more.

Alas! 'tis too late at thy fate to repine!
Poor shepherd! Amynta no more can be thine;
Thy tears are all fruitless, thy wishes are vain;
The moments neglected return not again.
O what had my youth with ambition to do!
Why left I Amynta! why broke I my vow!
O give me my sheep, and my sheep hook restore,
And I'll wander from love and Amynta no more.

## Lochaber.

95

Farewell to Lochaber, and farewell, my Jean, where heartſome with
Slow
thee I have mony days been; For Lochaber no more, Lochaber no more,
we'll may be return to Lochaber no more. Theſe tears that I ſhed, they are
all for my Dear, & no for the dangers attending on Weir; tho' bore on rough
ſeas to a far bloody Shore, may be to return to Lochaber no more.

Tho' hurricanes riſe, and riſe ev'ry wind,
They'll ne'er make a tempeſt like that in my mind.
Tho' loudeſt of thunder on louder waves roar,
That's naithing like leaving my love on the ſhore.
To leave thee behind me, my heart is ſair pain'd;
By eaſe that's inglorious, no fame can be gain'd:
And beauty and love's the reward of the brave,
And I muſt deſerve it before I can crave.

Then glory, my Jeany, maun plead my excuſe,
Since Honour commands me, how can I refuſe!
Without it I ne'er can have merit for thee;
And without thy favour, I'd better not be!
I gae then, my laſs, to win honour and fame,
And if I ſhould luck to come glorioully hame,
A heart I will bring thee with love running o'er,
And then I'll leave thee and Lochaber no more.

## The Mucking of Geordie's Byar.

96

As I went over yon meadow, And careleſsly paſsed a -
Andante
- long, I liſten'd with pleaſure to Jenny, While mourn - ful - ly
ſinging this Song. The mucking of Geordie's Byar, And the
ſhooling the Gruip ſo clean, Has aft gart me ſpend the night
ſleepleſs, And brought the ſalt tears in my een.

It was not my fathers pleaſure,
  Nor was it my mothers deſire,
That ever I puddl'd my fingers,
  Wi' the mucking o' Geordie's Byar.
    The mucking &c.

Though the roads were ever ſo filthy,
  Or the day, ſo ſcoury and foul,
I would ay be ganging wi' Geordie;
  I lik'd it far better than School.
    The mucking &c.

My brither abuſes me daily
  For being wi' Geordie ſo free,
My ſiſter ſhe ca's me hoodwinked,
  Becauſe he's below my degree.
    The mucking &c.

But well do I like my young Geordie,
  Altho' he was cunning and ſlee;
He ca's me his Dear and his Honey,
  And I'm ſure that my Geordie loos me
    The mucking &c.

# Bide ye Yet.

97

Gin I had a wee houfe, and a canty wee fire, A bonny wee
Andante
Wifie to praife and admire, A bonny wee Yardy a_fide a wee burn; fare-
Chorus
weel to the bodies that yammer and mourn! Sae bide ye yet, and
bide ye yet, ye lit_tle ken what may be_tide yeu yet. Some
bon_ny wee bo_dy may be my lot, and I'll ay be can_ty wi
Sym.
thinking o't.

When I gang afield, and come hame at e'en,
I'll get my wee wifie fou neat and fou clean,
And a bonny wee bairnie upon her knee,
That will cry, Papa, or Daddy, to me.
Cho.s Sae bide ye yet, &c.

And if there fhould happen ever to be
A diffrence atween my wee wifie & me,
In hearty good humour, altho' fhe be teaz'd,
I'll kifs her & clap her untill fhe be pleas'd:
Chos. Sae bide ye yet, &c.

## The Joyful Widower. Tune Maggy Lauder

98

I Married with a scolding wife, The fourteenth of November, She
Lively
made me weary of my life, By one un-ru-ly mem-her. Long
did I bear the heavy yoke, And ma-ny griefs attend-ed, But
Sing which of these you please
to my comfort be it spoke, Now, now her life is ended.

We liv'd full one-and-twenty years,
  A man and wife together;
At length from me her course she steer'd,
  And gone I know not whither:
Would I could guess, I do profess,
  I speak and do not flatter,
Of all the women in the world,
  I never would come at her.

Her body is bestowed well,
  A handsome grave does hide her;
But sure her soul is not in hell,
  The de'il would ne'er abide her.
I rather think she is aloft,
  And imitating thunder,
For why; methinks I hear her voice,
  Tearing the clouds asunder.

# Bonie Dundee.

99
"O whar did ye get that hauver meal bannock? O filly blind
Slow
body, O dinna ye fee; I gat it frae a young brifk Sodger Laddie, Be-
-tween Saint Johnfton and bonie Dundee. O gin I faw the
laddie that gae me't! Aft has he doudl'd me upon his knee; May Heaven pro-
-tect my bonie Scots laddie, And fend him fafe hame to his babie & me.

My blefsins upon thy fweet, wee lippie!
My bleffins upon thy bonie e'e brie!
Thy fmiles are fae like my blyth Sodger laddie,
Thou's ay the dearer, and dearer to me!
But I'll big a bow'r on yon bonie banks,
Whare Tay rins wimplin by fae clear;
And I'll cleed thee in the tartan fae fine,
And mak thee a man like thy dadie dear.

## Johnny and Mary.

100

S.
Down the burn, and thro the mead, His golden locks wav'd o'er his
Affettuoso
brow, Johnny lilting tun'd his reed, and Mary wip'd her bonny Mou.' Dear she
loo'd the well known Song, while her Johnny; blithe & bonny, sung her praise the
whole day long. Down the burn & thro the mead, his golden locks wav'd o'er his brow
Johnny lilt_ing tun'd his reed, and Ma_ry wip'd her bon_ny mou.'
S.
S.

Costly claiths she has but few;
Of rings and jewels nae great store;
Her face was fair, her love was true,
And Johnny wisely wish'd no more;
Love's the pearl the shepherd's prize;
O'er the mountain, near the fountain,
Love delights the shepherd's eyes.
Down the burn, &c.

Gold and titles give not health,
And Johnny cou'd nae these impart;
Youthfu' Mary's greatest wealth
Was still her faithfu' Johnny's heart:
Sweet the joys the lovers find,
Great the treasure, sweet the pleasure,
Where the heart is always kind.
Down the burn &c.

END OF VOLUME FIRST.

# THE SCOTS Musical Museum

Consisting of Six hundred Scots Songs

with proper Basses for the

PIANO FORTE &c.

Humbly Dedicated

To the Society

OF

Antiquaries of Scotland

BY JAMES JOHNSON

*In this publication the original simplicity of our Ancient National Airs is retained unincumbered with useless Accompaniments & graces depriving the hearers of the sweet simplicity of their native melodies.*

Volume 2 Pr. 7 s

Butterworth Scripsit

*Printed & Sold by JAMES JOHNSON Music Seller EDINBURGH to be had at T. PRESTON N.º 97 Strand LONDON, M.c FADYEN GLASGOW, & at all the principal* Music Sellers.

# PREFACE.

IN the first Volume of this work, two or three Airs not of Scots composition have been inadvertently inserted; which, whatever excellence they may have, was improper, as the Collection is meant to be solely the music of our own Country — The Songs contained in this Volume, both music and poetry, are all of them the work of Scotsmen — Wherever the old words could be recovered, they have been preferred; both as generally suiting better the genius of the tunes, and to preserve the productions of those earlier Sons of the Scottish Muses, some of whose names deserved a better fate than has befallen them — "Buried 'midst the wreck of things which were." Of our more modern Songs, the Editor has inserted the Authors' names as far as he could ascertain them; and as that was neglected in the first Volume, it is annexed here. — If he have made any mistakes in this affair, which he possibly may, he shall be very grateful at being set right.

Ignorance and Prejudice may perhaps affect to sneer at the simplicity of the poetry or music of some of these pieces; but their having been for ages the favorites of Nature's Judges — the Common People, was to the Editor a sufficient test of their merit.

Materials for the third Volume are in great forwardness;

Edin.r March 1. 1788.

# INDEX TO VOLUME SECOND.

Note, the Songs marked B, R, X, &c. are originals by different hands, but all of them Scots gentlemen, who have favoured the Editor, and the Public at large, with their compositions: these marked Z, are old verses, with corrections or additions.



I

# INDEX

# INDEX

## When Guilford good our Pilot ſtood.

Written for this Work by R. Burns. Tune, M. fr. icedan.

No. 101

*
When Guilford good our Pilot ſtood, An' did our hellim
Lively
thraw, man, Ae night, at tea, began a plea, Within A-me-ri-ca,
man: Then up they gat the maſkin-pat, And in the ſea did jaw, man; An
did nae leſs, in full Congreſs, Than quite refuſe our law, man.

2

Then thro' the lakes Montgomery takes,
I wat he was na ſlaw, man;
Down Lowrie's burn he took a turn,
And C-rl-t-n did ca', man;
But yet, whatreck, he, at Quebec,
Montgomery-like did fa', man,
Wi' ſword in hand, before his band,
Amang his en'mies a', man.

3

Poor Tammy G-ge within a cage
Was kept at Boſton ha', man:
Till Willie H-e took o'er the knowe
For Philadelphia, man:
Wi' ſword an' gun he thought a ſin
Guid Chriſtian bluid to draw, man;
But at New-York, wi' knife an' fork,
Sir-Loin he hacked ſma', man.

4

B-rg-ne gaed up, like ſpur an' whip,
Till Fraſer brave did fa', man,
Then loſt his way, ae miſty day,
In Saratoga ſhaw, man.
C-rnw-ll-s fought as lang's he dought
An' did the Buckſkins claw, man;
But Cl-nt-n's glaive frae ruſt to ſave
He hung it to the wa', man.

5

Then M-nt-gue, an' Guilford too,
Began to fear a fa', man;
And S-ckv-lle doure, wha ſtood the ſtoure,
The German Chief to thraw, man:
For Paddy B-rke, like ony Turk,
Nae mercy had at a', man;
An' Charlie F-x threw by the box,
An' lows'd his tinkler jaw, man.

6

Then R-ck-ngh-m took up the game
Till Death did on him ca', man;
When Sh-lb-rne meek held up his cheek
Conform to Goſpel law, man:
Saint Stephen's boys, wi' jarring noiſe
They did his meaſures thraw, man.
For N-rth an' F-x united ſtocks,
An' bore him to the wa', man.

## Continued.

7

Then Clubs an Hearts were Charlie's car-tes.
He swept the stakes awa', man,
Till the Diamond's Ace, of Indian race,
Led him a fair faux pas, man:
The Saxon lads, wi' loud placads,
On Chatham's Boy did ca', man;
An' Scotland drew her pipe an' blew,
'Up, Willie, waur them a', man.'

8

Behind the throne then Gr-nv-lle's gone,
A secret word or twa, man;
While slee D-nd-s arous'd the class
Be-north the Roman wa', man:

An' Chatham's wraith, in heav'nly graith,
(Inspired Bardies saw, man)
Wi' kindling eyes cry'd, 'Willie, rise!
'Would I hae fear'd them a', man.'

9

But, word an' blow, N-rth, F-x, and Co.
Gowff'd Willie like a ba', man,
Till Suthrons raise an' coost their claise
Behind him in a raw, man:
An' Caledon threw by the drone,
An' did her whittle draw, man;
An' swoor fu' rude, thro' dirt an' blood.
To mak it guid in law, man.

## Tranent Muir.

102

The Chevalier, being void of fear, Did march up Brislie brae, man,
And thro' Tranent, e'er he did stent, As fast as he could gae, man: While
Gen'ral Cope did taunt and mock, Wi' mony a loud huz_za, man, But
e'er next morn proclaim'd the cock, We heard a_no_ther craw man.

The brave Lochiel, as I heard tell,
Led Camerons on in clouds, man:
The morning fair, and clear the air,
They loos'd with devilish thuds, man;
Down guns they threw, & swords they drew,
And soon did chace them aff, man;
On Seaton Crafts they bust their chafts,
And gart them rin like daft, man.

The bluff dragoons swore blood and oon
They'd make the rebels run, man;
And yet they flee when them they see,
And winna fire a gun, man.
They turn'd their back, the foot they brak
Such terror seiz'd them a', man;
Some wet their cheeks some fyl'd their breeks
And some for fear did fa', man.

Continued.

The volunteers prick'd up their ears,
And vow gin they were croufe, man;
But when the bairns faw't turn to earn'ft,
They were not worth a loufe, man;
Maift feck gade hame; O fy for fhame!
They'd better ftaid awa', man,
Than wi' cockade to make parade,
And do nae good at a' man.

Menteith the great, when herfell f—t,
Un'wares did ding him o'er, man,
Yet wad na ftand to bear a hand,
But aff fou faft did fcour, man;
O'er Soutra hill, e'er he ftood ftill,
Before he tafted meat, man,
Troth he may brag of his fwift nag,
That bare him aff fae fleet, man.

And Simpfon keen to clear the een
Of rebels far in wrang, man;
Did never ftrive wi' piftols five,
But gallopp'd with the thrang, man:
He turn'd his back, and in a crak
Was cleanly out of fight, man;
And thought it beft, it was nae jeft
Wi' Highlanders to fight, man.

Mangft a' the gang nane bade the bang
But twa, and ane was tane, man;
For Campbell rade, but Myrie ftaid,
And fair he paid the kain, man;
Fell fkelps he got was war then fhot
Frae the fharp-edg'd claymore, man;
Frae many a fpout came running out
His reeking-het red gore, man.

But Gard'ner brave did ftill behave
Like to a hero bright, man;
His courage true, like him were few
That ftill defpifed flight, man;
For King and laws, and country's caufe,
In Honour's bed he lay, man;
His life, but not his courage, fled,
While he had breath to draw, man.

And Major Bowle, that worthy foul,
Was brought down to the ground, man;
His horfe being fhot, it was his lot
For to get mony a wound, man:
Lieutenant Smith, of Irifh birth,
Frae whom he call'd for aid, man,
Being full of dread, lap o'er his head,
And wadna be gainfaid, man.

He made fick hafte, fae fpur'd his beaft
'Twas little there he faw man:
To Berwick rade, and falfely faid,
The Scots were rebels a, man:
But let that end, for well 'tis kend
His ufe and wont to lie, man;
The Teague is naught, he never faught
When he had room to flee, man.

And Caddell dreft, amang the reft,
With gun and good claymore, man;
On gelding grey he rode that way,
With piftols fet before, man; (blood
The caufe was good, he'd fpend his
Before that he would yield, man;
But the night before he left the cor,
And never fac'd the field, man.

But gallant Roger, like a foger,
Stood and bravely fought, man:
I'm wae to tell, at laft he fell,
But mae down wi' him brought, man.
At point of death, wi' his laft breath,
(Some ftanding round in ring, man.)
On's back lying flat, he wav'd his hat,
And cry'd, God fave the King, man.

(dog
Some Highland rogues, like hungry
Neglecting to purfue, man,
About they fac'd, and in great hafte
Upon the booty flew, man;
And they as gain, for a' their pain,
Are deck'd wi' fpoils of war, man;
Fow bald can tell how her nainfell
Was ne'er fae pra before, man.

At the thorn tree, which you may fee
Beweft the meadow-mill, man,
There mony flain lay on the plain;
The clans purfuing ftill, man.
Sick unco' hacks, and deadly whacks,
I never faw the like, man,
Loft hands & heads coft them their dead
That fell near Prefton-dyke, man.

That afternoon, when a' was done,
I gaed to fee the fray, man;
But had I wift what after paft,
I'd better ftaid away, man:
On Seaton fands, wi' nimble hands,
They pick'd my pockets bare, man:
But I wifh ne'er to drie fick fear
For a' the fum and mair, man.

# Prælium Gillicrankianum.

To the foregoing Tune.

Grahamius notabilis coegerat Montanos,
Qui clypeis et gladiis fugarunt Anglicanos;
Fugerant Vallicolæ, atque Puritani,
Cacavere Batavi et Cameroniani.
Grahamius mirabilis, fortiſsimus Alcides,
Cujus Regi fuerat intemerata fides,
Agiles monticolas marte inſpiravit,
Et duplicatum numerum hoſtium profliga-vit.

Nobilis apparuit Fermilodunenſis,
Cujus in Rebelles ſtringebatur Enſis;
Nobilis et Sanguine, Nobilior virtute,
Regi devotiſsimus intus et in Cute;
Pitcurius heroicus, Hector Scoticanus,
Cui mens fidelis fuerat, et invicta manus,
Capita rebellium, is Excerebravit,
Hoſtes unitiſsimos Ille dimicavit.

Glengarius magnanimus atque Bellicoſus,
Functus ut Eneas, pro rege animoſus,
Fortis atque Strenuus, hoſtes Expugnavit,
Sanguine Rebellium Campos coloravit;
Surrexerat fideliter Donaldus Inſulanus,
Pugnaverat viriliter, cum Copiis Skyanis,
Pater atque Filij, non diſimularunt,
Sed pro Rege proprio unanimes pugnarunt.

MacLeanius, circumdatus tribo martiali,
Semper, devinctiſsimus familiæ regali,
Fortiter pugnaverat more Atavorum,
Deinde diſsipaverat Turmas Batavorum,
Strenuus Lochielius, multo Camerone,
Hoſtes Enſe peremit, et abrio pugione
Iſtos et intrepidos Orco dedicavit,
Impedimenta hoſtium Blaro reportavit.

MacNeillius de Bara, Glencous Kepoch-anus,
Balleehinus cum fratre, Stuartus Apianus,
Pro Jacobo ſeptimo, fortiter geſsere,
Pugiles fortiſsimi feliciter vicere.
Canonicus clariſsimus, Gallovidianus,
Acer et indomitus, conſilioque Sanus,
Ibi Dux adfuerat, ſpectabilis perſona,
Nam pro tuenda patria, hunc peperit Bellona;

Ducalidoni dominum Spreverat Gradivus,
Nobilis et juvenis, fortis et activus,
Nam cum nativum, principem, exulem, audiret
Redit ex Hungaria, ut regi inſerviret;
Hlic et adfuerat, Tutor Ranaldorum,
Qui Strenue pugnaverat, cum Copiis viror-um,
Et ipſe Capetaneus, ætate puerili,
Intentus eſt ad prælium, ſpiritu virili.

Glenmoriſtonus Junior, Optimus Bellator,
Subito jam factus, hactenus venator;
Perduelles Whiggeos, ut pecora proſtravit,
Enſe et fulmineo MacKaium fugavit.
Regibus et Legibus Scotici conſtantes,
Vos Clypeis et gladiis Pro principe pugnantes;
Veſtra eſt victoria, veſtra eſt et Gloria:
In Cantis et Hiſtoria perpes eſt Memoria.

Autore Herberto Kennedy, quondam in Academia Edinburgenſi Profeſsore,
Ex antiqua familia quandoque, de Haleaths, in valle Annandiæ orto.

## To the Weaver's gin ye go.

103

My heart was ance as blythe and free As ſimmer days were lang, But a bonie, weſtlin weaver lad Has gart me change my ſang.
Lively
Chos.
To the weaver's gin ye go, fair maids, To the weaver's gin ye go, I rede you right, gang ne'er at night, To the weaver's gin ye go.

My mither ſent me to the town
To warp a plaiden wab;
But the weary, weary warpin o't
Has gart me ſigh and ſab.
To the weaver's &c.

A bonie, weſtlin weaver lad
Sat working at his loom;
He took my heart as wi' a net
In every knot and thrum.
To the weaver's &c.

I ſat beſide my warpin-wheel,
And ay I ca'd it roun';
But every ſhot and every knock,
My heart it gae a ſtoun.
To the weaver's &c.

The moon was ſinking in the weſt
Wi' viſage pale and wan,
As my bonie, weſtlin weaver lad
Convoy'd me thro the glen.
To the weaver's &c.

But what was ſaid, or what was done,
Shame fa' me gin I tell;
But Oh! I fear the kintra ſoon
Will ken as weel's myſel!
To the weaver's &c.

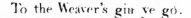

## Strephon and Lydia.

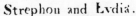

Tune, The Gordons has the guiding o't.

104

All lovely on the sultry beach, Expiring Strephon lay, No
Slow
hand the cordial draught to reach, Nor chear the gloomy way. Ill
fated youth! no parent nigh, To catch thy fleeting breath, No
bride, to fix thy swimming eye, Or smooth the face of Death.

Far distant from the mournful ſcene,
  Thy parents ſit at eaſe,
Thy Lydia rifles all the plain,
  And all. the ſpring, to pleaſe.
Ill fated youth! by fault of Friend,
  Not force of foe, depreſs'd,
Thou fall'st, alas! thyſelf, thy kind,
  Thy country, unredreſs'd!

## On a rock by ſeas ſurrounded.

Tune, Ianthy the lovely.

105

On a rock by ſeas ſur - round - - ed,

Continued.

Dis_tant far from fight of fhore, When the fhip-wreck'd
wretch con_found_ed, Hears the bel_low_ing tem_peft
Crefcendo il For
For.
F.
roar, Hopes of life do then for_fake him,
In this laft de_plor'd ex_treme; When
lo, his own loud fhricks a_wake him.
F.
And he finds it all a dream.
P

## Whiſtle, an' I'll come to you, my lad.

**Written for this Work by Robert Burns.**

106

O whiſtle, an' I'll come to you, my lad; O
whiſtle, an' I'll come to you, my lad: Though fath_er and
mither ſhould baith gae mad, O whiſtle, an' I'll come
to you, my lad. Come down the back ſtairs when ye
come to court me; Come down the back ſtairs when ye come to court
me; Come down the back ſtairs, and let naebody ſee; And come as ye
were na' coming to me, And come as ye were na' coming to me.

## I'm o'er young to Marry Yet.

107
I am my mam_my's ae bairn, Wi' unco folk I
Lively
weary, Sir, And ly_ing in a man's bed, I'm fley'd it
make me irie, Sir. I'm o'er young, I'm o'er young, I'm
o'er young to marry yet; I'm o'er young, 'twad be a sin To
tak me frae my mam_my yet.

Hallowmass is come and gane,
The nights are lang in winter, Sir;
And you an' I in ae bed,
In trowth, I dare na venture, Sir.
I'm o'er young &c.

Fu' loud and shill the frosty wind
Blaws thro' the leafless timmer, Sir;
But if ye come this gate again,
I'll aulder be gin simmer, Sir.
I'm o'er young &c.

## Hamilla.

Tune, The bonnieſt laſs in a' the warld.

108

Look where my dear Hamilla ſmiles, Hamilla, heav'nly char-
Slowiſh
-mer! ſee how with all their arts and wiles, The loves and graces arm her!
A bluſh dwells glowing on her cheek, Fair ſeat of youthful pleaſure!
There love in ſmiling language ſpeaks, There ſpreads the roſy treaſure.

O faireſt maid, I own thy power;
I gaze, I ſigh, and languiſh;
Yet ever, ever will adore,
And triumph in my anguiſh.

But eaſe, O charmer, eaſe my care,
And let my torments move thee;
As thou art faireſt of the fair,
So I the deareſt love thee.

## Love is the cauſe of my Mourning.

109

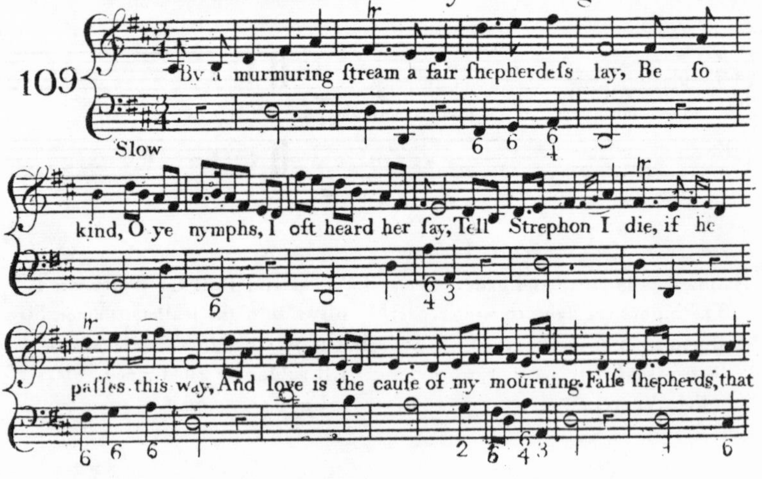
By a murmuring ſtream a fair ſhepherdeſs lay, Be ſo
Slow
kind, O ye nymphs, I oft heard her ſay, Tell Strephon I die, if he
paſſes this way, And love is the cauſe of my mourning. Falſe ſhepherds, that

## Continued.

tell me of beauty and charms, Deceive me, for Strephon's cold heart never
warms; Yet bring me this Strephon, I'll die in his arms; O Strephon. the
cauſe of my mourn_ing. But firſt, ſaid ſhe, let me go down to the
ſhades below, e'er ye let Strephon know that I have lov'd him ſo: Then on my
pale cheek no bluſhes will ſhew, That love is the cauſe of my mourn_ing.

Her eyes were ſcarce cloſed, when Strephon came by;
He thought ſhe'd been ſleeping, and ſoftly drew nigh;
But finding her breathleſs, Oh heavens! did he cry,
  Ah Chloris! the cauſe of my mourning.
Reſtore me my Chloris, ye nymphs, uſe your art:
They, ſighing, reply'd, 'Twas yourſelf ſhot the dart,
That wounded the tender young ſhepherdeſs' heart,
  And kill'd the poor Chloris with mourning
    Ah then, is Chloris dead,
    Wounded by me! he ſaid;
    I'll follow thee, chaſte maid,
    Down to the ſilent ſhade:
Then on her cold ſnowy breaſt leaning his head,
  Expir'd the poor Strephon with mourning.

# Bonnie May.

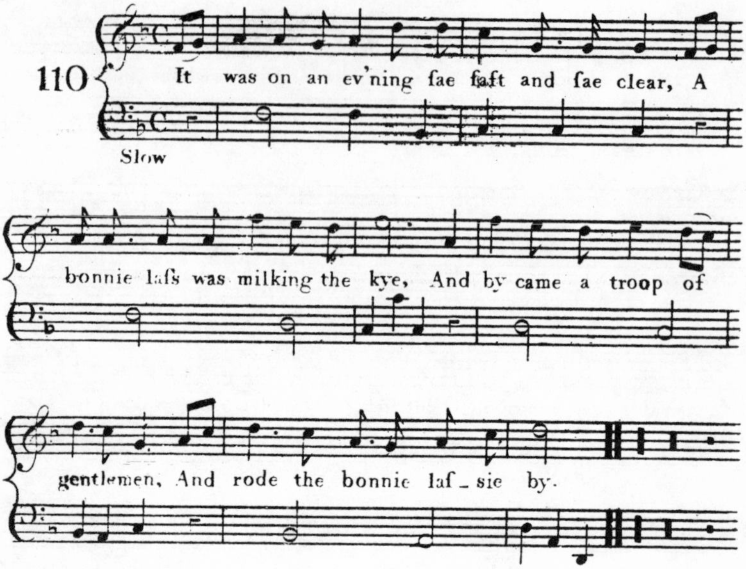
110
It was on an ev'ning ſae ſaft and ſae clear, A
Slow
bonnie laſs was milking the kye, And by came a troop of
gentlemen, And rode the bonnie laſ_sie by.

Then one of them ſaid unto her,
Bonnie laſsie, ſhew me the way
O if I do ſae it may breed me wae,
For langer I dare na ſtay.

But dark and miſty was the night
Before the bonnie laſs came hame;
Now where hae you been, my ae doughter.
I am ſure you was na your lane

O father, a tod has come o'er your lamb,
A gentleman of high degree,
And ay whan he ſpake he lifted his hat,
And bonnie, bonnie blinkit his ee.

But when twenty weeks were paſt & gane,
O twenty weeks and three,
The laſsie began to grow pale and wan,
And think lang for his blinkin ee.

O wae be to my father's herd,
An ill death may he die;
He bigged the bughts ſae far frae hame,
And wadna bide wi me.

It fell upon another fair evening,
The bonnie laſs was milking her kye,
And by came the troop of gentlemen,
And rode the bonnie laſsie by.

Then one of them ſtopt, and ſaid to her,
Wha's aught that baby ye are wi'.
The laſsie began for to bluſh, and think
To a father as gude as ye.

O had your tongue, my bonnie May,
Sae loud's I hear you lie;
O dinnae you mind the miſty night
I was in the bught with thee

Now he's come aff his milk-white ſteed,
And he has taen her hame:
Now let you father bring hame the kye,
You ne'er mair ſhall ca' them agen.

He was the laird of Auchentrone.
With fifty ploughs and three
And he has gotten the bonnieſt laſs
In a' the ſouth countrie.

## My Jo Janet.

111

O ſweet ſir, for your courteſie, When ye come by the
Lively
Baſs then, For the love ye bear to me, Buy me a keek - ing -
- glaſs then. Keek in - to the draw well, Jan - et, Jan - et; And
there ye'll ſee your bonny ſell, My Jo Janet.

Keeking in the draw-well clear,
What if I ſhou'd fa' in. then;
Syne a' my kin will ſay and ſwear,
I drown'd myſell for ſin, then.
Had the better by the brae,
Janet, Janet;
Had the better by the brae,
My jo Janet.

Good Sir, for your courteſie,
Coming thro' Aberdeen then,
For the love you bear to me,
Buy me a pair of ſheen then.
Clout the auld, the new are dear,
Janet, Janet;
A pair may gain ye ha'f a year,
My jo Janet.

But what if dancing on the green,
And ſkipping like a mawkin,
If they ſhould ſee my clouted ſheen,
Of me they will be tauking.
Dance ay laigh, and late at e'en,
Janet, Janet.
Syne a' their fauts will no be ſeen,
My jo Janet.

Kind Sir, for your courteſie,
When ye gae to the croſs then,
For the love ye bear to me,
Buy me a pacing horſe then.
Pace upo' your ſpinning wheel,
Janet, Janet,
Pace upo' your ſpinning wheel,
My jo Janet.

## He who presum'd to guide the Sun.

Tune, The Maids complaint

112
He who presum'd to guide the sun, Was crown'd with bad suc-
Slow
-cess; Tho' for his rash attempt undone, He'd glory'd ne'er the less.
Him you resemble, and aspire To lead our brightest fair; Like
him too, tho' consum'd by fire, You boast because you dare:

## The Birks of Aberfeldy.

Written for this Work by R. Burns. Tune, Birks of Abergeldie.

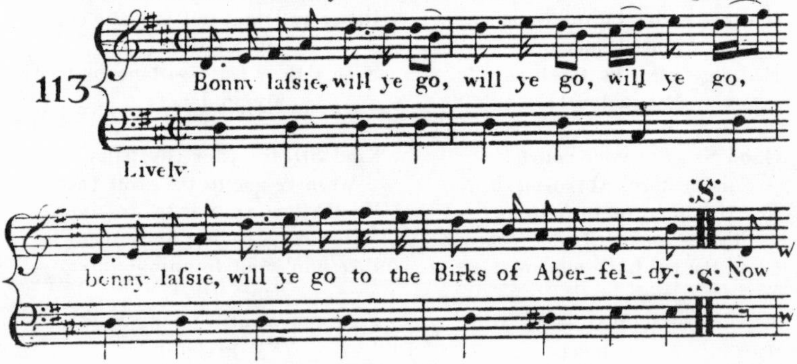
113
Bonny lassie, will ye go, will ye go, will ye go,
Lively
bonny lassie, will ye go to the Birks of Aber-fel-dy. Now
S.

## Continued.

Simmer blinks on flowery braes, And o'er the chryſ_tal ſtream_lets
plays; Come let us ſpend the lightſome days In the birks of A_ber-
_fel_dy. Bonny laſsie, will ye go, will ye go, will ye go,
Bonny laſsie, will ye go to the Birks of Aberfeldy?
S.
S.

The little birdies blythely ſing,
While o'er their heads the hazels hing;
Or lightly flit on wanton wing
  In the birks of Aberfeldy.
    Bonny laſsie, &c.

The hoary cliffs are crownd wi' flowers.
White o'er the linns the burnie pours,
And riſing weets wi' miſty ſhowers
  The birks of Aberfeldy.
    Bonny laſsie, &c.

The braes aſcend like lofty wa's,
The foamy ſtream deep-roaring fa's,
O'er-hung wi' fragrant-ſpreading ſhaws,
  The birks of Aberfeldy.
    Bonny laſsie, &c.

Let Fortune's gifts at random flee,
They ne'er ſhall draw a wiſh frae me.
Supremely bleſt wi' love and thee
  In the birks of Aberfeldy.
    Bonny laſsie, &c.

B

## Birks of Abergeldie.

BONNY laſsie, will ye go,
  Will ye go, will ye go,
Bonny laſsie, will ye go
  To the birks o' Abergeldie?
Ye ſhall get a gown of ſilk,
  A gown of ſilk, a gown of ſilk,
Ye ſhall get a gown of ſilk,
  And coat of calimancoe.

Na, kind Sir, I dare nae gang,
  I dare nae gang, I dare nae gang,
Na, kind Sir, I dare nae gang,
  My minnie ſhe'll be angry:
Sair, ſair wad ſhe flyte,
  Wad ſhe flyte, wad ſhe flyte,
Sair, ſair wad ſhe flyte,
  And ſair wad ſhe ban me.

# Mc Pherſon's Farewell.

Written for this Work by Robert Burns.

114
Slowiſh
Farewell, ye dungeon's dark and ſtrong, The wretch's deſtin-
-ie! Mc Pherson's time will not be long, On yonder gallows-tree.
Chorus
Sae rantingly, ſae wantonly, Sae daunting-ly gae'd he. He
play'd a ſpring and danc'd it round Be-low the gallows-tree.

O what is death but parting breath?
On many a bloody plain
I've dar'd his face, and in this place
I ſcorn him yet again!
Sae rantingly, &c.

I've liv'd a life of ſturt and ſtrife;
I die by treacherie:
It burns my heart I muſt depart
And not avenged be.
Sae rantingly, &c.

Untie theſe bands from off my hands,
And bring to me my ſword;
And there's no a man in all Scotland,
But I'll brave him at a word.
Sae rantingly, &c.

Now farewell, light, thou ſunſhine bright,
And all beneath the ſky!
May coward ſhame diſtain his name,
The wretch that dares not die!
Sae rantingly, &c.

# The Lowlands of Holland.

115

Slowiſh
The love that I have choſen. I'll there_with be con_
_tent, The ſaut_ſea ſhall be frozen Before that I repent; Re_
_pent it ſhall I ne_ver Un_til the day I die, But the
lowlands of Holland Hae twinn'd my love and me.

My love lies in the ſaut ſea,
  And I am on the ſide,
Enough to break a young thing's heart
  Wha lately was a bride:
Wha lately was a bonie bride
  And pleaſure in her e'e;
But the lowlands of Holland
  Hae twinn'd my love and me.

New Holland is a barren place,
  In it there grows no grain;
Nor any habitation
  Wherein for to remain:
But the ſugar canes are plenty,
  And the wine draps frae the tree;
And the lowlands of Holland
  Hae twinn'd my love and me.

My love he built a bonie ſhip
  And ſet her to the ſea,
Wi' ſeven ſcore brave mariners
  To bear her companie:

Threeſcore gaed to the bottom,
  And threeſcore died at ſea;
And the lowlands of Holland
  Hae twinn'd my love and me.

My love has built another ſhip
  And ſet her to the main,
He had but twenty mariners
  And all to bring her hame:
The ſtormy winds did roar again,
  The raging waves did rout,
And my love and his bonie ſhip
  Turn'd widderſhins about

There ſhall nae mantle croſs my back
  Nor kame gae in my hair,
Neither ſhall coal nor candle light
  Shine in my bower mair;
Nor ſhall I chuſe anither love
  Until the day I die,
Since the lowlands of Holland
  Hae twinn'd my love and me.

# The Maid of Selma.

116
In the hall I lay in night _ mine eyes half-clos'd with
Very Slow
fleep, _ Soft mufic came to mine ear, Soft mufic came,
to mine ear, It was the Maid of Selma. Her breafts were
white as the bofom of a Swan, Trembling on fwift _ rol_ ling
waves, She raif'd the nightly fong, For fhe knew that my
foul, was a ftre _ am that flow_ _ d at pleaf _ ant
founds; mix'd with the Harp a _ rofe her voice,

Continued.

mix'd with the Harp a _ rofe her Voice, She
came on my troub _ led foul, Like a beam
on the dark heaving oce _ an when it burfts from a
cloud and bright ens the foamy fide of a
wave; 'twas like the memory of joys that are
paft, plea _ fant and mourn _ full to the foul,
pleafant and mourn _ ful to the foul.

# The Highland Lafsie O.

117
*
Slowifh
Nae gen_tle dames, tho' ne'er fae fair, Shall e_ver
be my mufe's care; Their ti_tles a' are empty fhow; Gie
me my Highland Lafsie, O.
Chorus
With_in the glen fae bufhy,
O A_boon the plain fae rafhy O, I fet me down wi'
right gude will, To fing my Highland Lafsie, O.

O were yon hills and vallies mine;
Yon palace and yon gardens fine!
The world then the love fhould know
I bear my Highland Lafsie, O.
Within the glen &c.

But fickle fortune frowns on me,
And I maun crofs the raging fea;
But while my crimfon currents flow,
I love my Highland Lafsie, O.
Within the glen &c.

Altho' thro foreign climes I range,
I know her heart will never change,
For her bofom burns with honor's glow,
My faithful Highland Lafsie, O.
Within the glen &c.

For her I'll dare the billow's roar;
For her I'll trace a diftant fhore;
That Indian wealth may luftre throw
Around my Highland Lafsie, O.
Within the glen &c.

She has my heart, fhe has my hand,
By fecret truth and honor's band!
Till the mortal ftroke fhall lay me low,
I'm thine, my Highland Lafsie, O.
Farewel, the glen fae bufhy, O!
Farewel, the plain fae rafhy, O!
To other lands I now muft go
To fing my Highland Lafsie, O!

## The Northern Lafs.

Written for this Work by Robert Burns.

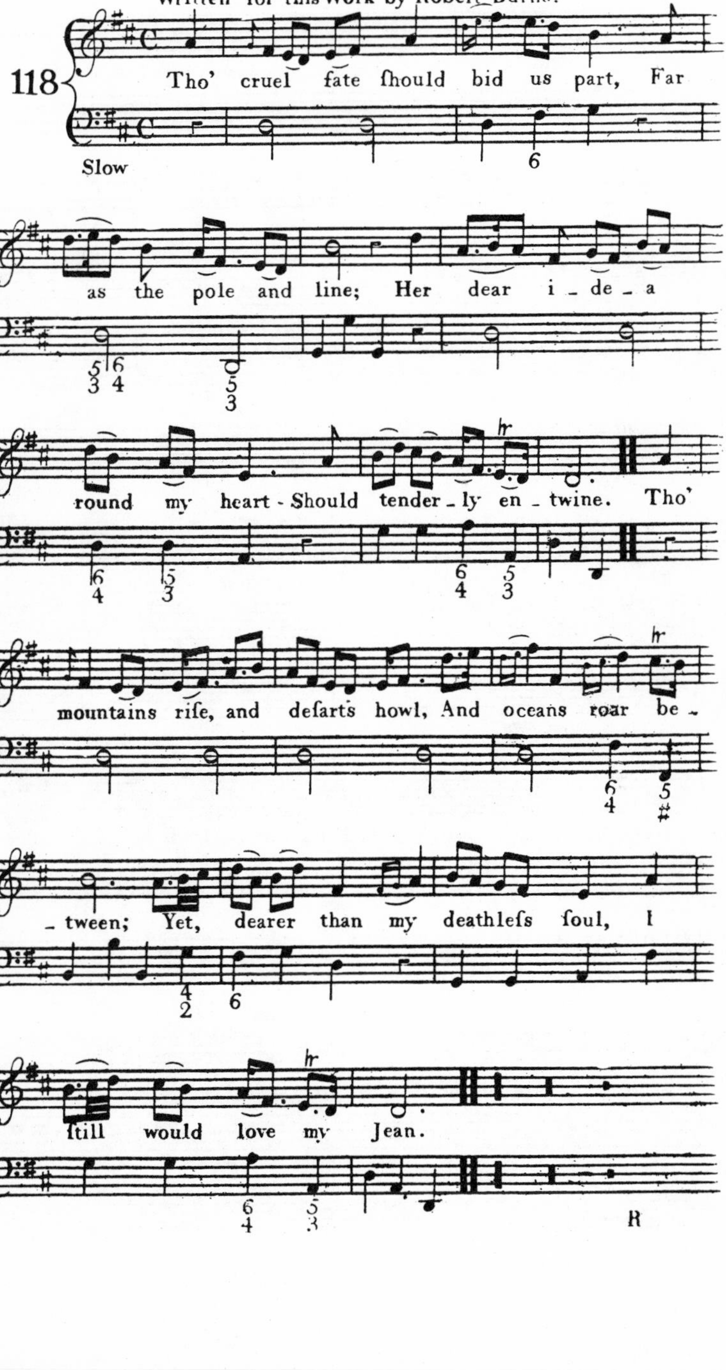

118
Slow
Tho' cruel fate fhould bid us part, Far as the pole and line; Her dear i_de_a round my heart-Should tender_ly en_twine. Tho' mountains rife, and defarts howl, And oceans roar be_tween; Yet, dearer than my deathlefs foul, I ftill would love my Jean.
R

## Song of Selma.

119

Plaintive
It is night. I am a_lone, for_lorn on the hill of
Storms. The Wind is heard in the Mountain, the Tor_rent
Shricks down the Rocks, no Hut receives me from the Rain; for_
_lorn on the Hill of Winds. Rife, Moon, from be hind thy
Clouds: Stars of the Night, ap_pear! Lend me Light to the

Continued.

Place where my Love Refts from the Toil of the chace; His
Bow near him un_ftrung, His Dogs Panting a_round him. But
here I muft fit a lone, by the Rock of the mof_sy
Stream; the ftream and the wind Roar, nor can I Hear the
voice of my Love, the voice of my Love.

# Fife and a' the lands about it.

120

Allan by his grief ex_cit_ed, Long the vic_tim
Slowish
of despair, Thus de_plor'd his passion slighted, Thus ad_
dress'd the scornful fair. Fife and all the lands a_
_bout it, Undesir_ing I _can see; Joy may crown my
days without it, Not, my charmer, with_out thee.

Must I then forever languish,
  Still complaining still endure;
Can her form create an anguish,
  Which her soul disdains to cure!
Why by hopeless passion fated,
  Must I still those eyes admire;
Whilst unheeded, unregretted,
  In her presence I expire!

Would thy charms improve their power,
  Timely think, relentless maid;
Beauty is, a short liv'd flower,
  Destined but to bloom and fade!

Let that heaven, whose kind impression
  All thy lovely features shew,
Melt thy soul to soft compassion
  For a suff'ring lover's woe.

See my colour quickly fading
  To a sad portentous pale:
See cold death thy scorn upbraiding,
  O'er my vital frame prevail.
Vain alas! expostulation,
  'Tis not thine her love to gain;
But with silent resignation
  Bid adieu to life and pain! D

## Were na my Heart light I wad die

121

There was ance a May, and ſhe loe'd na men; She
Slowiſh
biggit her bonny bow'r down in yon glen; But now ſhe cries dool & a
well-a-day. Come down the green gate, and come here a way.

When bonny young Johny cam o'er the ſea,
He ſaid he ſaw naething ſae lovely as me;
He hecht me baith rings and mony bra things:
And were na my heart light I wad die.
He had a wee titty that loed na me,
Becauſe I was twice as bonny as ſhe;
She rais'd ſick a pother 'twixt him and his mother,
That were na my heart light I wad die.
The day it was ſet, and the bridal to be,
The wife took a dwam, and lay down to die;
She main'd and ſhe grain'd out of dolour and pain,
Till he vow'd he never wad ſee me again.
His kin was for ane of a higher degree,
Said, What had he to do with the like of me!
Albeit I was bonny, I was na for Johny:
And were na my heart light I wad die.
They ſaid I had neither cow nor cauf,
Nor dribbles of drink rins thro' the draff,
Nor pickles of meal rins thro' the mill ee:
And were na my heart light I wad die.
His titty ſhe was baith wylie and ſlee,
She ſpy'd me as I came o'er the lee;
And then ſhe ran in and made a loud din,
Believe your ain een, an ye trow na me.
His bonnet ſtood ay fu' round on his brow;
His auld ane looks ay as well as ſome's new:
But now he lets't wear ony gate it will hing,
And caſts himſelf dowie upo' the corn bing.
And now he gaes drooping about the dykes,
And a' he dow do is to hund the tykes:
The live-lang night he ne'er ſteeks his eye,
And were na my heart light I wad die.
Were I young for thee, as I hae been,
We ſhou'd hae been galloping down on yon green,
And linking it on the lily-white lee;
And wow gin I were but young for thee.

## The Yellow-hair'd Laddie.

122

In April when primroſes paint the ſweet plain, And
Slowiſh
ſum_mer ap_proach_ing re_joic_eth the ſwain,
1st
joic_eth the ſwain. The yel_low_hair'd laddie wou'd
2d
of_ _ten_times go, To wilds and deep glens, where the
1st
2d
haw_thorn trees grow, haw_thorn trees grow.

There under the ſhade of an old ſacred thorn.
With freedom he ſung his loves ev'ning and morn;
He ſang with ſo ſaft and enchanting a ſound,
That ſilvans and fairies unſeen danc'd around.

The ſhepherd thus ſung, Tho' young Mary be fair,
Her beauty is daſh'd with a ſcornfu' proud air;
But Suſie was handſome, and ſweetly could ſing,
Her breath like the breezes perfum'd in the ſpring.

That Maddie, in all the gay bloom of her youth,
Like the moon was inconſtant, and never ſpoke truth;
But Suſie was faithful, good humour'd, and free,
And fair as the goddeſs who ſprung from the ſea.

That mamma's fine daughter, with all her great dow'r,
Was aukwardly airy, and frequently ſour;
Then ſighing he wiſhed, would parents agree,
The witty ſweet Suſie his miſtreſs might be.

## To the foregoing Tune.

Peggy WHEN firſt my dear laddie gade to the green hill,
And I at ewe-milking firſt ſey'd my young ſkill,
To bear the milk bowie nae pain was to me,
When I at the bughting forgather'd with thee.

Patie When corn-rigs wav'd yellow, and blue hether bells
Bloom'd bonny on moorland and ſweet riſing fells,
Nae birns, briers, or brechens gae trouble to me,
If I found the berries right ripen'd for thee.

Peggy When thou ran, or wreſtled, or putted the ſtane,
And came aff the victor, my heart was ay fain:
Thy ilka ſport manly gae pleaſure to me;
For nane can putt, wreſtle, or run ſwift as thee.

Patie Our Jenny ſings ſaftly the Cowden broom knows,
And Roſie lilts ſweetly the milking the ewes;
There's few Jenny Nettles like Nanſy can ſing,
At hro' the Wood,Laddie, Beſs gars our lugs ring;
But when my dear Peggy ſings, with better ſkill,
The Boatman, Tweedſide, or the Laſs of the Mill,
'Tis mony times ſweeter and pleaſant to me;
For tho' they ſing nicely, they cannot like thee.

Peggy How eaſy can laſſes trow what they deſire!
And praiſes ſae kindly increaſes Love's fire:
Give me ſtill this pleaſure, my ſtudy ſhall be,
To make myſelf better and ſweeter for thee.

## The auld Yellow-hair'd Laddie.

THE yellow-hair'd laddie ſat on yon burn brae,
Cries, milk the ewes laſſie, let nane of them gae;
And ay ſhe milked, and ay ſhe ſang,
The yellow-hair'd laddie ſhall be my goodman.
And ay ſhe milked, &c.

The weather is cauld, and my claithing is thin,
The ewes are new clipped they winna bught in,
They winna bught in, tho' I ſhou'd die,
O yellow-hair'd laddie, be kind to me.
They winna bught in, &c.

The good wife cries butt the houſe, Jenny come ben:
The cheeſe is to mak, and the butter to kirn:
Tho' butter, and cheeſe, and a' ſhou'd ſour,
I'll crack and kiſs wi my love ae ha'f hour;
It's ae ha'f hour, and we's e'en make it three,
For the yellow-hair'd laddie my huſband ſhall be.

# The Miller.

123

O Merry may the maid be That marries with the mil_
_ler, For foul day and fair day He's ay bringing till her. Has
ay a penny in his purſe, For dinner and for ſup_ per; And
gin he pleaſe, a good fat cheeſe, And lumps of yellow butter.
Slowiſh

When Jamie firſt did woo me,
  I ſpeir'd what was his calling;
Fair maid ſays he, O come and ſee,
  Ye're welcome to my dwalling:
Though I was ſhy, yet I cou'd ſpy
  The truth of what he told me.
And that his houſe was warm and couth,
  And room in it to hold me.

Behind the door a bag of meal,
  And in the kiſt was plenty,
Of good hard cakes his mither bakes,
  And bannocks were na ſcanty;
A good fat ſow, a ſleeky cow
  Was ſtandin in the byre,
Whilſt lazy pouſs with mealy mouſe
  Was playing at the fire

Good ſigns are theſe, my mither ſays,
  And bids me tak the miller;
For foul day and fair day
  He's ay bringing till her;
For meal and malt ſhe does na want,
  Nor ony thing that's dainty;
And now and then a keckling hen
  To lay her eggs in plenty.

In winter when the wind and rain
  Blaws o'er the houſe and byre,
He ſits beſide a clean hearth ſtane
  Before a rouſing fire;
With nut-brown ale he tells his tale
  Which rows him o'er fou nappy
Who'd be a king a petty thing,
  When a miller lives ſo happy.

## Wap at the Widow, my Laddie.

124
Lively
The widow can bake, the widow can brew, The widow can ſhape
and the widow can ſew, And mony braw things the widow can do, Then
wap at the widow, my laddie. With courage attack her baith early and
late, To kiſs her and clap her ye manna be blate; Speak well and do
better; for that's the beſt gate, To win a young widow, my laddie.

The widow ſhe's youthfu', and never ae hair
The waur of the wearing, and has a good ſkair
Of every thing lovely; ſhe's witty and fair,
And has a rich jointure, my laddie.
What cou'd you wiſh better your pleaſure to crown,
Than a widow, the bonnieſt toaſt in the town,
Wi' naething but draw in your ſtool and ſit down,
And ſport wi' the widow, my laddie.

Then till 'er and kill 'er wi' courteſie dead,
Tho' ſtark love and kindneſs be a' ye can plead;
Be heartſome and airy, and hope to ſucceed
Wi' a bonny gay widow, my laddie.
Strike iron while 'tis het, if ye'd have it to wald,
For Fortune ay favours the active and bauld,
But ruins the wooer that's thowleſs and cauld,
Unfit for the widow, my laddie.

## Braw, braw lads of Galla-water.

125

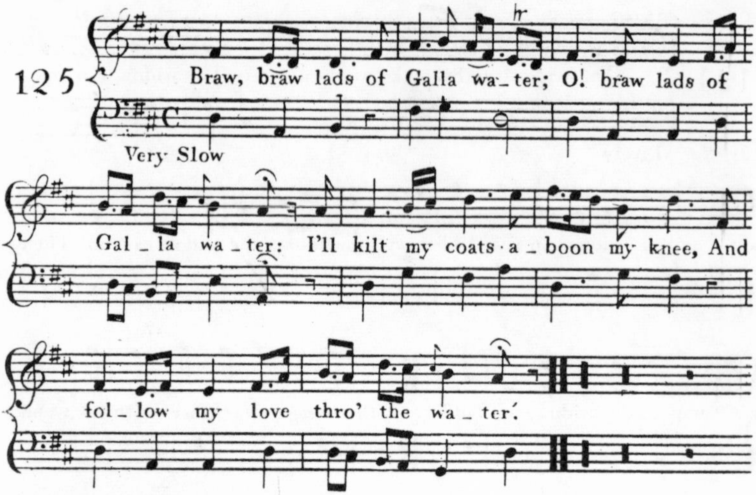
Braw, braw lads of Galla wa_ter; O! braw lads of
Very Slow
Gal_la wa_ter: I'll kilt my coats a_boon my knee, And
fol_low my love thro' the wa_ter.

Sae fair her hair, ſae brent her brow,
 Sae bonny blue her een, my dearie;
Sae white her teeth, ſae ſweet her mou',
 The mair I kiſs, ſhe's ay my dearie.

O'er yon bank, and o'er yon brae,
 O'er yon moſs amang the heather;
I'll kilt my coat aboon my knee,
 And follow my love thro' the water.

Down amang the broom, the broom,
 Down amang the broom, my dearie.
The laſſie loſt a ſilken ſnood,
 That coſt her mony a blirt and bleary.

### Same Tune.

NO repoſe can I diſcover
 Nor find joy without my lover;
Can I ſtay when ſhe's not near me;
 Cruel fates, once deign to hear me.

The charms of grandeur don't decoy me,
 Fair Eliza muſt enjoy me;
My crown and ſceptre I reſign,
 The ſhepherd's life ſhall ſtill be mine.

## The Young Man's Dream.

126

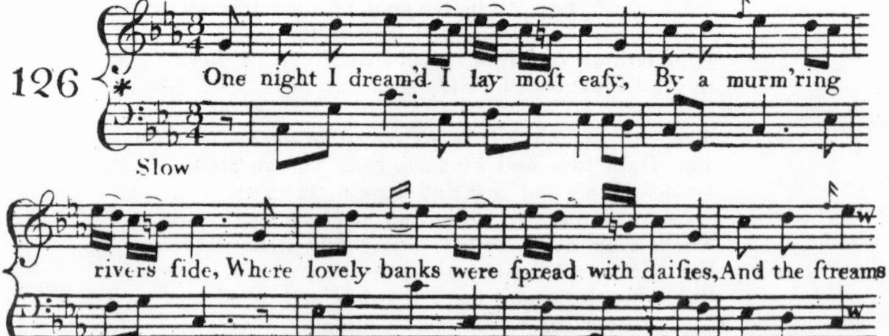
One night I dream'd I lay moſt eaſy, By a murm'ring
Slow
rivers ſide, Where lovely banks were ſpread with daiſies, And the ſtreams

## Continued.

did ſmoothly glide, While all around me and quite o_ver, Spreading

branches were diſplay'd, All in_ter_wov_en in due or_der

Soon became a pleaſant ſhade.

2

I ſaw my laſs come in moſt charming
  With a look and air ſo ſweet;
Ee'ry grace was moſt alarming
  Every beauty quite complete.
Cupid with his bow attended;
  Lovely Venus too was there;
As his bow young Cupid bended,
  Far away flew carking care.

3

On a bank of roſes ſeated,
  Charmingly my true love ſung;
While glad echo ſtill repeated
  And the hills and vallies rung:
At the laſt, by ſleep oppreſsed,
  On the bank my love did ly;
By young Cupid ſtill careſsed,
  While the graces round did fly.

The roſes red, the lily's bloſsom
  With her charms might not compare,
To view her cheeks and heaving boſom,
  Down they droop'd as in deſpair.
On her ſlumber I encroaching,
  Panting came to ſteal a kiſs;
Cupid ſmil'd at me approaching
  Seem'd to ſay,"There's nought amiſs.

With eager wiſhes I drew nigher,
  This fair maiden to embrace;
My breath grew quick, my pulſe beat
  Gazing on her lovely face. (higher,

The nymph awaking quickly check'd m
  Starting up, with angry tone;
"Thus, ſays ſhe do you reſpect me.
  "Leave me quick, and hence begone.
Cupid for me interpoſing,
  To my love did bow full low,
She from him her hands unlooſing,
  In contempt ſtruck down his bow.

Angry Cupid, from her flying,
  Cry'd out as he ſought the ſkies,
"Haughty nymphs their love denying,
  "Cupid ever ſhall deſpiſe."
As he ſpoke, old Care came wand'ring.
  With him ſtalk'd deſtructive Time:
Winter froze the ſtreams meand'ring,
  Nipt the Roſes in their prime.

Spectres then my love ſurrounded,
  At their back march'd chilling Death.
Whilſt ſhe, frighted and confounded,
  Felt their blaſting,pois'nous breath:
As her charms were ſwift decaying,.
  And the furrows ſeiz'd her cheek;
Forbear ye fiends! I vainly crying,
  Wak'd in the attempt to ſpeak.

T

## Same Tune.

O Molly Molly, my dear honey,
  Come and ſit thee down by me,
And tell to me what is the reaſon
  That I ſo ſlighted am by thee.
For if I ſpeak, you ſay I flatter,
  And if I ſpeak not how ſhall I ſpeed.
And if I chance to write a letter,
  Your anſwer is, I cannot read.

## O Mither dear.

Tune, Jenny dang the weaver.

127

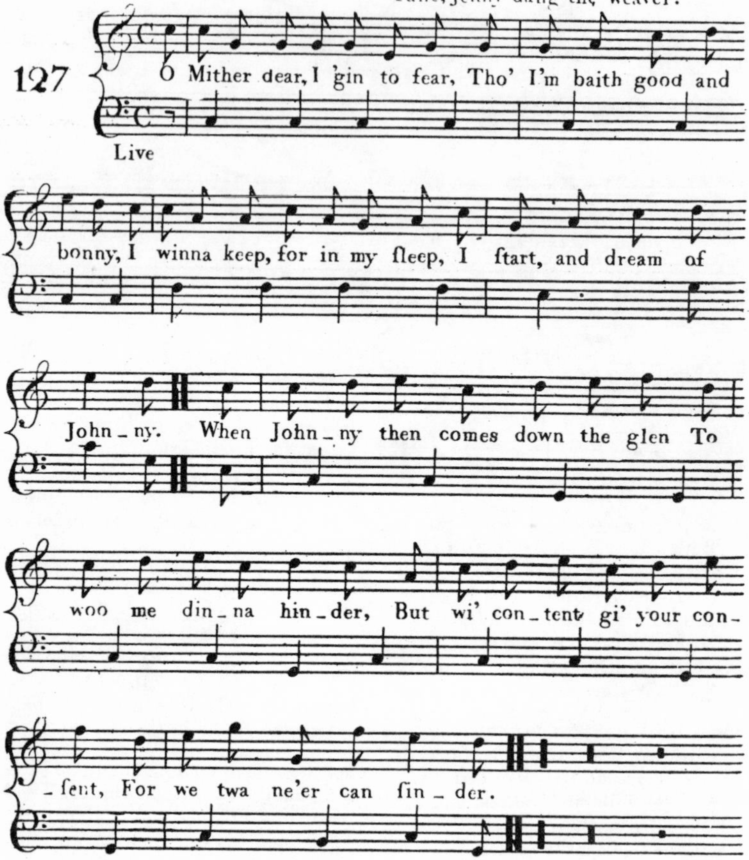
O Mither dear, I gin to fear, Tho' I'm baith good and
Live
bonny, I winna keep, for in my ſleep, I ſtart, and dream of
John_ny. When John_ny then comes down the glen To
woo me din_na hin_der, But wi' con_tent gi' your con-
_ſent, For we twa ne'er can ſin_der.

Better to marry, than miſcarry;
 For ſhame and ſkaith's the clink o't;
To thole the dool, to mount the ſtool,
 I downa bide to think o't;
Sae while tis time, I'll ſhun the crime,
 That gars poor Epps gae whingeing,
With haunches fow, and een ſae blew,
 To all the bedrals bingeing.

Had Eppy's apron bidden down,
 The kirk had ne'er a kend it;
But when the word's gane thro' the town,
 Alake, how can ſhe mend it!

Now Tam maun face the miniſter,
 And ſhe maun mount the pillar:
And that's the way that they maun gae,
 For poor folk hae nae ſiller.

Now had ye'r tongue, my doughter young,
 Replied the kindly mither,
Get Johnny's hand in haly band,
 Syne wap your wealth together.
I'm o' the mind, if he be kind,
 Ye'll do your part diſcreetly;
And prove a wife will gar his life,
 And thine go on right ſweetly.

## Befsy Bell, and Mary Gray.

128

O Befsy Bell, and Mary Gray, They are twa bon_ny
Lively
lafs_es; They bigg'd a bower on yon burn brae, And
theek'd it o'er with rafh_es. Fair Bef_sy Bell I
loo'd yeftreen, And thought I ne'er cou'd al_ter; But
Mary Gray's twa pawky een, Gard a' my fan_cy fal_ter.

Now Befsy's hair's like a lint tap,
 She fmiles like a May morning,
When Phæbus ftarts frae Thetis' lap,
 The hills with rays adorning.
White is her neck, foft is her hand,
 Her waift and feet fu' genty;
With ilka grace fhe can command
 Her lips; O wow! they're dainty.

And Mary's locks are like a craw,
 Her een like diamonds glances;
She's ay fae clean, redd up, and braw,
 She kills when e'er fhe dances;
Blyth as a kid, with wit at will,
 She blooming, tight, and tall is;
And guides her airs fae gracefu' ftill,
 O Jove! fhe's like thy Pallas.

Dear Befsy Bell, and Mary Gray,
 Ye unco fair opprefs us,
Our fancies jee between ye twa,
 Ye are fic bonny lafses.
Wae's me! for baith I canna get,
 To ane by law we're ftented,
Then I'll draw cuts, and tak my fate,
 And be with ane contented.

## Stay, my Charmer, can you leave me.

Written for this Work by R.Burns. Tune, An Gille dubh ciar dhubh.

129

* Stay, my charmer, can you leave me? Cruel, cruel to de_
Slow
ceive me! Well you know how much you grieve me: Cruel charmer, can you

go. Cruel charmer, can you go!

By my love so ill requited;
By the faith you fondly plighted;
By the pangs of lovers slighted:
Do not, do not leave me so!
Do not, do not leave me so!

B

## Lady Bothwell's Lament.

130

Balow, my boy, ly still and sleep; It grieves me
Very Slow
fore to hear thee weep: If thou'lt be silent, I'll be glad; Thy
mourning makes my heart full sad. Ba_low, my boy, thy
mother's joy, Thy father bred me great annoy. Balow ba_low, ba_

Continued.

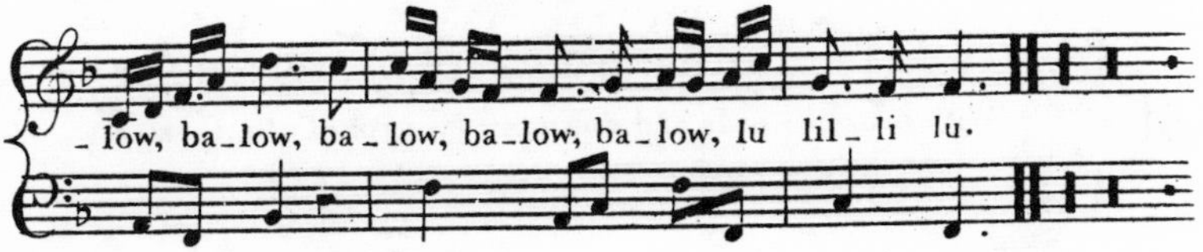
_low, ba_low, ba_low, ba_low, ba_low, lu lil_li lu.

Balow, my darling, ſleep a while,
And when thou wak'ſt then ſweetly ſmile;
But ſmile not as thy father did,
To cozen maids, nay, God forbid;
For in thine eye his look I ſee,
The tempting look that ruin'd me.
Balow, balow, &c.

When he began to court my love,
And with his ſugar'd words to move,
His tempting face, and flatt'ring chear,
In time to me did not appear;
But now I ſee that cruel he
Cares neither for his babe nor me.
Balow, balow, &c.

Fareweel, fareweel, thou falſeſt youth
That ever kiſs'd a woman's mouth;
Let never any after me
Submit unto thy courteſy:
For if they do, O! cruel thou
Wilt her abuſe, and care not how.
Balow, balow, &c.

I was too cred'lous at the firſt,
To yield thee all a maiden durſt;
Thou ſwore for ever true to prove,
Thy faith unchang'd, unchang'd thy love;
But, quick as thought, the change is wrought,
Thy love nae mair, thy promiſe nought.
Balow, balow, &c.

O gin I were a maid again,
From young mens flatt'ry I'd refrain,
For now unto my grief I find
They all are perjur'd and unkind;
Bewitching charms bred all my harms:
Witneſs my babe lyes in my arms.
Balow, balow, &c.

I tak my fate from bad to worſe,
That I muſt needs be now a nurſe,
And lull my young ſon on my lap:
From me, ſweet orphan, tak the pap:
Balow, my child, thy mother mild
Shall wail as from all bliſs exil'd.
Balow, balow &c.

Balow, my boy, weep not for me,
Whoſe greateſt grief's for wranging thee
Nor pity her deſerved ſmart,
Who can blame none but her fond heart
For, too ſoon truſting lateſt finds,
With faireſt tongues are falſeſt minds
Balow, balow, &c.

Balow, my boy, thy father's fled,
When he the thriftleſs ſon hath play'd.
Of vows and oaths forgetful, he
Preferr'd the wars to thee and me.
But now perhaps, thy curſe and mine
Make him eat acorns with the ſwine.
Balow, balow, &c.

But curſe not him; perhaps now he,
Stung with remorſe, is bleſsing thee.
Perhaps at death; for who can tell,
Whether the Judge of heaven & hell,
By ſome proud foe, has ſtruck the blow
And laid the dear deceiver low.
Balow, balow, &c.

I wiſh I were into the bounds
Where he lyes ſmother'd in his wounds
Repeating, as he pants for air,
My name, whom once he call'd his fair
No woman's yet ſo fiercely ſet,
But ſhe'll forgive, though not forget.
Balow, balow, &c.

If linen lacks, for my love's ſake,
Then quickly to him would I make
My ſmock once for his body meet,
And wrap him in that winding-ſheet
Ah me! how happy had I been,
If he had ne'er been wrapt therein.
Balow, balow, &c.

Balow, my boy, I'll weep for thee:
Too ſoon, alake, thou'lt weep for me:
Thy griefs are growing to a ſum;
God grant thee patience when they come
Born to ſuſtain thy mother's ſhame
A hapleſs fate, a baſtard's name.
Balow, balow, &c

## Woes my heart that we ſhou'd ſunder.

131

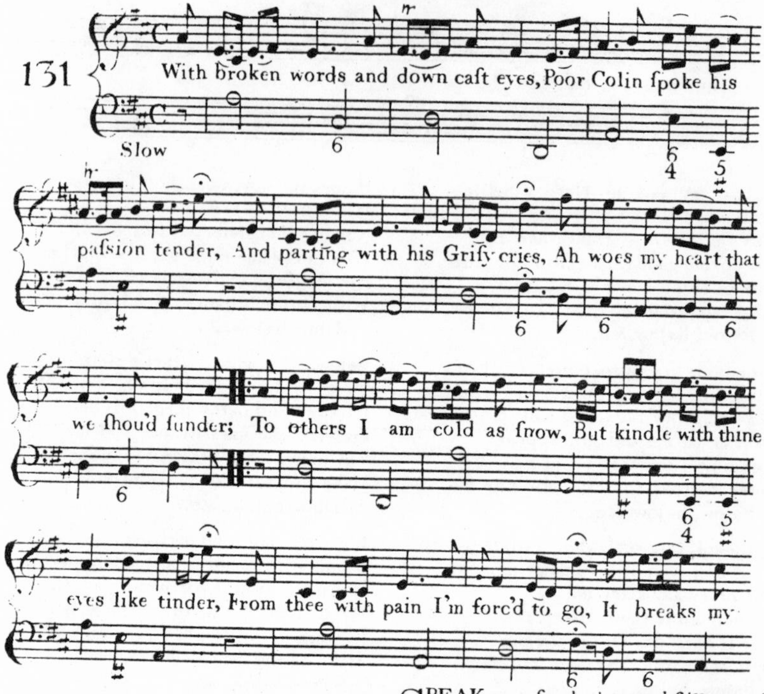
With broken words and down caſt eyes, Poor Colin ſpoke his
Slow
paſsion tender, And parting with his Griſy cries, Ah woes my heart that
we ſhou'd ſunder; To others I am cold as ſnow, But kindle with thine
eyes like tinder, From thee with pain I'm forc'd to go, It breaks my

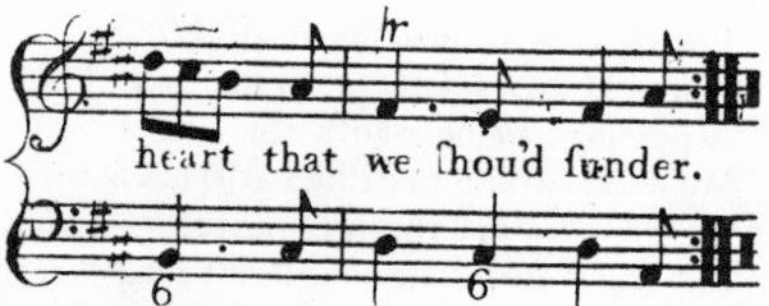
heart that we ſhou'd ſunder.

Chain'd to thy charms, I cannot range,
No beauty new my love ſhall hinder,
Nor time, nor place, ſhall ever change
My vows, tho' we're oblig'd to ſunder.
The image of thy graceful air,
And beauties which invite our wonder,
Thy lively wit, and prudence rare,
Shall ſtill be preſent, tho' we ſunder.

Dear nymph, believe thy ſwain in this,
You'll ne'er engage a heart that's kinder,
Then ſeal a promiſe with a kiſs,
Always to love me, tho' we ſunder.
Ye powers, take care of my dear laſs,
That as I leave her I may find her.
When that bleſs'd time ſhall come to paſs,
We'll meet again, and never ſunder.

SPEAK on, - ſpeak thus, and ſtill my grief,
Hold up a heart that's ſinking under
Theſe fears, that ſoon will want relief;
When Pate muſt from his Peggy ſunder.
A gentler face, and ſilk attire,
A lady rich in beauty's bloſsom,
Alake poor me! will now conſpire
To ſteal thee from thy Peggy's boſom,
No more the ſhepherd, who excell'd
The reſt, whoſe wit made them to wonder,
Shall now his Peggy's praiſes tell,
Ah! I can die, but never ſunder.
Ye meadows where we often ſtray'd,
Ye banks where we were wont to wander,
Sweet-ſcented rocks round which we play'd,
You'll loſe your ſweets when we're aſunder.
Again, ah! ſhall I never creep
Around the know with ſilent duty,
Kindly to watch thee, while aſleep,
And wonder at thy manly beauty.
Hear, heaven, while ſolemnly I vow,
Tho' thou ſhouldſt prove a wandring lover,
Thro' life to thee I ſhall prove true,
Nor be a wife to any other.

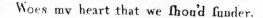

## Strathallan's Lament.

Written for this Work by Robert Burns.

132
Plaintive
Thick_est night, fur_round my dwelling! Howling
tempefts, o'er me rave! Turbid tor_rents, wintry fwel_ling,
Roaring by my lone_ly cave. Chryftal ftream_lets gen_tly
flowing, Bu_fy haunts of bafe mankind, Weftern breezes foftly
blow_ing, Suit not my dif_tracted mind.

In the caufe of Right engaged,
  Wrongs injurious to redress.
Honor's war we ftrongly waged,
  But the heavens deny'd fuccefs:
Ruin's wheel has driven o'er us,
  Not a hope that dare attend,
The wide world is all before us
  But a world without a friend!

## What will I do gin my Hoggie die.

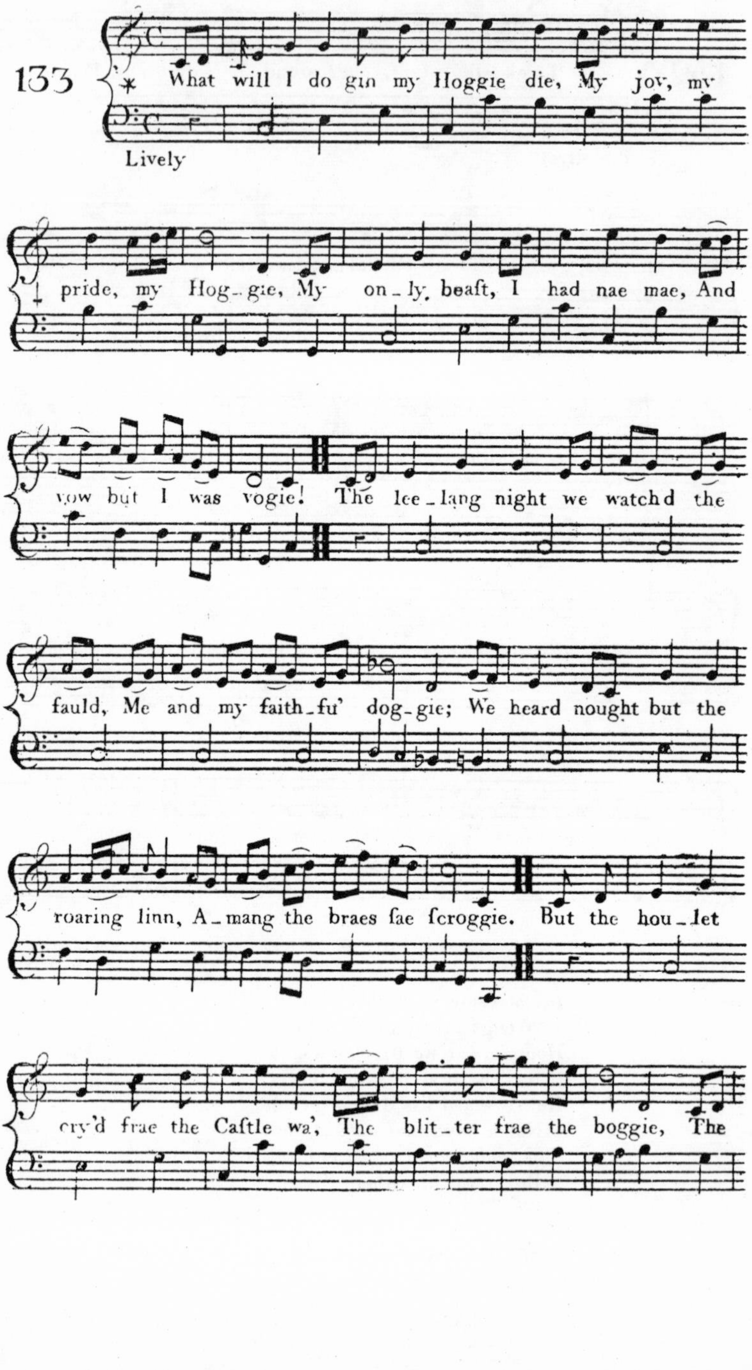
133
Lively
What will I do gin my Hoggie die, My joy, my pride, my Hog_gie, My only beaſt, I had nae mae, And vow but I was vogie! The lee_lang night we watchd the fauld, Me and my faith_fu' dog_gie; We heard nought but the roaring linn, A_mang the braes ſae ſcroggie. But the hou_let cry'd frae the Caſtle wa', The blit_ter frae the boggie, The

Continued

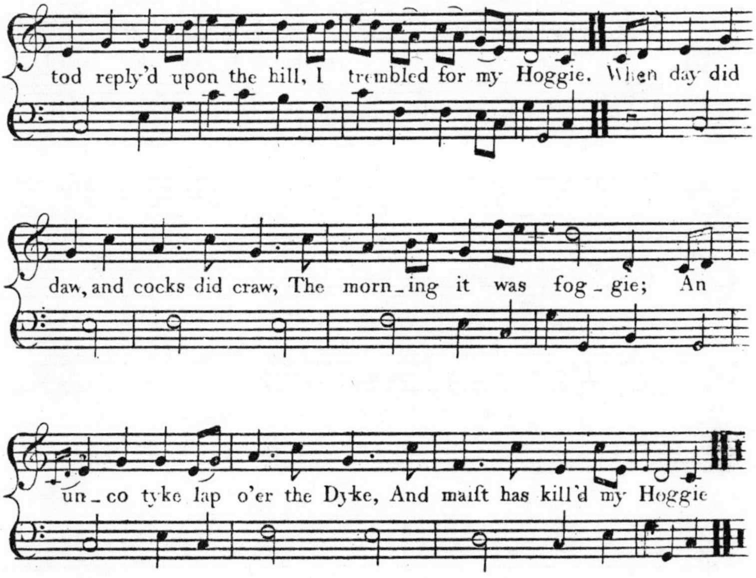
tod reply'd upon the hill, I trembled for my Hoggie. When day did
daw, and cocks did craw, The morn_ing it was fog_gie; An
un_co tyke lap o'er the Dyke, And maiſt has kill'd my Hoggie

## To the Foregoing Tune.

What words, dear Nancy, will prevail,
What tender accents move thee.
How ſhall I ſpeak the ſoft detail,
And ſhew how much I love thee!
The pains my ſoul is doom'd to bear,
Are far beyond expreſsion;
No riſing ſigh, nor falling tear
Can half reveal my paſsion.

Yet when the boſom rack'd with pain
It's latent woe diſcloſes,
'Tis nature's tribute to complain,
And ſorrow's ſelf repoſes.
Deluſive reſt! for grief and ſhame,
Unpitying ſhould'st thou hear me,
Shall reinforce the cruel flame,
The inceſsant pangs that tear me.

In apathy to ſpend my days,
I oft have wiſh'd with ardor,
Tho' hard thy image to eraze,
To bear it ſtill ſeem'd harder;
But vain my wiſhes, vain my toils,
Loſt freedom to recover;
From the harſh taſk my ſoul recoils.
A ſelf devoted lover.

You ſee by what degrees I pine,
Whilſt every look implores you,
While calmly you to fate reſign
The youth whoſe ſoul adores you.
Yet come it will the deſtin'd hour
When Death my ſoul ſhall ſever,
And love and beauty loſe their power
To torture me for ever.

## The Carle he came o'er the Craft.

134

Lively
The carle he came o'er the craft, And his beard new ſhaven, Glowr'd at me as he'd been daft, The carle trows that I'll hae him. Howt a_wa, I win_na hae him, No forſooth, I'll no hae him, New hoſe and new ſhoon And his beard new ſhav_en.


A ſiller broach he gae me nieſt,
  To faſten on my curchie nooked,
I wort awee upon my breaſt;
  But ſoon, alake! the tongue o't crook(ed;
And ſae may his; I winna hae him,
  Na, forſooth, I winna hae him,
Ane twice a bairn's a laſs's jeſt;
  Sae ony fool for me may hae him.

The carl has nae fault but ane,
  For he has lands and dollars plenty;
But wae's me for him! ſkin and bane
  Is no for a plump laſs of twenty.
Howt awa, I winna hae him,
  Na, forſooth, I winna hae him!
What ſignifies his dirty riggs,
  And caſh, without a man wi' them.

But ſhou'd my canker'd dady gar
  Me tak him 'gainſt my inclination,
I warn the fumbler to beware,
  That antlers dinna claim their ſtation.
Howt awa, I winna hae him!
  Na, forſooth, I winna hae him!
I'm fleed to crack the haly band,
  Sae lawty ſays, I ſhou'd nae hae him.

## Gae to the ky wi' me, Johnny.

135
Lively
O Gae to the ky wi' me, Johnny, Gae to the ky wi' me O
Gae to the ky wi' me, Johnny, And I'll be merry wi' thee. And
Was ſhe na wordy of kiſſes, And was ſhe na wordy of three, And
Chorus
was ſhe na wordy of kiſſes, That gaed to the ky wi' me O
Gae to the ky wi' me, Johnny, Gae to the ky wi' me; O
Gae to the ky wi' me, Johnny, And I'll be merry wi' thee

I hae a houſe a higgin,
Anither that's like to fa',
I have a laſſie wi' bairn,
Which grieves me warſt of a',
Gae to the ky, &c.

But if ſhe be wi' bairn,
As I trow weel ſhe be,
I have an auld mither at hame
Will doudle it on her knee.
Gae to the ky, &c.

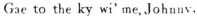

# Why hangs that cloud.

Tune, Hallow ev'n.

136

Why hangs that cloud u_pon thy brow, That beauteous
Slowish
heav'n e're while ferene! Whence do thefe ftorms and tempefts flow, Or
what this guft of pafsion mean? And muft then man_kind
lofe that light, Which in thine eyes was wont to fhine, And ly ob_
fcur'd in endlefs night, For each poor fil_ly fpeech of mine?

Dear child, how can I wrong thy name,
Since 'tis acknowledg'd at all hands,
That could ill tongues abufe thy fame,
Thy beauty can make large amends?
Or if I durft prophanely try,
Thy beauty's pow'rful charms t'upbraid,
Thy virtue well might give the lie,
Nor call thy beauty to its aid.

For Venus, every heart t' enfnare,
With all her charms has deck'd thy face,
And Pallas with unufual care,
Bids wifdom heighten every grace.
Who can the double pain endure;
Or who muft not refign the field
To thee, celeftial maid, fecure
With Cupid's bow, and Pallas' fhield?

If then to thee fuch pow'r is given,
Let not a wretch in torment live:
But fmile, and learn to copy heaven,
Since we muft fin ere it forgive.
Yet pitying Heaven not only does
Forgive th' offender and th' offence,
But even itfelf appeas'd beftows,
As the reward of penitence.

## Willy was a wanton wag.

137

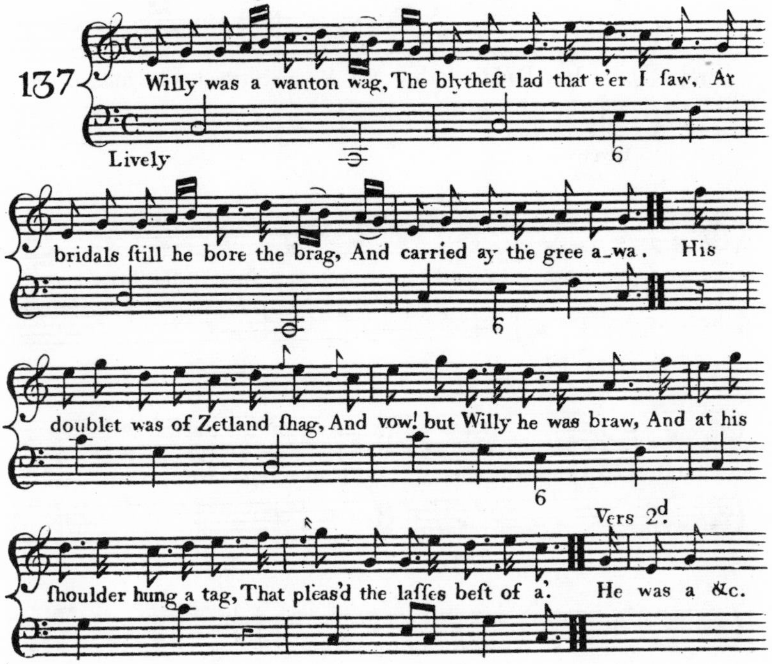
Willy was a wanton wag, The blytheſt lad that e'er I ſaw, At
Lively
6
bridals ſtill he bore the brag, And carried ay the gree a_wa. His
6
doublet was of Zetland ſhag, And vow! but Willy he was braw, And at his
6
Vers 2d.
ſhoulder hung a tag, That pleas'd the laſſes beſt of a'. He was a &c.

He was a man without a clag,
His heart was frank without a flaw;
And ay whatever Willy ſaid,
It was ſtill hadden as a law.
His boots they were made of the jag,
When he went to the weapon-ſhaw;
Upon the green nane durſt him brag,
The fiend a ane amang them a'.

And was not Willy well worth gowd?
He wan the love of great and ſma';
For after he the bride had kiſs'd,
He kiſs'd the laſſes hale-ſale a'.
Sae merrily round the ring they row'd,
When by the hand he led them a',
And ſmack on ſmack on them beſtow'd,
By virtue of a ſtanding law.

And was na Willy a great lown,
As ſhyre a lick as e'er was ſeen,
When he danc'd with the laſſes round,
The bridegroom ſpeer'd where he had been )

Quoth Willy, I've been at the ring,
With bobbing, faith, my ſhanks are fair.
Gae ca' your bride and maidens in,
For Willy he dow do nae mair.

Then reſt ye, Willy, I'll gae out,
And for a wee fill up the ring;
But ſhame light on his ſouple ſnout,
He wanted Willy's wanton fling.
Then ſtraight he to the bride did fare,
Says, Well's me on your bonny face;
With bobbing, Willy's ſhanks are fair,
And I'm come out to fill his place.

Bridegroom, ſhe ſays, you'll ſpoil the dance,
And at the ring you'll ay be lag,
Unleſs like Willy ye advance;
(O! Willy has a wanton leg:)
For wi't he learns us a' to ſteer,
And formaſt ay bears up the ring:
We will find nae ſic dancing here,
If we want Willy's wanton fling.

## Jumpin John.

138

Her Daddie forbad, her Minnie forbad, For_bidden ſhe
Lively
wad_na be: She wad_na trow't, the browſt ſhe brew'd Wad
Chorus
taſte ſae bit_ter_lie. The lang lad they ca'
jumpin John Be_guil'd the bonie laſs_ie, The lang lad they ca'
jumping John Be_guil'd the bonie laſs_ie.

A cow and a cauf, a yowe and a hauf,
And thretty gude ſhillins and three;
A vera gude tocher, a cotter-man's dochter,
The laſs wi' the bonie black e'e.
The lang lad &c.

## Hap me wi' thy Petticoat.

139

O Bell, thy looks have kill'd my heart, I paſs the day in
Slowiſh
pain, When night returns, I feel the ſmart And wiſh for thee in vain;
I'm ſtarving cold whilſt thou art warm, Have pi_ty and in_cline, And
grant me for a hap that Charming pet_ti_coat of thine.

My raviſh'd fancy in amaze
Still wanders o'er thy charms,
Deluſive dreams ten thouſand ways
Preſent thee to my arms.
But waking think what I endure,
While cruel you decline
Thoſe pleaſures, which alone can cure
This panting breaſt of mine.

I faint, I fail, I wildly rove,
Becauſe you ſtill deny
The juſt reward that's due to love,
And let true paſſion die.

Oh! turn, and let compaſſion ſeize
That lovely breaſt of thine;
Thy petticoat could give me eaſe,
If thou and it were mine.

Sure, Heaven has fitted for delight
That beauteous form of thine,
And thour't too good its law to ſlight,
By hind'ring the deſign.
May all the powers of love agree,
At length to make thee mine;
Or looſe my chains, and ſet me free
From ev'ry charm of thine.

## Up in the Morning Early.

140

Lively
Cauld blaws the wind frae eaſt to weſt, The drift is driving
fairly; Sae loud and ſhill's I hear the blaſt, I'm ſure its win_ter
fairly. Up in the morning's no for me, Up in the morning early; When
a' the hills are cover'd wi' ſnaw, I'm ſure it is winter fair_ly.

The birds ſit chittering in the thorn,
A. day they fare but ſparely;
And lang's the night frae e'en to morn,
I'm ſure it's winter fairly.
Up in the morning's, &c.

Z

## 141 The Tears of Scotland.

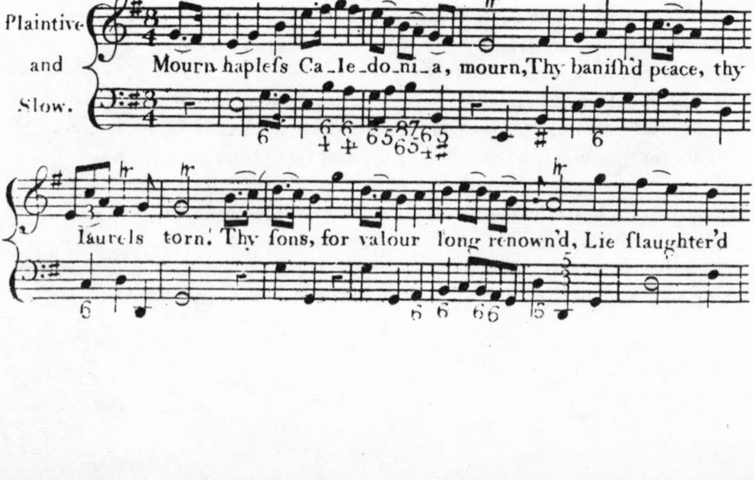
Plaintive and Slow.
Mourn hapleſs Ca_le_do_ni_a, mourn, Thy baniſh'd peace, thy
laurels torn! Thy ſons, for valour long renown'd, Lie ſlaughter'd

## Continued.

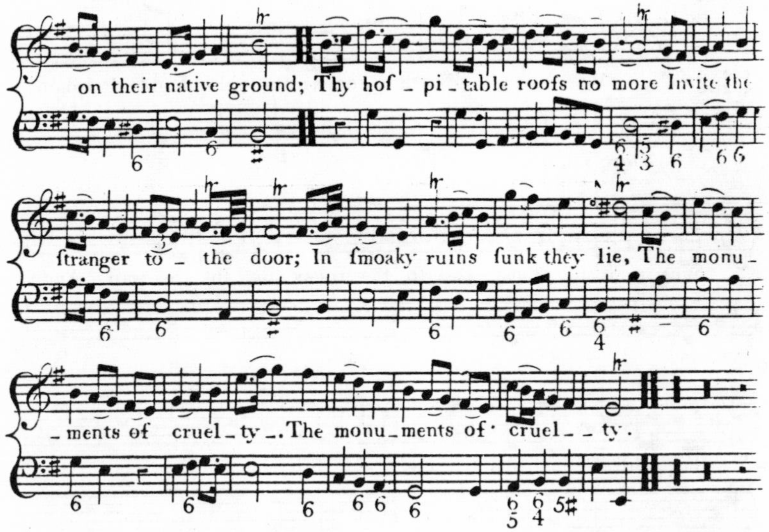
on their native ground; Thy hoſ _ pi _ table roofs no more Invite the
ſtranger to _ the door; In ſmoaky ruins ſunk they lie, The monu _
_ ments of cruel _ ty _. The monu _ ments of cruel _ _ ty.

The wretched owner ſees, afar,
His all become the prey of war;
Bethinks him of his babes and wife,
Then ſmites his breaſt, and curſes life.
Thy ſwains are famiſh'd on the rocks,
Where once they fed their wanton flocks:
Thy raviſh'd virgins ſhriek in vain;
Thy infants periſh on the plain.

What boots it then, in ev'ry clime,
Thro' the wide-ſpreading waſte of time,
Thy martial glory, crown'd with praiſe,
Still ſhone with undiminiſh'd blaze;
Thy tow'ring ſpirit now is broke,
Thy neck is bended to the yoke:
What foreign arms could never quell,
By civil rage, and rancour fell.

The rural pipe and merry lay
No more ſhall cheer the happy day:
No ſocial ſcenes of gay delight
Beguile the dreary winter night:
No ſtrains, but thoſe of ſorrow, flow,
And nought be heard but ſounds of woe,
While the pale phantoms of the ſlain
Glide nightly o'er the ſilent plain.

Oh baneful cauſe, oh fatal morn,
Accurs'd to ages yet unborn!
The ſons againſt their fathers ſtood;
The parent ſhed his children's blood.
Yet, when the rage of battle ceas'd,
The victor's ſoul was not appeas'd:
The naked and forlorn muſt feel
Devouring flames, and murd'ring ſteel

The pious mother doom'd to death,
Forſaken, wanders o'er the heath,
The bleak wind whiſtles round her head
Her helpleſs orphans cry for bread;
Bereſt of ſhelter, food, and friend,
She views the ſhades of night deſcend
And, ſtretch'd beneath th' inclement ſkies
Weeps o'er her tender babes, and dies.

Whilſt the warm blood bedews my veins
And unimpair'd remembrance reigns,
Reſentment of my country's fate
Within my filial breaſt ſhall beat;
And, ſpite of her inſulting foe,
My ſympathizing verſe ſhall flow:
"Mourn, hapleſs Caledonia, mourn
"Thy baniſh'd peace, thy laurels torn.

## Where winding Forth adorns the vale.

Tune, Cumbernauld-houſe.

142

Where winding Forth a_dorns the vale, Fond Strephon,
Slow
once a ſhepherd gay, Did to the rocks his lot be_wail, And
thus addreſst his plaintive lay. O Julia, more than lil_ly
fair, More blooming than the op'ning roſe, How can thy breaſt
re_lentleſs wear A heart more cold then winter's ſnows!

Yet nipping Winter's keeneſt reign
But for a ſhort-liv'd ſpace prevails;
Spring-time returns, and chears each ſwain,
Scented with Flora's fragrant gales.
Come, Julia, come, thy love obey,
Thou, miſtreſs of angelic charms,
Come ſmiling like the morn of May,
And center in thy Strephon's arms.

Elſe, haunted by the fiend deſpair,
He'll court ſome ſolitary grove,
Where mortal foot did ne'er repair,
But ſwains oppreſs'd with hapleſs love.
From the once pleaſing rural throng
Remov'd, he'll bend his lonely way,
Where Philomela's mournful ſong
Shall join his melancholy lay.

# The young Highland Rover.

Written for this Work by Robert Burns. Tune, Morag.

143

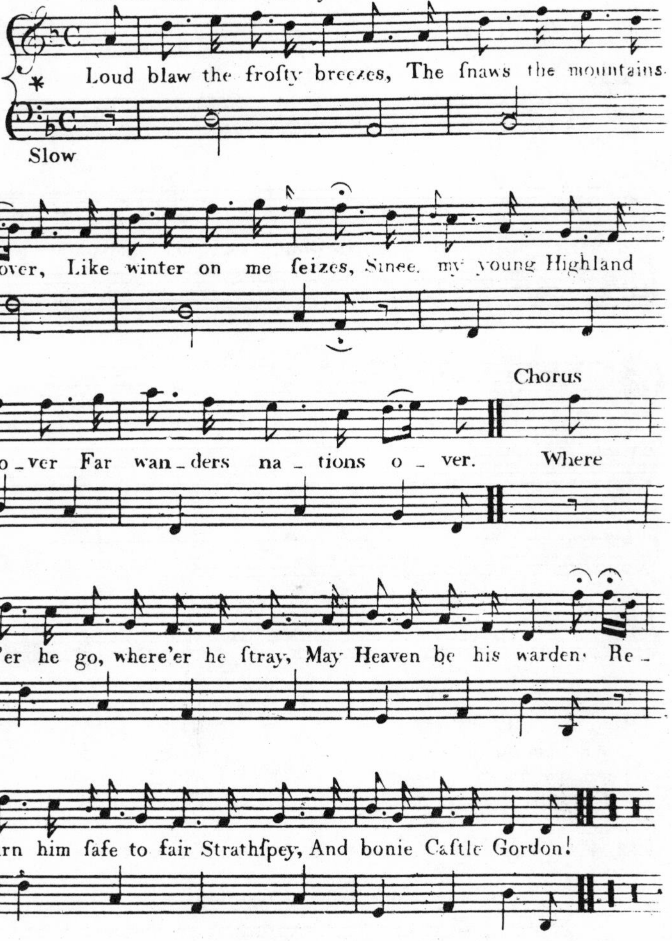
Loud blaw the frosty breezes, The snaws the mountains
Slow
cover, Like winter on me seizes, Since my young Highland
Chorus
Ro_ver Far wan_ders na_tions o_ver. Where
e'er he go, where'er he stray, May Heaven be his warden. Re_
_turn him safe to fair Strathspey, And bonie Castle Gordon!

The trees now naked groaning,
  Shall soon wi' leaves be hinging,
The birdies dowie moaning,
  Shall a' be blythely singing,
And every flower be springing.
Cho^s. Sae I'll rejoice the lee-lang day,
    When by his mighty Warden
  My youth's return'd to fair Strathspey
    And bonie Castle-Gordon.

## Dusty Miller.

144

Hey, the Duf_ty Mil_ler, And his dufty coat,
Lively
He will win a fhilling, Or he fpend a groat.
Duf_ty was the coat, Duf_ty was the col_our,
Dufty was the kifs That I got frae the Miller.

Hey, the dufty Miller,
And his dufty fack;
Leeze me on the calling
Fills the dufty peck:

Fills the dufty peck,
Brings the dufty filler;
I wad gie my coatie
For the dufty Miller.

## The Wedding-day.

145

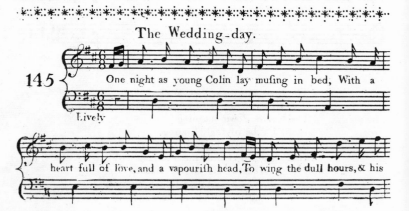

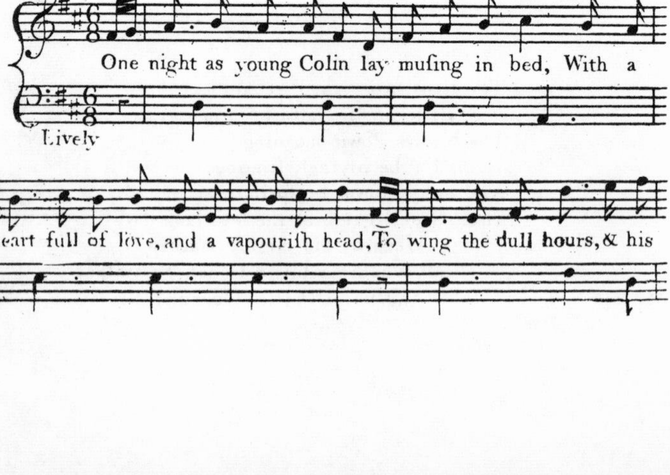
One night as young Colin lay mufing in bed, With a
Lively
heart full of love, and a vapourifh head, To wing the dull hours, & his

## Continued.

Sorrows allay, Thus ſweetly he ſung of his wedding day. What would I
give for a wedding day! Who would not wiſh for a wedding day! Wealth & am
-bition, I'd toſs ye away, With all you can boaſt, for a wedding-day.

Should heaven bid my wiſhes with freedom implore
One bliſs for the anguiſh I ſuffer'd before,
For Jeſsy, dear Jeſsy alone would I pray,
And graſp my whole wiſh on my wedding-day.
  Bleſs'd be th' approach of my wedding-day!
  Hail my dear nymph and my wedding-day!
  Earth, ſmile more verdant, and heaven ſhine more gay!
  For happineſs dawns with my wedding-day.

But Luna, who equally ſovereign preſides
O'er the hearts of the Ladies, and flow of the tides,
Unhappily changing, ſoon chang'd his wife's mind:
O Fate, could a wife prove ſo conſtant and kind!
  Why, was I born to a wedding-day!
  Curs'd, ever curs'd be my wedding-day!
  Colin, poor Colin thus changes his lay,
  And dates all his plagues from his wedding-day.

Ye Batchelors, warn'd by the Shepherds diſtreſs,
Be taught from your freedom to meaſure your bliſs.
Nor fall to the witchcraft of beauty a prey,
And blaſt all your joys on a wedding-day.
  Horns are the gift of a wedding-day,
  Want and a Scold crown a wedding-day,
  Happy the gallant, who wiſe when he may,
  Prefers a ſtout rope to a wedding-day.

# I dream'd I lay, &c.

146

*
I dream'd I lay where flowers were spring_ing,
Very Slow
Gaily in the funny beam; Lift'ning to the wild birds finging,
By a fal_ling, chryf_tal ftream: Straight the fky grew
black and daring; Thro' the woods the whirlwinds rave; Trees with aged
arms were war_ ing, O'er the fwelling, drumlie wave.

Such was my life's deceitful morning,
  Such the pleafures I enjoy'd;
But lang or noon, loud tempefts ftorming
  A' my flowery blifs deftroy'd.
Tho' fickle Fortune has deceivd me,
  She promis'd fair, and perform'd but ill:
Of mony a joy and hope bereav'd me,
  I bear a heart fhall fupport me ftill.

## I, who am ſore oppreſs'd with Love

Tune, Lovely laſs of Monorgon

147

Slowiſh
I, who am ſore oppreſs'd with love, Muſt like the
lonely turtle dove, To hills and ſhady groves repair, To vent my
grief and ſorrow there; Muſt now, a _ las! re_ _ ſolve to
part. At once with you and with my heart; For do you think my
heart can ſtay Be _ hind, when you are gone a _ way

No, no, my dear, whene'er we part,  
Take with you my poor bleeding heart;  
But uſe it kindly, for you know  
How much it lov'd you long ago:  
You know to what a great degree,  
Sighing for you, it waſted me,  
When one ſweet kiſs could well repay  
My pains and troubles all the day.

# A Cock Laird, fu' cadgie.

148

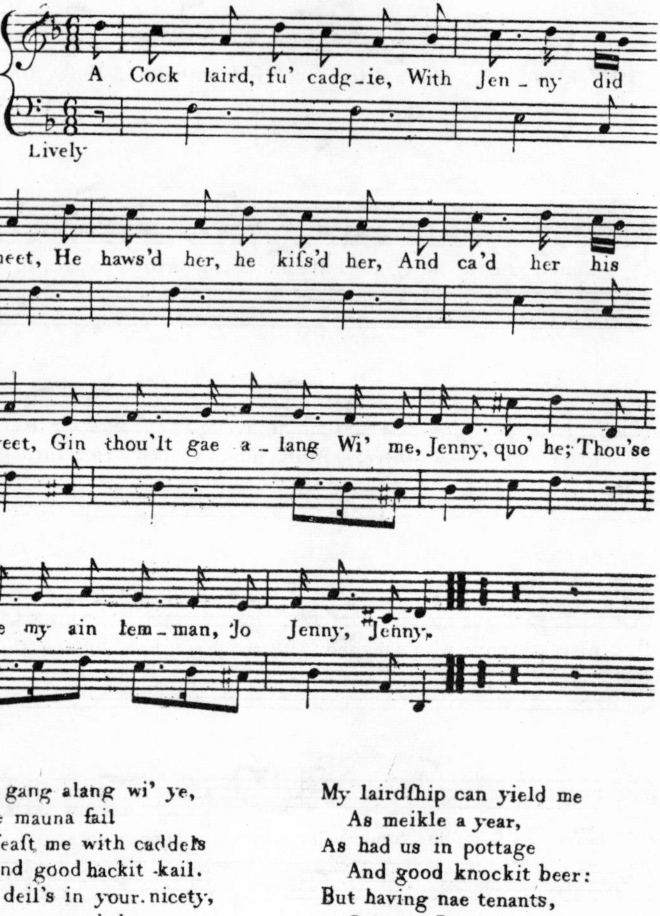
A Cock laird, fu' cadg-ie, With Jen-ny did
Lively
meet, He haws'd her, he kifs'd her, And ca'd her his
fweet, Gin thou'lt gae a-lang Wi' me, Jenny, quo' he; Thou'se
be my ain lem-man, Jo Jenny, Jenny.

If I gang alang wi' ye,
  Ye mauna fail
To feaft me with caddels
  And good hackit kail.
The deil's in your nicety,
  Jenny, quoth he,
Mayna bannocks of bear-meal
  Be as good for thee.

And I maun hae pinners
  With pearling fet round,
A fkirt of puddy,
  And a waiftcoat of brown,
Awa' with fick vanities,
  Jenny, quoth he,
For kurchis and kirtles
  Are fitter for thee.

My lairdfhip can yield me
  As meikle a year,
As had us in pottage
  And good knockit beer:
But having nae tenants,
  O Jenny, Jenny,
To buy ought I ne'er have
  A penny, quoth he.

The Borrowftoun merchants
  Will fell you on tick,
For we maun hae braw things,
  Albeit they foud break.
When broken, frae care
  The fools are fet free.
When we mak them lairds
  In the Abbey, quoth fhe.

## Duncan Davison.

149

Lively
* There was a lafs, they ca'd her Meg, And fhe held o'er the
moors to fpin; There was a lad that fol_low'd her, They
ca'd him Duncan Davifon. The moor was driegh, and Meg was
fkiegh, her favour Duncan could na win; For wi' the rock fhe
wad him knock, And ay fhe fhook the tem_per_pin.

As o'er the moor they lightly foor,
  A burn was clear, a glen was green,
Upon the banks they eas'd their fhanks,
  And ay fhe fet the wheel between:
But Duncan fwoor a haly aith
  That Meg fhould be a bride the morn,
Then Meg took up her fpinnin-graith,
  And flang them a out o'er the burn.

We will big a wee, wee houfe,
  And we will live like king and queen
Sae blythe and merry's we will be,
  When ye fet by the wheel at e'en.
A man may drink and no be drunk,
  A man may fight and no be flain;
A man may kifs a bony lafs,
  And ay be welcome backagain.

# Love will find out the way.

150
Quite over the mountains, And over the waves, Quite
Slow
over the fountains, And under the graves; O'er floods that are
deepeſt Which Neptune o_bey, O'er rocks that are ſteepeſt, Love will
find out the way, O'er floods that are deepeſt, Which Neptune O_
_bey, O'er rocks that are ſteepeſt, Love will find out the way.

Where there is no place
  For the glow-worm to lie;
Where there is no ſpace
  For the receipt of a fly;
Where the midge dare not venture,
  Leſt herſelf faſt ſhe lay;
But if love come, he will enter,
  And ſoon find out his way.

You may eſteem him
  A child in his force;
Or you may deem him
  A coward, which is worſe:
But if ſhe, whom love doth honour,
  Be conceal'd from the day,
Set a thouſand guards upon her,
  Love will find out the way.

Some think to loſe him,
  Which is too unkind;
And ſome do ſuppoſe him,
  Poor thing to be blind;
But if ne'er ſo cloſe ye wall him,
  Do the beſt that ye may,
Blind love, if ſo ye call him,
  He will find out the way.

You may train the eagle
  To ſtoop to your fiſt;
Or you may inveigle
  The Phœnix of the eaſt;
The Lioneſs ye may move her
  To give o'er her prey,
But you'll never ſtop a lover,
  He will find out his way.

## Ah! the poor Shepherd's mournful fate.

Tune, Gallaſhiels.

151

Slow
Ah! the poor ſhepherd's mournful fate, When doom'd to love, & doom'd to languiſh, To bear the ſcornful fair one's hate, Nor dare diſ_cloſe his anguiſh! Yet eager looks, & dying ſighs, My ſecret ſoul diſ_cover; While rapture trembling through mine eyes, Reveals how much I love her: The tender glance, the red'ning cheek, O'erſpread with riſing bluſhes, A thouſand various ways they ſpeak A thouſand various wiſhes.

For oh! that form ſo heavenly fair,
Thoſe languid eyes ſo ſweetly ſmiling,
That artleſs bluſh, and modeſt air,
So fatally beguiling!
Thy every look, and every grace,
So charm whene'er I view thee;

Till death o'ertake me in the chace,
Still will my hopes purſue thee.
Then when my tedious hours are paſt,
Be this laſt bleſsing given,
Low at thy feet to breathe my laſt,
And die in ſight of Heaven!

## My love has forſaken me.

152

Slow
* My love has for_ſaken me, Know ye for why! Be_cauſe he has flocks and herds, And none have I
Chorus
Whether I get him, whether I get him, Whether I get him or no, I care not three far_dins Whether I get him or no.

But the rot may come amongſt them,
And they may all die;
And then he'll be forſaken,
Ay, as weel as I.
Whether I get him, &c.

A thief will but rob me,
Take all that I have;
But an inconſtant lover
Will bring me to my grave.
Whether I get him, &c.

Meeting is a pleaſure,
And parting's a grief,
And an inconſtant lover
Is worſe than a thief.
Whether I get him, &c.

The grave it will rot me,
And bring me to duſt;
An inconſtant lover
No woman ſhould truſt.
Whether I get him, &c.

## My lov'd Celestia.

Tune, Benny Side

153
My lovd Ce_lestia is fo fair, So charming in each part, That ev'_ry feature is a fnare To catch my wounded heart. And, like the flutt' ring bird in vain. That labours to be freed, The more I ftruggle with my pain, A_las! the more I bleed.
Slow

Altho' the Heavens her heart have made
  Infenfible of care,
Yet will I gaze, nor hope for aid,
  But gazing I defpair:
Then tell me, ye who read the fkies
  The mystery difclofe,
Why, for the pleafure of my eyes
  I forfeit my repofe.

# Thro' the Wood, Laddie.

154

Slow
O Sandy, why leaves thou thy Nel_ly to mourn! Thy
presence cou'd ease me, When naething can please me, Now dowie I sigh
on the banks of the burn, Or thro' the wood, laddie, until thou return.
Tho' woods now are gay, and mornings so clear, While lav'rocks are
singing, and primroses springing; Yet none of them pleases my
eye or my ear, When thro' the wood, laddie, ye dinna ap_pear.

That I am forsaken, some spare na to tell:
I'm fash'd wi' their scorning,
Baith evening and morning:
Their jeering gaes aft to my heart wi' a knell,
When thro' the wood, laddie, I wander mysell.

Then stay, my dear Sandy, nae langer away,
But quick as an arrow,
Haste here to thy marrow,
Wha's living in langour till that happy day,
When thro' the wood, laddie, we'll dance, sing and play

## The Original words of Thro' the Wood, Laddie.

As Philermon and Phillis together did walk,
To the woods they did wander - To the woods they did wander.
As Philermon and Phillis together did walk,
To the woods they did wander, together did talk.
O could you, Philermon, this foreſt forſake,
And leave off to wander, - And leave off to wander,
O could you, Philermon, this foreſt forſake,
And leave off to wander, For Phillis's ſake.

If I this fine foreſt and woods ſhould give o'er,
And leave off to wander - And leave off to wander,
If I this fine foreſt and woods ſhould give o'er,
And leave off to wander, 'Tis thee I adore.
Juſt as they were talking, a Boy they eſpy'd,
With a bow and a quiver - With a bow and a quiver,
Juſt as they were talking, a Boy they eſpy'd,
With a bow and a quiver - his arrows faſt ty'd.

Young ſhepherd, ſaid he, To thee I am ſent,
From Venus my mother - From Venus my mother,
Young ſhepherd! ſaid he, to thee I am ſent,
From Venus my mother - Thy breaſt to torment:
With a bow ready bended, and a thundering dart,
Philermon was wounded - Philermon was wounded,
With a bow ready bended, and a thundering dart,
Philermon was wounded - quite thoro' the heart.

The Blind Boy in triumph went ſporting away,
And left poor Philermon - And left poor Philermon,
The blind boy in triumph went ſporting away,
And left poor Philermon - a victim and prey:
But the Nymph, with more pity, did whiſper him ſoft,
A cure I will tender - A cure I will tender,
But the Nymph, with more pity, did whiſper him ſoft,
A cure I will tender - Let the Boy fly aloft.

She kiſs'd and embrac'd him, and ſoothed his pain;
For Phillis was loving - For Phillis was loving,
She kiſs'd and embrac'd him, and ſoothed his pain;
For Phillis was loving - And loved again:
Then, down in yon meadow, there chaſtly we'll ſtay,
Thou Queen of my fancy Thou Queen of my fancy -
Then, down in yon meadow, there chaſtly we'll ſtay,
Thou Queen of my fancy, I'll embrace thee alway.

The beech and the hazel our covering ſhall be,
No canopy like them - no canopy like them -
The beech and the hazel our covering ſhall be
No canopy like them - While ſitting by thee:
With bracelets of roſes thine arms I will deck;
Gang thro' the wood, laddie - Gang thro' the wood, laddie.
With bracelets of roſes thine arms I will deck;
Gang thro' the wood, laddie - I'll ſhow my reſpect

# Where Helen Lies.

155

Plaintive
O that I were where Hel_en lies! Night and day on me ſhe cri_es; O that I were where Hel_en lies In fair Kirk_connel lee! O Helen, fair be_yond com_pare, A ringlet of thy flow_ing hair, I'll wear it ſtill for e_ver_mair Un_til the day I die.

Curs'd be the hand that ſhot the ſhot,
And curs'd the gun that gave the crack!
Into my arms bird Helen lap,
And died for ſake o' me.
O think na ye but my heart was ſair;
My love fell down, and ſpake nae mair;
There did ſhe ſwoon wi' meikle care,
On fair Kirkconnel lee.

I lighted down, my ſword did draw,
I cutted him in pieces ſma',
I cutted him in pieces ſma',
On fair Kirkconnel lee.

O Helen chaſte, thou'rt now at reſt,
If I were with thee I were bleſt,
Where thou lies low, and takes thy reſt
On fair Kirkconnel lee.

I wiſh my grave was growing green,
A winding ſheet put o'er my een,
And I in Helen's arms lying
In fair Kirkconnel lee!
I wiſh I were where Helen lies.
Night and day on me ſhe cries.
O that I were where Helen lies
On fair Kirkconnel lee!

# Theniel Menzies bonie Mary.

Tune, Ruffians Rant

156

In coming by the brig o' Dye; At Darlet we a blink did
Lively but not too faſt
tarry; As day was dawin in the ſky, We drank a health to bonie Mary.
Theniel Menzies' bonie Mary, Theniel Menzies' bonie Mary, Charlie
Grigor tint his plaidie, Kiſsin Theniel's bonie Mary.

Her een ſae bright, her brow ſae white,
Her haffet locks as brown's a berry;
And ay they dimpl't wi' a ſmile,
The roſy cheeks o' bonie Mary.
Theniel Menzies,' &c.

We lap and danc'd the lee-lang day,
Till Piper lads were wae and weary;
But Charlie gat the ſpring to pay
For kiſsin Theniel's bonie Mary.
Theniel Menzies' &c.

Z

## To the foregoing Tune.

A' the lads o' Thornie-bank
When they gae to the ſhore o' Bucky,
They'll ſtep in and tak a pint
Wi' Lady Onlie, honeſt lucky.
Cho.s Lady Onlie, honeſt lucky,
Brews gude ale at ſhore o' Bucky;
I wiſh her ſale for her gude ale,
The beſt on a' the ſhore o' Bucky

Her houſe ſae bien, her curch ſae clean.
I wat ſhe is a dainty Chuckie!
And cheary blinks the ingle gleede
O' Lady Onlie, honeſt lucky.
Cho.s Lady Onlie, &c

Z

# The Banks of the Devon.

Written for this Work by Burns.  Tune, Bhannerach dhon na chri.

157
Slow
How pleaſant the banks of the clear-winding Devon, With
green-ſpreading buſhes and flow'rs blooming fair! But the bon-ni-eſt
flow'r on the banks of the Devon Was once a ſweet bud on the braes of the
Ayr. Mild be the ſun on this ſweet-bluſhing Flower, In the
gay, roſy morn as it bathes in the dew; And gentle the fall of the
ſoft vernal ſhower, That ſteals on the evening each leaf to renew.

O ſpare the dear bloſsom, ye orient breezes,
With chill, hoary wing as ye uſher the dawn!
And far be thou diſtant, thou reptile that ſeizeſt
The verdure and pride of the garden or lawn!
Let Bourbon exult in his gay, gilded Lillies,
And England triumphant diſplay her proud Roſe;
A fairer than either adorns the green vallies
Where Devon, ſweet Devon, meandering flows.

B

## Waly, Waly.

158

O Waly, waly, up yon bank, And waly, waly down yon brae, &
Very Slow
waly by yon river side, Where I and my love wont to gae! O
waly, waly, love is bonny, A little while when it is new, But
when 'tis auld, it waxes cauld, And wears away like morning dew!


I leant my back unto an aik,
  I thought it was a trusty tree;
But first it bow'd, and syne it brak,
  And sae did my fause love to me.
When cockle-shells turn siller bells,
  And mussels grow on ev'ry tree;
When frost and snaw shall warm us a',
  Then shall my love prove true to me.

Now Arthur's seat shall be my bed,
  The sheets shall ne'er be fyl'd by me,
Saint Anton's well shall be my drink,
  Since my true-love's forsaken me.
O Mart'mas wind, when wilt thou blow,
  And shake the green leaves off the tree!
O gentle death, when wilt thou come
  And tak a life that wearies me!

'Tis not the frost that freezes fell,
  Nor blawing snaw's inclemency;
'Tis not sic cauld that makes me cry
  But my love's heart grown cauld to me
When we came in by Glasgow town,
  We were a comely sight to see;
My love was cled in velvet black
  And I mysel in cramasie.

But had I wist before I kiss'd
  That love had been sae ill to win;
I'd lockt my heart in a case of gold,
  And pin'd it with a siller pin.
Oh, oh! if my young babe were born,
  And set upon the nurse's knee;
And I mysel were dead and gane;
  For maid again I'll never be.

# The Shepherd Adonis.

159

The Shepherd A do_nis Being weary'd with
Slow
ſport, He, for a re_tirement, To the woods did re_ſort;
He threw by his club, And he laid him_ſelf down; He
envy'd no monarch, Nor wiſh'd for a crown.

He drank of the burn,
And he ate frae the tree,
Himſelf he enjoy'd;
And frae trouble was free:
He wiſh'd for no nymph,
Tho' never ſae fair,
Had nae love nor ambition,
And therefore no care.

But as he lay thus
In an ev'ning ſae clear,
A heav'nly ſweet voice
Sounded ſaft in his ear;
Which came frae a ſhady
Green neighbouring grove,
Where bonny Amynta
Sat ſinging of love.

He wander'd that way,
And found wha was there;
He was quite confounded
To ſee her ſae fair:
He ſtood like a ſtatue,
Not a foot cou'd he move,
Nor knew he what griev'd him;
But he fear'd it was love.

The nymph ſhe beheld him
With a kind modeſt grace,
Seeing ſomething that pleas'd her
Appear in his face;
With bluſhing a little,
She to him did ſay,
O ſhepherd, what want ye,
How came you this way.

His ſpirits reviving,
The ſwain to her ſaid,
I was ne'er ſae ſurpris'd
At the ſight of a maid;
Until I beheld thee,
From love I was free;
But now I'm ta'en captive,
My faireſt, by thee.

## Duncan Gray.

160

*
Wea ry fa' you, Dun_can Gray, Ha, ha the
Lively
gird_in o't, Wae gae by you, Dun_can Gray,
Ha, ha the gird_in o't; When a' the lave gae
to their play, Then I maun ſit the lee lang day And
jeeg the cradle wi' my tae, And a' for the girdin o't.

Bonie was the Lammas moon,
  Ha, ha the girdin o't;
Glowrin a' the hills aboon,
  Ha, ha the girdin o't;
The girdin brak, the beaſt cam down,
I tint my curch and baith my ſhoon,
And Duncan, ye're an unco loun
  Wae on the bad girdin o't.

But Duncan, gin ye'll keep your aith,
  Ha, ha the girdin o't,
I'ſ bleſs you wi' my hindmoſt breath
  Ha, ha the girdin o't;
Duncan, gin ye'll keep your aith,
The beaſt again can bear us baith,
And auld Meſs John will mend the
  And clout the bad girdin o't. (ſkaith

# Dumbarton's Drums.

161

Dumbarton's drums beat bonny O, When they mind me
Slowifh
of my dear Johny O. How happy am I When my foldier is by, While he
kiffes and bleffes his Annie O. 'Tis a foldier alone can delight me
O, For his graceful look do invite me O: While guarded in his arms, I'll
fear no wars alarms, Neither danger nor death fhall e'er fright me O.

My love is a handfome laddie O:
Genteel, but ne'er foppifh nor gaudy O:
Tho' commiffions are dear,
Yet I'll buy him one this year;
For he fhall ferve no longer a cadie O.
A foldier has honour and bravery O,
Unacquainted with rogues & their knavery O:
He minds no other thing
But the ladies or the king:
For every other care is but flavery O

Then I'll be the captain's lady O:
Farewell all my friends and my daddy O:
I'll wait no more at home,
But I'll follow with the drum,
And whene'er that beats I'll be ready O.
Dumbarton's drums found bonny O,
They are fprightly like my dear Johny O:
How happy fhall I be,
When on my foldier's knee,
And he kiffes and bleffes his Annie O!

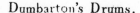

## Cauld Kail in Aberdeen.

162

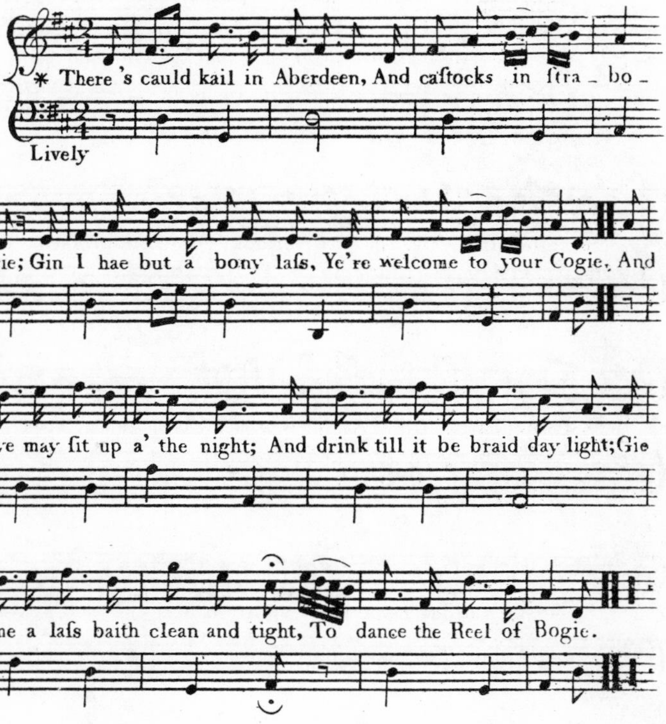
* There 's cauld kail in Aberdeen, And caſtocks in ſtra _ bo _
Lively
_ gie; Gin I hae but a bony laſs, Ye're welcome to your Cogie, And
ye may ſit up a' the night; And drink till it be braid day light; Gie
me a laſs baith clean and tight, To dance the Reel of Bogie.

In Cotillons the French excel;
John Bull, in Countra-dances;
The Spaniards dance Fandangos well,
Mynheer an All' mande prances:
In Fourſome Reels the Scots delight,
The Threeſome maiſt dance wondrous light;
But Twaſome ding a' out o' ſight,
Danc'd to the Reel of Bogie.

Come, Lads, and view your Partners well,
Wale each a blythſome Rogie;
I'll tak this Laſsie to myſel,
She ſeems ſae keen and vogie:
Now, Piper lad, bang up the Spring;
The Countra faſhion is the thing,
To prie their mou's e're we begin
To dance the Reel of Bogie.

Now ilka lad has got a laſs,
Save yon auld doited Fogie,
And ta'en a fling upo' the graſs,
As they do in Stra'bogie.
But a' the laſses look ſae fain,
We canna think ourſel's to hain;
For they maun hae their Come-again
To dance the Reel of Bogie.

Now a' the lads hae done their beſt,
Like true men of Stra'bogie;
We'll ſtop a while and tak a reſt,
And tipple out a Cogie:
Come now, my lads, & tak your glaſs,
And try ilk other to ſurpaſs,
In wiſhing health to every laſs
To dance the Reel of Bogie

## For lake of Gold.

163

For lake of Gold ſhe's left me Oh! And of all that's
Slowiſh
6 56 5 6

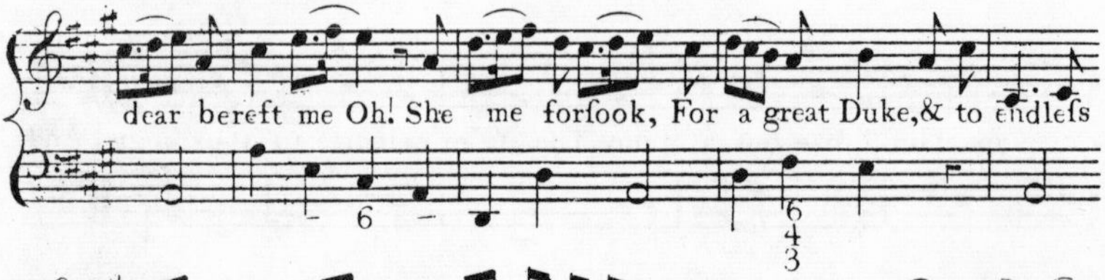
dear bereft me Oh! She me forſook, For a great Duke,& to endleſs
6 6 4 3

care has left me Oh! A ſtar & garter has more art, Than youth, a
6 6 5 4 3 6 6 6

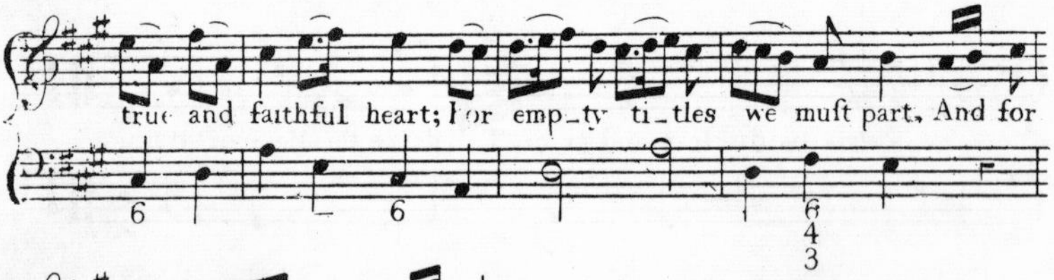
true and faithful heart; For emp_ty ti_tles we muſt part, And for
6 6 6 4 3

glitt'ring ſhow ſhe left me Oh!
6

No cruel fair ſhall ever move
My injur'd heart again to love,
Thro' diſtant climates I muſt rove,
Since Jeanie ſhe has left me, Oh!
Ye pow'rs above, I to your care
Commit my lovely, charming fair,
Your choiceſt bleſsings on her ſhare,
Tho' ſhe's for ever left me, Oh!

## Katharine Ogie.

164
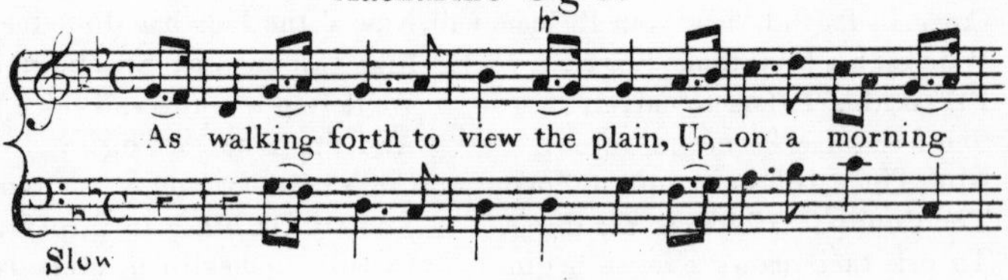
As walking forth to view the plain, Up_on a morning
Slow

Continued.

ear _ ly, While May's ſweet ſcent did chear my brain, From
flow'rs which grew ſo rarely; I chanc'd to meet a
pretty maid, She ſhin'd tho' it was foggy: I aſk'd her
name, Sweet Sir, ſhe ſaid, My name is Katharine Ogie.

I ſtood a while, and did admire,
To ſee a nymph ſo ſtately;
So briſk an air there did appear,
In a country-maid ſo neatly:
Such natural ſweetneſs ſhe diſplay'd,
Like a lillie in a bogie;
Diana's ſelf was ne'er array'd
Like this ſame Katharine Ogie.

Thou flow'r of females, Beauty's queen,
Who ſees thee ſure muſt prize thee;
Though thou art dreſt in robes but mean,
Yet theſe cannot diſguiſe thee;
Thy handſome air and graceful look,
Far excells any clowniſh rogie;
Thou'rt match for laird, or lord, or duke,
My charming Katharine Ogie.

O were I but a ſhepherd ſwain,
To feed my flock beſide thee;
At boughting time to leave the plain,
In milking to abide thee,
I'd think myſelf a happier man,
With Kate, my club, and dogie
Than he that hugs his thouſands ten,
Had I but Katharine Ogie

Then I'd deſpiſe th imperial throne,
And ſtateſmen's dangerous ſtations;
I'd be no king I'd wear no crown,
I'd ſmile at conqu'ring nations:
Might I careſs and ſtill poſſeſs
This laſs of whom I'm vogie;
For theſe are toys, and ſtill look leſs,
Compar'd with Katharine Ogie.

But I fear the gods have not decreed
For me ſo fine a creature,
Whoſe beauty rare makes her exceed
All other works in nature.
Clouds of deſpair ſurround my love,
That are both dark and foggy:
Pity my caſe, ye powers above,
Elſe I die for Katharine Ogie.

# The Ploughman.

165

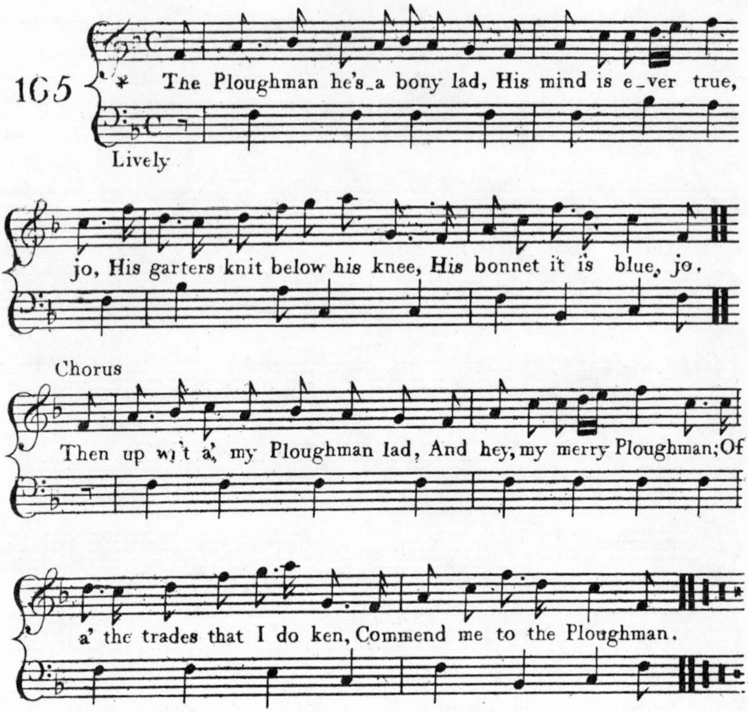
The Ploughman he's_a bony lad, His mind is e_ver true,
Lively
jo, His garters knit below his knee, His bonnet it is blue, jo.
Chorus
Then up wi't a', my Ploughman lad, And hey, my merry Ploughman; Of
a' the trades that I do ken, Commend me to the Ploughman.

My Ploughman he comes hame at e'en,
He's aften wat and weary:
Cast off the wat, put on the dry,
And gae to bed, my Dearie.
Up wi't a' &c.

I will wash my Ploughman's hose,
And I will dress his o erlay;
I will mak my Ploughman's bed,
And chear him late and early.
Up wi't a' &c.

I hae been east, I hae been west,
I hae been at Saint Johnston,
The boniest sight that e'er I saw
Was th' Ploughman laddie dancin.
Up wi't a' &c.

Snaw-white stockins on his legs,
And siller buckles glancin;
A gude blue bannet on his head,
And O but he was handsome!
Up wi't a' &c.

Commend me to the Barn yard,
And the Corn-mou, man;
I never gat my Coggie fou
Till I met wi' the Ploughman.
Up wi't a' &c.

Tune, Here's a Health to my true love, &c.

166

To me what are riches en_cumbred with care. To
Slow
me what is pomp's in_ſig_ni_fi_cant glare? No
minion of fortune, no pageant of ſtate, Shall e_ver
in_duce me to en_vy his fate.

Let rakes in a paramour's love acquieſce,
  Or jealouſies ſtifle, in noiſy exceſs,
Such pleaſures I court as my ſoul can review,
  Nor tumults attend, nor compunctions purſue.

Their perſonal graces let fops idolize,
  Whoſe life is but death in a ſplendid diſguiſe;
But ſoon the pale tyrant his right ſhall reſume,
  And all their falſe luſture be hid in the tomb.

Let the meteor diſcovery attract the fond ſage,
  In fruitleſs reſearches for life to engage,
Content with my portion the reſt I forego,
  Nor labour to gain diſappointment and woe.

Contemptibly fond of contemptible ſelf,
  While miſers their wiſhes concenter in pelf,
Let the godlike delight of imparting be mine;
  Enjoyment reflected is pleaſure divine.

Extenſive dominion and abſolute power,
  May tickle ambition perhaps for an hour,
But power in poſſeſſion ſoon loſes its charm
  While conſcience remonſtrates, and terror alarms.

With vigour. O teach me, kind heaven, to ſuſtain,
  Thoſe ills which in life to be ſuffer'd remain;
And, when 'tis allow'd me the goal to deſcry
  For [illegible] ſpecies. I liv'd, for [illegible] ſelf let me die

## Hey, Jenny, come down to Jock.

167

Jocky he came here to woo, On ae feaſt-day when
Lively
we were fu; And Jenny pat on her beſt array, When ſhe
heard that Joc-ky was come that way.
6
5
6
4
2
6

Jenny ſhe gaed up the ſtair,
Sae privily to change her ſmock;
And ay ſae loud as her mither did rair,
Hey, Jenny, come down to Jock.

Jenny ſhe came down the ſtair,
And ſhe came bobbin and bekin ben;
Her ſtays they were lac'd,& her waiſt it was jimp,
And a bra' new-made manco gown.

Jocky took her by the hand,
O Jenny, can ye fancy me?
My father is dead,& has left me ſome land,
And bra' houſes twa or three;

And I will gie them a' to thee,
A haith, quo' Jenny, I fear you mock:
Then foul fa' me gin I ſcorn thee;
If ye'll be my Jenny, I'll be your Jock.

Jenny lookit, and ſyne ſhe leugh,
Ye firſt maun get my mither's conſent:
A weel, goodwife, and what ſay ye?
Quo' ſhe, Jock, I'm weel content.

Jenny to her mither did ſay,
O mither, fetch us ſome gude meat;
A piece of the butter was kirn'd the day,
That Jocky and I thegither may eat.

Jocky unto Jenny did ſay,
Jenny, my dear, I want nae meat;
It was nae for meat that I came here,
But a' for the love of you, Jenny, my dear.

Then Jocky and Jenny were led to their bed,
And Jocky he lay neiſt the ſtock;
And five or ſix times ere break of day,
He aſk'd at Jenny how ſhe lik'd Jock?

Quo' Jenny, Dear Jock, you gie me content,
I bleſs my mither for gieing conſent:
And on the next morning before the firſt coc
Our Jenny did cry, I dearly love Jock.

Jenny ſhe gaed up the gait,
Wi' a green gown as ſide as her ſmock;
And ay ſae loud as her mither did rair,
Vow ſirs! has nae Jenny got Jock.

## O'er Bogie.

168
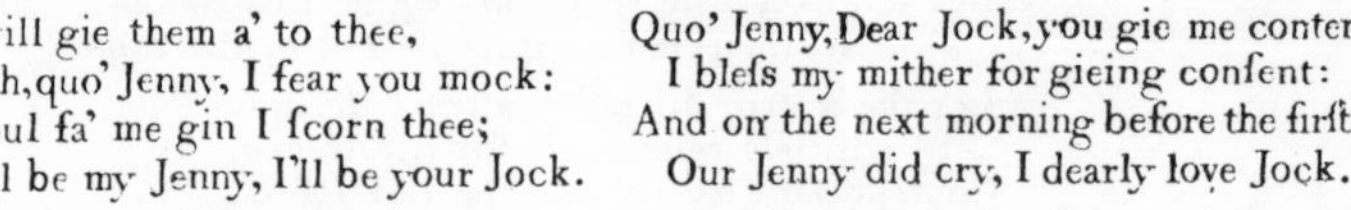
I will a-wa' wi' my love, I will a-wa wi' her; Tho'
6
6

## Continued.

a' my kin had ſworn and ſaid, I will awa wi her. I'll
O'er Bog - ie, o'er Bog - ie, o'er Bog - ie wi' her, Tho'
a' my kin had ſworn and ſaid, I will a - wa wi' her.

If I can get but her conſent,
 I dinna care a ſtrae;
Tho' ilka ane be diſcontent,
 Awa' wi' her I'll gae.
  I'll o'er Bogie, &c.

For now ſhe's miſtreſs of my heart,
 And wordy of my hand,
And well I wat we ſhanna part
 For ſiller or for land.
  I'll o'er Bogie, &c.

Let rakes delight to ſwear and drink,
 And beaus admire fine lace,
But my chief pleaſure is to blink
 On Betty's bonny face.
  I'll o'er Bogie, &c.

There a' the beauties do combine,
 Of colour, treats, and air,
The ſaul that ſparkles in her een
 Makes her a jewel rare.
  I'll o'er Bogie, &c.

Her flowing wit gives ſhining life
 To a' her other charms;
How bleſs'd I'll be when ſhe's my wife,
 And lock'd up in my arms!
  I'll o'er Bogie, &c.

There blythly will I rant and ſing,
 While o'er her ſweets I range,
I'll cry, Your humble ſervant, King
 Shame fa' them that wad change.
  I'll o'er Bogie, &c.

A kiſs of Betty and a ſmile,
 Albeit ye wad lay down,
The right ye hae to Britain's iſle,
 And offer me ye'r crown.
  I'll o'er Bogie, &c.

## Same Tune.

WELL, I agree, ye're ſure of me;
 Next to my fa her gae;
Make him content to give conſent,
 He'll hardly ſay you nay:
For you have what he wad be at,
 And will commend you weel,
Since parents auld think love grows caul
 Where bairns want milk and meal.
Shou'd he deny, I care na by,
 He'd contradict in vain,
Tho' a' my kin had ſaid and ſworn,
 But thee I will have nane:
Then never range, nor learn to change
 Like theſe in high degree:
And if ye prove faithful in love,
 You'll find nae faut in me

# Lafs wi' a Lump of Land.

169

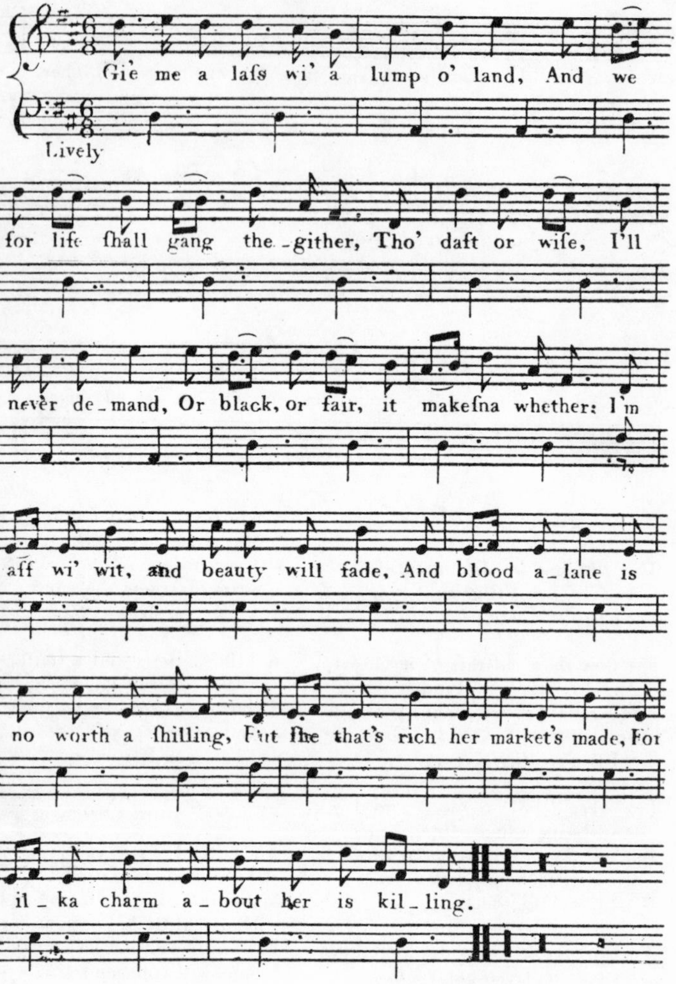
Gie me a lafs wi' a lump o' land, And we
Lively
for life fhall gang the_gither, Tho' daft or wife, I'll
never de_mand, Or black, or fair, it makefna whether: I'm
aff wi' wit, and beauty will fade, And blood a_lane is
no worth a fhilling, But fhe that's rich her market's made, For
il_ka charm a_bout her is kil_ling.

Gi'e me a lafs wi' a lump of land,
And in my bofom I'll hug my treafure;
Gin I had ance her gear in my hand,
Should love turn dowf, it will find pleafure.
Laugh on wha likes, but there's my hand,
I hate with poortith, tho' bonny, to meddle,
Unlefs they bring cafh, or a lump of land,
Theyse ne'er get me to dance to their fiddle.

There's meikle good love in bands & bags
And filler & gowd's a fweet complection;
For beauty, and wit, and virtue in rags,
Have tint the art of gaining affection:
Love tips his arrows with wood and parks
And caftles, & riggs, & muirs & meadows:
And naething can catch our modern fparks.
But well tocher'd laffes, or jointur'd-
-widows.

## Hey Tutti Taiti.

170

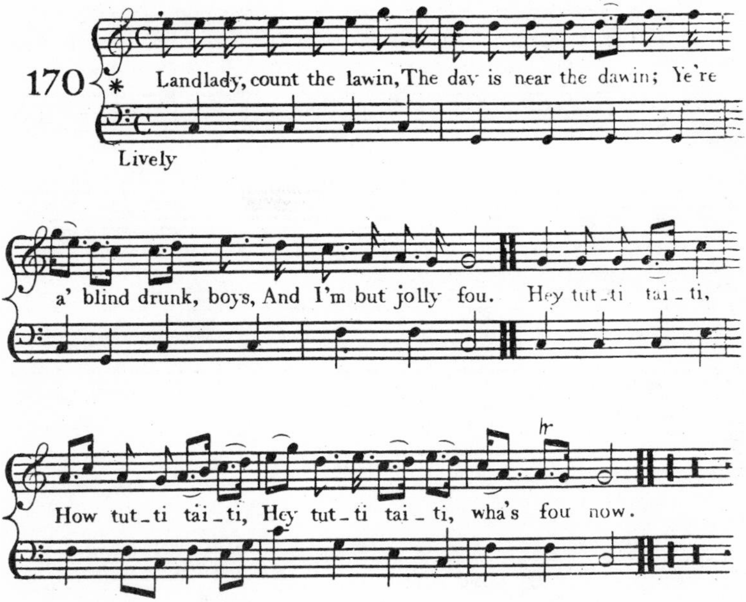
*
Landlady, count the lawin, The day is near the dawin; Ye're
Lively
a' blind drunk, boys, And I'm but jolly fou. Hey tut_ti tai_ti,
How tut_ti tai_ti, Hey tut_ti tai_ti, wha's fou now.

Cog an ye were ay fou,
Cog an ye were ay fou,
I wad ſit and ſing to you,
If ye were ay fou.
Hey tutti &c

Weel may we a' be!
Ill may we never ſee!
God bleſs the king
And the companie!
Hey tutti &c

### Same Tune.

HERE is to the king, Sir,
Ye ken wha I mean, Sir,
And to every honeſt man
That will do't again.
Chorus.
Fill up your bumpers high,
We'll drink a' your barrels dry;
Out upon them, fy! fy!
That winna do't again.

Here's to the Chieftans
Of the Scots Highland clans;
They hae done it mair than ance,
And will do't again.
Fill up &c.

When you hear the trumpet ſounds,
Tutti taiti to the drum;
Up your ſwords, and down your gun
And to the louns again.
Fill up &c.

Here is to th king o' Swedes,
Freſh laurels crown his head!
Pox on every ſneaking blade
That winna do't again!
Fill up &c.

But to mak a' things right, now,
He that drinks maun fight too,
To ſhew his heart's upright too,
And that he'll do't again.
Fill up &c.

# The young Laird and Edinburgh Katy.

171

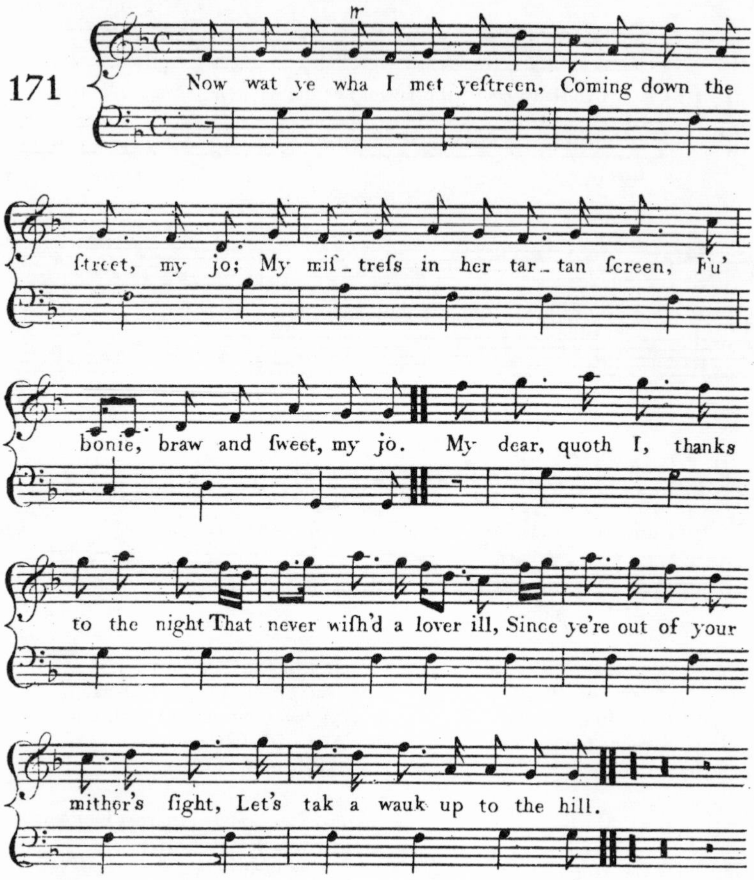
Now wat ye wha I met yestreen, Coming down the
street, my jo; My mis_tress in her tar_tan screen, Fu'
bonie, braw and sweet, my jo. My dear, quoth I, thanks
to the night That never wish'd a lover ill, Since ye're out of your
mither's sight, Let's tak a wauk up to the hill.

O Katy, wiltu' gang wi' me,
And leave the dinsome town a while,
The blossom's sprouting frae the tree,
And a' the simmer's gawn to smile:
The mavis, nightingale, and lark,
The bleating lambs and whistling hind,
In ilka dale, green shaw, and park,
Will nourish health, and glad ye'r mind.

Soon as the clear goodman of day
Bends his morning draught of dew,
We'll gae to some burn-side and play,
And gather flow'rs to busk ye'r brow;
We'll pou the daisies on the green,
The lucken gowans frae the bog:
Between hands now and then we'll lean,
And sport upo' the velvet fog.

There's up into a pleasant glen,
A wee piece frae my father's tow'r,
A canny, saft, and flow'ry den,
Where circling birks have form'd a bow'r;
Whene'er the sun grows high and warm,
We'll to that cauler shade remove,
There will I lock thee in my arms,
And love and kiss, and kiss and love.

## Katy's Anſwer.

172

My mither's ay glowran o'er me, Tho' ſhe did the
ſame before me, I canna get leave To look to my love, Or
elſe ſhe'll be like to devour me. Right fain wad I tak ye'r
of _ fer, Sweet Sir, but I'll tine my tocher; Then, Sandy, ye'll
fret, And wyte ye'er poor Kate, When e'er ye keek in your toom coffer.

For tho' my father has plenty
Of ſiller and pleniſhing dainty,
Yet he's unco ſweer
To twin wi' his gear,
And ſae we had need to be tenty.

Tutor my parents wi' caution,
Be wylie in ilka motion,
Brag weel o' ye'r land,
And there's my leal hand,
Win them, I'll be at your devotion.

# Raving winds around her blowing.

Written for this Work by R. Burns. Tune, Mc Grigor of Roro's Lament.

173

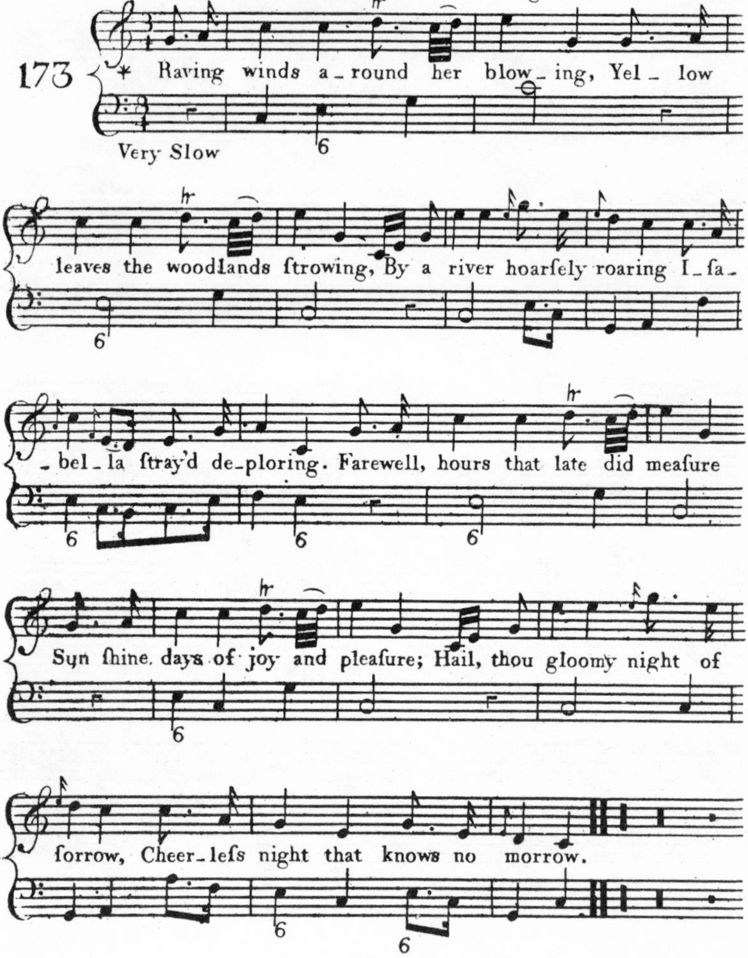
* Raving winds a_round her blow_ing, Yel_low
Very Slow
leaves the woodlands strowing, By a river hoarsely roaring I_sa_
_bel_la stray'd de_ploring. Farewell, hours that late did measure
Sun shine, days of joy and pleasure; Hail, thou gloomy night of
sorrow, Cheer_less night that knows no morrow.

O'er the Past too fondly wandering,
On the hopeless Future pondering;
Chilly Grief my life-blood freezes,
Fell Despair my fancy seizes.
Life, thou soul of every blessing;
Load to Misery most distressing;
Gladly how would I resign thee,
And to dark Oblivion join thee!

## Ye gods, was Strephon's picture bleſt.

Tune, 14th. of October.

174

Ye gods, was Strephon's picture bleſt, With the fair
Slow
heav'n of Chloe's breaſt! Move ſofter, thou fond flutt'ring heart, Oh
gent_ly throb,_ too fierce thou art. Tell me, thou bright_eſt
of thy kind, For Strephon was the bliſs deſign'd, For Strephon's sake dear
charming maid, Didſt thou pre_fer his wand'ring ſhade?

And thou, bleſs'd ſhade, that ſweetly art
Lodg'd ſo near my Chloe's heart,
For me the tender hour improve,
And ſoftly tell how dear I love.
Ungrateful thing! it ſcorns to hear
Its wretched maſter's ardent prayer,
Ingroſſing all that beautous heaven,
That Chloe, laviſh maid, has given.

I cannot blame thee; were I lord
Of all the wealth theſe breaſts afford,
I'd be a miſer too, nor give
An alms to keep a god alive.

Oh! ſmile not thus, my lovely fair,
On theſe cold looks that lifeleſs are;
Prize him whoſe boſom glows with fire,
With eager love and ſoft deſire.

'Tis true, thy charms, O pow'rful maid.
To life can bring the ſilent ſhade:
Thou canſt ſurpaſs the painter's art,
And real warmth and flames impart.
But oh! it ne'er can love like me,
I ever lov'd and lov'd but thee:
Then, charmer, grant my fond requeſt.
Say, Thou canſt love, and make me bleſt

## How long and dreary is the Night.

A Galick Air.

175

Slow
How long and drea_ry is the Night, When
I am frae my dearie! I fleeplefs lye frae e'en to
morn, Tho' I were ne'er fo weary. I fleeplefs lye frae
e'en to morn, Tho' I were ne'er fo weary.

When I think on the happy days
I fpent wi' you, my dearie;
And now what lands between us lie,
How can I be but eerie!
And now what lands, &c.

How flow ye move, ye heavy hours,
As ye were wae and weary!
It was na fae ye glinted by,
When I was wi' my dearie.
It was na fae ye glinted, &c.

* * * * * * * * * * * * * * * * * * * * * * * * * * *

## Since robb'd of all that charmd my views.

Tune, Mifs Hamilton's delight

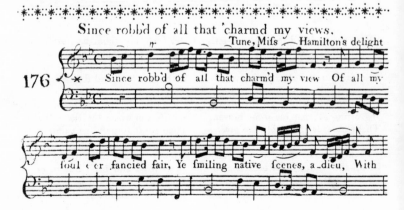

176

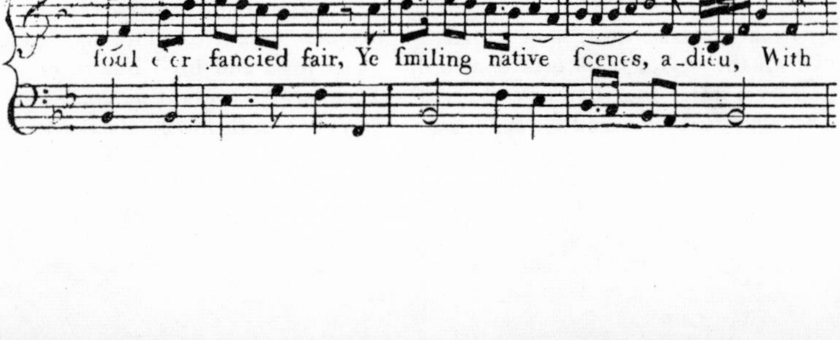
Since robb'd of all that charm'd my view Of all my
foul e'er fancied fair, Ye fmiling native fcenes, a_dieu, With

Continued.

each de_light_ful object there! Oh, when my heart re_
volves the joys Which in your ſweet re_ceſs I knew, The laſt dread
ſhock which life deſtroys, Is heaven, com_par'd with loſing you!

Ye vales, which to the rapturd eye,
  Diſclos'd the flow'ry pride of may;
Ye circling hills, whoſe ſummits high
  Bluſh'd with the morning's earlieſt ray;
Where heedleſs oft, how far I ſtray'd,
  And pleas'd my ruin to purſue,
I ſung my dear, my cruel maid;
  Adieu, for ever, ah adieu!

Ye dear aſsociates of my breaſt,(ſwell;
  Whoſe hearts with ſpeechleſs ſorrow
And thou, with hoary age oppreſt,
  Dear author of my life, farewel.
For me, alas! thy fruitleſs tears,
  Far, far remote from friends, and home,
Shall blaſt thy venerable years,
  And bend thee pining to the tomb.

Sharp are the pangs by nature felt,
  From dear relations torn away;
Yet ſharper pangs, my vitals melt,
  To hopeleſs love a deſtin'd prey.
While ſhe, as angry heav'n, and main,
  Deaf to the helpleſs ſailor's prayer,
Enjoys my ſoul-conſuming pain,
  And wantons with my deep deſpair.

From curſed gold what ills ariſe,
  What horrors lifes fair proſpect ſtain;
Friends blaſt their friends with angry eyes,
  And brothers bleed by brothers ſlain.

From curſed gold I trace my woe;
  Could I this ſplendid miſchief boaſt
Nor would my tears, unpitied flow
  Nor would my ſighs in air be loſt.

Ah! when a mother's cruel care.
  Nurs'd me an infant on the breaſt,
Had early fate ſurpriz'd me there,
  And wrapt me in eternal reſt;(beat
Then had this breaſt ne'er learn'd to
  And tremble with unpitied pain
Nor had a maid's relentleſs hate,
  Been, ev'n in death, deplor'd in vain

Oft, in the pleaſing toils of love
  With ev'ry winning art I try'd
To catch the coyly flutt'ring dove
  With killing eyes & plumy pride
But far on nimble pinnions borne
  From love's warm gales & flow'ry plains
She ſought the northern climes of ſcorn
  Where ever freezing winter reigns

Ah me had heaven and ſhe prov'd kind
  Then full of age, & free from care,
How bleſt had I my life reſign'd
  Where firſt I breath'd this vital air·
But ſince no flatt'ring hope remains
  Let me my wretched lot purſue:
Adieu, dear friends & native ſcenes
  To all but grief and love adieu!

# The Bonny Earl of Murray.

177

Ye Highlands and ye Lowlands, Oh! where have you been? They have ſlain the Earl of Murray, And they laid him on the green! They have ſlain the Earl of Mur_ray, And they laid him on the green.
Very Slow

Now wae be to thee, Huntley!
And wherefore did you ſae?
I bade you bring him wi' you,
But forbade you him to ſlay.
I bade &c.

He was a bra' gallant,
And he rid at the ring,
And the bonny Earl of Murray,
Oh! he might have been a king.
And the &c.

He was a bra' gallant,
And he play'd at the ba',
And the bonny Earl of Murray
Was the flower amang them a'.
And the &c.

He was a bra' gallant,
And he play'd at the glove;
And the bonny Earl of Murray,
Oh! he was the Queen's love.
And the, &c.

Oh! lang will his lady
Look o'er the caſtle Down,
Ere ſhe ſee the Earl of Murray
Come ſounding through the town.
Ere ſhe, &c.

# Young Damon.

Tune, Highland Lamentation.

178

Plaintive
A_midſt a ro_ſy bank of flowers, Young Damon
mourn'd his for_lorn fate, In ſighs he ſpent his lang_uid
hours, And breath'd his woes in lone_ly ſtate. Gay
joy no more ſhall eaſe his mind, No wan_ton
ſports can ſooth his care, Since ſweet A_man_da
prov'd unkind, And left him full of black deſ_pair.

His looks, that were as freſh as morn,
  Can now no longer ſmiles impart;
His penſive ſoul on ſadneſs borne,
  Is rack'd and torn by Cupid's dart.
Turn, fair Amanda, cheer your ſwain,
  Unſhroud him from this vail of woe;
Range every charm to ſoothe the pain,
  That in his tortur'd breaſt doth grow.

## Musing on the roaring Ocean.

Written for this Work by R.Burns. Tune, Druimion dubh.

179

Musing on the roaring ocean, Which di _ vides my
love and me. Weary _ ing Heav'n in warm de _ vo _ tion,
For his weal wher _ e'er he be.

Hope and Fear's alternate billow
 Yielding late to Nature's law,
Whisp'ring spirits round my pillow
 Talk of him that's far awa.

Ye whom Sorrow never wounded,
 Ye who never shed a tear,
Care-untroubled, joy-surrounded,
 Gaudy Day to you is dear.

Gentle Night, do thou befriend me;
 Downy Sleep, the curtain draw;
Spirits kind, again attend me,
 Talk of him that's far awa. R

## Blythe was she. Written by R. Burns.

180

Blythe, Blythe and merry was she, Blythe was she but & ben:
Blythe by the banks of Ern, And blythe in Glen _ turit glen. By
Oughtertyre grows the aik, On Yarrow banks, the birken shaw; But

## Continued.

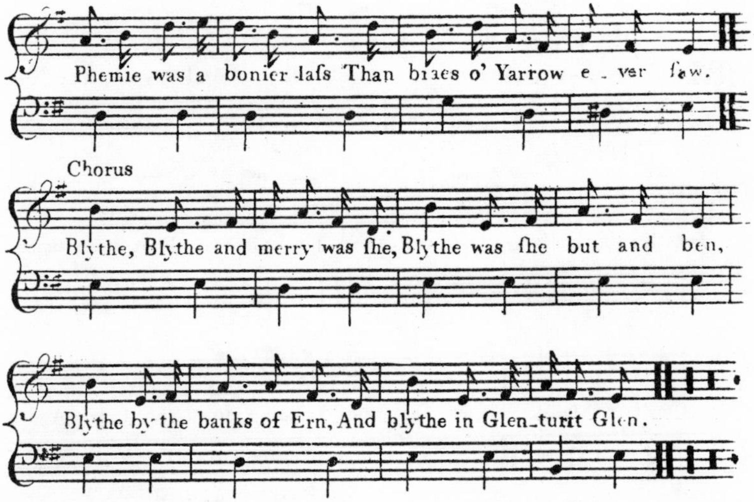
Phemie was a bonier laſs Than braes o' Yarrow e - ver ſaw.
Chorus
Blythe, Blythe and merry was ſhe, Blythe was ſhe but and ben,
Blythe by the banks of Ern, And blythe in Glen_turit Glen.

Her looks were like a flow'r in may,
Her ſmile was like a ſimmer morn;
She tripped by the banks of Ern,
As light's a bird upon a thorn.
Blythe, &c.

Her bony face it was as meek
As ony lamb upon a lee;
The evening ſun was ne'er ſae ſweet
As was the blink o' Phemie's e'e.
Blythe, &c.

The Highland hills I've wander'd wide
And o'er the Lawlands I hae been;
But Phemie was the blytheſt laſs
That ever trode the dewy green.
Blythe, &c.

B

## To the Foregoing Tune.

SHE took me in, ſhe ſet me down,
She hecht to keep me lawin-free;
But, wylie Carlin that ſhe was!
She gart me birl my bawbie.
Blythe, blythe, blythe was ſhe,
Blythe was ſhe butt and ben;
Weel ſhe lo'ed a Hawick gill,
And leugh to ſee a tappit hen.

I lo'ed the liquor weel eneugh,
But, wae's my heart, my caſh ran done,
Lang or I had quench'd my drouth,
And laith was I to pawn my ſhoon!
Blythe, blythe, &c.

When we had three times toomd the ſtowp,
And the nieſt chappin new begun,
Wha ſtarted in to heeze our hope,
But Andrew wi' his cutty gun.
Blythe, blythe, &c.

The Carlin brought her kebbuck ben,
And girdle-cakes weel toaſted brown:
Weel did the canny kimmer ken
It gart the ſwats gae glibber down.
Blythe, blythe, &c.

We ca'd the bicker aft about,
Till dawin we ne'er jeed our bum:
And ay the cleaneſt drinker out
Was Andrew an' his cutty gun.
Blythe, blythe, &c.

He did like ony Mavis ſing,
While ſhe below his oxter ſat;
He ca'd her ay his bonie thing,
And mony a ſappy kiſs ſhe gat.
Blythe, blythe, &c.

I hae been eaſt, I hae been weſt,
I hae been far ayont the ſun,
But the clevereſt lad that e'er I ſaw
Was Andrew wi his cutty gun.
Blythe, blythe, &c.

# Johuy Faa, or the Gypſie laddie.

181

The gypſies came to our Lord's yett, And vow but they ſang
Slow
ſweetly; They ſang ſae ſweet, and ſae compleat, That down came
the fair lady. When ſhe came tripping down the ſtair, And
a' her maids be_fore her; As ſoon as they ſaw her
weel_fair'd face, They cooſt the gla_mer o'er her.

Gae tak frae me this gay mantile,
And bring to me a plaidie;
For if kith and kin and a' had ſworn,
I'll follow the gypſie laddie.
Yeſtreen I lay in a weel-made bed,
And my good lord beſide me;
This night I'll ly in a tenant's barn,
Whatever ſhall betide me.

Oh. come to your bed ſays Johny Faa,
Oh. come to your bed, my deary;
For I vow and ſwear by the hilt of my ſword,
That your lord ſhall nae mair come near ye.
I'll go to bed to my Johny Faa,
And I'll go to bed to my deary;
For I vow and ſwear by what paſt yeſtreen,
That my lord ſhall nae mair come near me.

I'll make a hap to my Johny Faa,
And I'll make a hap to my deary;
And he's get a' the coat gaes round,
And my lord ſhall nae mair come near m
And when our lord came hame at e'en,
And ſpeir'd for his fair lady,
The tane ſhe cry'd, and the other reply'd,
She's awa wi' the gypſie laddie.

Gae ſaddle to me the black, black ſteed,
Gae ſaddle and mak him ready;
Before that I either eat or ſleep,
I'll gae ſeek my fair lady.
And we were fifteen well made men,
Altho' we were nae bonny
And we are a' put down for ane,
The earl of Caſsilis' lady.

# To Daunton me.

182

*
Slowiſh
The blude red roſe at Yule may blaw The ſimmer lillies bloom in ſnaw, The froſt may freeze the deepeſt ſea, But an auld man ſhall ne_ver daunton me. To daunton me, And me ſae young, Wi' his fauſe heart and flatt'ring tongue, That is the thing you ne'er ſhall ſee For an auld man ſhall never daunton me,

For a' his meal and a' his maut,
For a' his freſh beef and his ſaut,
For a' his gold and white monie,
An auld man ſhall never daunton me.
To daunton me, &c.

His gear may buy him kye and yowes,
His gear may buy him glens & knowes.
But me he ſhall not buy nor fee,
For an auld man ſhall never daunton me
To daunton me, &c.

He hirples twa-fauld as he dow,
Wi' his teethleſs gab and his auld beld pow,
And the rain rains down frae his red bleard e'e,
That auld man ſhall never daunton me.
To daunton me, &c.

## Polwart on the Green.

183

At Polwart on the green, If you'll meet me the
Slowifh
morn, Where laſses do con_veen,, To dance about the thorn:
A kind_ly welcome you ſhall meet, Frae her wha likes to view,
A lover and a lad compleat, The lad and lover you.

Let dorty dames ſay na,
  As lang as e'er they pleaſe,
Seem caulder than the ſnaw,
  While inwardly they bleeze;
But I will frankly ſhaw my mind,
  And yield my heart to thee;
Be ever to the captive kind,
  That langs nae to be free.

At Polwart on the green,
  Among the new mawn hay,
With ſangs and dancing keen
  We'll paſs the heartſome day.
At night, if beds be o'er thrang laid,
  And thou be twin'd of thine,
Thou ſhall be welcome, my dear lad
  To take a part of mine.

## Abſence.

A Song in the manner of Shenſtone.

184

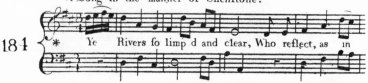

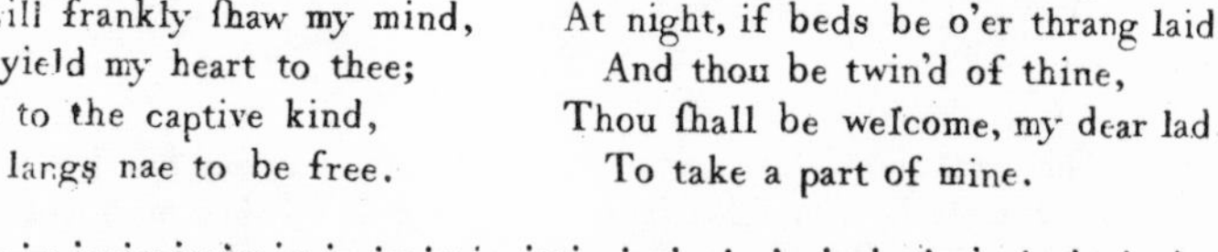
Ye Rivers ſo limp d and clear, Who reflect, as in

Continued.

cadence you ſlow, all the beauties that va_ry the year, All the flow'rs
on your margins that grow: How bleſt on your banks cou'd I dwell:
Were Me_liſ_sa the pleaſure to ſhare, And teach your ſweet
e_ _choes to tell, With what fondneſs I doat on the fair.


Ye harveſts that wave in the breeze
As far as the view can extend,
Ye mountains umbrageous with trees
Whoſe tops ſo majeſtic aſcend;
Your landſkip what joy to ſurvey,
Were Meliſsa with me to admire!
Then the harveſts would glitter how gay,
How majeſtic the mountains aſpire!

In penſive regret whilſt I rove
The fragrance of flowers to enhale,
Or w tch from the paſture and grove
Each muſic that floats in the gale,
Alas! the deluſion how vain!
No odours nor harmony pleaſe,
A heart agonizing with pain,
Which tries every poſture for eaſe.

If anxious to flatter my woes
Or the languor of abſence to chear,
Her breath I would catch in the roſe
Or her voice in the nightingale hear;
To cheat my deſpair of its prey
What object her charms can aſsume,
How harſh is the nightingales lay,
How inſipid the roſes perfume!

Ye Zephyrs that viſit my fair,
Ye Sun beams around her that play,
Does her ſympathy dwell on my care,
Does ſhe number the hours of my ſtay:
Firſt periſh ambition and wealth,
Firſt periſh all elſe that is dear, (-lth
E'er one ſigh ſhould eſcape her by ſtea
E'er my abſence ſhould coſt her one tear

(-more
When, when, ſhall her beauties once
This deſolate boſom ſurpriſ
Ye fates, the bleſt moment reſtore
When I baſk'd in the beams of her eyes
When with ſweet emulation of heart
Our kindneſs we ſtruggled to ſhew,
But the more that we ſtrove to impart
We felt it more ardently glow.

## I had a Horſe, and I had nae mair

185

I had a horſe, & I had nae mair, I gat him frae my daddy; My
Very Slow
purſe was light, and my heart was ſair, But my wit it was fu' ready.
And ſae I thought me on a time, Outwittens of my dad_dy, To
fee myſell to a lawland laird, Wha had a bonny la_dy.

I wrote a letter, and thus began,
Madam, be not offended,
I'm o'er the lugs in love wi' you,
And care not tho' ye kend it:
For I get little frae the laird,
And far leſs frae my daddy,
And I would blythly be the man
Would ſtrive to pleaſe my lady.

She read my letter, and ſhe leugh,
Ye needn been ſae blate, man,
You might hae come to me yourſell,
And tald me o' your ſtate, man:
You might hae come to me yourſell,
Outwittens o' ony body,
And made John Gouckſton of the laird,
And kiſs'd his bonny lady.

Then ſhe pat ſiller in my purſe,
We drank wine in a cogie;
She fee'd a man to rub my horſe,
And wow but I was vogie!
But I gat ne'er ſae ſair a fleg
Since I came frae my daddy,
The laird came rap rap to the yett,
Whan I was wi' his lady.

Then ſhe pat me below a chair,
And hap'd me wi' a plaidie;
But I was like to ſwarf wi' fear,
And wiſh'd me wi' my daddy.
The laird went out he ſaw na me,
I went whan I was ready:
I promis'd, but I ne'er gade back
To ſee his bonny lady

## Talk not of love, it gives me pain. By a Lady.

Tune, Banks of Spey.

186

* Talk not of love, it gives me pain, For love has
Very Slow
been my foe; He bound me with an iron chain, And
plung'd me deep in woe. But friendſhip's pure and laſting
joys, My heart was form'd to prove; There, welcome win and
wear the prize, But ne_ver talk of love.

Your friendſhip much can make me bleſt,
Oh, why that bliſs deſtroy!
Why urge the only, one requeſt
You know I will deny!
Your thought, if love muſt harbour there,
Conceal it in that thought;
Nor cauſe me from my boſom tear
The very friend I ſought.

## O'er the water to Charlie.

187

Come boat me o'er, come row me o'er, Come boat me o'er to
Lively
Charlie; I'll gie John Rofs another bawbee, To boat me o'er to Charlie.
We'll o'er the water, we'll o'er the fea, We'll o'er the water to Charlie; Come
weal, come woe, we'll gather and go, And live or die wi' Charlie.

I lo'e weel my Charlie's name,
Tho' fome there be abhor him:
But O, to fee auld Nick gaun hame,
And Charlie's faes before him!
We'll o'er &c.

I fwear and vow by moon and ftars,
And fun that fhines fo early!
If I had twenty thoufand lives,
I'd die as aft for Charlie.
We'll o'er &c.

## Up and warn a' Willie.

188

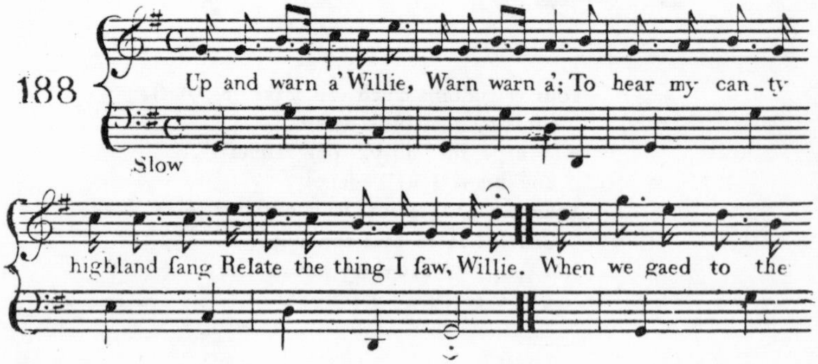
Up and warn a' Willie, Warn warn a'; To hear my can_ty
Slow
highland fang Relate the thing I faw, Willie. When we gaed to the

Continued

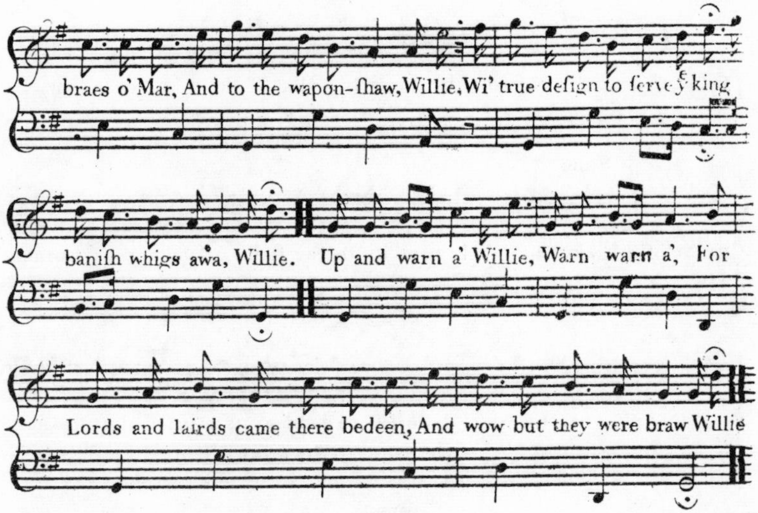
braes o' Mar, And to the wapon-ſhaw, Willie, Wi' true deſign to ſerve ye king
banish whigs awa, Willie. Up and warn a' Willie, Warn warn a', For
Lords and lairds came there bedeen, And wow but they were braw Willie

But when the ſtandard was ſet up,
Right fierce the wind did blaw, Willie;
The royal nit upon the tap
Down to the ground did fa', Willie.
Up and warn a', Willie,
Warn, warn a';
Then ſecond ſighted Sandy ſaid
We'd do nae gude at a', Willie.

But when the army join'd at Perth
The braveſt e're ye ſaw, Willie,
We didna doubt the rogues to rout,
Reſtore our king and a', Willie.
Up and warn a', Willie,
Warn, warn a';
The pipers play'd frae right to left
O whirry whigs awa, Willie.

But when we march'd to Sherra-muir
And there the rebels ſaw, Willie;
Brave Argyle ttack'd our right,
Our flank and front and a' Willie.
Up and warn a', Willie,
Warn, warn a';
Traitor Huntly ſoon gave way
Seaforth, S^t Clair and a' Willie.

But brave Glengary on our right,
The rebel's left did claw, Willie,
He there the greateſt ſlaughter made
That ever Donald ſaw, Willie.
Up and warn a', Willie,
Warn, warn a',
And Whittam ſ_t his breeks for fear
And faſt did rin awa, Willie.

For he ca'd us a Highland mob
And ſoon he'd ſlay us a' Willie,
But we chas'd him back to Stirling brig
Dragoons and foot and Willie.
Up and warn a', Willie,
Warn, warn a';
At length we rallied on a hill
And briſkly up did draw, Willie

But when Argyle did view our line
And them in order ſaw, Willie,
He ſtreight gaed to Dumblane again
And back his left did draw, Willie.
Up and warn a' Willie,
Warn warn a';
Then we to Auchterairder march'd
To wait a better fa' Willie.

Now if ye ſpier wha wan the day,
I've tell'd you what I ſaw Willie.
We baith did fight and baith did beat
And baith did rin awa Willie
Up and warn a' Willie
Warn warn a;
For ſecond ſighted Sandie ſaid
We'd do nae gude at a' Willie

## A Rose bud by my early walk.

189

A rose bud by my early walk, A down a corn - in -
Slow
closed bawk, Sae gently bent its thorny stalk, All on a dewy morning.
Ere twice the shades o' dawn are fled, In a' its crimson glory spread, &
drooping rich the dewy head, It scents the ear - ly morning. Ere
twice the shades o' dawn are fled, In a' its crimson glory spread, And
drooping rich the dewy head, It scents the ear - ly morning.

Within the bush her covert nest
A little linnet fondly prest,
The dew sat chilly on her breast
Sae early in the morning.
She soon shall see her tender brood,
The pride, the pleasur o' the wood,
Amang the fresh green leaves bedew'd,
Awauk the early morning.

So thou, dear bird, young Jeany fair,
On trembling string or vocal air,
Shalt sweetly pay the tender care
That tents thy early morning.
So thou - sweet Rose bud - young and gay,
Shalt beauteous blaze upon the day,
And bless the Parent's evening ray
That watch'd thy early morning.

## To a Blackbird.

By a Lady.

Tune; Scots Queen.

190

* Go on ſweet bird, and ſoothe my care, Thy tune_ful
Slow
notes will huſh deſpair; Thy plaintive warblings void of art, Thrill
ſweet_ly thro' my ach_ing heart. Now chuſe thy mate, and
fond_ly love, And all the charm_ing tranſport prove; While
I a lovelorn ex_ile live, Nor tranſ_port or re_ceive or
give, Nor tran_ſport or re_ceive or give.

For thee is laughing nature gay;
For thee ſhe pours the vernal day:
For me in vain is nature dreſt,
While joy's a ſtranger to my breaſt!
Theſe ſweet emotions all enjoy;
Let love and ſong thy hours employ!
Go on, ſweet bird, and ſoothe my care:
Thy tuneful notes will huſh deſpair

## Hooly and Fairly.

191

Oh! what had I a do for to marry; My wife she drinks
Lively
naithing but sack and ca_na_ry, I to her friends complain'd right early:
O gin my wife wou'd drink hooly and fair_ly hooly and fair_ly,
hooly and fairly O gin my wife wou'd drink hooly and fair_ly.

First she drank Crummie, and syne she drank Garie;
Now she has druken my bonny grey mairie,
That carried me thro' the dub and the lairie, O gin my wife, &c.
She has druken her stockins sae has she her shoon.
And she has druken her bonny new gown:
Her wee bit dud sark that co'erd her fu' rarely, O gin my wife, &c.
If she'd drink but her ain things I wad na much care,
But she drinks my claiths that I canna well spare;
To the kirk and the market I gang fu' barely: O gin my wife, &c.
The vera gray mittens that gaed on my han's
To her neebour wife she has laid them in pawns;
My bane-headed staff that I lo'ed sae dearly, O gin my wife, &c.
If there's ony siller, she maun keep the purse;
If I seek but a baubee she'll scauld and she'll curse,
She gangs like a queen, I scrimped and sparely: O gin my wife, &c.
I never was given to wrangling nor strife,
Nor eer did refuse her the comforts of life;
E'er it come to a war I'm ay for a parley: O gin my wife, &c.
A pint wi' her cummers I wad her allow;
But when she sits down she fills hersell fow;
And when she is fow she's unco camstairie. O gin my wife, &c.
And when she comes hame she lays on the lads;
She ca's the lasses baith limmers and jads;
And I, my ain sell, an auld cuckold carlie; O gin my wife, &c.

## Auld Rob Morris.

192

There's Auld Rob Morris that wins in yon glen, He's the
Slowifh
king of good fallows, and wale of auld men: Has
four-fcore of black fheep, and four fcore too; And
auld Rob Morris is the man ye maun loo.

Doughter. Had your tongue, mither, and let that abee,
For his eild and my eild can never agree:
They'll never agree, and that will be feen;
For he is fourfcore, and I'm but fifteen.

Mither. Had your tongue, doughter, and lay by your pride,
For he's be the bridegroom, and ye's be the bride:
He fhall ly by your fide, and kifs ye too;
Auld Rob Morris is the man ye maun loo.

Doughter. Auld Rob Morris I ken him fou weel,
His back fticks out like ony peet-ereel
He's out fhin'd, in-knee'd, and ringle-eye'd too:
Auld Rob Morris is the man I'll ne'er loo.

Mither. Tho' auld Rob Morris be an elderly man,
Yet his auld brafs it will buy a new pan;
Then, doughter, ye fhoudna be fae ill to fhoo
For auld Rob Morris is the man ye maun loo.

Doughter. But auld Rob Morris I never will hae,
His back is fo ftiff, and his beard is grown gray
I had rather die than live wi' him a year;
Sae mair of Rob Morris I never will hear.

# And I'll kiſs thee yet, yet.

Tune, Braes o' Balquhidder.

193

And I'll kiſs thee yet, yet, An I'll kiſs thee o'er again; An
Slowiſh
I'll kiſs thee yet, yet, My bony Peg-gy Ali-ſon. When
in my arms, wi' a' thy charms, I claſp my countleſs treaſure, O! I
ſeek nae mair o' Heav'n to ſhare, Than ſic a moment's pleaſure O! When
in my arms, wi' a' thy charms, I claſp my countleſs treaſure, O! I
ſeek nae mair o' Heav'n to ſhare, Than ſic a moment's pleaſure O!

An I'll kiſs thee yet, yet,
An I'll kiſs thee o'er again;
An I'll kiſs thee yet, yet,
bony Peggy Aliſon.

And by thy een ſae bony blue,
I ſwear I'm thine forever O!
And on thy lips I ſeal my vow,
And break it ſhall I never O.
And by thy een, &c.

## Rattlin, roarin Willie.

194

O Rat_tlin, roarin Willie, O he held to the fair, An'
Lively
for to fell his fid_dle And buy fome o_ther ware; But
par_ting wi' his fid_dle, The faut tear blin't his e'e; And
Rattlin, roarin Willie Ye're wel_come hame to me.


O Willie, come fell your fiddle,
 O fell your fiddle fae fine;
O Willie, come fell your fiddle,
 And buy a pint o' wine;
If I fhould fell my fiddle,
 The warl' would think I wa mad,
For mony a rantin day
 My fiddle and I hae had.

As I cam by Crochallan
 I cannily keekit ben,
Rattlin, roarin Willie
 Was fitting at yon boord_en',
Sitting at yon boord_en',
 And amang guid companie;
Rattlin, roarin Willie,
 Ye're welcome hame to me.

## Where braving angry winter's ftorms.

Written by Robᵗ Burns. Tune, N. Gows Lamentation for Abercairny.

195

Slowifh

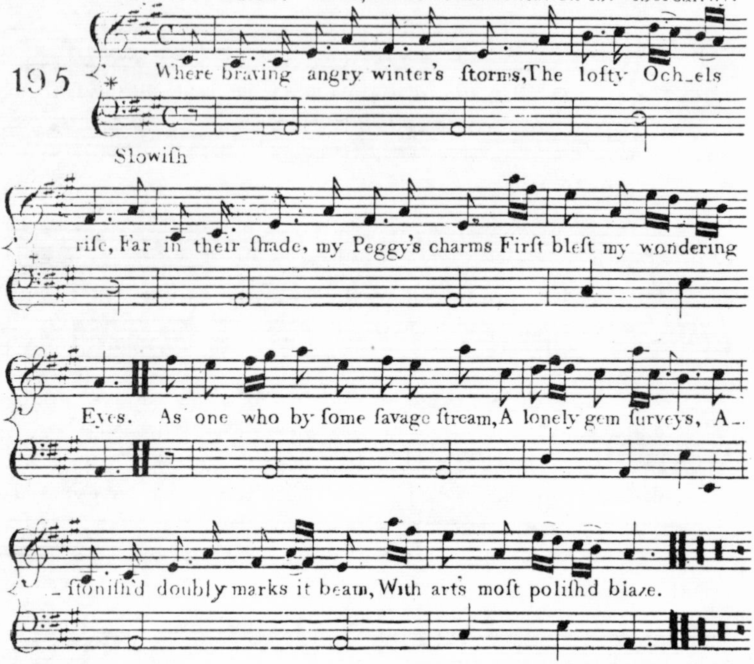
Where braving angry winter's ftorms, The lofty Och_els
rife, Far in their fhade, my Peggy's charms Firft bleft my wondering
Eyes. As one who by fome favage ftream, A lonely gem furveys, A_
_ftonifh'd doubly marks it beam, With arts moft polifh'd blaze.

Bleft be the wild, fequefter'd fhade,
And bleft the day and hour,
Where Peggy's charms I firft furvey'd,
When firft I felt their pow'r!

The tyrant death with grim controul
May feize my fleeting breath,
But tearing Peggy from my foul
Muft be a ftronger death.

R

## Tibbie, I hae feen the day.

Written for this Work by Robᵗ Burns. Tune, Invercalds Reel.

196

Slowifh

O Tibbie, I hae feen the day, Ye would na been fae fhy; For
laik o' gear ye lightly me, But trowth, I care na by. Yes _

Continued.

_treen I met you on the moor, Ye ſpak na, but gaed by like ſtoure; Ye
geck at me be_cauſe I'm poor, But fient a hair care I.
Chorus
O Tibbie, I hae ſeen the day, Ye would na been ſae ſhy; For
laik o' gear ye lightly me, But trowth I care na by.


I doubt na, laſs, but ye may think,
Becauſe ye hae the name o' clink,
That ye can pleaſe me at a wink,
Whene'er ye like to try.
Tibbie, I hae &c.

But ſorrow tak him that's ſae mean,
Altho' his pouch o' coin were clean,
Wha follows ony ſaucy quean
That looks ſae proud and high.
Tibbie, I hae &c.

Altho' a lad were e'er ſae ſmart,
If that he want the yellow dirt,
Ye'll caſt your head anither airt,
And anſwer him fu' dry
Tibbie, I hae &c.

But if he hae the name o' gear,
Ye'll faſten to him like a brier,
Tho' hardly he for ſenſe or lear
Be better than the kye.
Tibbie, I hae &c.

But, Tibbie, laſs, tak my advice,
Your daddie's gear maks you ſae nice;
The deil a ane wad ſpier your price,
Were ye as poor as I.
Tibbie, I hae &c.

## Nancy's Ghost.

Tune, Bonie Kate of Edinburgh.

197

Where waving pines fa_lute the fkies, And fil_ver
Slow
ftreams me_and_ring flow, Where verdant mountains gently rife, Thus
Sandy fung his tale of woe. Ah Ket_ty, cruel per_jur'd
maid, why haft thou ftole my heart away; Why thus for_fa_ken
am I laid, To fpend in tears and fighs the day!

The cooing turtle hears my moan,
My briny tears increafe the ftream,
The mountains echo back my groan
Whilft thou, fair tyrant, art my theme,
O blooming maid, indulgent prove,
And wipe the tears from Sandy's eyes,
O grant him kind returns of love,
Or Sandy bleeds and falls and dies.

Thus Sandy fung but turning round,
Beheld fweet Nancy's injur'd fhade,
He trembling faw he fhook and groan'd,
Fear and difmay his guilt betray'd:

"Ah, haplefs man, thy perjur'd vow
"Was to thy Nancy's heart a grave!
"The damps of death bedew'd my brow,
"While you the dying maid could fave!"

Thus fpake the vifion, and withdrew,
From Sandy's cheeks the crimfon fled;
Guilt and Defpair their arrows threw,
And now behold the traitor dead.
Remember fwains my artlefs ftrain,
To plighted faith be ever true,
And let no injur'd maid complain,
She finds falfe Sandy live in you.

D

## Clarinda.

Written for this Work by Robert Burns.

198
Slow and Expreſsive
Clar_in_da, miſtreſs of my ſoul, The meaſur'd
time is run! The wretch beneath the dreary pole, So
marks his lateſt ſun.

To what dark cave of frozen night
  Shall poor Sylvander hie;
Depriv'd of thee, his life and light.
  The Sun of all his joy.

We part – but by theſe precious drops,
  That fill thy lovely eyes.
No other light ſhall guide my ſteps,
  Till thy bright beams ariſe.

She, the fair Sun of all her ſex
  Has bleſt my glorious day:
And ſhall a glimmering Planet fix
  My worſhip to its ray.

# Cromlet's Lilt.

199

Slow
Since all thy vows, falſe maid, Are blown to air, And my poor heart betray'd To ſad deſ_pair,
In_to ſome wil_der_neſs, My grief I will ex_preſs,
And thy hard heart_ed_neſs, O cru_el fair.

Have I not graven our loves
On every tree
In yonder ſpreading Groves,
Tho' falſe thou be:
Was not a ſolemn oath
Plighted betwixt us both,
Thou thy faith, I my troth,
Conſtant to be.

Some gloomy place I'll find,
Some doleful ſhade,
Where neither ſun nor wind
E'er entrance had:
Into that hollow cave,
There will I ſigh and rave,
Becauſe thou doſt behave
So faithleſsly.

Wild fruit ſhall be my meat,
I'll drink the ſpring,
Cold earth ſhall be my ſeat:
For covering,

I'll have the ſtarry ſky
My head to canopy,
Until my ſoul on high
Shall ſpread its wing.

I'll have no funeral fire,
Nor tears for me;
No grave do I deſire,
Nor obſequies.
The courteous red_breaſt he,
With leaves will cover me,
And ſing my elegy,
With doleful voice.

And when a ghoſt I am,
I'll viſit thee;
O thou deceitful dame,
Whoſe cruelty
Has kill'd the kind'ſt heart,
That e'er felt Cupid's dart,
And never can deſert
From loving thee.

## The Winter it is Past

200

* The winter it is paſt, and the ſum_mers come at
Very Slow
laſt And the ſmall birds ſing on ev'_ry tree The
hearts of theſe are glad but mine is very ſad. For my
Lover has part_ed from me

The roſe upon the brier, by the waters running clear,
  May have charms for the linnet or the bee;
Their little loves are bleſt and their little hearts at reſt,
  But my Lover is parted from me.

My love is like the ſun, in the firmament does run,
  Forever is conſtant and true;
But his is like the moon that wanders up and down,
  And every month it is new.

All you that are in love and cannot it remove,
  I pity the pains you endure:
For experience makes me know that your hearts are full of woe,
  A woe that no mortal can cure.

END OF VOLUME SECOND

# THE SCOTS Musical Museum

Consisting of Six hundred Scots Songs

with proper Basses for the

PIANO FORTE &c.

Humbly Dedicated

To the Society

OF

Antiquaries of Scotland

BY JAMES JOHNSON

*In this publication the original simplicity of our Ancient National Airs is retained unincumbered with useless Accompaniments & graces depriving the hearers of the sweet simplicity of their native melodies.*

Volume 3 Pr. 7^s

Butterworth Scripsit

Printed & Sold by JAMES JOHNSON Music Seller EDINBURGH to be had at T PRESTON N.o 97 Strand LONDON, M.c FADYEN GLASGOW. & at all the principal Music Sellers.

# PREFACE.

NOW that the Editor gives this third Volume of The Scots Musical Museum to the Public he hopes it will not be found unworthy of the Volumes already Published. ___ As this is not one of those many Publications which are hourly ushered into the World merely to catch the eye of Fashion in her frenzy of a day, the Editor has little to hope or fear from the herd of readers. Consciousness of the well-known merit of our Scotish Music, and the national fondness of a Scotch-man for the productions of his own country, are at once the Editor's motive and apology for this Undertaking; and where any of the Pieces in the Collection may perhaps be found wanting at the Critical Bar of the First, he appeals to the honest prejudices of the Last.

Edin^r. February 2^d. 1790

# INDEX TO VOLUME THIRD.

Note, the Songs marked B. R. X. &c. are originals by different hands, but all of them Scots gentlemen, who have favoured the Editor and the Public at large with their compositions: these marked Z, are old verses, with corrections or additions.

# INDEX.

# INDEX.



## U



## W



## Y

## Tune your Fiddles, &c.

Tune, Marquis of Huntly's Reel.

No. 201

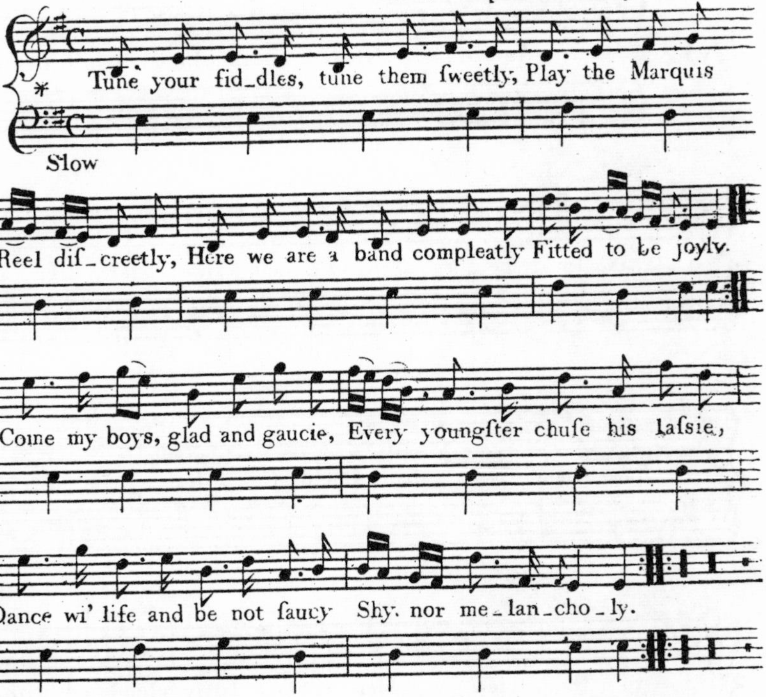
Tune your fid_dles, tune them ſweetly, Play the Marquis
Slow
Reel diſ_creetly, Here we are a band compleatly Fitted to be joyly.
Come my boys, glad and gaucie, Every youngſter chuſe his laſsie,
Dance wi' life and be not ſaucy Shy. nor me_lan_cho_ly.

Lay aſide your ſowre grimaces,
Clouded brows and drumly faces,
Look about and ſee their Graces,
How they ſmile delighted!
Now's the ſeaſon to be merry,
Hang the thoughts of Charon's ferry,
Time enough to turn camſtary
When we're old and doited.
Now's the ſeaſon &c.

Butler put about the claret
Thro' us all divide and ſhare it,
Gordon-Caſtle well can ſpare it
It has claret plenty.
Wine's the true. inſpiring liquor
Draffy drink may pleaſe the Vicar,
When he graſps the foaming bicker
Vicars are not dainty.
Wine's the true &c.

We'll extol our noble maſter
Sprung from many a brave ânceſtor
Lord preſerve him from diſaſter,
So we pray in duty.
Proſper too our pretty Dutcheſs
Safe from all diſtreſsful touches,
Keep her out of Pluto's clutches;
Long in health and beauty.
Proſper too our &c.

Angels guard their gallant boy,
Make him long his fathers joy,
Sturdy like the Heir of Troy,
Stout and briſk and healthy:
Pallas grant him every bleſsing
Wit and ſize and ſtrength encreaſing,
Plutus, what's in thy poſseſsing,
Make him rich and wealthy.
Pallas grant &c.

Youth ſolace him with thy pleaſure
In refin'd and worthy meaſure,
Merit gain him choiceſt treaſure
From the Royal Donor.
Famous may he be in ſtory,
Full of days and full of glory,
To the grave when old and hoary
May he go with honour.
Famous may &c.

Gordons join our hearty praiſes
Honeſt tho' in homely phraſes
Love our chearful ſpirits raiſes
Lofty as the lark is;
Echoes waft our wiſhes daily
Thro' the grove and thro' the alley
Sound o'er every hill and valley
Bleſsings on our Marquis.
Echoes waft &c.

## Gladſmuir.

202

As o_ver Gladſ_muir's blood ſtain'd field, Sco-
-tia, Im_pe_ri_al God_deſs flew;. Her lif__ted
ſpear and ra__diant ſhield Con_ſpi_cuous bla_zing
to the view. Her vi_ſage lately cloud_ed with deſ_
_pair, Now re_a_ſum'd its. firſt ma_jeſ_tic air.

Such ſeen as oft in battle warm
She glow'd through many a martial age;
Or mild to breathe the civil charm
In pious plans and counſel ſage:
For, o'er the mingling glories of her face
A manly greatneſs heighten'd female grace.
Loud as the trumpet rolls its ſound,
Her voice the Pow'r celeſtial rais'd;
While her victorious ſons around
In ſilent joy and wonder gaz'd:
The ſacred muſes heard th' immortal lay,
And thus to earth the notes of fame convey.

Continued.

'Tis done! my ſons. 'tis nobly done.
Victorious over tyrant pow'r;
How quick the race of fame was run.
The work of ages in one hour:
Slow creeps th' oppreſsive weight of ſlaviſh reigns,
One glorious moment roſe, and burſt your chains.
But late, forlorn, dejected, pale,
A prey to each inſulting foe;
I ſought the grove and gloomy vale,
To vent in ſolitude my woe:
Now to my hand the balance fair reſtor'd;
Once more I wield on high th' imperial ſword.
What arm has this deliverance wrought?
'Tis he. the gallant youth appears;
O warm in fields, and cool in thought.
Beyond the ſlow advance of years!
Haſte, let me, reſcu'd now from future harms,
Strain cloſe the filial virtue in my arms.
Early I nurs'd this royal youth,
Ah! ill detain'd on foreign ſhores;
I fill'd his mind with love of truth,
With fortitude and wiſdom's ſtores:
For when a noble action is decreed,
Heav'n forms the Hero for the deſtin'd deed.
Nor could the ſoft ſeducing charms
Of mild Heſperia's blooming ſoil,
Ee'r quench his noble thirſt of arms,
Of generous deeds and honeſt toil:
Fir'd with the warmth a country's love imparts,
He fled their weakneſs, but admir'd their arts.
With him I plough'd the ſtormy main;
My breath inſpir'd the auſpicious gale;
Reſerv'd for Gladſmuir's glorious plain,
Through dangers wing'd his daring ſail:
Where, firm'd with inborn worth he durſt oppoſe
His ſingle valour to an hoſt of foes.
He came! he ſpoke! and all around,
As ſwift as heav'n's quick darted flame,
Shepherds turn'd warriors at the ſound,
And every boſom beat for fame:
They caught heroic ardour from his eyes,
And at his ſide the willing heroes riſe.
Rouſe England! rouſe, fame's nobleſt ſon,
In all thy ancient ſplendor ſhine;
If I the glorious work begun,
O let the crowning palm be thine:
I bring a Prince, for ſuch is heav'n's decree,
Who overcomes but to forgive and free.
So ſhall fierce wars and tumults ceaſe,
While plenty crowns the ſmiling plain;
And induſtry, fair child of peace,
Shall in each crowded city reign:
So ſhall theſe happy realms for ever prove
The ſweets of Union, Liberty, and Love.

# Gill Morice.

203

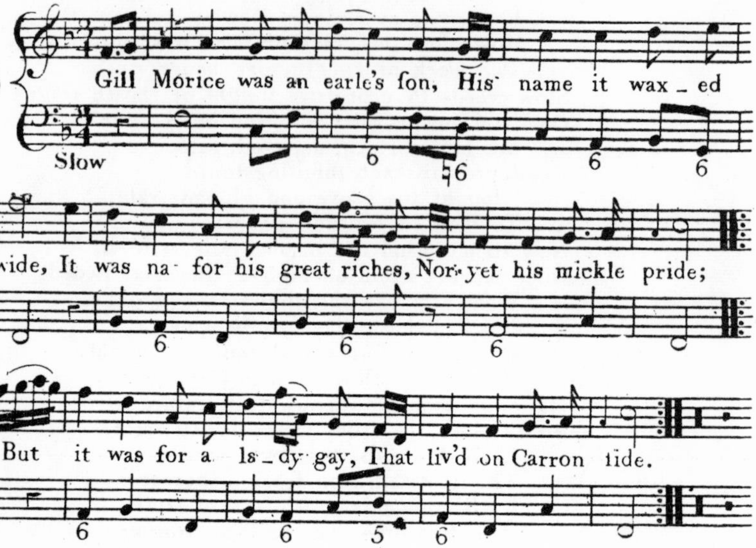
Gill Morice was an earle's ſon, His name it wax_ed
Slow
wide, It was na for his great riches, Nor yet his mickle pride;
But it was for a la_dy gay, That liv'd on Carron ſide.

Where will I get a bonny boy,
  That will win hoſe and ſhoon,
That will gae to Lord Barnard's ha',
  And bid his lady cum.
Ye maun rin this errant, Willie,
  And ye may rin wi' pride;
When other boys gae on their feet,
  On horſeback ye ſall ride.

Oh no! oh no! my maſter dear!
  I dare na for my life;
I'll nae gae to the bauld baron's
  For to tryſt furth his wife.
My bird Willie, my boy Willie,
  My dear Willie, he ſaid,
How can ye ſtrive againſt the ſtream,
  For I ſall be obey'd.

But, oh my maſter dear, he cry'd,
  In green wood ye're your lain;
Gi' o'er ſic thoughts, I wou'd ye red,
  For fear ye ſhou'd be ta'en.
Haſte, haſte, I ſay, gae to the ha',
  Bid her come here wi' ſpeed;
If ye refuſe my high command,
  I'll gar thy body bleed.

Gae bid her tak this gay mantel,
  'Tis a' goud but the hem;
Bid her cum to the good green wood,
  And bring nane but her lain:
And there it is, a ſilken ſark;
  Her ain hand ſew'd the ſleeve;
And bid her cum to Gill Morice;
  Speer nae bauld baron's leave.

I will gae your black errand,
  Tho' it be to thy coſt;
Sen ye by me will nae be warn'd,
  In it ye ſall find froſt.
The baron he's a man of might,
  He ne'er could 'bide a taunt,
As ye will ſee before it's night,
  How ſma' ye'll hae to vaunt.

Now, ſen I maun your errand rin,
  Sae ſair againſt my will,
I'ſe make a vow, and keep it true,
  It ſal be done for ill.
And when he came to broken brigg,
  He bent his bow and ſwam;
And when he came to graſs growing,
  Set down his feet and ran. &c. &c. &c.

## I love my Love in ſecret.

204

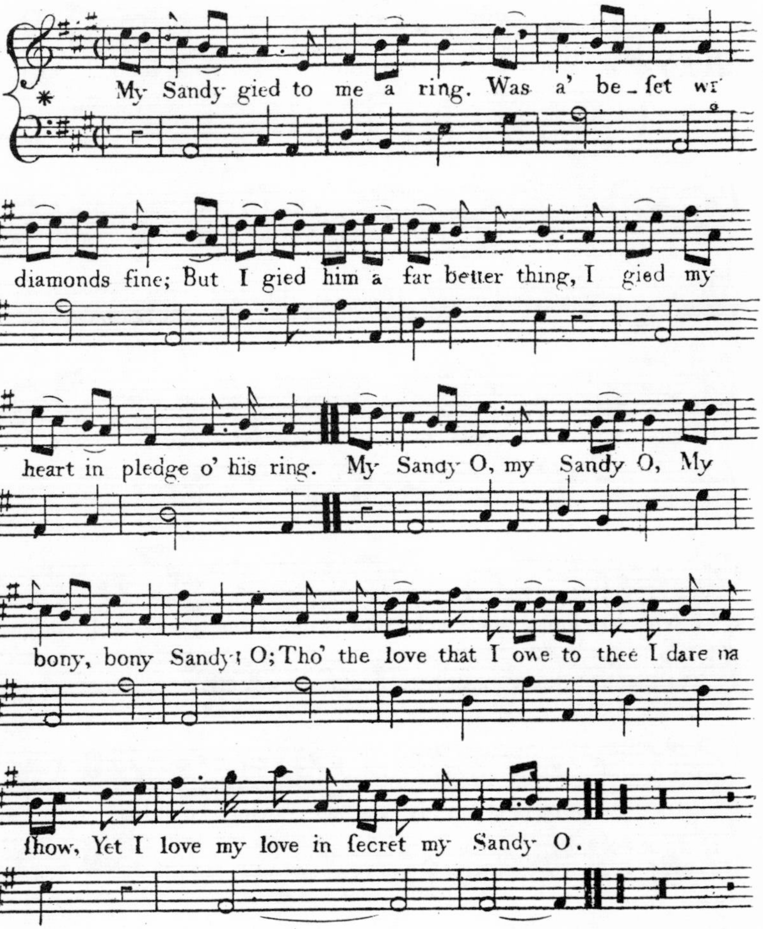
My Sandy gied to me a ring. Was a' be_ſet wi'
diamonds fine; But I gied him a far better thing, I gied my
heart in pledge o' his ring. My Sandy O, my Sandy O, My
bony, bony Sandy O; Tho' the love that I owe to thee I dare na
ſhow, Yet I love my love in ſecret my Sandy O.

My Sandy brak a pieceo' gowd,
While down his cheeks the ſaut tears row'd;
He took a hauf and gied it to me,
And I'll keep it till the hour I die.
My Sandy O &c.

## Same Tune.

THE ſmiling plains profuſely gay,
Are dreſs'd in all the pride of May,
The birds on ev'ry ſpray above,
To rapture wake the vocal grove.

But ah Miranda without thee,
Nor ſpring nor ſummer ſmills on me.
All lonely in the ſecret ſhade;
I mourn thy abſence, charming maid

O ſoft as love! as honour fair,
Serenely ſweet as vernal air.
Come to my arms for you alone,
Can all my abſence paſt atone.
O come! and to my bleeding heart,
The ſov'reign balm of love impart;
Thy preſence laſting joy ſhall bring.
And give the year eternal ſpring

## When I upon thy bosom lean.

Tune, Scots Recluse.

205

Slow
* When I upon thy bosom lean, And fond_ly clasp thee
a', my ain, I glo_ry in the sa_cred ties That made us
ane, wha ance were twain: A mutual flame in_spires us baith, The
ten_der look, the mel_ting kiss: Even years shall ne'er des_
_troy our love, But on_ly gie us change o' bliss.

Hae I a wish? it's a' for thee;
I ken thy wish is me to please;
Our moments pass sae smooth away
That numbers on us look and gaze,
Weel pleas'd they see our happy days,
Nor envy's sel finds aught to blame;
And ay when weary cares arise,
Thy bosom still shall be my hame.

I'll lay me there, and take my rest,
And if that aught disturb my dear,
I'll bid her laugh her cares away,
And beg her not to drap a tear:
Hae I a joy? it's a' her ain;
United still her heart and mine;
They're like the woodbine round the tree,
That's twin'd till death shall them disjoin.

## Colonel Gardener.

Tune, Sawnie's Pipe

206

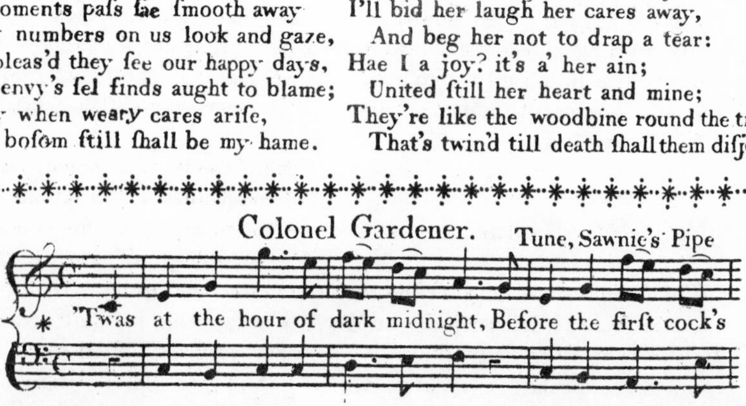
* 'Twas at the hour of dark midnight, Before the first cock's

Continued.

crow_ing, When weſt_land winds ſhook Stirling's towers, With
hol_low mur_murs blowing; When Fan_ny fair, all woe be_
_gone, Sad on her bed was ly_ing, And from the ruin'd
towers ſhe heard The boding ſcreech owl cry_ing,

O diſmal night! ſhe ſaid, and wept,
  O night preſaging ſorrow,
O diſmal night! ſhe ſaid, and wept,
  But more I dread to-morrow.
For now the bloody hour draws nigh,
  Each hoſt to Preſton bending;
At morn ſhall ſons their fathers ſlay,
  With deadly hate contending.

Even in the viſions of the night,
  I ſaw fell death wide ſweeping;
And all the matrons of the land,
  And all the virgins, weeping.
And now ſhe heard the maſsy gates
  Harſh on their hinges turning;
And now through all the caſtle heard
  The woeful voice of mourning.

Aghaſt, ſhe ſtarted from her bed,
  The fatal tidings dreading;
O ſpeak, ſhe cry'd, my father's ſlain!
  I ſee, I ſee him bleeding!

A pale corpſe on the ſullen ſhore,
  At morn, fair maid, I left him;
Even at the threſh-hold of his gate,
  The foe of life bereft him.

Bold, in the battle's front, he fell,
  With many a wound deformed:
A braver Knight, nor better man,
  This fair iſle ne'er adorned.
While thus he ſpoke, the grief-ſtruck maid
  A deadly ſwoon invaded;
Loſt was the luſtre of her eyes,
  And all her beauty faded.

Sad was the ſight, and ſad the news,
  And ſad was our complaining;
But oh! for thee, my native land
  What woes are ſtill remaining.
But why complain. the hero's ſoul
  Is high in heaven ſhining:
May providence defend our iſle
  From all our foes deſigning.

# Tibbie Dunbar.

Written for this Work by Robert Burns. Tune, Johnny M^c^ Gill.

207

* O wilt thou go wi' me, fweet Tibbie Dun_bar; O
wilt thou go wi' me, fweet Tib_bie Dunbar; Wilt thou ride on a
horfe, or be drawn in a car, Or walk by my fide, O fweet
Tibbie Dun_bar. I care na thy daddie, his lands and his
money, I care na thy kin, fae high and fae lord_ly: But
fay thou wilt hae me for bet_ter for waur, And
come in thy coatie fweet Tibbie Dunbar.

# Jenny, was fair and unkind.

Tune. Scots Jenny.

208
Slow
When weſt winds did blow with a ſoft, gentle breeze, And
ſweet blooming verdure did clothe all the trees, I went forth one morning to
hail the new ſpring, And hear the ſweet ſongſters all warble and ſing.
I ſaw the green foreſt, I ſaw the gay plain, But na_ture to
me was delightful in vain, For love had in_vaded the peace of my
mind, And Jenny, dear Jenny, was fair and un_kind.

Ye Powers, who reſide in the regions above,
Deprive me of life, or inſpire her with love!
Make Jenny's fair boſom to feel for my pain,
That I may ſweet peace and contentment regain.
Then in a retreat with my dear I would dwell;
Contentment ſhould guard us in ſome humble cell;
Remote, we'll live happy, tho' ſimple our fare;
Our health all our wealth, and to love all our care.

## My Harry was a Gallant gay.

Tune, Highlander's Lament.

209

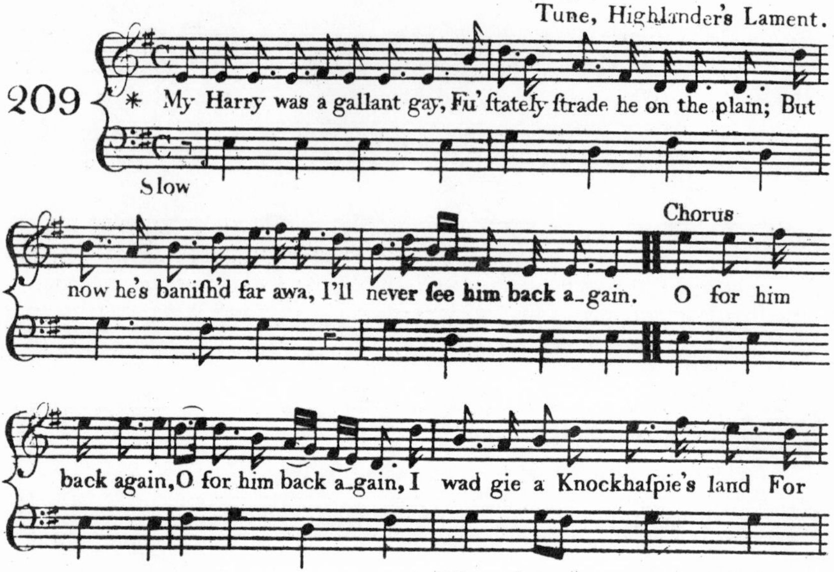
* My Harry was a gallant gay, Fu' stately strade he on the plain; But
Slow
Chorus
now he's banish'd far awa, I'll never see him back a_gain. O for him
back again, O for him back a_gain, I wad gie a Knockhaspie's land For

Highland Harry back again.

When a' the lave gae to their bed,
I wander dowie up the glen;
I set me down and greet my fill,
And ay I wish him back again.
O for him &c.
O were some villains hangit high,
And ilka body had their ain!
Then I might see the joyfu' sight,
My Highlan Harry back again.
O for him &c.

## The Highland Character.

210

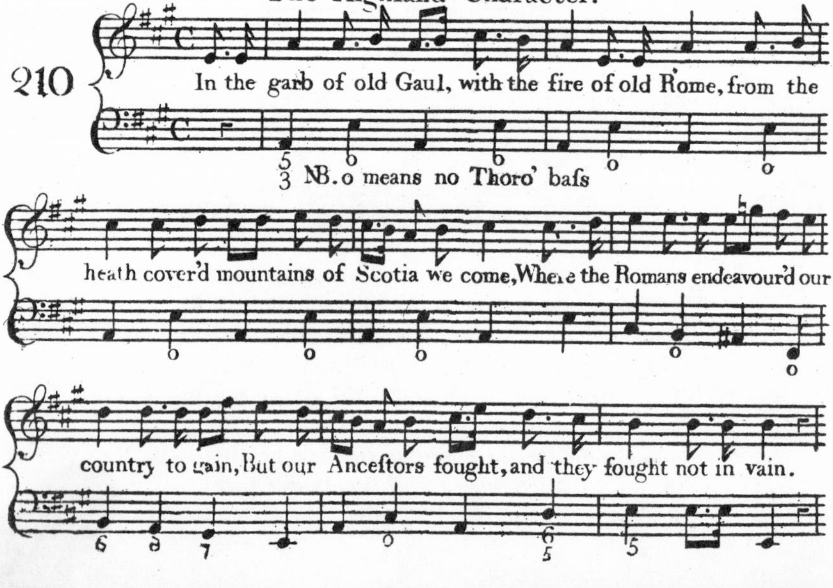
In the garb of old Gaul, with the fire of old Rome, from the
NB. o means no Thoro' bass
heath cover'd mountains of Scotia we come, Where the Romans endeavour'd our
country to gain, But our Ancestors fought, and they fought not in vain.

## Continued.

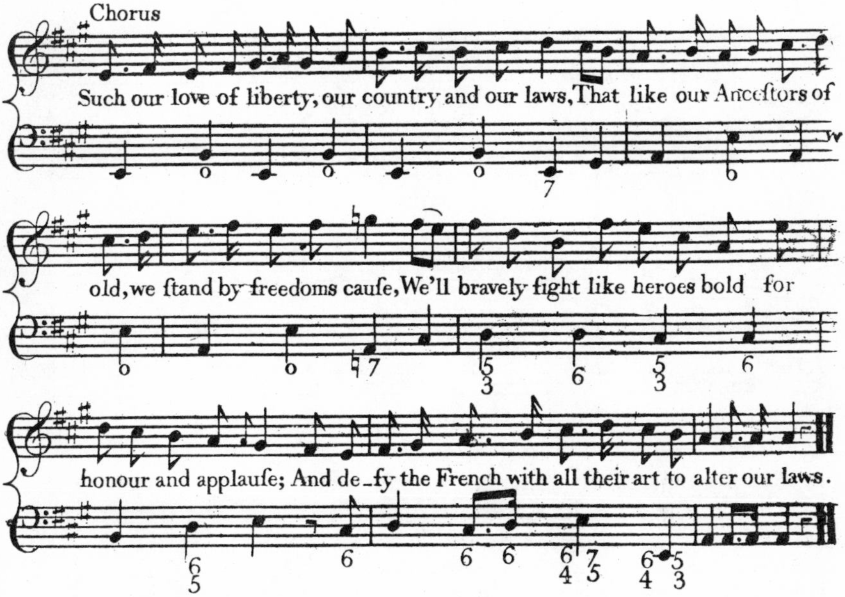
Chorus
Such our love of liberty, our country and our laws, That like our Anceſtors of
old, we ſtand by freedoms cauſe, We'll bravely fight like heroes bold for
honour and applauſe; And de_fy the French with all their art to alter our laws.

No effeminate cuſtoms our ſinews unbrace,
No luxurious tables enervate our race;
Our loud ſounding pipe bears the true martial ſtrain,
So do we the old Scottiſh valour retain.
Such our love &c.

We're tall as the oak on the mount of the vale,
Are ſwift as the roe which the hound doth aſſail,
As the full moon in autumn our ſhields do appear,
Minerva would dread to encounter our ſpear.
Such our love &c.

As a ſtorm in the ocean when Boreas blows,
So are we enrag'd when we ruſh on our foes;
We ſons of the mountains, tremendous as rocks,
Daſh the force of our foes with our thundering ſtrokes.
Such our love &c.

Quebec and Cape Breton, the pride of old France,
In their troops fondly boaſted till we did advance;
But when our claymores they ſaw us produce,
Their courage did-fail and they ſued for a truce.
Such our love &c.

In our realm may the fury of faction long ceaſe,
May our councils be wiſe, and our commerce increaſe;
And in Scotia's cold climate may each of us find,
That our friends ſtill prove true and our beauties prove kind
Cho^s. Then we'll defend our liberty, our country and our laws,
And teach our late poſterity to fight in Freedoms cauſe,
That they like our Anceſtors bold, for honour and applauſe,
May defy the French, with all their art, to alter our laws

## Leader haughs and Yarrow.

211

The morn was fair, ſaft was the air, All nature's ſweets were
ſpringing, The buds did bow with ſilver dew, Tenthouſand birds were ſinging;
When on the bent, with blyth content, Young Jamie ſang his marrow, Nae
bonnier laſs e'er trod the graſs, On Leader haughs and Yarrow.

How ſweet her face, where ev'ry grace
In heavenly beauty's planted;
Her ſmiling een, and comely mein,
That nae perfection wanted;
I'll never fret, nor ban my fate,
But bleſs my bonny marrow:
If her dear ſmile my doubts beguile,
My mind ſhall ken nae ſorrow.

Yet tho' ſhe's fair, and has full ſhare
Of ev'ry charm inchanting,
Each good turns ill, and ſoon will kill
Poor, me, if love be wanting.
O bonny laſs! have but the grace
To think ere ye gae further,
Your joys maun flit, if you commit
The crying ſin of murder.

My wand'ring ghaiſt will ne'er get reſt,
And day and night affright ye;
But if ye're kind, wi' joyful mind
I'll ſtudy to delight ye;
Our years around with love thus crown'd
From all things joy ſhall borrow:
Thus none ſhall be more bleſt than we,
On Leader-haughs and Yarrow.

O ſweeteſt Sue. tis only you
Can make life worth my wiſhes,
If equal love your mind can move
To grant this beſt of bliſſes.
Thou art my ſun, and thy leaſt frown
Would blaſt me in the bloſſom;
But if thou ſhine, and make me thine,
I'll flouriſh in thy boſom.

## The Taylor fell thro' the bed, &c.

212

* The Taylor fell thro' the bed, thimble an' a, The
Tay_lor fell thro' the bed thim_ble an' a'; The
blank_ets were thin and the ſheets they were ſma', The
Tay_lor fell thro' the bed, thim_ble an' a'.

The ſleepy bit laſsie ſhe dreaded nae ill,
The ſleepy bit laſsie ſhe dreaded nae ill;
The weather was cauld and the laſsie lay ſtill,
She thought that a Taylor could do her nae ill.

Gie me the groat again, cany young man,
Gie me the groat again, cany young man;
The day it is ſhort and the night it is lang,
The deareſt ſiller that ever I wan.

There's ſomebody weary wi' lying her lane,
There's ſomebody weary wi' lying her lane,
There's ſome that are dowie, I trow wad be fain
To ſee the bit Taylor come ſkippin again.

## Ay waukin, O.

213

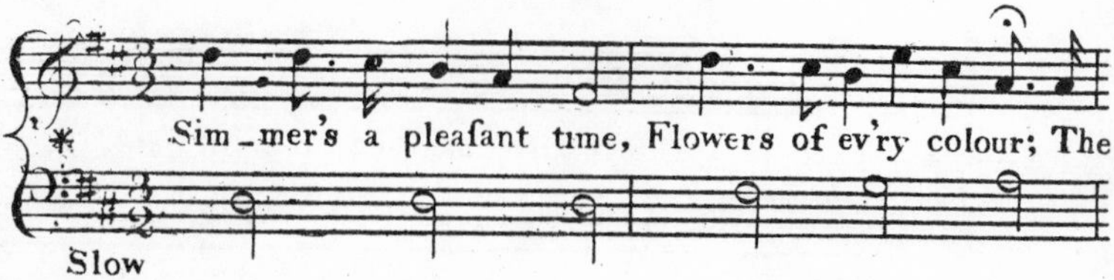
Sim_mer's a pleasant time, Flowers of ev'ry colour; The
Slow

water rins o'er the heugh, And I long for my true lover! Ay waukin, O,

Waukin still and weary: Sleep I can get nane, For thinking on my Dearie.

When I sleep I dream,
  When I wauk I'm irie;
Sleep I can get nane
  For thinking on my Dearie.
    Ay waukin &c.

Lanely night comes on,
  A' the lave are sleepin:
I think on my bony lad
  And I bleer my een wi' greetin.
    Ay waukin &c.

## The Breast knots.

214

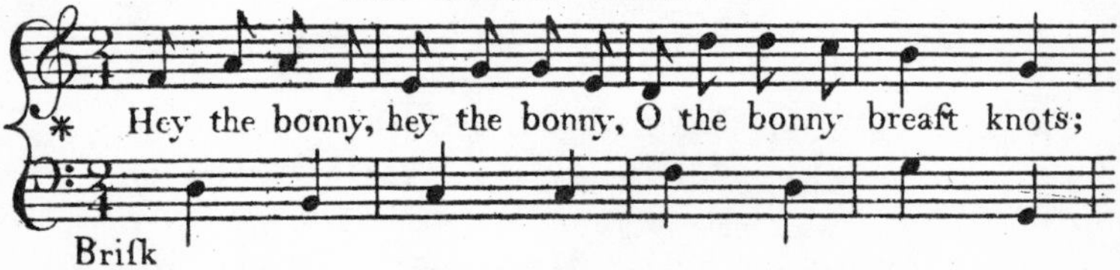
Hey the bonny, hey the bonny, O the bonny breast knots;
Brisk

Tight and bonny were they a', When they got on their breast knots. There

was a bridal in this town, And till't the lass_es a' were boun', With

Continued.

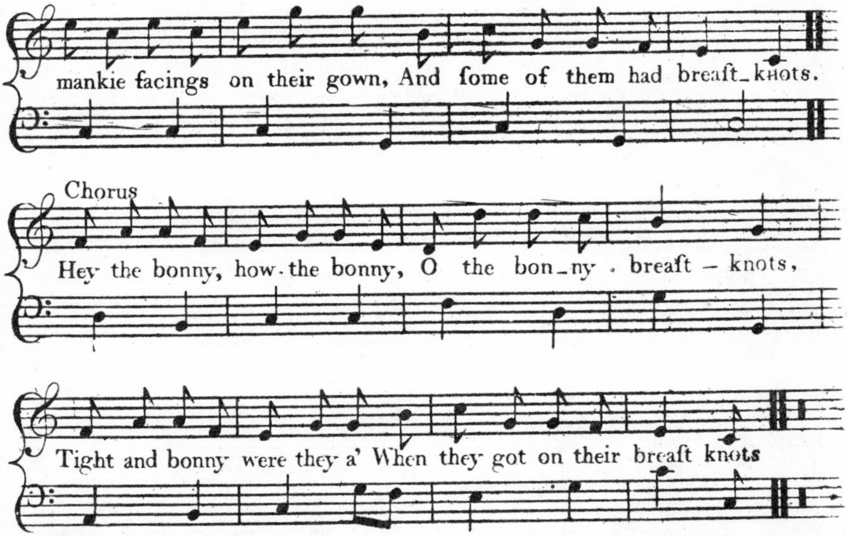
mankie facings on their gown, And ſome of them had breaſt_knots.
Chorus
Hey the bonny, how the bonny, O the bon_ny breaſt – knots,
Tight and bonny were they a' When they got on their breaſt knots

And there was mony a luſty lad,
As ever handled grape and gaud,
I wat their manhood well they ſhaw'd,
At ruffling of the breaſt-knot.
Hey the bonny &c.

At nine o' clock they did conveen,
Some clad in blue, ſome clad in green,
Wi' glancing buckles in their ſheen,
And flowers upon their waiſt-coat.
Hey the bonny &c.

The bride by this time was right fain,
When that ſhe ſaw ſae light a train,
She pray'd the day might keep frae rain,
For ſpoiling of their breaſt knots.
Hey the bonny &c.

Forth came the wives a' wi' a phraſe,
And wiſh'd the laſſie happy days,
And muckle thought they of her claiths,
And ſpecially the breaſt-knots.
Hey the bonny &c.

Forth ſpake the mither, ſan ſhe ſaw,
The bride and maidens a' ſae bra',
Wi' cackling clouts, black be their fa',
They have made a bonny caſt o't.
Hey the bonny &c.

Next down their breakfaſt it was ſet,
Some barley lippies of milk meat,
It leiped them it was ſae het,
As ſoon as they did taſte o't.
Hey the bonny &c

Till ſome frae them the ſpoons they threw,
And ſwore that they had burnt their mou
And ſome into their cutty blew,
I wat their will they miſt not.
Hey the bonny &c.

When ilka ane had claw'd their plate,
The piper lad he looked blate
Altho' they ſaid that he ſhould eat,
I trow he loſt the beſt o't.
Hey the bonny &c.

Syne forth they got a' wi' a loup,
O'er creels and deals and a' did coup,
The piper ſaid, wi' them d _ l ſcoup
He'd make a hungry feaſt o't.
Hey the bonny &c.

Syne off they got a' wi' a fling,
Each laſs unto her lad did cling,
And a' cry'd for a different ſpring,
The bride ſhe ſought the breaſt-knot.
Hey the bonny &c.

Fan they ty'd up their marriage band
At the bridegroom's they neiſt did land,
Forth came auld Madge wi' her ſplit ma
And bread and cheeſe a hiſt o't (wn
Hey the bonny &c.

She took a quarter and a third,
On the bride's head ſhe gae a gird,
Till farls flew athort the yird,
And parted round the reſt o't.
Hey the bonny &c.

The bride then by the hand they took
Twice, thrice they led her round y$^e$ crook
Some ſaid goodwife well mat ye brook
And ſome great count they caſt not.
Hey the bonny &c

All ran to kilns and barns in rank,
Some ſat on deals & ſome on planks.
The piper lad ſtood on his ſhanks,
And dirled up the breaſt knot.
Hey the bonny &c.

## Beware o' bonie Ann.

215

*
Slow
Ye gallants bright I red you right, Be_ware o'
bonie Ann; Her come_ly face ſae fu' o' grace, Your
heart ſhe will tre_pan. . Her een ſae bright, like ſtars by
night, Her ſkin is like the ſwan; Sae jimp_ly lac'd her
gen_ty waiſt, That ſweet_ly ye might ſpan.

Youth, grace and love attendant move,
And pleaſure leads the van:
In a' their charms and conquering arms,
They wait on bonie Ann.
The captive bands may chain the hands,
But loove enſlaves the man:
Ye gallants braw, I red you a'
Beware o' bonie Ann. X

## This is no mine ain houſe.

216

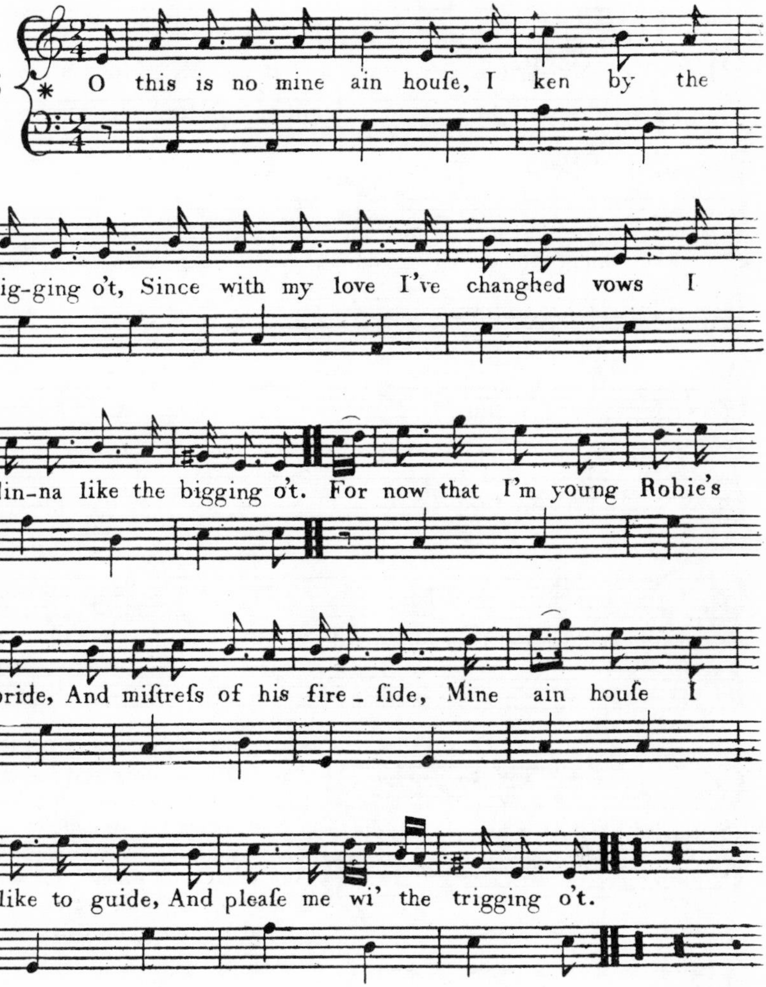
O this is no mine ain houſe, I ken by the rig-ging o't, Since with my love I've changhed vows I din-na like the bigging o't. For now that I'm young Robie's bride, And miſtreſs of his fire _ ſide, Mine ain houſe I like to guide, And pleaſe me wi' the trigging o't.

Then farewell to my father's houſe,
  I gang where love invites me;
The ſtricteſt duty this allows,
  When love with honour meets me.
When Hymen moulds me into ane,
  My Robie's nearer than my kin,
And to refuſe him were a ſin,
  Sae lang's he kindly treats me.

When I am in mine ain houſe,
  True love ſhall be at hand ay
To make me ſtill a prudent ſpouse,
  And let my man command ay;
Avoiding ilka cauſe of ſtrife,
  The common peſt of married life,
That makes ane wearied of his wife.
  And breaks the kindly band ay.

## My Wife's a wanton, wee thing.

217

My Wife's a wanton, wee thing, My wife's a wanton
Lively
wee thing, My wife's a wanton wee thing, She win_na be_
guid_ed by me. She play'd the loon or ſhe was married, She
play'd the loon or ſhe was married, She play'd the loon or ſhe was

married, She'll do it again or ſhe die.

She ſell'd her coat and ſhe drank it,
She ſell'd her coat and ſhe drank it,
She row'd herſell in a blanket,
She winna be guided for me.
She mind't na when I forbade her,
She mind't na when I forbade her,
I took a rung and I claw'd her,
And a braw gude bairn was ſhe.

## Laddie lie near me.

218

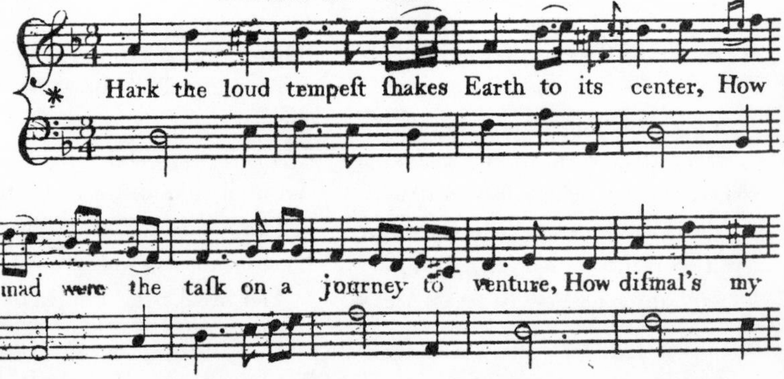
Hark the loud tempeſt ſhakes Earth to its center, How
mad were the taſk on a journey to venture, How diſmal's my

Continued.

proſpect! of life, I am weary, O liſ_ten my love I be_
_ſeech thee to hear me. Hear me, hear me, in ten_der_neſs
hear me, All the long winter night Laddie be near me.

Nights tho' protracted, tho' piercing the weather,
Yet ſummer was endleſs, when we were together;
Now ſince thy, abſence I feel moſt ſeverely.
Joy is extinguiſh'd and being is dreary
Dreary, dreary painful and dreary
All the long winter night Laddie be near me

Seize the ſweet moments while yet they invite thee,
Pleaſures here ſlighted, hereafter may ſlight thee..
Diſtance and time may no longer endear thee,
Come, my dear youth while thy preſence can chear me.
Chear me, chear me heaven knows it would chear me
All the long winter night Laddie be near me.

What is my fault my ſoul's darling acquaint me,
Let jealous fury no longer torment thee,
Judge for thy ſelf how, I love and revere thee
Heaven and thy heart from ſuſpicion will clear me
Clear me, clear me juſtice muſt clear me
All the long winter night Laddie lie near me.

D

## Old Words

LANG hae we parted been,
Laſsie my dearie;
Now we are met again,
Laſsie lie near me.
Cho.<sup></sup>

Near me, near me,
Laſsie lie near me
Lang haſt thou lien thy lane,
Laſsie lie near me.

A' that I hae endur'd,
Laſsie, my dearie,
Here in thy arms is cur'd,
Laſsie lie near me.
Chos. Near me.

# The brisk young Lad.

219
Lively
* There came a young man to my dad_die's door, My
daddie's door, my daddie's door, There came a young man to my
daddie's door Came seeking me to woo. And wow, but he was a
braw young lad, A brisk young lad and a braw young lad, And
wow but he was a braw young lad, Came seeking me to woo.

But I was bakin when he came,
When he came, when he came;
I took him in and gae him a scone,
To thow his frozen mou'.
And wow but, &c.

I set him in aside the bink,
I gae him bread, and ale to drink,
And ne'er a blyth styme wad he blink,
Until his wame was fou.
And wow but, &c

Gae, get ye gone, ye cauldrife wooer,
Ye sour-looking, cauldrife wooer,
I Straightway show'd him to the door,
Saying, come nae mair to woo.
And wow but, &c.

There lay a duck-dub before the door,
Before the door, before the door,
There lay a duck-dub before the door,
And there fell he I trow.
And wow but, &c.

Out came the goodman, and high he shouted,
Out came the goodwife, and low she louted,
And a' the town-neighbours were gather'd about it,
And there lay he I trow.
And wow but, &c.

Then out came I, and sneer'd and smil'd,
Ye came to woo, but ye're a' beguil'd,
Ye'ave fa'en i' the dirt, and ye're a' befyl'd
We'll hae nae mair of you.
And wow but, &c.

# The Gardener wi' his Paidle.

220
Slowiſh
When ro_ſy May comes in wi' flowers, To deck her
gay, green ſpreading bowers; Then buſy, buſy are his hours, The
Gardner wi' his paidle. The chryſ_tal wa_ters gent_ly
fa'; The merry birds are lov_ers a'; The ſcen_ted breezes
round him blaw, The Gardener wi' his paidle.

When purple morning ſtarts the hare
To ſteal upon her early fare;
Then thro' the dews he maun repair,
The Gardener wi' his paidle,
When day, expiring in the weſt,
The curtain draws of Nature's reſt;
He flies to her arms he lo'es the beſt,.
The Gardener wi' his paidle.

## Bonny Barbara Allan.

221

It was in and a_bout the Mar_tinmas time, When the

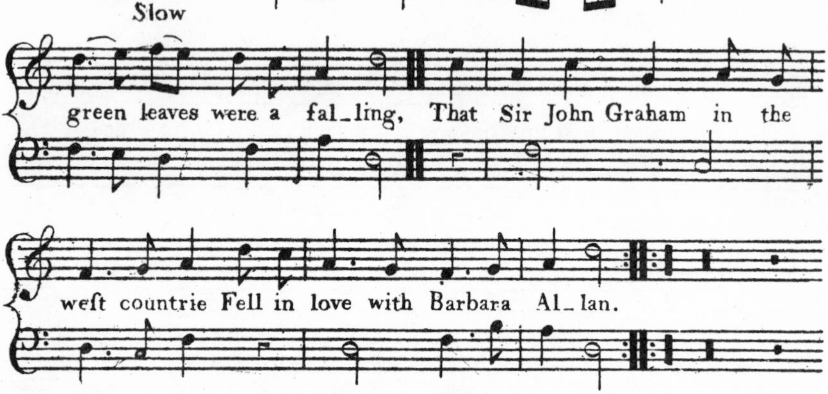
Slow
green leaves were a fal_ling, That Sir John Graham in the
west countrie Fell in love with Barbara Al_lan.

He ſent his man down thro' the town,
To the place where ſhe was dwelling;
O haſte and come to my maſter dear,
Gin ye be Barbara Allan.

O hooly, hooly roſe ſhe up,
To the place where he was lying,
And when ſhe drew the curtin by,
Young man, I think youre dying.

O its I'm ſick, and very very ſick,
And 'tis a' for Barbara Allan.
O the better for me ye's never be,
Tho' your heart's blood were a ſpilling.

O dinna ye mind, young man, ſaid ſhe,
When ye the cups was fillin
That ye made the healths gae round and (round,
And ſlighted Barbara Allan.

He turn'd his face unto the wa',
And death was with him dealing,
Adieu, adieu, my dear friends a',
And be kind to Barbara Allan.

And ſlowly, ſlowly raiſe ſhe up,
And ſlowly, ſlowly left him;
And ſighing, ſaid, ſhe cou'd not ſtay,
Since death of life had reft him.

She had nae gane a mile but twa,
When ſhe heard the deid bell knelling,
And ev'ry jow that the deid bell geid,
It cry'd, woe to Barbara Allan.

O mother, mother, mak my bed,
O make it ſaft and narrow;
Since my love died for me to-day,
I'll die for him to-morrow.

## Young Philander.

222

Young Philander woo'd me lang but I was peeviſh & forbad him, I

wou'd na tent his loving ſang, But now I wiſh I wiſh I had him. Ilk

Continued.

morning when I view my glaſs. Then I perceive my beauty going, When the
wrinkles ſeize the face, Then we may bid a_dieu to wooing. My
beauty anes ſo much admir'd, I find it fading faſt, and flying; My
cheeks which coral like appear'd, Grow pale the broken blood-decaying;

Ah! we may ſee ourſelves to be
Like ſummer fruit that is unſhaken;
When ripe, they ſoon fall down and die,
And by corruption quickly taken.
Uſe then your time, ye virgins fair,
Employ your day before 'tis evil;
Fifteen is a ſeaſon rare,
But five an twenty is the devil.
Juſt when ripe, conſent unto 't,
Hug nae mair your lanely pillow,
Women are like other fruit,
They loſe their reliſh when too mellow.

If opportunity be loſt,
You'll find it hard to be regained;
Which now I may tell to my coſt,
Tho' but myſel nane can be blamed.
If then your fortune you reſpect,
Take the occaſion when it offers;
Nor a true lover's ſuit neglect,
Leſt you be ſcoff'd for being ſcoffers.
I, by his fond expreſſions, thought (ing
That in his love he'd ne'er prove chang
But now, alas! 'tis turn'd to nought,
And, paſt my hope, he's gane a ranging

Dear maidens, then, take my advice,
And let na coyneſs prove your ruin:
For if ye be o'er fooliſh nice,
Your ſuiters will give over wooing.
Then maidens auld you nam'd will be,
And in that fretful rank be number'd,
As lang as life; and when ye die,
With leading apes be ever cumber'd.
A puniſhment, and hated band,
With which we cannot be contented,
Then be not wiſe behind the hand,
That the miſtake may be prevented.

## On a bank of Flowers.

Written for this Work by Robert Burns.

223

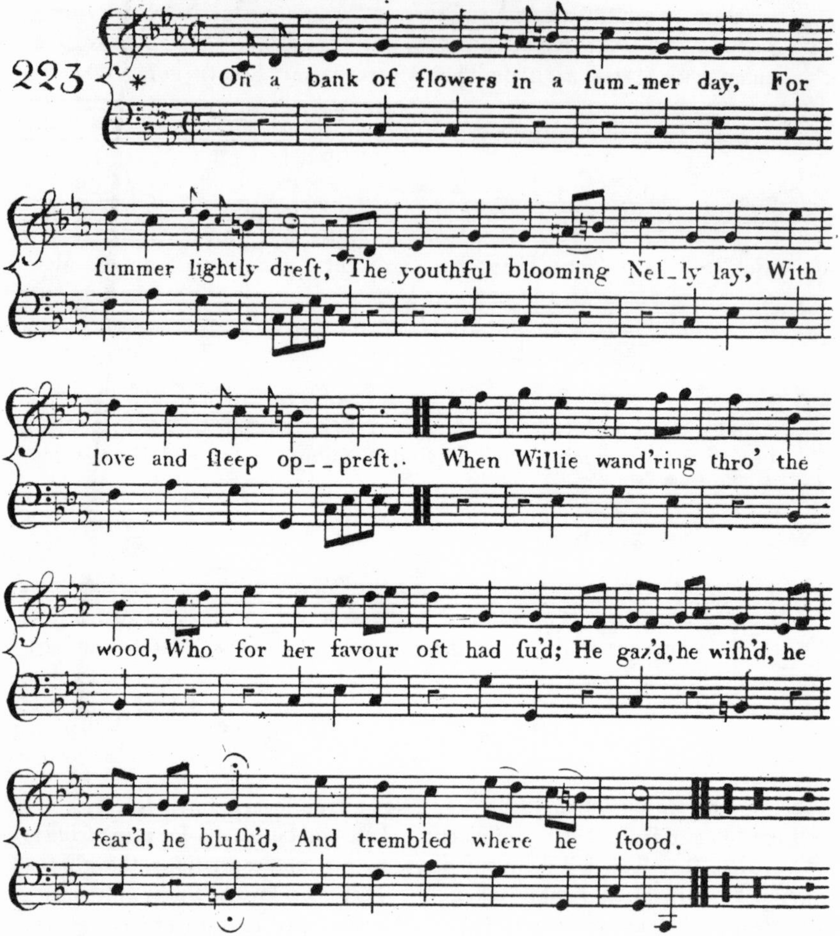
On a bank of flowers in a sum_mer day, For
summer lightly drest, The youthful blooming Nel_ly lay, With
love and sleep op_ _prest.. When Willie wand'ring thro' the
wood, Who for her favour oft had su'd; He gaz'd, he wish'd, he
fear'd, he blush'd, And trembled where he stood.

Her closed eyes like weapons sheath'd
Were seal'd in soft repose;
Her lips still as she fragrant breath'd
It richer dy'd the rose.
The springing lilies sweetly prest,
Wild, wanton kiss'd her rival breast;
He gaz'd, he wish'd, he fear'd, he blush'd,
His bosom ill at rest.

Her robes light waving in the breeze,
Her tender limbs embrace;
Her lovely form, her native ease,
All harmony and grace:
Tumultuous tides his pulses roll,
A faltering, ardent kiss he stole;
He gaz'd, he wish'd, he fear'd, he blush'd,
And sigh'd his very soul.

As flies the partridge from the brake
On fear-inspired wings,
So Nelly starting, half-awake,
Away affrighted springs:
But Willy follow'd, _as he should,
He overtook her in the wood;
He vow'd, he pray'd, he found the maid
Forgiving all and good.

## The day returns, my bosom burns,

Written for this Work by Robert Burns. Tune, Seventh of November.

224

The day returns, my bosom burns, The bliss_ful
day we twa did meet, Tho' winter wild in tempest toil'd, Ne'er
summer_sun was half sae sweet. Then a' the pride that loads the
tide, And crosses o'er the sul_try line; Than kingly robes, than
crowns and globes, Heav'n gave me more it made thee mine.-

While day and night can bring delight,
Or nature aught of pleasure give;
While joys above, my mind can move,
For thee and thee alone I live!
When that grim foe of life below
Comes in between to make us part;
The iron hand that breaks our band,
It breaks my bliss _ it breaks my heart

## My love she's but a Lassie yet.

225

My love she's but a lassie yet, My love she's but a lassie yet, We'll
let her stand a year or twa, She'll no be half sae saucy yet. I
rue the day I sought her O, I rue the day I sought her O, Wha
gets her needs na say he's woo'd, But he may say he's bought her O.

Come draw a drap o' the best o't yet,
Come draw a drap o' the best o't yet:
Gae seek for pleasure whare ye will,
But here I never misst it yet.

We're a' dry wi' drinking o't,
We're a' dry wi' drinking o't:
The minister kisst the fidler's wife,
He could na preach for thinkin o't.

## The Gaberlunzie-man.

226

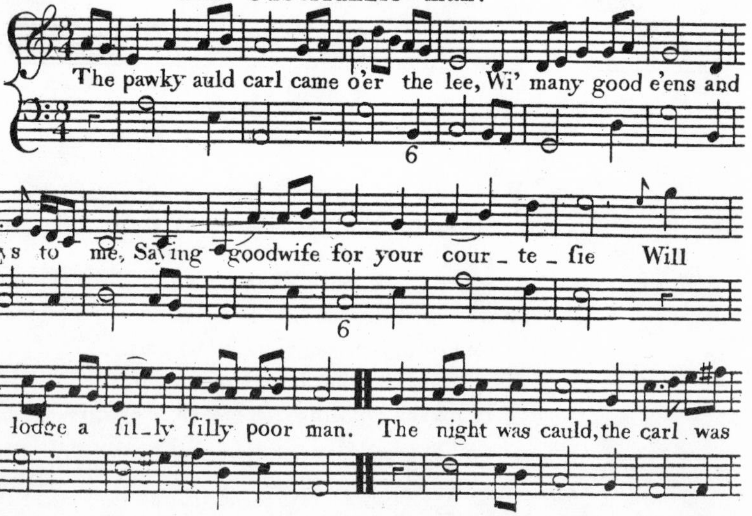
The pawky auld carl came o'er the lee, Wi' many good e'ens and
days to me, Saying goodwife for your cour_te_sie Will
ye lodge a sil_ly silly poor man. The night was cauld, the carl was
6
6

Continued.

wat, And down a_yont the ingle he ſat, My daughter's ſhoulders
he gan to clap And cadgi_ly cadgi_ly ranted and ſang.

O vow! quo' he, were I as free,
As firſt when I ſaw this country,
How blyth and merry wad I be!
And I wad never think lang.
He grew canty, and ſhe grew fain;
But little did her auld minny ken
What thir ſlee twa together were ſay'ng,
When wooing they were ſae thrang.

And O! quo' he, an ye were as black
As e'er the crown of my dady's hat,
'Tis I wad lay thee by my back,
And awa wi' me thou ſhou'd gang.
And O! quo' ſhe, an I were as white,
As e'er the ſnaw lay on the dike,
I'd clead me braw and lady-like,
And awa' wi' thee I would gang.

Between the twa was made a plot;
They raiſe a wee before the cock,
And wilily they ſhot the lock,
And faſt to the bent are they gane.
Up in the morn the auld wife raiſe,
And at her leiſure pat on her claiſe;
Syne to the ſervants bed ſhe gaes,
To ſpeer for the ſilly poor man.

She gaed to the bed where the beggar (lay,
The ſtrae was cauld, he was away,
She clapt her hands, cry'd, Walladay!
For ſome of our gear will be gane.
Some ran to coffers, and ſome to kiſts,
But nought was ſtown that cou'd be miſt,
She danc'd her lane, cry'd praiſe be bleſt!
I have lodg'd a leal poor man.

Since naething's awa', as we can learn,
The kirn's to kirn, and milk to earn,
Gae butt the houſe, laſs, and wauken my
And bid her come quickly ben. (bairn,

The ſervant gade where the daughter lay
The ſheets was cauld, ſhe was away,
And faſt to her goodwife did ſay,
She's aff wi' the gaberlunzie-man.

O fy gar ride, and fy gar rin,
And haſte ye find theſe traytors again;
For ſhe's be burnt, and he's be ſlain,
The wearifu' gaberlunzie-man.
Some rade upo' horſe, ſome ran a foot,
The wife was wood and out o' her wit;
She cou'd na gang, nor yet cou'd ſhe ſit,
But ay ſhe curs'd and ay ſhe bann'd.

Mean time far hind out o'er the lee
Fu' ſnug in a glen, where nane could ſee,
The twa with kindly ſport and glee,
Cut frae a new cheeſe a whang:
The priving was good, it pleas'd them baith
To lo'e her for ay, he gae her his aith.
Quo' ſhe, To leave thee I will be laith,
My winſome gaberlunzie-man.

O kend my minny I were wi' you,
Ill-fardly wad ſhe crook her mou',
Sick a poor man ſhe'd never trow,
After the gaberlunzie-man.
My dear, quo' he, ye're yet o'er young,
And ha' nae learn'd the beggars tongue,
To follow me frae town to town,
And carry the gaberlunzie on.

Wi' cauk and keel I'll win your bread,
And ſpindles & whorles for them wha need.
Whilk is a gentle trade indeed,
To carry the gaberlunzie on.
I'll bow my leg, and crook my knee,
And draw a black clout o'er my eye,
A cripple or blind they will ca' me,
While we ſhall be merry and ſing.

# Cauld frosty morning.

227

* 'Twas past ane o clock in a cauld frosty morning, When cankert No_
_vember blaws over the plain, I heard the kirk bell re_peat the loud warning, As,
restless, I sought for sweet slumber in vain: Then up I a_rose, the silver moon
shining bright; Mountains & vallies appearing all hoary white, Forth I would
go a_mid the pale, silent night, To seek the fair one, the cause of my pain.

Sae gently I staw to my lovely Maid's chamber,
  And rapp d at her window, low down on my knee;
Begging that she would awauk from sweet slumber,
  Awauk from sweet slumber and pity me.
For, that a stranger to a' pleasure, peace and rest,
  Love into madness had fired my tortur'd breast,
And that I should be of a' men the maist unblest,
  Unless she would pity my sad miserie!

My true-love arose and whispered to me,
  (The moon looked in, and envy'd my love's charms;)
"An innocent maiden, ah, would you undo me!"
  I made no reply, but leapt into her arms:
Bright Phebus peep'd over the hills and found me there;
  As he has done, now, seven lang years and mair:
A faithfuller, constanter, kinder, more loving Pair,
  His sweet chearing beam nor enlightens nor warms

# The black Eagle.

228

Hark! yonder Eagle lone_ly wails; His faithful bosom
grief as_sails: Last night I heard him in my dream, When
death and woe were all the theme. Like that poor bird I make my
moan, I grieve for dearest Delia gone, With him to gloomy
rocks I fly, He mourns for love and so do I.

'Twas mighty love that tam'd his breast,
'Tis tender grief that breaks his rest.
He droops his wings, he hangs his head,
Since she he fondly lov'd was dead.
With Delia's breath my joy expir'd,
'Twas Delia's smiles my fancy fir'd;
Like that poor Bird, I pine, and prove
Nought can supply the place of love.

Dark as his feathers was the fate
That robb'd him of his darling Mate.
Dimm'd is the lustre of his eye,
That wont to gaze the sun bright sky.
To him is now for ever lost
The heartfelt bliss he once could boast.
Thy sorrows, hapless bird, display
An image of my soul's dismay

## Jamie come try me.

229

Jamie come try me, Jamie come try me, If thou would win my love Jamie come try me. If thou ſhould aſk my love, Could I de_ny thee? If thou would win my love Jamie come try me.
Very Slow

If thou ſhould kiſs me, love,
Wha could eſpy thee?
If thou wad be my love,
Jamie come try me.
Jamie come &c.

## Magie's Tocher.

230

The meal was dear ſhort ſyne, The maut & a' the gither, And Maggie was juſt in her prime, When Willie made courtſhip till her. Twa piſtols charg'd be_gueſs, To gie the cour_ting ſhot, And ſyne came ben the laſs, Wi' ſwats drawn frae the butt, He

## Continued.

firſt ſpeer'd at the guidman, And ſyne at Giles the mither, An
ye wad gi's a bit land, We'd buckle us e'en the gither.

My doughter ye ſhall hae,
  I'll gi' you her by the hand:
But I'll part wi' my wife by my fay,
  Or I part wi' my land.
Your tocher it ſall be good,
  There's nane ſall hae its maik,
The laſs bound in her ſnood,
  And Crummie wha kens her ſtake:
With an auld bedden o' claiths,
  Was left me by my mither,
They're jet black o'er wi' flaes,
  Ye may cuddle in them the gither.

Ye ſpeak right well, guidman,
  But ye maun mend your hand,
And think o' modeſty,
  Gin ye'll not quat your land:
We are but young, ye ken,
  And now we're gawn the gither;
A houſe is but and ben,
  And Crummie will want her fother.
The bairns are coming on,
  And they'll cry, O their mither;
We have nouther pat nor pan,
  But four bare legs the gither.

Your tocher's be good enough
  For that you need nae fear,
Twa good ſtilts to the pleugh,
  And ye your ſell maun ſteer:
Ye ſhall hae twa good pocks
  That anes were o' the tweel,
The t' ane to had the grots,
  The ither to had the meal;
With an auld kiſt made of wands,
  And that ſall be your coffer,
Wi' aiken woody bands,
  And that may had your tocher.

Conſider well, guidman,
  We hae but borrowed gear,
The horſe that I ride on
  Is Sandy Wilſon's mare:
The ſaddle's nane of my ain,
  And thae's but borrow'd boots,
And when that I gae hame,
  I maun tak to my koots:
The cloak is Geordy Watt's,
  That gars me look ſae crouſe;
Come fill us a cogue of ſwats,
  We'll make nae mair toom ruſe.

I like you weel, young lad,
  For telling me ſae plain,
I married when little I had
  O' gear that was my ain:
But ſin that things are ſae,
  The bride ſhe maun come furth,
Tho' a' the gear ſhe'll hae,
  It'll be but little worth.

A bargain it maun be,
  Fy cry on Giles the mither:
Content am I, quo' ſhe,
  E'en gar the hiſſie come hither.
The bride ſhe gade till her bed,
  The bridegroom he came till her;
The fidler crap in at the fit,
  And they cuddl'd it a' the gither.

## My bony Mary.

231

Go, fetch to me a pint o' wine, And fill it in a
fil_ver taſ_ſie; That I may drink be_fore I go A
fer_vice to my bo_nie laſsie. The boat rocks at the Pier o'
Leith, Fu' loud the wind blaws frae the Ferry, The ſhip rides by the
Ber_wick_law, And I maun leave my bo_ny Mary.

The trumpets ſound, the banners fly,
  The glittering ſpears are ranked ready,
The ſhouts o' war are heard a far,
  The battle cloſes deep and bloody:
It's not the roar o' ſea or ſhore,
  Wad make me langer wiſh to tarry;
Nor ſhouts o' war that's heard afar,
  It's leaving thee, my bony Mary!

# The lazy miſt.

Written for this Work by Robert Burns.

232

The lazy miſt hangs from the brow of the hill, Concealing ye
courſe of the dark winding rill; How languid the ſcenes, late ſo
ſprightly, appear, As Autumn to Winter reſigns the pale year. The
foreſts are leafleſs, the meadows are brown, And all the gay
foppery of ſummer is flown: Apart let me wander, apart let m
muſe, How quick Time is flying, how keen Fate pur – ſues,

How long I have liv'd – but how much liv'd in vain;
How little of life's ſcanty ſpan may remain:
What aſpects, old Time, in his progreſs, has worn;
What ties, cruel Fate, in my boſom has torn.
How fooliſh, or worſe, till our ſummit is gain'd.
And downward, how weaken'd how darken'd, how pain'd.
Life is not worth having with all it can give
For ſomething beyond it poor man ſure muſt live.

B.

## The Captain's Lady.

233

* O mount and go, Mount and make you ready, O
mount and go, And be the Captain's Lady. When the drums do beat,
And the cannons rattle, Thou ſhall ſit in ſtate, And ſee thy love in
battle. When the drums do beat, And the cannons rattle, Thou ſhalt
ſit in ſtate, And ſee thy love in battle. Chos. O mount & go &c.

When the vanquiſh'd foe
Sues for peace and quiet,
To the ſhades we'll go
And in love enjoy it.
Chos. O Mount &c.

## Johnie Cope.

234

* Sir John Cope trode the north right far, Yet ne'er a re_bel

## Continued.

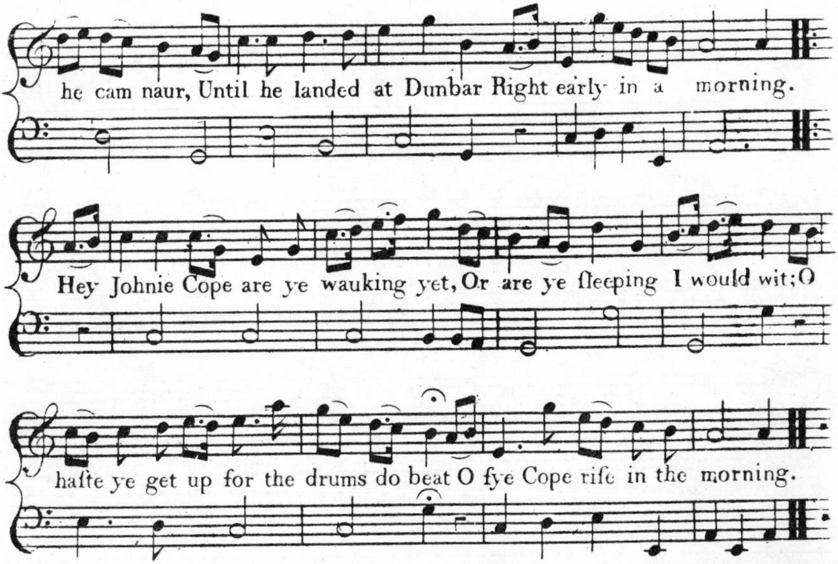
he cam naur, Until he landed at Dunbar Right early in a morning.
Hey Johnie Cope are ye wauking yet, Or are ye ſleeping I would wit; O
haſte ye get up for the drums do beat O fye Cope riſe in the morning.

He wrote a challenge from Dunbar,
Come fight me Charlie an ye daur;
If it be not by the chance of war
I'll give you a merry morning.
Hey Johnie Cope &c.

When Charlie look'd the letter upon
He drew his ſword the ſcabbard from-
"So Heaven reſtore to me my own,
"I'll meet you, Cope, in the morning."
Hey Johnie Cope &c.

Cope ſwore with many a bloody word
That he would fight them gun and ſword,
But he fled frae his neſt like an ill ſcar'd (bird,
And Johnie he took wing in y^e morning
Hey Johnie Cope &c.

It was upon an afternoon,
Sir Johnie march'd to Preſton town
He ſays, my lads come lean you down,
And we'll fight the boys in the morning.
Hey Johnie Cope &c.

But when he ſaw the Highland lads
Wi' tartan trews and white cockauds,
Wi' ſwords & guns & rungs & gauds,
O Johnie he took wing in the morning.
Hey Johnie Cope &c.

On the morrow when he did riſe,
He look'd between him and the ſkies.
He ſaw them wi' their naked thighs,
Which fear'd him in the morning
Hey Johnie Cope &c.

O then he flew into Dunbar,
Crying for a man of war; (tar,
He thought to have paſs'd for a ruſtic
And gotten awa in the morning.
Hey Johnie Cope &c.

Sir Johnie into Berwick rade,
Juſt as the devil had been his guide;
Gien him the warld he would na ſtay'd
To foughten the boys in the morning
Hey Johnie Cope &c.

Says the Berwickers unto Sir John.
O what's become of all your men.
In faith ſays he, I dinna ken,
I left them a' this morning
Hey Johnie Cope &c.

Says Lord Mark Car ye are na blate,
To bring us the new's o' your ain defeat
I think you deſerve the back o' the gate
Get out o' my ſight this morning.
Hey Johnie Cope &c.

# I Love my Jean.

Written for this Work by R: Burns. Tune, Miss Admiral Gordon's Strathspey.

235

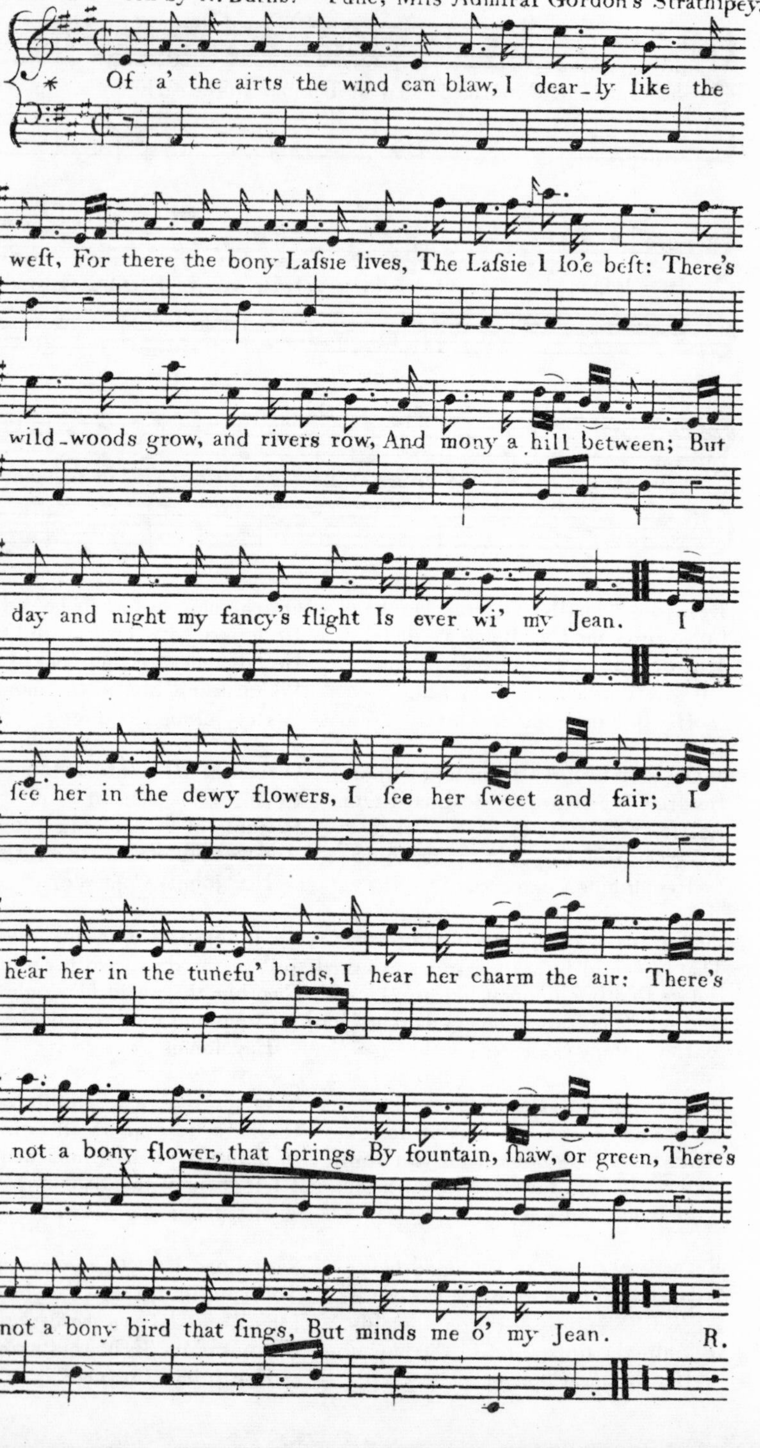
Of a' the airts the wind can blaw, I dear_ly like the
west, For there the bony Lassie lives, The Lassie I lo'e best: There's
wild_woods grow, and rivers row, And mony a hill between; But
day and night my fancy's flight Is ever wi' my Jean. I
see her in the dewy flowers, I see her sweet and fair; I
hear her in the tunefu' birds, I hear her charm the air: There's
not a bony flower, that springs By fountain, shaw, or green, There's
not a bony bird that sings, But minds me o' my Jean. R.

Tune, O dear mother, what ſhall I do.

236

O dear Peggy, love's be_guiling, We ought not to
Slowiſh
truſt his ſmiling; Better far to do as I do, Leſt a harder
luck be_tide you. Laſ_ses, when their fancy's carried,
Think of nought but to be married, Run_ _ning to a
life deſ_troys Hartſome, free, and youth_fu' joys.

## Old Words.

O dear minny, what ſhall I do?
O dear minny, what ſhall I do?
O dear minny, what ſhall I do?
Daft thing, doylt thing, do as I do.

If I be black, I canna be lo'ed;
If I be fair, I canna be gude;
If I be lordly, the lads will look by me:
O dear minny, what ſhall I do.
Cho[s] O dear minny &c.

## The linkin laddie.

237

Waes me that e'er I made your bed! Waes me that eer I ſaw ye, For
Slowiſh
now I've loſt my maiden head, And I ken na how they ca' ye! My
name's weel kend in my ain countrie, They ca' me the linkin laddie: An
ye had na been as willing as I, Shame fa' them wad e'er hae bade ye

## Alloa Houſe.

238

The ſpring time returns, and cloeths the green plains, And
Al_lo_a ſhines, more chearful and gay; The lark tunes his throat & the
neighbouring ſwains Sing merri_ly round me where_e_ver I ſtray.

Continued.

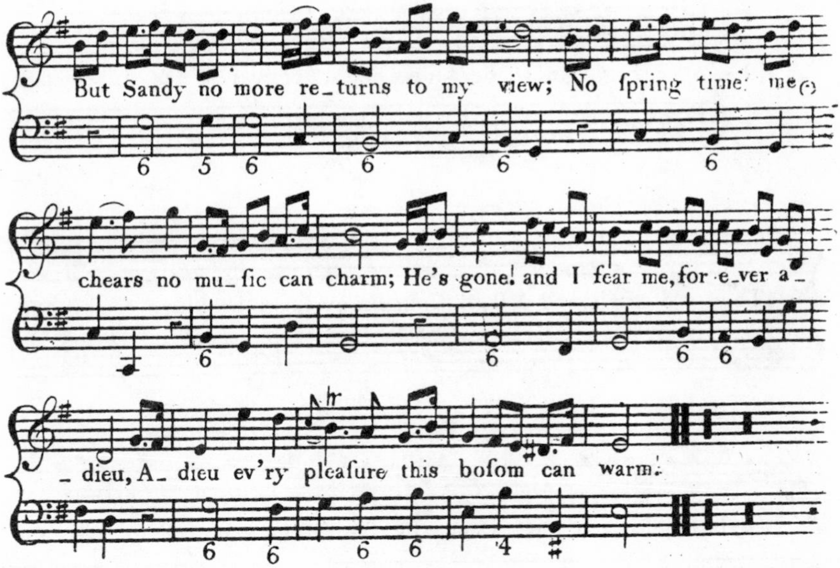
But Sandy no more re_turns to my view; No spring time me
chears no mu_sic can charm; He's gone! and I fear me, for e_ver a_
_dieu, A_ dieu ev'ry pleasure this bosom can warm!

O Alloa House! how much art thou chang'd!
How silent, how dull to me is each grove!
Alone I here wander where once we both rang'd,
Alas! where to please me my Sandy once strove!
Here Sandy I heard the tales that you told;
Here listened too fond, whenever you sing;
Am I grown less fair, then, that you are turn'd cold,
Or foolish, believ'd a false, flattering tongue.

So spoke the fair maid; when sorrow's keen pain,
And shame, her last falt'ring accents supprest;
For fate at that moment brought back her dear swain,
Who heard, and, with rapture, his Nelly addrest.
My Nelly, my fair, I come, O my love,
No pow'r shall thee tear again from my arms,
And, Nelly! no more thy fond shepherd reprove,
Who knows thy fair worth, and adores all thy charms.

She heard; and new joy shot thro' her soft frame;
And will you, my love! be true, she reply'd.
And live I to meet my fond shepherd the same!
Or dream I that Sandy will make me his bride!
O Nelly! I live to find thee still kind;
Still true to thy swain, and lovely as true:
Then adieu! to all sorrow; what soul is so blind,
As not to live happy for ever with you.

## Tune, Carle, an' the king come.

239

Peggy, now the king's come, Peggy, now the kings come,
Thou may dance, and I ſhall ſing, Peggy, ſince the king's come. Nae
mair the hawkies ſhalt thou milk, But change thy plaiding -coat for
ſilk, And be a lady of that Ilk, Now Peggy, ſince the king's come.


## Old Words.

Chorus

CARL an the king come,  
Carl an the king come;  
Thou ſhalt dance and I will ſing,  
Carl an the king come.

An ſomebodie were come again,  
Then ſomebodie maun croſs the main,  
And every man ſhall hae his ain,  
Carl an the king come.  
Cho.ˢ Carl an &c.

I trow we ſwapped for the warſe,  
We gae the boot and better horſe;  
And that we'll tell them at the croſs,  
Carl an the king come.  
Cho.ˢ Carl an &c.

Coggie an the king come,  
Coggie an the king come,  
I'ſe be fou and thou'ſe be toom,  
Coggie an the king come.  
Cho.ˢ Coggie an &c.

## The Siller Crown.

240

And ye fall walk in filk at_tire, And filler hae to
fpare, Gin ye'll con fent to be his bride, Nor
think o' Don_ald mair. O, wha wad buy a fil_ken
gown, Wi' a poor bro_ken heart Or what's to me a
fil_er crown Gin frae my love I part.

The mind whafe every wifh is pure
Far dearer is to me,
And e'er I'm forc'd to break my faith,
I'll lay me down and die:
For I hae pledged my virgin troth
Brave Donalds fate to fhare,
And he has gi'en to me his heart
Wi' a' its virtues rare

His gentle manners wan my heart,
He, gratefu' took the gift;
Cou'd I but think, to feek it back
It wou'd be war than theft.
For langeft life, can ne'er repay
The love he bears to me,
And e'er I'm forced to break my troth
I'll lay me down and die.

## S^t. Kilda Song.

241

By the ſtream ſo cool and clear, And thro' the caves where
Slow with Expreſsion
breezes. lan_guiſh, Sooth_ing ſtill my ten_der an_guiſh,
Hoping ſtill to find my lover, I have wander'd far and
near, O where ſhall I the youth diſcover.

Sleeps he in your breezy ſhade,
Ye rocks with moſs and ivy waving,
On ſome bank where wild waves laving,
Murmur through the twiſted willow;
On that bank, O were I laid,
How ſoft ſhould be my lover's pillow!

## The Mill Mill O.

242

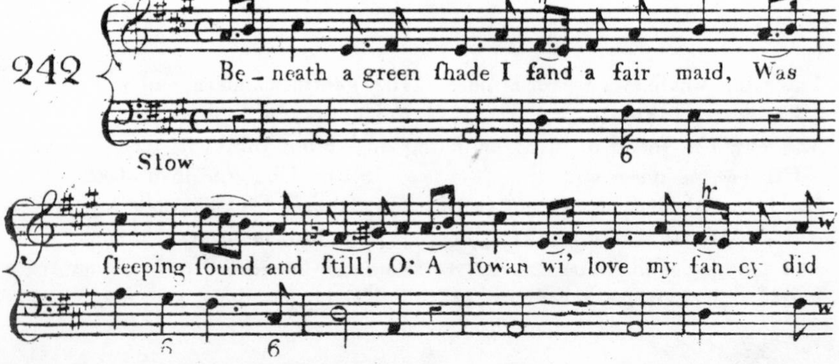
Be_neath a green ſhade I fand a fair maid, Was
Slow
ſleeping ſound and ſtill! O: A lowan wi' love my fan_cy did

## Continued.

rove A_round her wi' good will O: Her boſom I preſt; but
ſunk in her reſt, She ſtir'dna my joy to ſpill O: While kindly ſhe
ſlept, cloſe to her I crept, And kiſs'd & kiſs'd her my fill O

Oblig'd by command in Flanders to land,
  T' employ my courage and ſkill_.O,
Frae her quietly I ſtaw, hoiſt ſails and awa,
  For the wind blew fair on the billow
Twa years brought me hame, where loud-fraiſing fame
  Tald me with a voice right ſhrill_.O,
My laſs, like a fool, had mounted the ſtool,
  Nor kend wha had done her the ill_.O.

Mair fond of her charms, with my ſon in her arms,
  I ferlying ſpeir'd how ſhe fell_.O,
Wi' the tear in her eye, quoth ſhe, Let me die,
  Sweet Sir, gin I can tell_.O.
But love gave command, I took her by the hand,
  And bade a' her fears expel_.O,
And nae mair look wan, for I was the man
  Wha had done her the deed myſel_.O.

My bonny ſweet laſs, on the gowany graſs,
  Beneath the Shilling-hill_.O
If I did offence, I'ſe make ye amends
  Before I leave Peggy's mill_.O.
O the mill, mill_.O, and the kill, kill_.O,
  And the coggin of the wheel_.O;
The ſack and the ſieve, a' that ye maun leave,
  And round with a ſodger reel_.O.

# The Waefu Heart.

243

Gin living worth cou'd win my heart, You woud na
Very Slow
ſpeak in vain, But in the darkſome grave it's laid Ne_
_ver to riſe a _ gain. My wae_fu' heart lies low wi'
his Whoſe heart was on_ly mine And oh! what a heart was
that to loſe, But I maun no re _ _pine

Yet oh gin heav'n in mercy ſoon
Wou'd grant the boon I crave,
And tak this life now naething worth
Sin Jamie's in his grave.
And ſee his gentle ſpirit come
To ſhow me on my way,
Surpriſ'd nae doubt, I ſtill am here,
Sair wondring at my ſtay.

I come, I come, my Jamie dear
And oh! wi' what gude will
I follow, wharſoe'er ye lead,
Ye canna lead to ill.
She ſaid, and ſoon a deadlie pale
Her faded cheek poſseſt,
Her waefu' heart forgot to beat
Her ſorrows ſunk to reſt.

# Laſs gin ye lo'e me, tell me now

244
Moderato
I ha'e laid a herring in ſa't, Laſs gin ye lo'e me
tell me now I ha'e brew'd a forpet o' ma't an I
canna come il_ka day to woo. I ha'e a calf will ſoon be a cow,
Laſs gin ye loe me tell me now, I ha'e a pig will
ſoon be a ſow, an' I canna come il_ka day to woo.

I've a houſe on yonder muir,
Laſs gin ye lo'e me tell me now,
Three ſparrows may dance upon the floor,
And I canna come ilka day to woo;
I ha'e a butt and I ha'e a benn
Laſs gin ye lo'e me tak me now;
I ha'e three chickens and a fat hen,
And I canna come ony mair to woo.

I've a hen wi' a happity leg,
Laſs gin ye lo'e me tak me now,
Which ilka day lays me an egg,
And I canna come ilka day to woo.
I ha'e a kebbock upon ı ſhelf,
Laſs gin ye lo'e me tak me now,
I downa eat it a' my ſelf
And I winna come ony mair to. woo.

## The Lover's addrefs to Rofe bud. By a Lady.

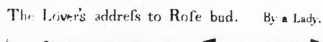

245

Sweet nurfling of the tears of morning, By Zephyr's balmy
kifs_ _es preft, O foon thy par_ent ftem adorning, Thou fhalt
fpread thy fra_grant breaft. Yet not too foon be fond of fhining,
Beauty's days are bright but few, This hour in prime, the
next de_clining I's charms will pall u_pon the view.
Slow

Emma fair flow'r all hearts now warming,
She muft yield to Fate's decree,
Soon like her, thou fhalt be charming,
Soon fhe'll fade and pafs like thee.
As thou art the faireft blofsom,
Thy bleft lot fhall envy move;
Go breath thy fweets on Emma's bofom,
Seat of innocence and love.

Love will teach thee when refigning,
On that breaft thy blufhing pride,
How thy modeft head declining,
May deck her beauties, yet not hide.
If fome hand too boldly daring
There difturbs thy bleft repofe,
Be not of thy vengeance fparing,
Sheath thy prickles in my foes.

## Ceafe, ceafe my dear friend to explore.

246

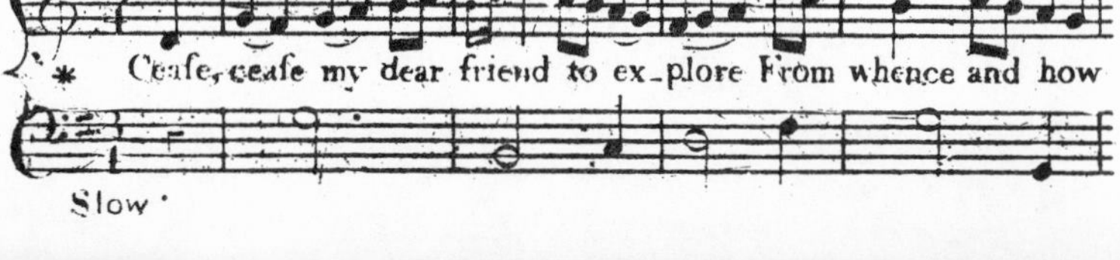
Ceafe, ceafe my dear friend to ex_plore From whence and how
Slow

Continued.

piercing my smart, Let the charms of the nymph I a_dore Ex_
_cuse and in_terpret my heart, Then how much I admire you shall
prove, When like me you are taught to ad_mire, And imagine how
boundless my love, When you number the charms that in_spire.

Than sunshine more dear to my sight,
To my life more essential than air,
To my soul she is perfect delight,
To my sense all that's pleasing and fair,
The swains who her beauty behold
With transport applaud ev'ry charm,
And swear that the breast must be cold
Which a beam so intense cannot warm.

Ah. say will she slightly forego,
A conquest, tho' humble, yet sure;
Will she leave a poor shepherd to woe,
Who for her ev'ry bliss would procure.
Alas. too presaging my fears,
Too jealous my soul of it's bliss,
Methinks she already appears,
To foresee, and elude my address

Does my boldness offend my dear maid,
Is my fondness loquacious, and free,
Are my visits too frequently paid,
Or my converse unworthy of thee.

Yet when grief was too big for my breast
And labour'd in sighs to complain,
It's struggles I oft have supprest.
And silence impos'd on my pain.

And oft while, by tenderness caught
To my charmer's retirement I flew,
I reproach'd the fond absence of thought
And in blushing confusion, withdrew.
My speech, tho' too little refin'd,
Tho' simple and aukward my mien,
Yet still shouldst thou deign to be kind,
What a wonderful change might be seen.

Ah! Strephon how vain thy desire,
Thy numbers and music how vain,
While merit and fortune conspire.
The smiles of the nymph to obtain.
Yet cease to upbraid the soft choice
Tho' it ne'er should determine for thee
If thy heart in her joy may rejoice
Unhappy thou never canst be _

# Auld Robin Gray.

247

When the ſheep are in the fauld & the ky at hame, &
a' the warld to ſleep are gane, The waes of my heart fa' in
ſhow'rs frae my ee, When my gudeman lyes ſound by me.

Young Jamie lood me well and he ſought me for his bride,
  But ſaving a crown he had naething beſide,
To make that crown a pound my Jamie gade to ſea,
  And the crown and the pound were baith for me.
He had nae been awa a week but only twa,
  When my mother ſhe fell ſick and the cow was ſtown awa,
My father brake his arm and my Jamie at the ſea.
  And auld Robin Gray came a courting me.
My father coudna work and my mother coudna ſpin,
  I toil'd day and night but their bread I coudna win,
Auld Rob maintain'd them baith and wi' tears in his ee,
  Said Jenny for their ſakes O marry me.
My heart it ſaid nay I look'd for Jamie back,
  But the wind it blew high and the ſhip it was a wrack,
The ſhip it was a wrack why didna Jenny die,
  And why do I live to ſay waes me.
Auld Robin argued ſair tho' my mother didna ſpeak,
  She look'd in my face till my heart was like to break,
So they gied him my hand tho' my heart was in the ſea,
  And auld Robin Gray is gudeman to me.
I hadna been a wife a week but only four,
  When ſitting ſae mournfuly at the door,
I ſaw my Jamie's wreath for I coudna think it he,
  Till he ſaid I'm come back for to marry thee.
O ſair did we greet and mickle did we ſay,
  We took but ae kiſs and we tore ourſelves away,
I wiſh I were dead but I'm no like to die,
  And why do I live to ſay waes me.
I gang like a ghaiſt and I carenae to ſpin,
  I darena think on Jamie for that wad be a ſin,
But I'll do my beſt a gudewife to be,
  For auld Robin Gray is kind to me.

## Leith Wynd

Jenny.
248
Slowish
Were I a_ssur'd you'd con_stant prove, You should nae mair complain; The ea_sy maid be_set wi' love, Few words will quickly gain: For I must own, now since you're free This too fond heart of mine Has lang, a black_sole true to thee, Wish'd to be pair'd with thine.

### ROGER.

I'm happy now; ah! let my head
  Upon thy breast recline;
The pleasure strikes me near-hand dead;
  Is Jenny then sae kind.
O let me briz thee to my heart,
  And round my arms entwine:
Delightfu' thought! we'll never part,
  Come, press thy mouth to mine.

## Whiſtle o'er the lave o't.

249

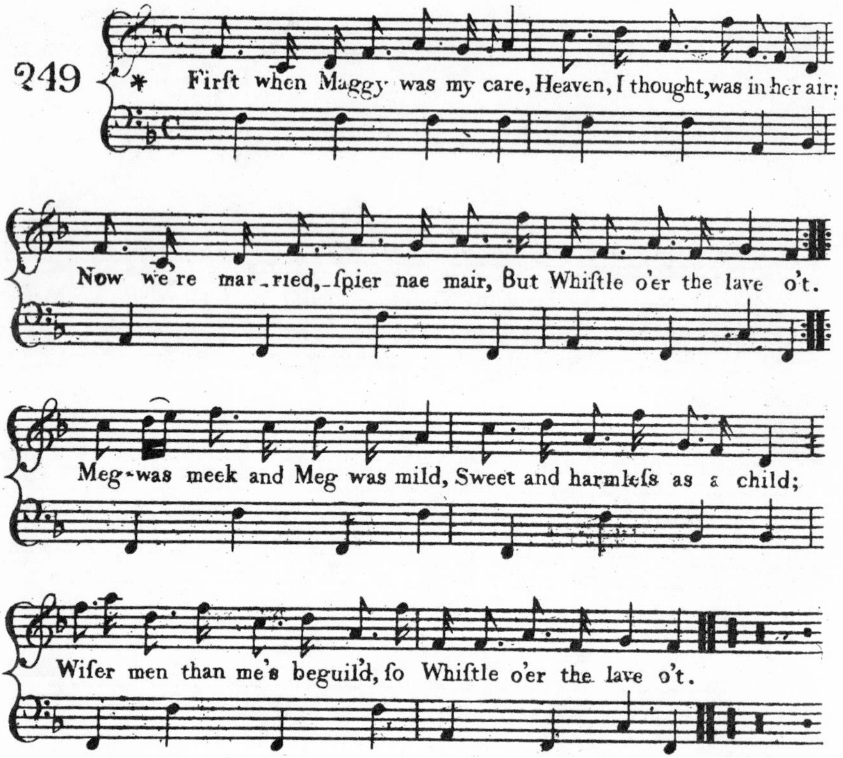
* First when Maggy was my care, Heaven, I thought, was in her air;
Now we're mar-ried, ſpier nae mair, But Whiſtle o'er the lave o't.
Meg-was meek and Meg was mild, Sweet and harmleſs as a child;
Wiſer men than me's beguil'd, ſo Whiſtle o'er the lave o't.

How we live, my Meg and me,
How we love and how we gree;
I carena by how few may ſee,
Whiſtle o'er the lave o't.

Wha I wiſh were maggots meat,
Diſh'd up in her winding-ſheet;
I could write - but Meg maun ſee't,
Whiſtle o'er the lave o't.

X

## Tak your auld cloak about ye.

250

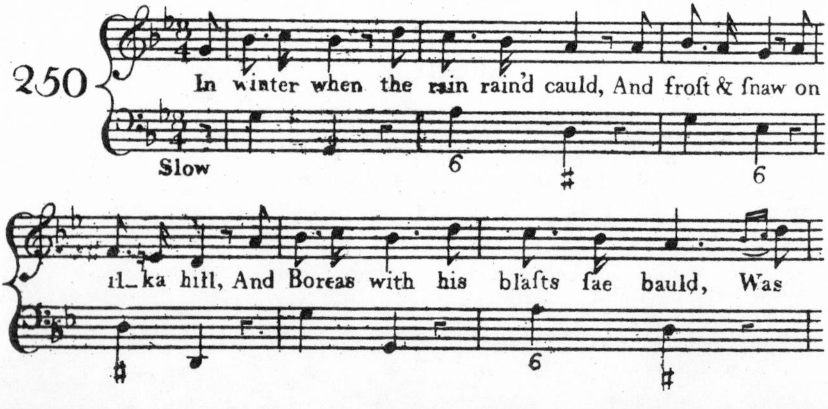
In winter when the rain rain'd cauld, And froſt & ſnaw on
Slow
il-ka hill, And Boreas with his blaſts ſae bauld, Was

Continued.

threat'ning a' our ky to kill. Then Bell my wife, wha loves na ſtrife.
She ſaid to me right haſtily, Get up good _ man ſave
Cromie's life, And tak your auld cloak a _ bout ye.

My Cromie is a uſefu' cow,
  And ſhe is come of a good kyne;
Oft has ſhe wet the bairns' mou,
  And I am laith that ſhe ſhould tyne;
Get up, goodman, it is fou time,
  The ſun ſhines in the liſt ſae hie;
Sloth never made a gracious end,
  Go tak your auld cloak about ye.

My cloak was anes a good grey cloak,
  When it was fitting for my wear;
But now its ſcantly worth a groat,
  For I have worn't this thirty year;
Let's ſpend the gear that we have won,
  We little ken the day we'll die;
Then I'll be proud, ſince I have ſworn
  To have a new cloak about me.

In days when our King Robert rang,
  His trews they coſt but half a crown;
He ſaid they were a groat o'er dear,
  And ca'd the taylor thief and loun.
He was the king that wore a crown,
  And thou the man of laigh degree,
'Tis pride puts a' the country down,
  Sae tak thy auld cloak about ye.

Every land has its ain laugh,
  Ilk kind of corn it has its hool,
I think the warld is a' run wrang,
  When ilka wife her man wad rule;
Do ye not ſee Rob, Jock, and Hab,
  As they are girded gallantly,
While I ſit hurklen in the aſe.
  I'll have a new cloak about me.

Goodman, I wat 'tis thirty years
  Since we did ane anither ken;
And we have had between us twa
  Of lads and bonny laſſes ten;
Now they are women grown and men,
  I wiſh and pray well may they be,
And if you prove a good huſband,
  E'en tak your auld cloak about ye.

Bell my wife, ſhe loves na ſtrife,
  But ſhe wad guide me, if ſhe can;
And to maintain an eaſy life,
  I aft maun yield, tho' I'm gudeman:
Nought's to be won at woman's hand,
  Unleſs ye gi'e her a' the plea;
Then I'll leave off where I began,
  And tak my auld cloak about me.

## Happy Clown

251

Hid from himfelf, now by the dawn, He ftarts as frefh as
Lively
rof_es blawn; And rang_es o'er the heights and lawn
After his bleeting flocks. Healthful and in_no_cently gay, He
chants and whift_les out the day; Untaught to fmile, and
then be_tray Like court_ly weather_cocks.

Life happy, from ambition free,
Envy, and vile hypocrify,
Where truth and love with joy agree,
  Unfullied with a crime:

Unmov'd with what difturbs the great,
In proping of their pride and ftate:
He lives, and unafraid of fate,
  Contented fpends his time.

# Donald and Flora.

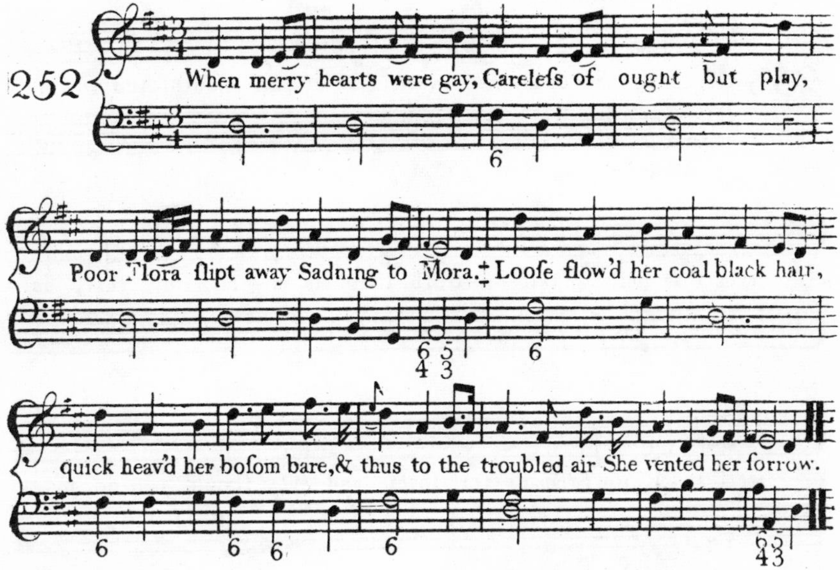
252
When merry hearts were gay, Carelefs of ought but play,
Poor Flora flipt away Sadning to Mora.‡ Loofe flow'd her coal black hair,
quick heav'd her bofom bare, & thus to the troubled air She vented her forrow.

'Loud howls the northern blaft,
Bleak is the dreary wafte;
'Hafte thee O Donald hafte
'Hafte to thy Flora.
'Twice twelve long months are o'er,
'Since in a foreign fhore,
'You promis'd to fight no more,
But meet me in Mora.

"Where now is Donald dear,
(Maids cry with taunting fneer
"Say is he ftill fincere
"To his lov'd Flora. _
'Parents upbraid my moan;
'Each heart is turn'd to ftone _
'Ah Flora, thou'rt now alone
"Friendlefs in Mora!

'Come then, oh come away,
'Donald no longer ftay _
'Where can my rover ftray
'From his dear Flora. _
'Ah fure he ne'er could be
'Falfe to his vows and me _
'O Heaven! is not yonder he
'Bounding in Mora.

Never O wretched fair!
Sigh'd the fad mefsenger,)
Never fhall Donald mair
'Meet his lov'd Flora!

'Cold, cold beyond the main,
'Donald thy love lies flain; _
'He fent me to foothe thy pain
'Weeping in Mora.

'Well fought our gallant men
'Headed by brave Burgoyne,
'Our heros were thrice led on
'To Britifh glory. _
'But ah! tho' our foes did flee,
'Sad was the lofs to thee,
'While ev'ry frefh victory
'Drown'd us in forrow.

"Here take this trufty blade,
(Donald expiring faid,)
"Give it to yon dear maid
"Weeping in Mora. _
"Tell her oh Allan tell,
"Donald thus bravely fell,
"And that in his laft farewell
"He thought on his Flora."

Mute ftood the trembling fair
Speechlefs with wild defpair,
Then ftriking her bofom bare
Sigh'd out poor Flora! _
Oh Donald! oh welladay!
Was all the fond heart could fay
At length the found died away
Feebly in Mora.

A fmall valley in Athole, fo named by the two lovers.

# By the delicious warmneſs of thy mouth.

.Patie Sings
253
By the de_licious warmneſs of thy mouth, And rowing
Slow
eyes that ſmiling tell the truth I gueſs my laſ_ſie, that, as
well as I, You're made for love; and Why ſhould you de_ny.
Peggy Sings
But ken ye, lad, gin we confeſs o'er ſoon, Ye think us cheap, & ſyne the
wooing's done: The maiden that o'er quickly tines her power, Like
un_ripe fruit, will taſte but hard and ſowr.
NB. The 2d Meaſure muſt be repeated for Paties laſt verſe

Patie Sings

But gin they hing o'er lang upon the tree,
Their ſweetneſs they may tine; and ſae may ye:
Red cheeked you completely ripe appear,
And I ha'e thol'd and woo'd a lang haff-year.

Peggy ſinging, falls into Patie's arms.

Then dinna pu me, gently thus I fa'
Into my Patie's arms, for good and a':
But ſtint your wiſhes to this kind embrace,
And mint nae farer till we've got the grace.

Patie (with his left hand about her waiſt.)

O charming armfu' hence ye cares away,
I'll kiſs my treaſure a' the live_lang day;
A' night I'll dream my kiſses o'er again,
Till that day come that ye'll be a' my ain.

Sung by both.

254

Sun gallop down the weſtlin ſkies, Gang ſoon to bed, and
Briſkly
quickly riſe, O laſh your ſteeds poſt time a_way, And
haſte a_bout our bridal day! And if ye're wearied, honeſt light,
Sleep, gin ye like, a week that night, And if ye're wearied,
honeſt light, Sleep, gin ye like, a week that night

## O, were I on Parnaſsus Hill,

Written for this Work by R: Burns. Tune, My love is lost to me.

255

O were I on Par_naſsus hill; Or had o' He_li_
Slow
_con my fill; That I might catch po_ _e_tic ſkill, To
ſing how dear I love thee. But Nith maun be my Muſ_es
well, My Muſe maun be thy bo_nie ſell; On Cor_ſincon I'll
glowr and ſpell, And write how dear I love thee.

Then come, ſweet Muſe, inſpire my lay!
For a' the lee_lang ſimmer's day,
I coudna ſing, I coudna ſay,
How much, how dear, I love thee.
I ſee thee dancing o'er the green,
Thy waiſt ſae jimp, thy limbs ſae clean,
Thy tempting lips, thy roguiſh een_
By Heaven and Earth I love thee.

By night, by day, a_field at hame,
The thoughts o' thee my breaſt inflame
And ay I muſe and ſing thy name,
I only live to love thee.
Tho' I were doom'd to wander on,
Beyond the ſea, beyond the ſun,
Till my laſt, weary ſand was run;
Till then _and then I love thee.

R.

## Song of Selma.

256
Plaintive
Ullin, Carril and Ryno, Voices of the days of old, let me
hear you while yet it is dark, to pleafe and a_wake my foul. I hear you
not ye fons of fong; in what hall of the Clouds is your Reft; do you
touch the fhadowy Harp, Robed with morning mift, where the rif_ing
Sun comes forth from his greenheaded waves from his greenheaded waves.

# The Captive Ribband.

A Galic Air.

257

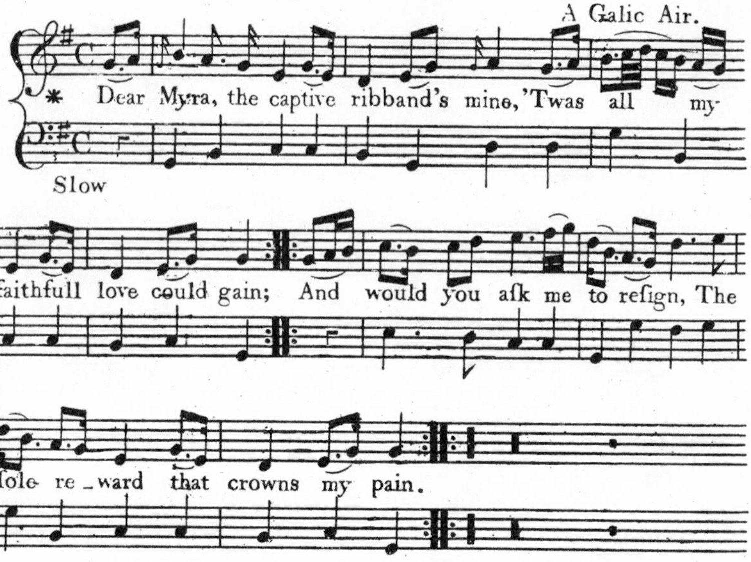
* Dear Myra, the captive ribband's mine, 'Twas all my
Slow
faithfull love could gain; And would you ask me to resign, The
sole re_ward that crowns my pain.

Go bid the hero who has run
Thro' fields of death to gather fame,
Go bid him lay his laurels down
And all his well earn'd praise disclaim.

The Ribband shall its freedom lose,
Lose all the bliss it had with you,
And share the fate I would impose
On thee, wert thou my captive too.

It shall upon my boson live,
Or clasp me in a close embrace;
And at its fortune if you grieve-
Retrieve its doom and take its place.

* * * * * * * * * * * * * * * * * * * * * * * * * * *

# There's a youth in this City.

A Galic Air.

258

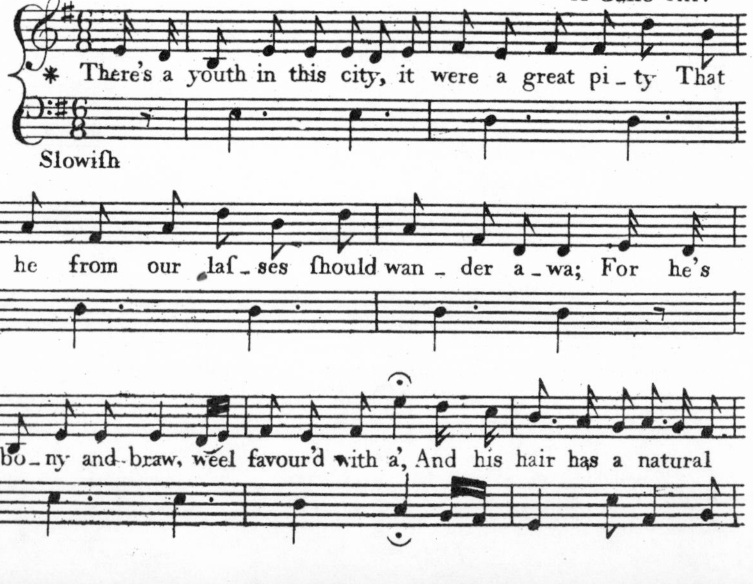
* There's a youth in this city, it were a great pi_ty That
Slowish
he from our las_ses should wan_der a_wa; For he's
bo_ny and braw, weel favour'd with a', And his hair has a natural

Continued.

buckle and a'. His coat is the hue of his bon_net fae blue; His
fecket is white as the new driven fnaw; His hofe they are blae, & his
fhoon like the flae, And his clear fil_ler buc_kles they
dazzle us a'. His coat is the hue of his bon_net fae blue; His
fecket is white as the new driven fnaw; His hofe they are blae and his
fhoon like the flae, And his clear filler buckles they dazzle us a'.

For beauty and fortune the laddie's been courtin;
  Weel-featur'd, weel-tocher'd, weel mounted and braw;
But chiefly the filler, that gars him gang till her,
  The Pennie's the jewel that beautifies a'.
There's Meg wi' the mailin that fain wad a haen him
  And Sufie whafe daddy was laird o' the Ha;
There's lang-tocher'd Nancy maift fetters his fancy
  But th' laddie's dear fel he lo'es dearest of a'.

# My heart's in the Highlands,

Tune, Failte na miofg.

259

* My heart's in the Highlands, my heart is not here; My
Slow
heart's in the Highlands a chafing the deer; A chafing the wild deer, and
following the roe, My heart's in the Highlands, wherever I go. Fare-
-well to the Highlands, farewell to the north, The birth place of
Valour, the country of Worth, Wher-ever I wander, wher-ever I
rove, The hills of the Highlands for ever I love.

Farewell to the mountains high cover'd with fnow;
Farewell to the ftraths and green vallies below:
Farewell to the forefts and wild hanging woods;
Farewell to the torrents and loud pouring floods.
My heart's in the Highlands, my heart is not here,
My heart's in the Highlands a chafing the deer:
Chafing the wild deer, and following the roe;
My heart's in the Highlands, wherever I go.

## John Anderson my Jo.

Written for this Work by Robert Burns.

260

John Ander_son my jo, John, When we were first Ac_
Lively
_quent; Your locks were like the ra_ven, Your bony brow was
brent; But now your brow is beld, John, Your
locks are like the snaw; But bles_ings on your
frosty pow, John Ander_son my Jo.

John Anderson my jo, John,
  We clamb the hill the gither;
And mony a canty day John,
  We've had wi' ane anither:
Now we maun totter down, John,
  And hand in hand we'll go;
And sleep the gither at the foot,
  John Anderson my Jo.

## Ah, why thus Abandon'd &c.

261

Ah, why thus abandon'd to mourning and woe, Why thus, lonely
Philomel, why flows thy sad strain? For spring shall return & a lover be_stow,
And thy bosom no trace of dejection retain; Yet if pity inspire thee ah, cease not thy
lay, Mourn sweetest complainer, man calls thee to mourn, O soothe him whose
pleasures like thine pass a_way, Full swiftly they pass but they never re_turn.

## Deil tak the Wars.

262

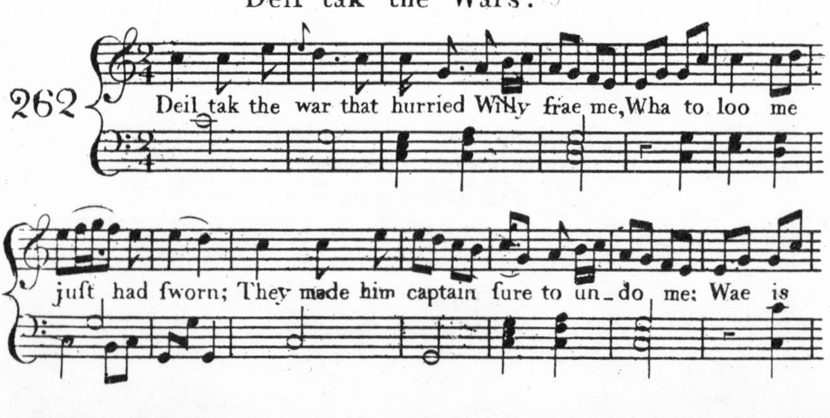
Deil tak the war that hurried Willy frae me, Wha to loo me
just had sworn; They made him captain sure to un_do me: Wae is

Continued.

me, he'll ne'er re _ turn! A thouſand loons abroad will fight him, He frae
thouſands ne'er will run; Day & night I did in _ vite him, To ſtay ſafe from
ſword or gun; I us'd alluring graces With muckle kind embraces, Now ſighing no
crying, then tears dropping fall; And had he my ſoft arms preferr'd to war's a _
_ larms, My love grown mad without the man of Gad I fear in my fit I had granted all.

I waſh'd and patch'd to make me look provoking,
  Snares they ſaid would catch the men;
And on my head a huge commode ſat cocking,
  Which made me ſhew as tall again:
For a new gown I paid muckle money,
  Which with golden flowers did ſhine:
My love well might think me gay and bonny,
  Nae Scots laſs was e'er ſo fine.
    My petticoat I ſpotted,
    Fringe too with thread I knotted,
Lac'd ſhoes and ſilken hoſe garter'd o'er the knee;
    But oh! the fatal thought,
    To Willy theſe are nought,
Wha rid to towns, and rifled wi' dragoons,
When he, ſilly loon, might hae plunder'd me.

# Awa whigs awa.

263

A_ _wa whigs a_wa, A_ _wa whigs a_wa, Ye're but a
pack o' traitor louns, Ye'll do nae gude at a'. Our thriſsles
flouriſh'd freſh and fair, And bonie bloom'd our roſ_es; But
whigs cam like a froſt in June, And wither'd a' our poſies.
Chorus
A_ _wa whigs a_wa, A_ wa whigs a_wa, Ye're but a pack o'
trai_tor louns, Ye'll do nae gude at a'.

Our ancient crown's fa'n in the duſt;
Deil blin them wi the ſtoure o't,
And write their names in his black beuk
Wha gae the whigs the power o't!
Cho.[s] Awa whigs &c.

Our ſad decay in church and ſtate
Surpaſses my deſcriving:
The whigs cam o'er us for a curſe,
And we hae done wi' thriving.
Cho.[s] Awa whigs &c.

Grim Vengeance lang has taen a nap,
But we may ſee him wauken:
Gude help the day when royal heads
Are hunted like a maukin.
Cho.[s] Awa whigs &c.

## Ca' the ewes to the knowes,

264

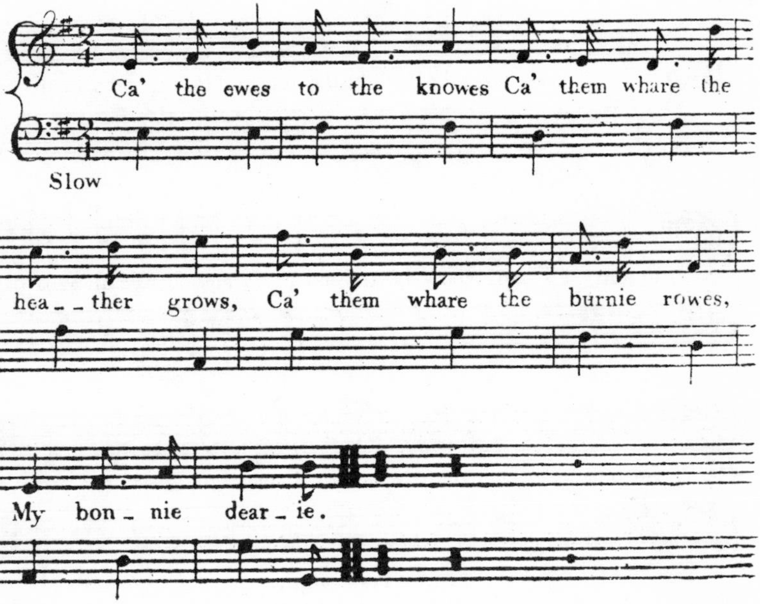
Ca' the ewes to the knowes Ca' them whare the
Slow
hea _ _ ther grows, Ca' them whare the burnie rowes,
My bon _ nie dear _ ie.

As I gaed down the water-ſide,
There I met my ſhepherd-lad,
He row'd me ſweetly in his plaid,
An he ca'd me his dearie.
Cho.[s] Ca' the ewes &c.

Ye ſall get gowns and ribbons meet
Cauf-leather ſhoon upon your feet.
And in my arms ye'se lie and ſleep,
And ye ſall be my dearie.
Cho.[s] Ca' the ewes &c.

Will ye gang down the water-ſide
And ſee the waves ſae ſweetly glide
Beneath the hazels ſpreading wide,
The moon it ſhines fu' clearly.
Cho.[s] Ca' the ewes &c.

If ye'll but ſtand to what ye've ſaid,
I'se gang wi' you, my ſhepherd lad,
And ye may rowe me in your plaid,
And I ſall be your dearie.
Cho.[s] Ca' the ewes &c.

I was bred up at nae ſic ſchool,
My ſhepherd-lad, to play the fool,
And a' the day to ſit in dool,
And nae body to ſee me:
Cho.[s] Ca' the ewes &c.

While waters wimple to the ſea;
While day blinks in the lift ſae hie:
Till clay-cauld death ſall blin' my e'e,
Ye ſall be my dearie,
Cho.[s] Ca' the ewes &c.

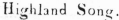

## Highland Song.

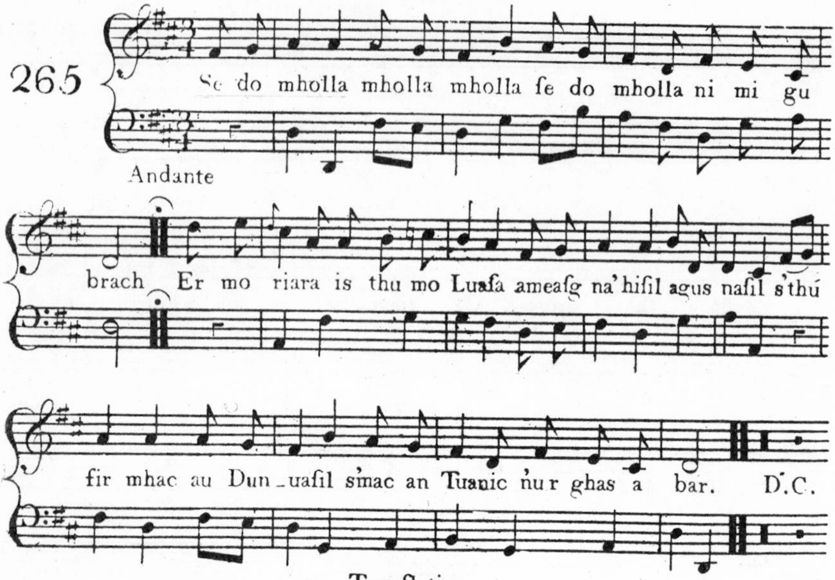
265
Se do mholla mholla mholla ſe do mholla ni mi gu
Andante
brach Er mo riara is thu mo Luaſa ameaſg na' hiſil agus naſil s'thu
fir mhac au Dun_uaſil s'mac an Tuanic ṅu r ghas a bar. D.C.

Tranſlation.

Thy praiſe I'll ever celebrate.
Truly thou art my Lover either among the lowly or high, thou art the true ſon of the Gentleman, and alſo the Farmer's ſon when the Harveſt comes on.

* * * * * * * * * * * * * * * * * * * * * * * * * * *

## The Jolly Beggar.

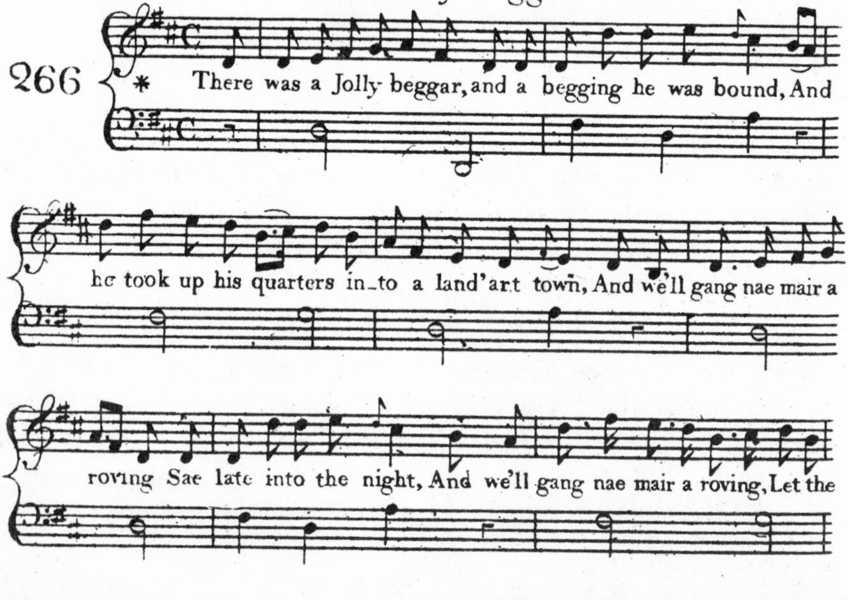
266
*
There was a Jolly beggar, and a begging he was bound, And
he took up his quarters in_to a land'art town, And we'll gang nae mair a
roving Sae late into the night, And we'll gang nae mair a roving, Let the

Continued.

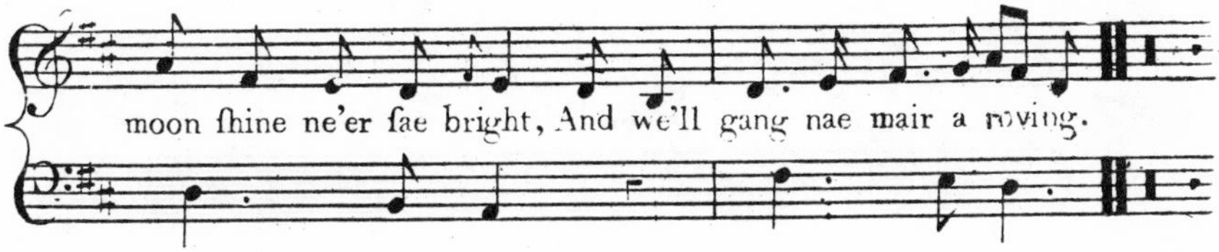
moon ſhine ne'er ſae bright, And we'll gang nae mair a roving.

He wad neither ly in barn, nor yet wad he in byre,
But in ahint the ha' door, or elſe afore the fire.
And we'll gang nae mair, &c.

The beggar's bed was made at e'en wi' good clean ſtraw and hay,
And in ahint the ha' door, and there the beggar lay.
And we'll gang nae mair, &c.

Up raiſe the goodman's dochter, and for to bar the door,
And there ſhe ſaw the beggar ſtandin i' the floor.
And we'll gang nae mair, &c.

He took the laſſie in his arms, and to the bed he ran,
O hooly, hooly wi' me, Sir, ye'll waken our goodman.
And we'll gang nae mair, &c.

The beggar was a cunnin' loon, and ne'er a word he ſpak
Until he got his turn done, ſyne he began to crack.
And we'll gang nae mair, &c.

Is there ony dogs into this town, Maiden, tell me true;
And what wad ye do wi' them, my hinny and my dow.
And we'll gang nae mair, &c.

They'll rive a' my mealpocks, and do me meikle wrang.
O dool for the doing o't, are ye the poor man.
And we'll gang nae mair, &c.

Then ſhe took up the mealpocks and flang them o'er the wa',
The d_l gae wi' the mealpocks, my maidenhead and a'.
And we'll gang nae mair, &c.

I took ye for ſome gentleman, at leaſt the Laird of Brodie;
O dool for the doing o't! are ye the poor bodie.
And we'll gang nae mair, &c.

He took the laſſie in his arms, and gae her kiſſes three,
And four-and-twenty hunder mark to pay the nurice-fee.
And we'll gang nae mair, &c.

He took a horn frae his ſide, and blew baith loud and ſhrill,
And four-and-twenty belted knights came ſkipping o'er the hill.
And we'll gang nae mair, &c

And he took out his little knife, loot a' his duddies fa',
And he was the braweſt gentleman that was amang them a'
And we'll gang nae mair, &c.

The beggar was a cliver loon, and he lap ſhoulder height,
O ay for ſicken quarters as I gat yeſternight.
And we'll gang nae mair, &c.

## I loe na a Laddie but ane.

267

I loe nae a laddie but ane, He loes na a lassie but
Slowish
me; He's willin' to make me his ain, An' his ain I am willin' to
be. He coft me a rokley o' blue, A pair o' mit_tens o'
green An' his price was a kiss o' my mou; An' I
paid him the debt yes_treen.

My mither's ay makin' a phrase,
"That I'm lucky young to be wed;"
But lang 'ere she countit my days,
O' me she was brought to bed:
Sae mither, just settle your tongue,
An' dinna be flytin' sae bauld,
For we can do the thing when we're young,
That we canna do weel when we're auld.

### Same Tune.

Let ithers brag weel o' their gear,
Their land, and their lordlie degree;
I carena for ought but my dear,
For he's ilka thing lordlie to me:
His words mair than sugar are sweet!
His sense drives ilk fear far awa!
I listen poor fool! and I greet
Yet oh how sweet are the tears as they fa!

"Dear lassie," he cries wi' a jeer,
"Ne'er heed what the auld anes will say;
"Tho' we've little to brag o' _ ne'er fear,
"What's gowd to a heart that is wae.
"Our laird has baith honours and wealth;
"Yet see! how he's dwining wi' care:
"Now we, tho' we've naithing but health,
"Are cantie and leil evermair.

"O Menie! the heart that is true,
"Has something mair costlie than gear;
"Ilk e'en, it has naithing to rue;
"Ilk morn, it has naithing to fear:
"Ye warldlings! gae, hoard up your store,
"And tremble for fear ought ye tyne:
"Guard your treasures wi' lock, bar & door
"While thus in my arms I lock mine!"

He ends wi' a kiss and a smile _
Waes me! can I tak it amiss,
When a lad sae unpractis'd in guile
Smiles saftly, and ends wi' a kiss!
Ye lasses wha loo to torment
Your lemans wi' fause scorn and strife,
Play your pranks _ for I've gien my consent
And this night I'll tak Jamie for life.

## I'll mak you be fain to follow me.

268

As late by a ſodger I chanced to paſs, I heard him a courtin a
Lively
bony young laſs; My hin_ny, my life, my deareſt, quo he, I'll
mak you be fain to fol_low me. Gin I ſhould fol_low you a
poor ſodger lad. Ilk ane o' my cummers wad think I was mad; For
battles I never ſhall lang to ſee, I'll never be fain to follow thee.

To follow me, I think ye may be glad,
A part o' my ſupper, a part o' my bed,
A part o' my bed, wherever it be,
I'll mak you be fain to follow me.
Come try my knapſack on your back,
Alang the king's high-gate we'll pack;
Between Saint Johnſton and bony Dundee,
I'll mak you be fain to follow me.

# The Bridal o't.

Tune, Lucy Campbel.

269

They ſay that Jockey'll ſpeed weel o't, They ſay that Jockey'll
ſpeed weel o't, For he grows brawer ilka day, I hope we'll hae a bridal o't.
For yeſternight nae farder gane, The backhouſe at the ſide wa' o't, He
there wi' Meg was mirden ſeen, I hope we'll hae a bridal o't.

An we had but a bridal o't,
  An we had but a bridal o't,
We'd leave the reſt unto gude luck
  Altho' there ſhould betide ill o't:
For bridal days are merry times
  And young folks like the coming o't,
And Scribblers they bang up their rhymes
  And Pipers they the bumming o't.

The laſses like a bridal o't,
  The laſses like a bridal o't,
Their braws maun be in rank and file
  Altho' that they ſhould guide ill o't:
The boddom o' the kiſt is then
  Turn'd up unto the immoſt o't,
The end that held the keeks ſae clean
  Is now become the teemeſt o't.

The bangſter at the threſhing o't,
  The bangſter at the threſhing o't,
Afore it comes is fidgin fain
  And ilka day's a claſhing o't;
He'll ſell his jerkin for a groat,
  His linder for anither o't,
And e'er he want to clear his ſhot,
  His ſark'll pay the tither o't.

The Pipers and the Fiddlers o't,
  The Pipers and the Fiddlers o't,
Can ſmell a bridal unco far
  And like to be the middlers o't:
Fan thick and threefald they convene
  Ilk ane envies the tither o't,
And wiſhes nane but him alane
  May ever ſee anither o't.

Fan they hae done wi' eating o't,
  Fan they hae done wi' eating o't,
For dancing they gae to the green,
  And aiblins to the beating o't:
He dances beſt that dances faſt,
  And loups at ilka reeſing o't,
And claps his hands frae hough to hough,
  And furls about the feezings o't.

## Merry hae I been teethin a heckle.

Tune, Boddich na' mbrigs, or Lord Breadalbine's March.

270

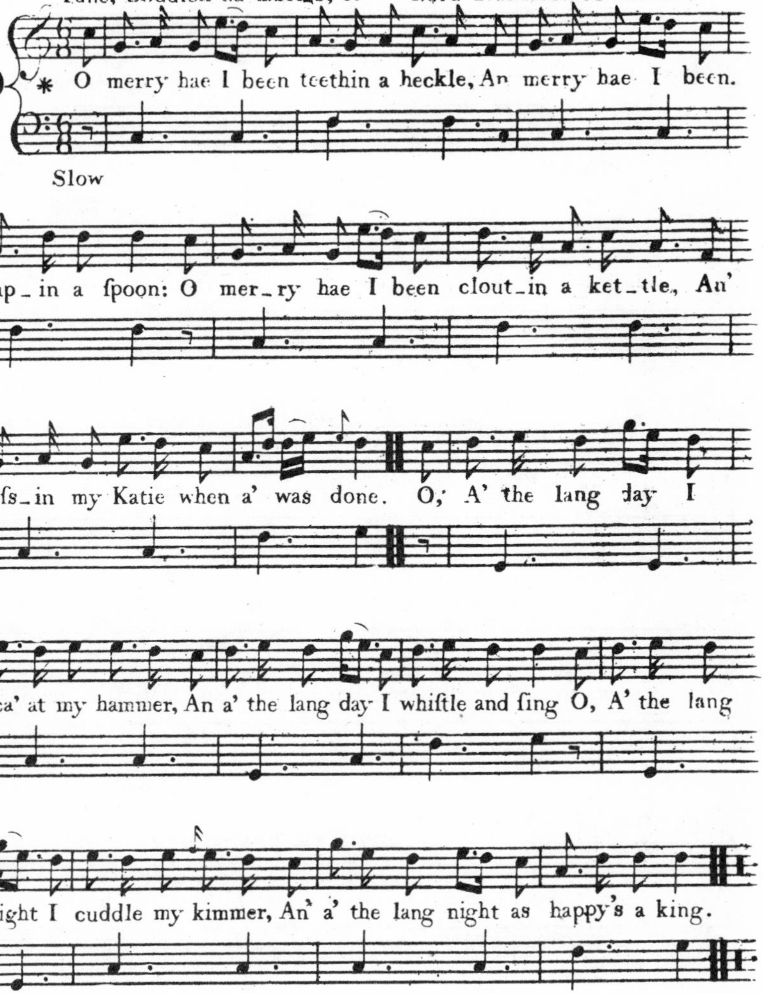
* O merry hae I been teethin a heckle, An merry hae I been.
Slow
ſhap_in a ſpoon: O mer_ry hae I been clout_in a ket_tle, An'
kiſs_in my Katie when a' was done. O, A' the lang day I
ca' at my hammer, An a' the lang day I whiſtle and ſing O, A' the lang
night I cuddle my kimmer, An a' the lang night as happy's a king.

Bitter in dool I lickit my winnins
O' marrying Beſs, to gie her a ſlave:
Bleſt be the hour ſhe cool'd in her linnens,
And blythe be the bird that ſings on her grave!

Come to my arms, my Katie, my Katie,
An' come to my arms and kiſs me again!
Druken or ſober here's to thee, Katie!
And bleſt be the day I did it again.

## A Mother's lament for the death of her son.

Written for this Work by R: Burns. Tune, Finlayston House

271

Fate gave the word, the ar_row sped, And pierc'd my
Slow
Darling's heart: And with him all the joys are fled Life
can to me im_part. By cru_el hands the sap_ling
drops, In dust dis_ho_nor'd laid: So fell the pride of
all my hopes, My a_ges fu_ture shade.

The mother linnet in the brake
  Bewails her ravish'd young;
So I, for my lost Darling's sake,
  Lament the live day long.
Death, oft I've fear'd thy fatal blow,
  Now, fond, I bare my breast,
O, do thou kindly lay me low
  With him I love at rest!

B.

## The White Cockade.

272

* My love was born in Aberdeen, The boniest lad that
Lively
e'er was seen, But now he makes our hearts fu' sad, He
takes the field wi' his White Cockade. O he's a ranting, ro_ving
lad, He is a brisk an' a bonny lad, Be_tide what may, I
will be wed, And follow the boy wi' the White Cockade.

I'll sell my rock, my reel, my tow,
My gude gray mare and hawkit cow;
To buy mysel a tartan plaid,
To follow the boy wi' the White Cockade.
Cho[s]. O he's a ranting, roving lad,

## Oran gaoil, a gallic ſong tranſlated by a Lady.

273

* As on an eminence I ſtood a muſing, A heaven _ ly
form broke forth on my ſight; She darted a look from her
two lovely diamonds, Than vaniſhing left me o'erwhelm'd with de _
_ light. O. on my faithful faithful, faithful, on my faithful
boſom re _ cline, Thoſe ſparkling, black eyes that make conqueſt of
thouſands, In _ ſenſible he, would not wiſh to be thine!

Aw'd by her mien and heavenly like motion,
I follow'd the goddeſs who raviſh'd my eye;
I would _but Oh, Heavens! could I but deſcribe her,
Thouſands like me would adore her and die!
O! on my faithful &c.

Her complection is like to the delicate ſnow;
Lilies and roſes compar'd with her ſkin,
Soon loſe their hue and ſink back in confuſion,
Unable to bear the bright rays of the ſun.
O! on my faithful &c.

# Sandy o'er the Lee.

274
Spiritoso
I winna marry o_ny man but Sandy o'er the lee. I
winna marry ony man but Sandy o'er the lee. I winna hae the dominie for
gude he canna be, But I will hae my San_dy lad, my
Sandy o'er the lee, For he's aye a kifsing kifsing aye a kifsing
me, he's aye a kifsing, kifsing aye a kifsing me.

I will not have the minifter for all his godly looks,
Nor yet will I the lawyer have, for all his wily crooks:
I will not have the plowman lad, nor yet will I the miller.
But I will have my Sandy lad, without one penny filler
For he's aye a kifsing kifsing &c.

I will not have the foldier lad for he gangs to the war,
I will not have the failor lad becaufe he fmells of tar;
I will not have the lord nor laird for all their mickle gear,
But I will have my Sandy lad my Sandy o'er the moor.
For he's aye a kifsing kifsing &c.

# Todlen Hame.

275

When I have a ſax_pence under my thum, Then
Slowiſh
I'll get cred_it in il_ka town: But ay when I'm poor they
Chorus
bid me gae by; O! poverty parts good company. Todlen hame,
tod_len hame, O! Cou'dna my love come tod_len hame.

Fair fa the goodwife, and ſend her good ſale,
She gi'es us white bannocks to drink her ale,
Syne if her tippony chance to be ſma',
We'll tak a good ſcour o't, and ca't awa'.
Todlen hame, todlen hame,
As round as a neep come todlen hame.

My kimmer and I lay down to ſleep,
And twa pint ſtoups at our bed-feet;
And ay when we waken'd we drank them dry:
What think you of my wee kimmer and I.
Todlen butt and todlen ben,
Sae round as my love comes todlen hame.

Leez me on liquor, my todlen dow,
Ye're ay ſae good-humour'd when weeting your mou';
When ſober ſae ſour, ye'll fight wi' a flee,
That it's a blyth ſight to the bairns and me,
Todlen hame, todlen hame,
When round as a neep ye come todlen hame.

## The Braes o' Ballochmyle.

Written for this Work by Robert Burns.

276

The Catrine woods were yellow seen, The flowers decay'd on
Catrine lee, Nae lav'rock sang on hillock green, But nature
sickend on the e'e. Thro' faded groves Ma_ri_a sang, Her_
sel in beau_ty's bloom the while, And ay the wild wood
echoes rang, Fare_weel the braes o' Ballochmyle.

Low in your wintry beds, ye flowers,
Again ye'll flourish fresh and fair;
Ye birdies dumb, in with'ring bowers,
Again ye'll charm the vocal air.
But here alas! for me nae mair;
Shall birdie charm, or floweret smile;
Fareweel the bonnie banks of Ayr,
Fareweel, fareweel! sweet Ballochmyle.

# The rantin dog the Daddie o't.

Tune, East nook o' Fife.

277

O wha my babie-clouts will buy, O Wha will tent me when I
Lively
cry; Wha will kiss me where I lie. The rantin dog the daddie o't. O
Wha will own he did the faut, O wha will buy the groan_in maut, O
Wha will tell me how to ca't. The rantin dog the daddie o't.

When I mount the Creepie-chair,
Wha will sit beside me there,
Gie me Rob, I'll seek nae mair,
The rantin dog the Daddie o't.

Wha will crack to me my lane;
Wha will mak me fidgin fain;
Wha will kiss me o'er again.
The rantin dog the Daddie o't. Z

# The Shepherd's Preference.

278

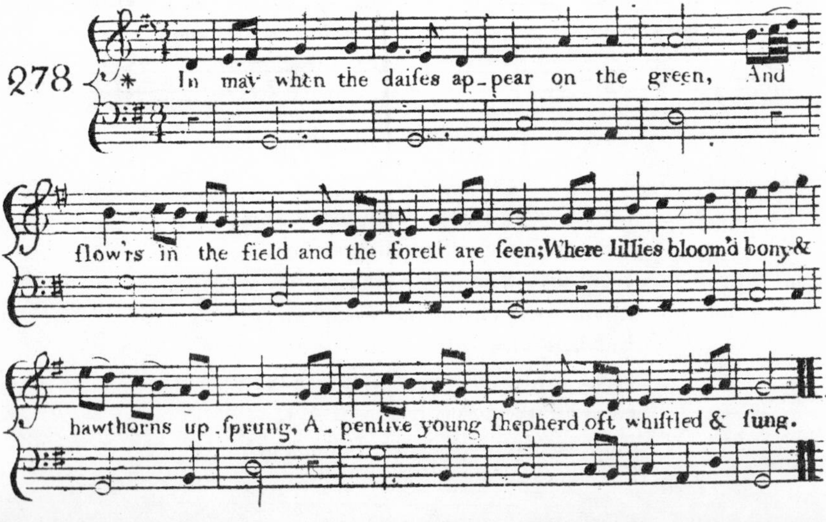
In may when the daises ap_pear on the green, And
flow'rs in the field and the forest are seen; Where lillies bloom'd bony &
hawthorns up sprung, A_ pensive young shepherd oft whistled & sung.

## Continued.

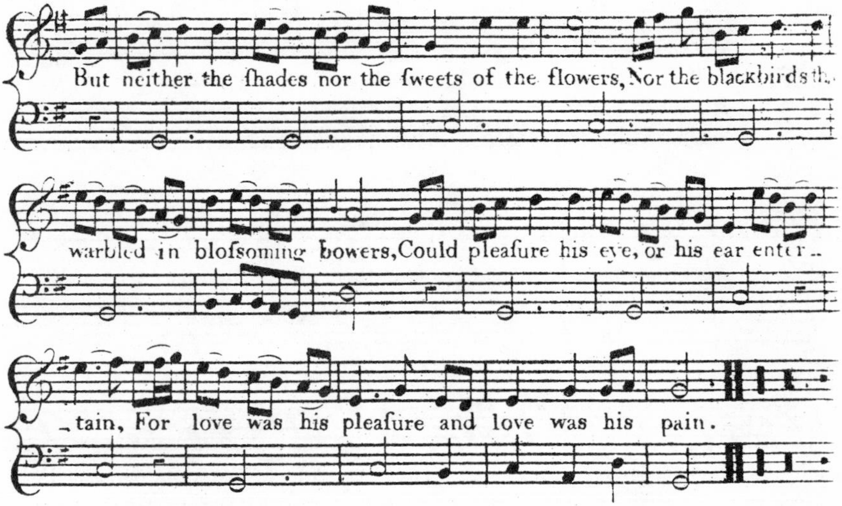
But neither the ſhades nor the ſweets of the flowers, Nor the blackbirds th..
warbled in bloſsoming bowers, Could pleaſure his eye, or his ear enter..
..tain, For love was his pleaſure and love was his pain.

The ſhepherd thus ſung, while his flocks all around,
  Drew nearer and nearer and ſigh'd to the ſound;
Around, as in chains, lay the beaſts of the wood,
  With pity diſarm'd, with muſic ſubdu'd.
Young Jeſsy is fair as the ſpring's early flower,
  And Mary ſings ſweet as the bird, in her bower:
But Peggy is fairer and ſweeter than they
  With looks like the morning with ſmiles like the day.

In the flower of her youth in the bloom of eighteen,
  Of virtue the goddeſs, of beauty the queen,
One hour in her preſence, an age far excells,
  Amid courts, where ambition with miſery dwells;
How fair to the ſhepherd the new ſpringing flowers,
  When may and when morning lead on the gay hours
But Peggy is brighter and fairer than they,
  She's fair as the morning and lovely as may.

How ſweet to the ſhepherd the wild woodland ſound,
  When larks ſing above him, and lambs bleat around:
But Peggy far ſweeter can ſpeak and can ſing
  Than the notes of the warblers that welcome the ſpring.
When in beauty ſhe moves by the brook of the plain,
  You would call her a Venus. new ſprung from the main,
When ſhe ſings and the woods with their echoes reply,
  You would think that an angel was warbling on high.

How ſprightly the ſwains, in her preſence appear
  All the charms ſhe improves that embelliſh the ear
She heightens each pleaſure, ſhe ſoftens each woe,
  She is all of celeſtial we fancy below.
Ye Pow'rs that preſide over mortal eſtate,
  Whoſe nod governs nature, whoſe pleaſure is fate,
O grant me, O grant me the heaven of her charms:
  May I live in her preſence and die in her arms.

## My Mary dear, departed ſhade.

Written for this Work by R: Burns. Tune, Captn. Cook's death &c.

279

Thou ling'ring ſtar, with leſs'ning ray, That lov'ſt to
greet the ear_ly morn, A_gain thou uſherſt in the day My
Mary from my ſoul was torn. O Mary! dear departed Shade! Where
is thy place of bliſsful reſt? Seeſt thou thy Lov_er
_lowly laid? Hear'ſt thou the groans that rend his breaſt?


That ſacred hour can I forget,
Can I forget the hallow'd grove
Where, by the winding Ayr, we met
To live one day of parting love!
Eternity cannot efface
Thoſe records dear of tranſports paſt;
Thy image at our laſt embrace,
Ah, little thought we 'twas our laſt!

Ayr gurgling kiſs'd his pebbled ſhore,
O'erhung with wild-woods thickening green;
The fragrant birch & hawthorn hoar
Twin'd amorous round the raptur'd ſcene;
The flowers ſprang wanton to be preſt,
The birds ſang love on every ſpray,
Till too, too ſoon the glowing weſt
Proclaim'd the ſpeed of winged day.

Still o'er theſe ſcenes my mem'ry wakes
And fondly broods with miſer-care;
Time but th' impreſsion ſtronger makes,
As ſtreams their channels deeper wear:
My Mary, dear departed Shade!
Where is thy place of bliſsful reſt?
Seeſt thou thy Lover lowly laid?
Hear'ſt thou the groans that rend his breaſt.

## Hardyknute: Or, The Battle of Largs.

280

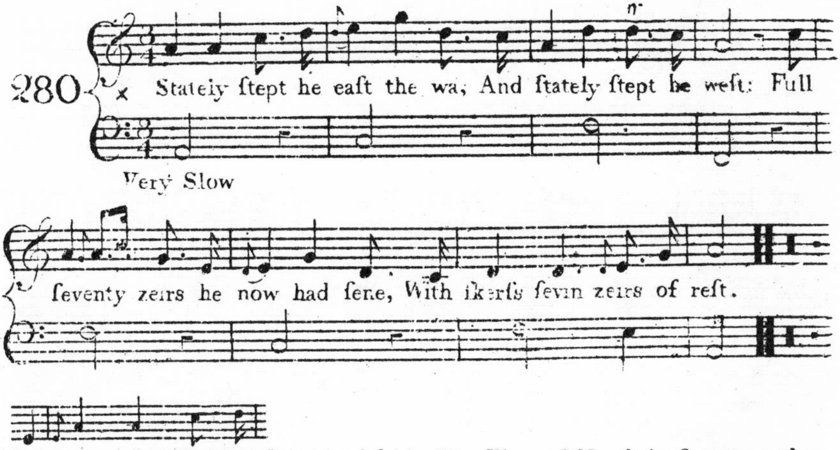
Stately ſtept he eaſt the wa, And ſtately ſtept he weſt: Full
Very Slow
ſeventy zeirs he now had ſene, With ſkerſs ſevin zeirs of reſt.

He livit quhen Britons breach of faith
Wroucht Scotland meikle wae;
And ay his ſword tauld to their ſkaith,
He was their deidly fae.

Hie on a hill his caſtle ſtude,
With halls and towirs a hicht,
And guidly chambers fair to ſe
Quhair he lodgit mony a knicht,

His dame ſae peirleſs anes and fair,
For chaſt and bewtie deimt,
Nae marrow had in all the land,
Saif Elenor the queen.

Full thirtein ſons to him ſcho bare,
All men of valour ſtout;
In bludy ficht with ſword in hand
Nyne loſt their lives bot doubt;

Four zit remain, lang may they live
To ſtand by liege and land:
Hie was their fame, hie was their micht,
And hie was their command.

Great luve they bare to Fairly fair,
Their ſiſter ſaft and deir;
Her girdle ſhawd her middle gimp,
And gowden gliſt her hair.

Quhat waefou wae her bewtie bred,
Waefou to zung and auld,
Waefou I trow to kyth and kin,
As ſtory ever tauld!

The King of Norſe in ſummer tyde,
Puſt up with powir and micht,
Landed in fair Scotland the yle,
With mony a hardy knicht.

The tydings to our gude Scots king
Came, as he ſat at dyne,
With noble chiefs in braif aray,
Drinking the blude-reid wyne.

"To horſe, to horſe, my royal Liege,
Zours faes ſtand on the ſtrand,
Full twenty thouſand glittering ſpears
The King of Norſe commands."

"Bring me my ſteed Mage dapple gray
Our gude King raiſe and cry'd,
"A truſtier beaſt in all the land
A Scots king nevir ſeyd.

Go, little page, tell Hardyknute,
That lives on hill ſae hie,
To draw his ſword, the dreid of faes.
And haſt and follow me."

The little page flew ſwift as dart
Flung by his maſters arm:
"Cum down, cum down, Lord Hardyknute
And rid zour King frae harm."

Then reid reid grew his dark-brown cheiks
Sae did his dark-brown brow;
His luiks grew kene, as they were wont,
In dangers great, to do. &c.

## Eppie Adair.

281

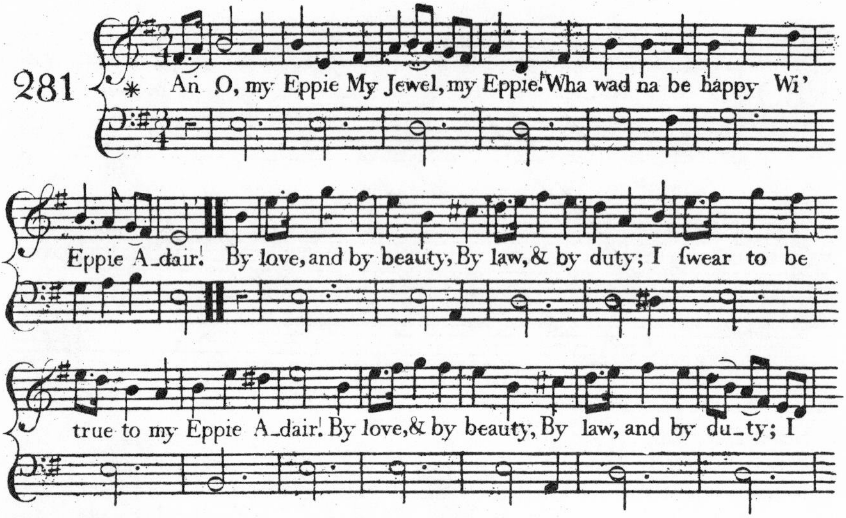
An O, my Eppie My Jewel, my Eppie! Wha wad na be happy Wi'
Eppie A_dair! By love, and by beauty, By law, & by duty; I swear to be
true to my Eppie A_dair! By love, & by beauty, By law, and by du_ty; I

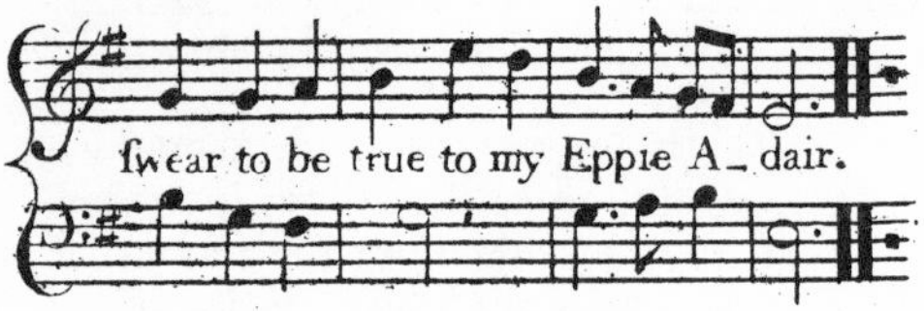
swear to be true to my Eppie A_dair.

A' pleasure exile me,
Dishonour defile me,
If e'er I beguile thee,
My Eppie Adair!

## The Battle of Sherra-moor.

Written for this Work by Robt. Burns. Tune, Cameronian Rant.

282

O cam ye here the fight to shun, Or herd the sheep wi' me, man, or
were ye at the Sherra moor, Or did the bat_tle see, man. "I
saw the bat_tle sair and teugh, And ree_kin_red ran
mony a sheugh, My heart for fear gae sough for sough To

Continued.

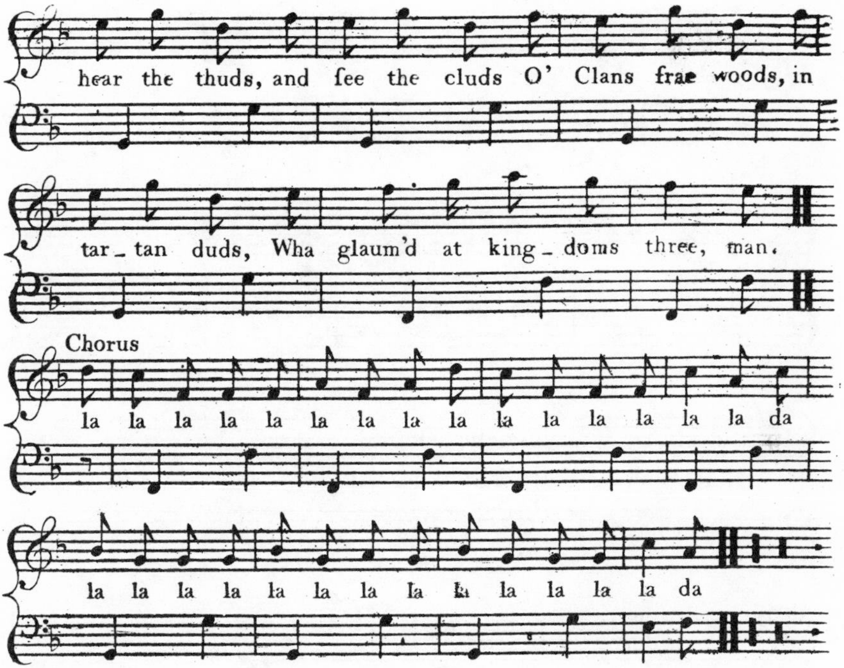
hear the thuds, and see the cluds O' Clans frae woods, in
tar_tan duds, Wha glaum'd at king_doms three, man.
Chorus
la la la la la la la la la la la la la la la da
la la la la la la la la la la la la la da

The red-coat lads wi' black cockauds
To meet them were na slaw, man,
They rush'd, and push'd & blude outgush'd,
And mony a bouk did fa' man:
The great Argyle led on his files,
I wat they glanc'd for twenty miles,
They hough'd the Clans like nine-pin kyles
They hack'd & hash'd while braid swords cla-sh'd,
And thro' they dash'd, & hew'd & smash'd,
Till fey men di'd awa, man.
Chos. la la la, &c.
But had ye seen the philibegs
And skyrin tartan trews, man,
When in the teeth they dar'd our Whigs,
And covenant Trueblues, man;
In lines extended lang and large,
When baiginets o'erpower'd the charge,
And thousands hasten'd to the charge;
Wi' Highland wrath they frae the sheath
Drew blades o' death, till out o' breath
They fled like frighted dows, man."
Chos. la la la, &c.
"O how deil Tam can that be true,
The chace gaed frae the north, man;
I saw mysel, they did pursue
The horse-men bach to Forth, man
And at Dunblane in my ain sight
They took the brig wi'a their might,
And straught to Stirling wing'd their fli-ght,
But, cursed lot! the gates were shut
And mony a huntit poor Red-coat
For fear amaist did swarf man.
Chos. la la la, &c.
My sister Kate cam up the gate
Wi' crowdie unto me, man;
She swoor she saw some rebels run
To Perth and to Dundee, man:
Their left-hand General had nae skill;
The Angus lads had nae gude will,
That day their neebour's blude to spill;
For fear by foes that they should lose
Their cogs o' brose, they scar'd at blows
And hameward fast did flee, man.
Chos. la la la, &c.
They've lost some gallant gentlemen
Amang the Highland clans, man;
I fear my Lord Panmuir is slain,
Or in his en'mies hands, man:
Now wad ye sing this double flight,
Some fell for wrang & some for right,
And mony bade the warld gudenight;
Say pell and mell, wi' muskets knell
How Tories fell and Whigs to h_ll
Flew off in frighted bands, man
Chos. la la la, &c

## Sandy and Jockie.

283

Twa bony lads were San_dy and Jock_ _ie;
Jockie was lo'ed but Sandy un_luc_ky, Jockie was
laird baith of hills and of val_lies, But San_dy was
nought but the king o' gude fellows, Jockie lo'ed Madgie, for
Madgie had money, And Sandie lo'ed Mary, for Mary was
bony: Ane wedded for Love, Ane wedded for treasure, So
Jockie had siller, And Sandy had pleasure.
6 6 6 6 6 6

# The Bonie Banks of Ayr.

Written for this Work by Robert Burns.

284

Slow
The gloomy night is gath'ring fast, Loud roars the wild, in
-constant blast, Yon murky cloud is foul with rain, I see it
driving o'er the plain; The hunter now has left the moor, The scatter'd
coveys meet secure, The hunter now has left the moor, the scattered coveys
meet secure, while here I wander prest with care, Along the lonely banks of Ayr

The Autumn mourns her rip'ning corn
By early Winter's ravage torn;
Across her placid, azure sky,
She sees the scowling tempest fly:
Chill runs my blood to hear it rave,
I think upon the stormy wave,
Where many a danger I must dare,
Far from the bonie banks of Ayr.

'Tis not the surging billow's roar,
'Tis not that fatal, deadly shore;
Tho' Death in ev'ry shape appear,
The wretched have no more to fear:
But round my heart the ties are bound
That heart transpierc'd with many a wo
These bleed afresh, those ties I tear,
To leave the bonie banks of Ayr.

Farewell, old Coila's hills and dales,
Her heathy moors and winding vales;
The scenes where wretched fancy roves
Pursuing past, unhappy loves!
Farewell, my friends! farewell, my foes
My peace with these, my love with those
The bursting tears my heart declare,
Farewell, the bonie banks of Ayr

## John o' Badenyond.

235

Slow
When first I came to be a man of twenty years or ſo, I
thought myſelf a handſome youth, and fain the world would know; In
beſt attire I ſtept abroad, with ſpirits briſk and gay, And
here and there, and every where, was like a morn in May.
No care I had, nor fear of want, but rambled up and down; And
for a beau I might have paſs'd in country or in town I
ſtill was pleas'd where'er I went, and when I was a_lone, I

Continued.

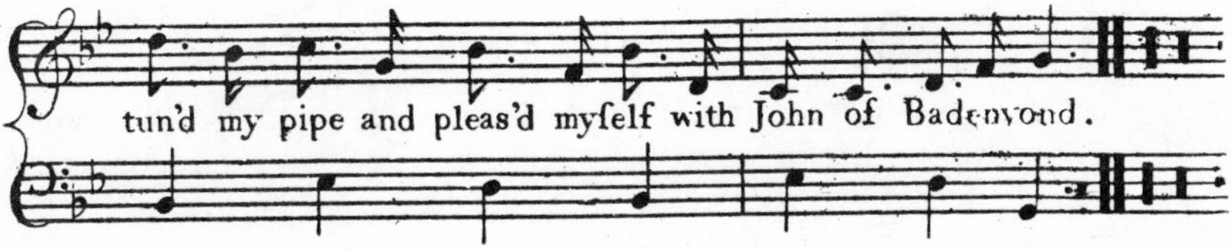
tun'd my pipe and pleas'd myſelf with John of Badenyond.

Now in the days of youthful prime a miſtreſs I muſt find,
For love, they ſay, gives one an air, and ev'n improves the mind,
On Phillis fair, above the reſt, kind fortune fix'd my eyes;
Her piercing beauty ſtruck my heart, and ſhe became my choice:
To Cupid then, with hearty pray'r, I offer'd many a vow,
And danc'd, and ſung, and ſigh'd and ſwore, as other lovers do:
But when at laſt I breath'd my flame, I found her cold as ſtone;
I left the girl, and tun'd my pipe, to John of Badenyond.

When love had thus my heart beguil'd, with fooliſh hopes and vain,
To friendſhip's port I ſteer'd my courſe, and laugh'd at lover's pain;
A friend I got by lucky chance, 'twas ſomething like divine,
An honeſt friend's a precious gift, and ſuch a gift was mine:
And now whatever might betide a happy man was I,
In any ſtrait I knew to whom I freely might apply:
A ſtrait ſoon came, my friend I try'd, he laugh'd and ſpurn'd my moan
I hy'd me home, and pleas'd myſelf with John of Badenyond.

I thought I ſhould be wiſer next, and would a patriot turn,
Began to doat on Johnny Wilkes, and cry up Parſon Horne;
Their noble ſpirit I admir'd and prais'd their manly zeal,
Who had with flaming tongue and pen maintain'd the public weal:
But e'er a month, or two was paſt, I found myſelf betray'd;
'Twas Self and Party after all, for all the ſtir they made,
At laſt I ſaw theſe factious knaves inſult the very throne,
I curs'd them a', and tun'd my pipe, to John of Badenyond.

What next to do I mus'd a while, ſtill hoping to ſucceed,
I pitch'd on books for company, and gravely try'd to read;
I bought and borrow'd every where, and ſtudied night and day;
Nor miſt what Dean or Doctor wrote, that happened in my way;
Philoſophy I now eſteem'd the ornament of youth;
And carefully thro' many a page, I hunted after truth:
A thouſand various ſchemes I try'd and yet was pleas'd with none,
I threw them by, and tun'd my pipe to John of Bade yond.

And now ye youngſters every where, who want to make a ſhow,
Take heed in time, nor vainly hope for happineſs below,
What you may fancy pleaſure here is but an empty name
For girls, and friends, and books, and ſo, you'll find them all the ſame.
Then be adviſ'd, and warning take from ſuch a man as me,
I'm neither Pope nor Cardinal, nor one of high degree:
You'll find diſpleaſure every where; then do as I have done,
E'en tune your pipe, and pleaſe yourſelf with John of Badenyond

# Frennett Hall.

286

When Frennett caſtle's ivied wa's Thro' yallow leaves were ſeen; When birds forſook the ſapleſs boughs, And bees the faded green;
Then Lady Frennet, vengeful dame, Did wander frae the ha', To the wild foreſt's dewie gloom, A _ mong the leaves that fa'.

Slow

Her page, the ſwifteſt of her train,
  Had clumb a lofty tree,
Whaſe branches to the angry blaſt
  Were ſoughing mournfullie:
He turn'd his een towards the path
  That near the caſtle lay,
Where good lord John and Rothemay
  Were rideing down the brae.

Swift darts the eagle from the ſky,
  When prey beneath is ſeen;
As quickly he forgot his hold,
  And perch'd upon the green:
O hie thee, hie thee! lady gay,
  Frae this dark wood awa:
Some viſitors of gallant mein
  Are haſting to the ha'.

Then round ſhe rowed her ſilken plaid,
  Her feet ſhe did na ſpare,
Until ſhe left the foreſt ſkirts
  A lang bow-ſhot and mair.
O where, O where, my good lord John,
  O tell me where you ride?
Within my caſtle-wall this night
  I hope you mean to bide.

Kind nobles, will ye but alight,
  In yonder bower to ſtay;
Saft eaſe ſhall teach you to forget
  The hardneſs of the way.
Forbear entreaty, gentle dame,
  How can we here remain?
Full well you ken your huſband dear
  Was by our father ſlain.

The thoughts of which with fell revenge
  Your angry boſom ſwell:
Enraged you've ſworn that blood for bloo[d]
  Should this black paſſion quell.
O fear not, fear not, good lord John,
  That I will you betray,
Or ſue requittal for a debt
  Which nature cannot pay.

Bear witneſs, a' ye powers on high,
  Ye lights that 'gin to ſhine,
This night ſhall prove the ſacred cord
  That knits your faith and mine.
The lady ſlee with honeyed words
  Entic d thir youths to ſtay:
But morning ſun nere ſhone upon
  Lord John nor Rothemay.

## Young Jockey was the blytheſt lad.

287

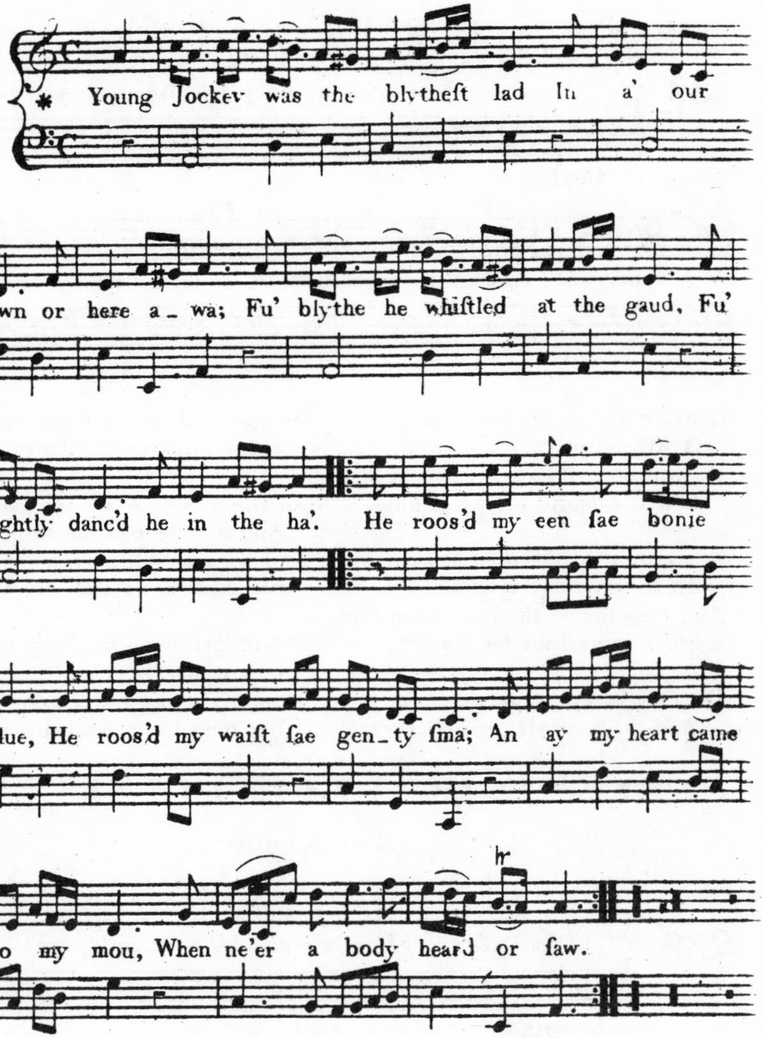
* Young Jockey was the blytheſt lad In a' our
town or here a_wa; Fu' blythe he whiſtled at the gaud, Fu'
lightly danc'd he in the ha'. He roos'd my een ſae bonie
blue, He roos'd my waiſt ſae gen_ty ſma; An ay my heart came
to my mou, When ne'er a body heard or ſaw.

My Jockey toils upon the plain
  Thro' wind and weet, thro' froſt and ſnaw;
And o'er the lee I leuk fu' fain
  When Jockey's owſen hameward ca.
An ay the night comes round again
  When in his arms he taks me a';
An ay he vows he'll be my ain
  As lang's he has a breath to draw.

## A waukrife Minnie.

288

Whare are you gaun, my bony lafs, Whare are you gaun, my
Lively

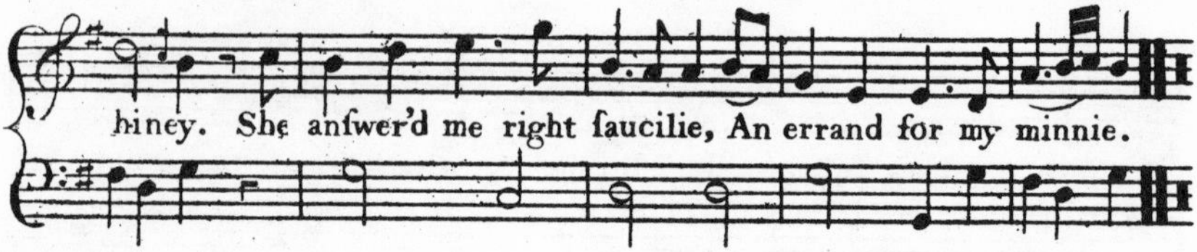
hiney. She anfwer'd me right faucilie, An errand for my minnie.

O whare live ye, my bony lafs,
O whare live ye, my hiney.
By yon burn-fide, gin ye maun ken,
In a wee houfe wi' my minnie.

But I foor up the glen at e'en,
To fee my bony lafsie;
And lang before the grey morn cam,
She was na hauf fae faucey.

O weary fa the waukrife cock,
And the foumart lay his crawin!
He wauken'd the auld wife frae her fleep
A wee blink or the dawin.

An angry wife I wat fhe raife,
And o'er the bed fhe brought her;
And wi' a meikle hazel rung
She made her a weel pay'd dochter

O fare thee weel, my bony lafs!
O fare thee weel, my hinnie!
Thou art a gay and a bony lafs,
But thou has a waukrife minnie.

* * * * * * * * * * * * * * * * * * * * * * * * * *

## Tullochgorum.

289

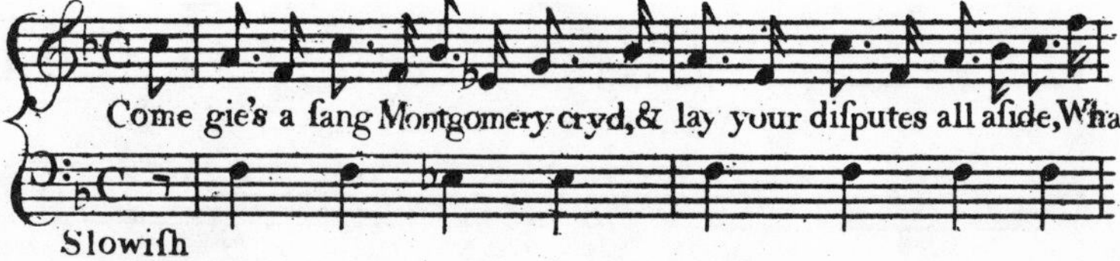
Come gie's a fang Montgomery cryd, & lay your difputes all afide, What
Slowifh

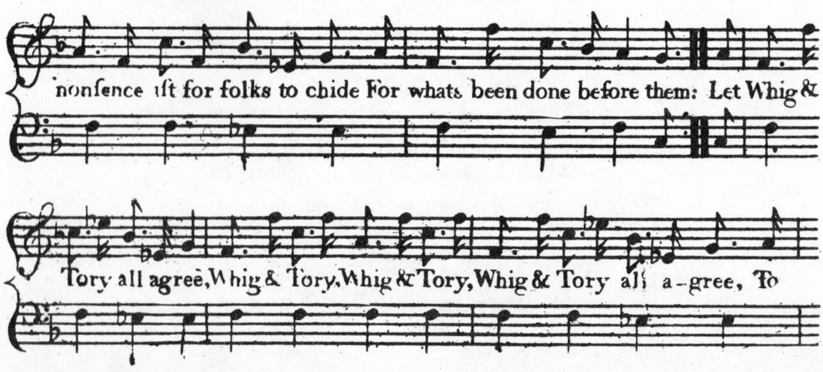
nonfence ift for folks to chide For whats been done before them: Let Whig &
Tory all agree, Whig & Tory, Whig & Tory, Whig & Tory all a-gree, To

Continued.

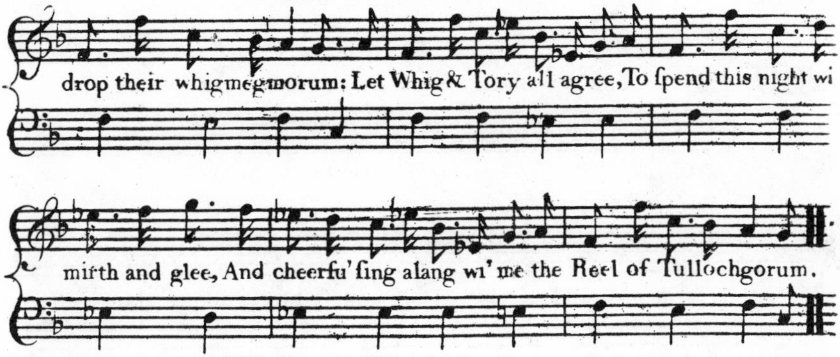
drop their whigmegmorum: Let Whig & Tory all agree, To ſpend this night wi
mirth and glee, And cheerfu' ſing alang wi' me the Reel of Tullochgorum.

Tullochgorum's my delight,
It gars us a' in ane unite,
And ony ſumph that keeps up ſpite,
In conſcience I abhor him.
Blithe and merry we's be a',
Blithe and merry, blithe and merry,
Blithe and merry we's be a,
To make a chearfu' quorum.
Blithe and merry, we's be a',
As lang's we ha'e a breath to draw,
And dance, 'till we be like to fa',
The reel of Tullochgorum.

There needs na' be ſo great a phraſe
Wi' dringing dull Italian lays,
I wadna gi'e our ain Strathſpeys
For half a hundred ſcore o'em:
They re douff and dowie at the beſt,
Douff and dowie, douff and dowie;
They're douff and dowie at the beſt,
Wi' a' their variorum:
They're douff and dowie at the beſt,
Their Allegros, and a' the reſt,
They cannot pleaſe a Scotiſh taſte,
Compar'd wi' Tullochgorum.

Let warldly minds themſelves oppreſs
Wi' fear of want, and double ceſs;
And ſilly fauls themſelves diſtreſs
Wi' keeping up decorum:
Shall we ſae ſour and ſulky ſit,
Sour and ſulky, ſour and ſulky;
Shall we ſae ſour and ſulky ſit,
Like auld Philoſophorum.
Shall we ſae ſour and ſulky ſit,
Wi' neither ſenſe, nor mirth. nor wit,
And canna riſe to ſhake a fit,
At the reel of Tullochgorum.

May choiceſt bleſsings ſtill attend
Each honeſt-hearted open friend,
And calm and quiet be his end,
Be a' that's good before him!
May peace and plenty be his lot,
Peace and plenty, peace and plenty;
May peace and plenty be his lot,
And dainties a' great ſtore o'em!
May peace and plenty be his lot,
Unſtain'd by any vicious blot;
And may he never want a groat
That's fond of Tullochgorum.

But for the diſcontented fool,
Who wants to be oppreſsion's tool,
May envy gnaw his rotten ſoul,
And blackeſt fiends devore him!
May dool and ſorrow be his chance,
Dool and ſorrow, dool and ſorrow,
May dool and ſorrow be his chance,
And honeſt ſouls abhor him.
May dool and ſorrow be his chance,
And a' the ills that come frae France
Whoe'er he be that winna dance
The reel of Tullochgorum.

# For a' that an' a' that.

Written for this Work by Robert Burns.

290
* Tho' womens minds like win - ter winds May
Slow
shift and turn and a' that. The noblest breast adores them maist, A
consequence I draw that. For a' that and a' that, And
twice as mickle as a' that, The bony lass that I lo'e best she'll
be my ain for a' that

Great love I bear to all the Fair,
Their humble slave an' a' that;
But lordly, Will, I hold it still,
A mortal sin to thraw that.
For a' that &c.

In rapture sweet this hour we meet,
Wi' mutual love an' a that;
But for how lang the flie may stang,
Let inclination law that.
For a' that &c.

Their tricks and craft hae put me daft,
They've taen me in an' a' that,
But clear your decks and here's, The sex!
I like the jads for a' that!

For a' that an' a' that,
And twice as meikle's a' that;
The bony lass that I lo'e best,
She'll be my ain for a that.

# Willie brew'd a peck o' maut.

Written for this Work by Robert Burns.

291

O Willie brew'd a peck o' maut, And Rob and Al_lan
cam to see; Three blyther hearts, that lee lang night, Ye
Chorus
wad na found in Christendie. We are na fou, We're nae that
fou, But just a drappie in our e'e; The cock may craw the
day may daw, And ay we'll taste the barley bree.

Here are we met, three merry boys,
Three merry boys I trow are we;
And mony a night we've merry been,
And mony mae we hope to be!
Cho.s We are na fou, &c.

It is the moon, I ken her horn,
That's blinkin in the lift sae hie;
She shines sae bright to wyle us hame
But by my sooth she'll wait a wee.—
Cho.s We are na fou, &c.

Wha first shall rise to gang awa,
A cuckold, coward loun is he!
Wha first beside his chair shall fa',
He is the king amang us three.
Cho.s We are na fou, &c.

## Killiecrankie.

292

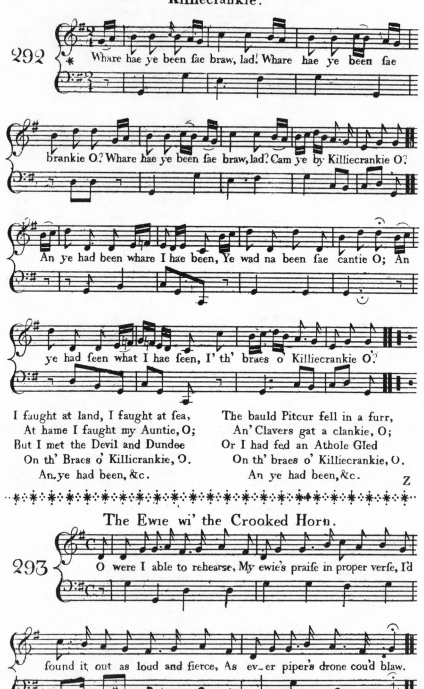

Whare hae ye been sae braw, lad! Whare hae ye been sae
brankie O? Whare hae ye been sae braw, lad? Cam ye by Killiecrankie O?
An ye had been whare I hae been, Ye wad na been sae cantie O; An
ye had seen what I hae seen, I' th' braes o' Killiecrankie O?

I faught at land, I faught at sea,
At hame I faught my Auntie, O;
But I met the Devil and Dundee
On th' Braes o' Killicrankie, O.
An ye had been, &c.

The bauld Pitcur fell in a furr,
An' Clavers gat a clankie, O;
Or I had fed an Athole Gled
On th' braes o' Killiecrankie, O.
An ye had been, &c.

Z

## The Ewie wi' the Crooked Horn.

293

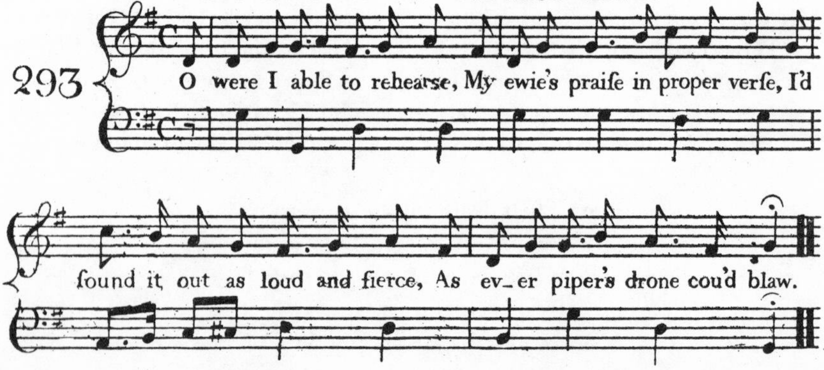
O were I able to rehearse, My ewie's praise in proper verse, I'd
sound it out as loud and fierce, As ev_er piper's drone cou'd blaw.

## Continued.

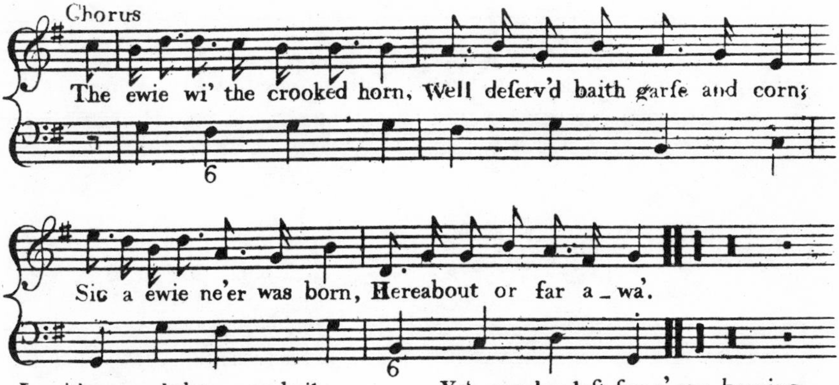
Chorus
The ewie wi' the crooked horn, Well deſerv'd baith garſe and corn;
6
Sic a ewie ne'er was born, Hereabout or far a_wa'.
6

I neither needed tar nor keil,
To mark her upo' hip or heel,
Her crooked horn it did as well,
To ken her by amo' them a'
The ewie, &c.
She never threaten'd ſcab nor rot,
But keeped ay her ain jog trot,
Baith to the fauld and to the cot,
Was never ſweer to lead nor ca'.
The ewie, &c.
Cauld or hunger never dang her,
Wind or rain could never wrang her,
Ance ſhe lay a wook an' langer
Out aneath a wreath o' ſnaw.
The ewie, &c.
When other ewies lap the dyke,
And ate the kail for a' the tyke,
My ewie never play'd the like
But tees'd about the barn yard wa'.
The ewie, &c.
A better nor a thriftier beaſt,
Nae honeſt man cou'd weel ha' wiſt,
For ſilly thing ſhe never miſt,
To hae ilk year a lamb or twa.
The ewie, &c.
The firſt ſhe had I gae to Jock,
To be to him a kind of ſtock,
And now the laddie has a flock,
Of mair nor thirty head te ca.
The ewie, &c.
The neeſt I gae to Jean; and now,
The bairn's ſae bra', has fauld ſae
That lads ſae thick come her to woo,
They're fain to ſleep on hay or ſtraw
The ewie, &c.
I looked ay at even for her,
For fear the fumart might devour her,
Or ſome meſhanter had come o'er her,
If the beaſtie bade awa'.
The ewie, &c.

Yet monday laſt for a' my keeping,
I canna ſpeak it without greeting.
A villain came when I was ſleeping,
And ſtaw my ewie, horn and a'.
The ewie, &c.
I ſought her ſair upo' the morn
And down beneath a buſs of thorn
I got my ewie's crooked horn,
But ah! my ewie was awa'.
The ewie, &c.
But an I had the lown that did it,
I've ſworn and ban'd as well as ſaid it
Tho' a' the warld ſhou'd forbid it,
I ſhou'd gi'e his neck a thraw.
The ewie, &c.
I never met wi' ſick a turn
As this, ſince ever I was born,
My ewie wi' the crooked horn,
Peur ſilly ewie ſtown awa'.
The ewie, &c.
O had ſhe died of crook or cauld,
As ewies die when they are auld,
It wad na been by mony fauld,
Sae fair a heart to nane o's a'.
The ewie, &c.
For a' the claith that we hae worn,
Frae her and hers ſae aften ſhorn,
The loſs of her we cou'd ha'e born,
Had fair ſtrae death tane her awa.
The ewie, &c.
But ſilly thing to loſe her life,
Aneath a greedy villain's knife,
I'm really fear'd that our goodwife
Sall never win aboon't ava.
The ewie, &c.
O all ye bards beneath Kinghorn,
Call up your muſes let them mourn,
Our ewie wi' the crooked horn,
Is ſtown frae' us and fell'd and a.
The ewie, &c.

# The blue-eyed Lafsie.

Written for this Work by Robert Burns.

294

I gaed a waefu' gate, yeftreen, A gate, I fear, I'll
dearly rue; I gat my death frae twa fweet een, Twa
lovely e'en o' bonie blue. 'Twas not her golden ring_lets
bright; Her lips like rofes, wat wi' dew, Her heav_ing bofom,
li_ly-white, It was her een fae bonie blue.

She talk'd, fhe fmil'd, my heart fhe wyl'd,
She charm'd my foul I wift na how;
And ay the ftound, the deadly wound,
Cam frae her een fae bonie blue.
But fpare to fpeak, and fpare to fpeed;
She'll aiblins liften to my vow:
Should fhe refufe, I'll lay my dead
To her twa een fae bonie blue.

# The Banks of Nith.

Written for this Work by R. Burns. Tune, Robie donna gorach.

295

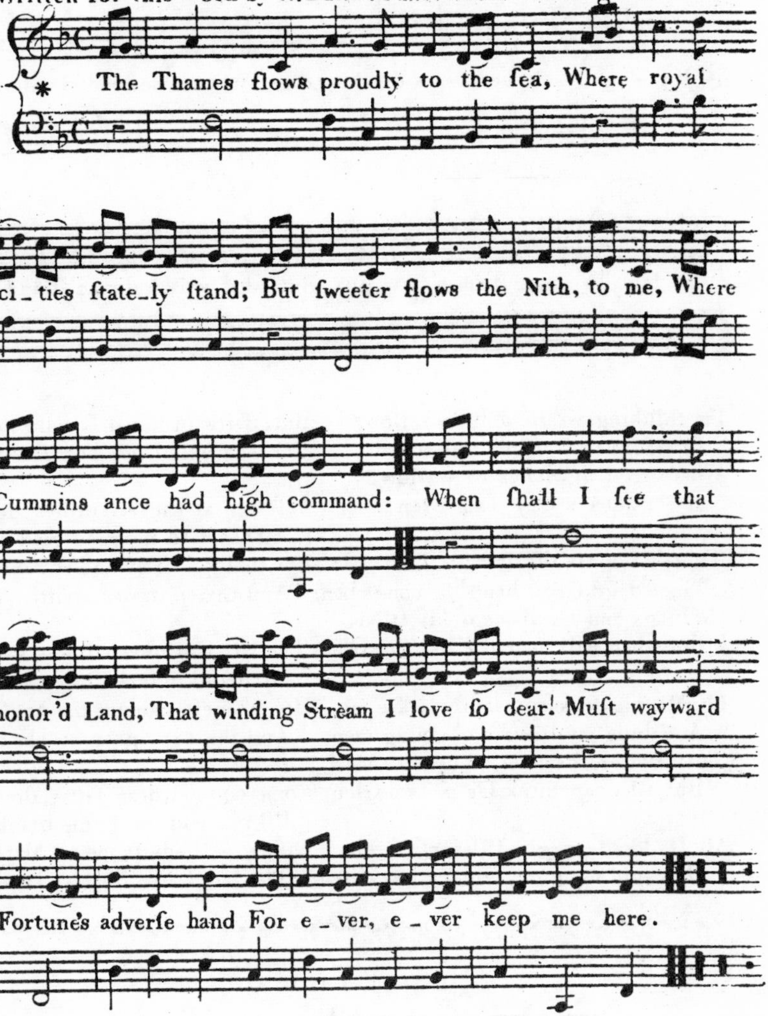
*
The Thames flows proudly to the sea, Where royal
ci_ties state_ly stand; But sweeter flows the Nith, to me, Where
Cummins ance had high command: When shall I see that
honor'd Land, That winding Stream I love so dear! Must wayward
Fortune's adverse hand For e_ver, e_ver keep me here.

How lovely, Nith, thy fruitful vales,
  Where bounding hawthorns gayly bloom,
And sweetly spread thy sloping dales
  Where lambkins wanton through the broom.
Tho wandering, now, must be my doom,
  Far from thy bonie banks and braes,
May there my latest hours consume,
  Amang the friends of early days!

## Tam Glen.

Written for this Work by Robert Burns.

296

*
My heart is a breaking,dear Tittie, Some counſel unto me come

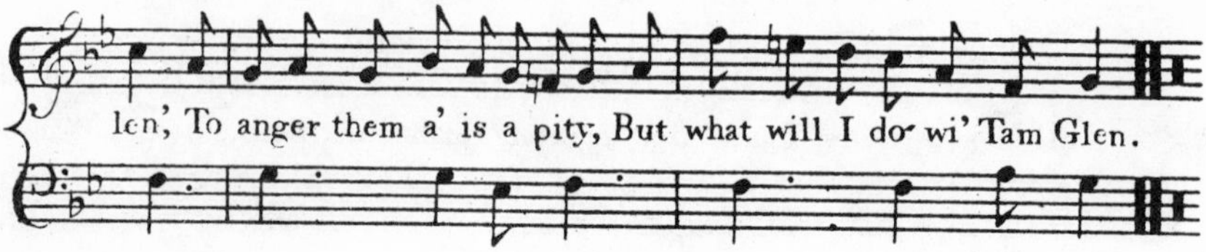
len', To anger them a' is a pity, But what will I do wi' Tam Glen.

I'm thinking, wi' ſic a braw fellow,
In poortith I might mak a fen:
What care I in riches to wallow,
If I mauna marry Tam Glen.

There's Lowrie the laird o' Dumeller,
"Gude day to you brute" he comes ben:
Ie brags and he blaws o' his ſiller,
But when will he dance like Tam Glen.

My Minnie does conſtantly deave me,
And bids me beware o' young men;
They flatter, ſhe ſays, to deceive me,
But wha can think ſae o' Tam Glen.

My Daddie ſays, gin I'll forſake him,
He'll gie me gude hunder marks ten:
But, if its' ordain'd I maun take him,
O wha will I get but Tam Glen.

Yeſtreen at the Valentines' dealing,
My heart to my mou gied a ſten;
For thrice I drew ane without failing,
And thrice it was written, Tam Glen.

The laſt Halloween I was waukin
My droukit ſark-ſleeve, as ye ken;
His likeneſs cam up the houſe ſtaukin,
And the very grey breeks o' Tam Glen!

Come counſel, dear Tittie, don't tarry;
I'll gie you my bonie black hen,
Gif ye will adviſe me to Marry
The lad I lo'e dearly, Tam Glen.

## Drap o' capie o.

297
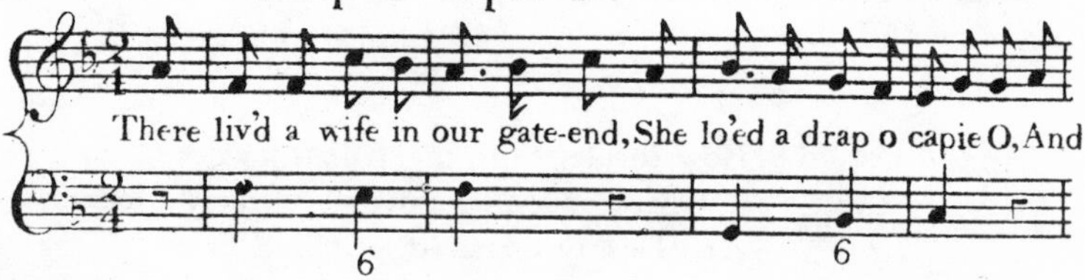
There liv'd a wife in our gate-end, She lo'ed a drap o capie O, And
6
6

a' the gear that e'er ſhe gat, She ſlipt it in her gabie O: Up
6
6

Continued.

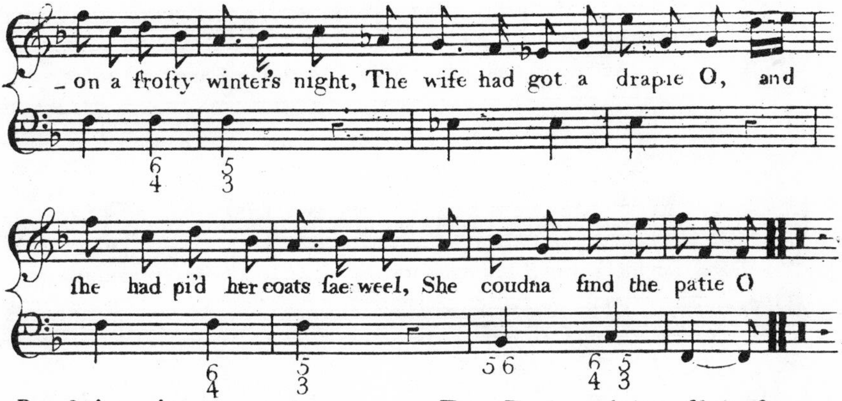
_ on a froſty winter's night, The wife had got a drapie O, and
ſhe had pi'd her coats ſae weel, She coudna find the patie O

But ſhe's awa' to her goodman,
They ca'd him Tamie Lamie-O,
Gae ben and fetch to me the can,.
That I may get a dramie-O.
Tamie was an honeſt man,
Himſelf he took a drapie-O,
It was nae weil out o'er his craig,
Till ſhe was on his tapie-O.

Quoth ſhe, the deil flee o'er your craig,
Ye greedy druken coofie O!
My wee drap drink, I had nae mair,
And I maun die o' drouthie_O,
She paid him weil, baith back and ſide,
And ſair ſhe creiſh'd his backie-O,
And made his ſkin baith blue and black,
And gar'd his ſhoulders crackie-O.

Then he's awa' to the malt barn,
And he has ta'en a pockie-O,
He put her in, baith head and tail,
And caſt her o'er his backie-O.
The carling ſpurr'd wi' head and feet,
The carle he was ſae ackie-O,
To ilka wa' that he came by,
He gar'd her head play knackie-O.

Goodman, I think you'll murder me,
My brains you out will knockie O,
He gi'd her ay the other hitch,
Lie ſtill, you devil's buckie-O.
Goodman, I'm like to make my burn,
O let me out, dear Tamie-O,
He ſet her down upon a ſtane,
And bade her pie a damie-O.

Then Tamie took her aff the ſtane,
And put her in the pockie-O,
And when ſhe did begin to ſpur,
He lent her ay a knockie-O.
Away he went to the mill-dam,
And there ga'e her a duckie-O,
And ilka chiel that had a ſtick,
Play'd thump upon her backie-O

And when he took her hame again,
He did hing up the pockie-O,
At her bed-ſide, as I hear ſay,
Upon a little knagie-O.
And ilka day that ſhe up-roſe,
In naithing but her ſmockie-O,
Sae ſoon as ſhe look'd o'er the bed,
She might behold the pockie-O

Now all ye men, baith far and near,
That have a drunken tutie-O,
Duck you your wives in time of year,
And I'll lend you the pockie-O,
The wife did live for nineteen years,
And was fu' frank and cuthie-O,
And ever ſince ſhe got the duck,
She never had the drouthie-O

At laſt the carling chanc'd to die,
And Tamie did her bury-O,
And for the public benefit,
He has gar'd print the curie-O
And this he did her motto make;
Here lies an honeſt luckie-O,
Who never left the drinking trade,
Until ſhe got a duckie-O

## On the reſtoration of the forfeited Eſtates 1784.

Tune, As I came in by Auchindown.

298

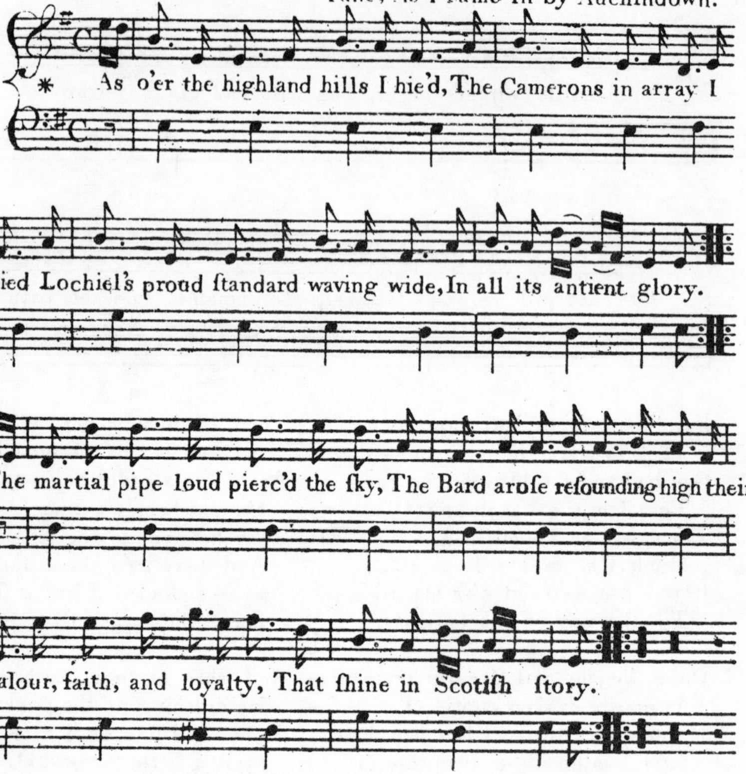
As o'er the highland hills I hie'd, The Camerons in array I
ſpied Lochiel's proud ſtandard waving wide, In all its antient glory.
The martial pipe loud pierc'd the ſky, The Bard aroſe reſounding high their
valour, faith, and loyalty, That ſhine in Scotiſh ſtory.

No more the trumpet calls to arms,
  Awaking battle's fierce alarms,
But every heroe's boſom warms,
  With ſongs of exultation,
While brave Lochiel at length regains,
  Thro' toils of war his native plains,
And won by glorious wounds, attains,
  His high paternal ſtation.

Let now the voice of joy prevail,
  And echoe wide from hill to vale;
Ye warlike Clans ariſe and hail,
  Your laurell'd Chiefs returning.
O'er ev'ry mountain every iſle,
  Let peace in all her luſter ſmile.
And diſcord ne'er her day defile,
  With ſullen ſhades of mourning.

M^c. Leod, M^c Donald join the ſtrain,
  M^c Pherſon, Fraſer, and M^c. Lean,
Thro' all your bounds let gladneſs reign,
  Both Prince and patriot praiſing

Whoſe generous bounty richly pours,
  The ſtreams of plenty round your ſhore
To Scotia's hills their pride reſtores,
  Her faded honours raiſing.

Let all the joyous banquet ſhare,
  Nor e'er let Gothic grandeur dare,
With ſcowling brow to overbear
  A Vaſsal's rights invading
Let Freedom's conſcious Sons diſdain
  To croud his fawning timed train,
Nor even own his haughty reign
  Their dignity degrading.

Ye northern Chiefs, whoſe rage unbroke,
  Has ſtill repell'd the tyrants ſhock,
Who ne'er have bow'd beneath her yoke
  With ſervile baſe proſtration,
Let each now train his truſty band
  'Gainſt foreign Foes alone to ſtand
With undivided heart and hand
  For freedom, King, and Nation.

# The Campbell's are comin.

299

The Campbells are comin O_ho, Oho. The Campbells are comin O_
_ho, Oho! The Campbells are comin to bonie Lochleven, The Campbells are
comin O_ho, Oho! Upon the Lomons I lay, I lay, Upon the Lomons I lay, I
lay, I looked down to bonie Lochleven And ſaw three bonie perches play.
Chorus
The Campbelſs are comin O_ho, Oho! The Campbells are comin O_ho, Oho. The
Compbells are comin to bonie Lochleven, The Campbells are comin Oho, Oho!

Great Argyle he goes before,
He maks his cannons and guns to roar,
Wi' ſound o' trumpet, pipe and drum
The Campbells are comin Oho, Oho!
Cho.ˢ The Campbells &c.

The Campbells they are a' in arms
Their loyal faith and truth to ſhow,
Wi' banners rattling in the wind,
The Campbells are comin Oho, Oho!
Cho.ˢ The Campbells &c.

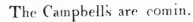

## Get up and bar the Door.

300

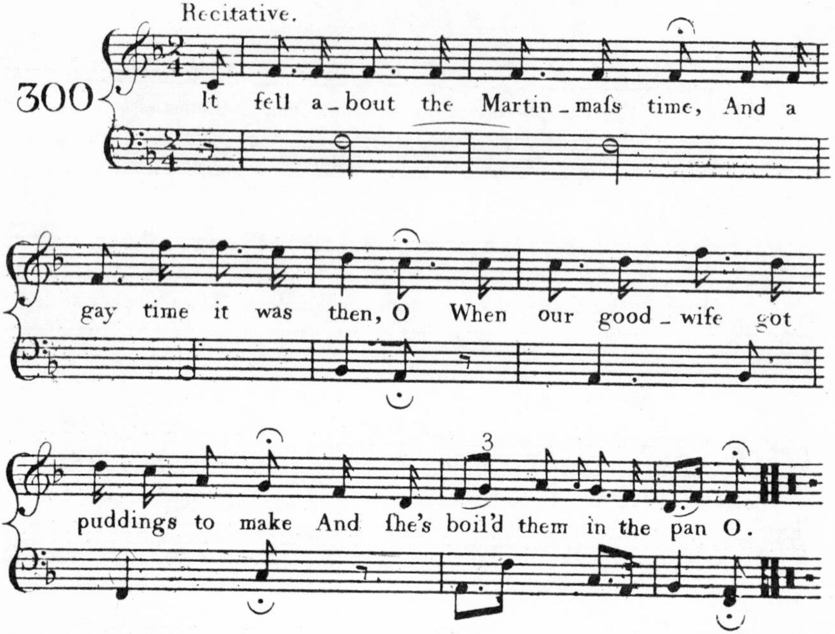
Recitative.
It fell a_bout the Martin_maſs time, And a
gay time it was then, O When our good_wife got
puddings to make And ſhe's boil'd them in the pan O.
3

The wind ſae cauld blew ſouth & north,
And blew into the floor, O.
Quoth our goodman, to our goodwife,
"Gat up and bar the door" O.

"My hand is in my hus'if ſkap,
Goodman, as ye may ſee O,
And it ſhou'd nae be barr'd this hundred year,
It's no be barr'd for me O."

They made a paction 'tween them twa,
They made it firm and ſure; O
That the firſt who ſhould ſpeak the foremoſt word,
Shou'd riſe and bar the door O

Then by there came two gentlemen,
At twelve o clock at night, O
And they could neither ſee houſe nor hall,
Nor coal nor candle light O.

Now, whether is this a rich man's houſe,
Or whether is it a poor. O
But never a word wad ane o' them ſpeak,
For barring of the door, O.

And firſt they ate the white puddings,
And then they ate the black O.
Though muckle thought the goodwife to herſel,
Yet ne'er a word ſhe ſpake O.

Then ſaid the one unto the other,
"Here, man, tak ye my knife O
Do ye tak aff the auld man's beard,
And I'll kiſs the goodwife. O

"But there's nae water in the houſe,
And what ſhall we do than." O
"What ails ye at the pudding broo,
That boils into the pan O."

O up then ſtatted our goodman,
An angry man was he, O
"Will ye kiſs my wife before my een,
And ſcald me wi' pudding bree." O

Then up and ſtarted our goodwife,
Gied three ſkips on the floor, O
"Goodman, you've ſpoken the foremoſt word,
Get up and bar the door, O."

END OF VOLUME THIRD.

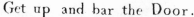

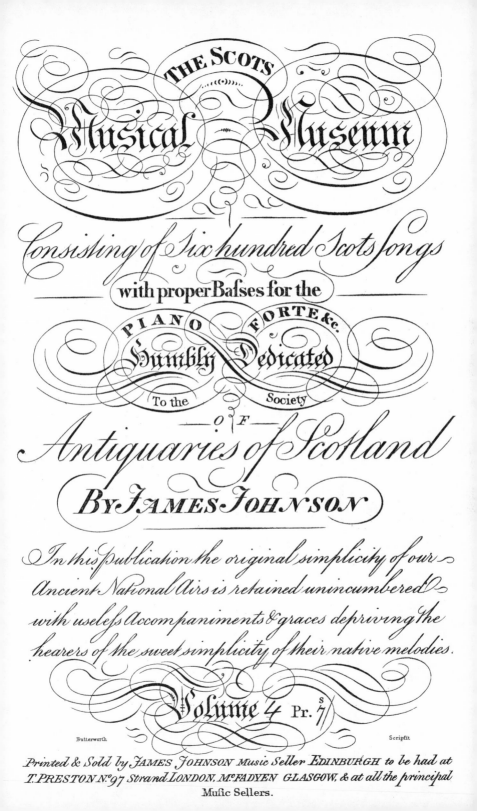

# THE SCOTS Musical Museum

Consisting of Six hundred Scots Songs

with proper Basses for the

PIANO FORTE &c.

Humbly Dedicated

To the Society

of

# Antiquaries of Scotland

## BY JAMES JOHNSON

In this Publication the original simplicity of our Ancient National Airs is retained unincumbered with useless Accompaniments & graces depriving the hearers of the sweet simplicity of their native melodies.

Volume 4 Pr. 7s

Butterworth Scripsit

Printed & Sold by JAMES JOHNSON Music Seller EDINBURGH to be had at T. PRESTON No. 97 Strand LONDON, McFADYEN GLASGOW, & at all the principal Music Sellers.

# PREFACE.

WHEN the Editor Publiſhed the third Volume of this work, he had reaſon to conclude that one volume more would finiſh the Publication. — Still however, he has a conſiderable number of Scots Airs and Songs more than his plan allowed him to include in this fourth volume. — Theſe, though in all probability they will not amount to what he has hitherto publiſhed as one volume, he ſhall yet give to the world; that the Scots Muſical Muſeum may be a Collection of every Scots Song extant. — To thoſe who object that his Publication contains pieces of inferior, or little value, the Editor anſwers, by referring to his plan — All our Songs cannot have equal merit. Beſides, as the world have not yet agreed on any unerring balance, any undiſputed ſtandard, in matters of Taſte, what to one perſon yields no manner of pleaſure, may to another be a high enjoyment.

Edin.r August 13. 1792.

# INDEX TO VOLUME FOURTH.

Note, the Songs marked B. R. X. &c. are originals by different hands, but all of them Scots gentlemen, who have favoured the Editor and the Public at large with their compoſitions: theſe marked Z, are old verſes, with corrections or additions.

# INDEX

# INDEX



---

As the authentic Prose history of the Whistle is curious, we shall here subjoin it. _ In the train of Anne, Princess of Denmark, when she came to Scotland with her husband, James the Sixth, there came over also a Danish gentleman of gigantic Stature and great prowess, and a matchless devotee of Bacchus. He had a curious ebony Ca', or Whistle, which, at the beginning of the orgies he laid on the table, and whoever was last able to blow the Whistle, every body else being disabled by the potency of the bottle, was to carry off the Whistle as a trophy of victory. _ The Dane produced credentials of his victories, without a single defeat, at the courts of Copenhagen, Stockholm, Moscow, Warsaw, and several of the petty courts of Germany; and challenged the Scotish Bacchanalians to the alternative of trying his prowess, or else of acknowledging their inferiority. _ After many overthrows on the part of the Scots the Dane was encountered by Sir Robert Lowrie of Maxwelton, ancestor to the present Sir Robert, who after three days & nights Claret-shed, left the scandinavian dead-drunk, "And blew on the Whistle his requiem shrill." _ Sir Walter Lowrie, son to Sir Robert before mentioned, afterwards lost the Whistle to Walter Riddel of Glenriddel, who had married the sister of Sir Walter. _ On Friday, the Sixteenth of October 1790, the Whistle was once more contended for, as related in the Ballad, by the present Sir Robert Lowrie of Maxwelton; Robt. Riddel Esqr. of Glenriddel, lineal descendant and representative of Walter Riddel, who won the Whistle, and in whose Family it had continued; and Alexr. Fergusson, Esqr. of Craigdarroch, likewise descended of the great Sir Robert, which last gentleman carried off the hard-won honors of the Field.

# Craigie-burn Wood

Written for this Work by Robert Burns.

No. 301

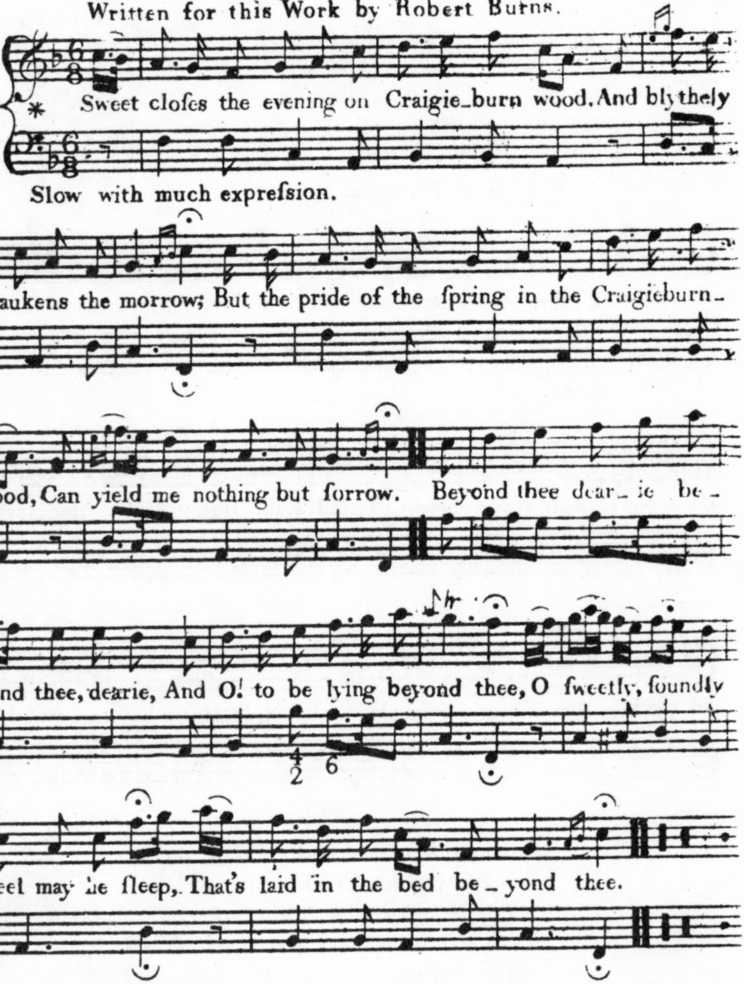
Sweet closes the evening on Craigie-burn wood, And blythely
Slow with much expression.
awaukens the morrow; But the pride of the spring in the Craigieburn-
-wood, Can yield me nothing but sorrow. Beyond thee dear-ie be-
-yond thee, dearie, And O! to be lying beyond thee, O sweetly, soundly
weel may he sleep, That's laid in the bed be-yond thee.

I see the spreading leaves and flowers,
  I hear the wild birds singing;
But pleasure they hae nane for me
  While care my heart is wringing.
    Beyond thee, &c.

I can na tell, I maun na tell
  I dare na for your anger
But secret love will break my heart,
  If I conceal it langer
    Beyond thee, &c.

I see thee gracefu', straight and tall,
  I see thee sweet and bonie,
But Oh, what will my torments be,
  If thou refuse thy Johnie!
    Beyond thee, &c.

To see thee in another's arms,
  In love to lie and languish,
'Twad be my dead, that will be seen,
  My heart wad burst wi' anguish.
    Beyond thee, &c.

But Jeanie, say thou wilt be mine,
  Say, thou loes nane before me;
And a' my days o' life to come
  I'll gratefully adore thee.
    Beyond thee, &c.

## Frae the friends and Land I love.

Tune, Carron Side

302

*
Frae the friends and Land I love, Driv'n by Fortunes
Very Slow & Plaintive.
fel_ly ſpite, Frae my beſt Belov'd I rove never mair to taſte delight
Never mair maun hope to find Eaſe frae toil, re_lief frae care
When Remembrance wracks the mind, Pleaſures but un vail Deſpair

Brighteſt climes ſhall mirk appear,
  Deſart ilka blooming ſhore;
Till the Fates, nae mair ſevere,
  Friendſhip, Love and Peace reſtore.
Till Revenge, wi' laurell'd head
  Bring our Baniſhed hame again;
And ilk loyal, bonie lad
  Croſs the ſeas and win his ain.

## Hughie Graham.

303
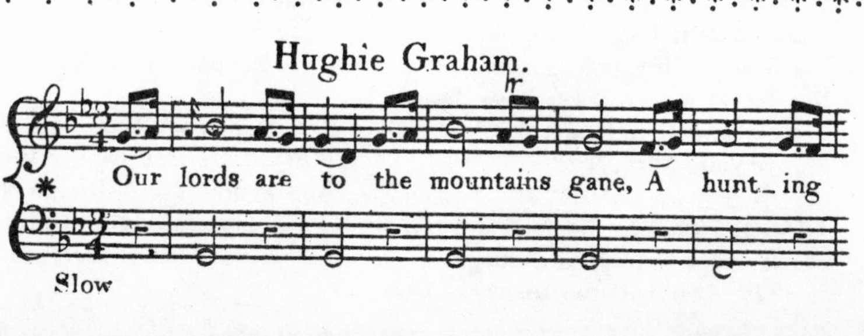
*
Our lords are to the mountains gane, A hunt_ing
Slow

Continued.

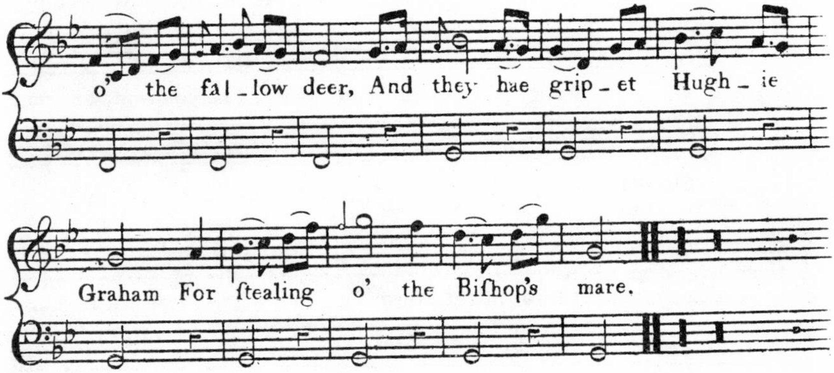
o' the fal_low deer, And they hae grip_et Hugh_ie
Graham For ſtealing o' the Biſhop's mare.

And they hae tied him hand and foot,
And led him up thro' Stirling town;
The lads and laſses met him there,
Cried, Hughie Graham thou art a loun.

O lowſe my right hand free, he ſays,
And put my braid ſword in the ſame;
He's no in Stirling town this day,
Daur tell the tale to Hughie Graham.

Up then beſpake the brave Whitefoord,
As he ſat by the biſhop's knee,
Five hundred white ſtots I'll gie you,
If ye'll let Hughie Graham gae free.

O haud your tongue, the biſhop ſays,
And wi' your pleading let me be;
For tho' ten Grahams were in his coat,
Hughie Graham this day ſhall die.

Up then beſpake the fair Whitefoord,
As ſhe ſat by the biſhop's knee;
Five hundred white pence I'll gee you,
If ye'll gie Hughie Graham to me.

O haud your tongue now lady fair,
And wi' your pleading let it be,
Altho' ten Grahams were in his coat,
Its for my honor he maun die.

They've taen him to the gallows knowe,
He looked to the gallows tree,
Yet never colourleft his cheek,
Nor ever did he blin' his e'e.

At length he looked round about,
To ſee whatever he could ſpy;
And there he ſaw his auld father,
And he was weeping bitterly.

O haud your tongue, my father dear
And wi' your weeping let it be;
Thy weeping's ſairer on my heart
Than a' that they can do to me.

And ye may gie my brother John,
My ſword that's bent in the middle clear
And let him come at twelve o' clock.
And ſee me pay the biſhop's mare.

And ye may gie my brother James, (-n
My ſword that's bent in the middle brow
And bid him come at four o' clock,
And ſee his brother Hugh cut down.

Remember me to Maggy my wife,
The nieſt time ye gang o'er the moor,
Tell her, ſhe ſtaw the biſhop's mare,
Tell her, ſhe was the biſhop's whore.

And ye may tell my kith and kin,
I never did diſgrace their blood;
And when they meet the biſhop's cloak.
To mak it ſhorter by the hood

## My Goddess Woman.

Tune, The Butcher boy

304

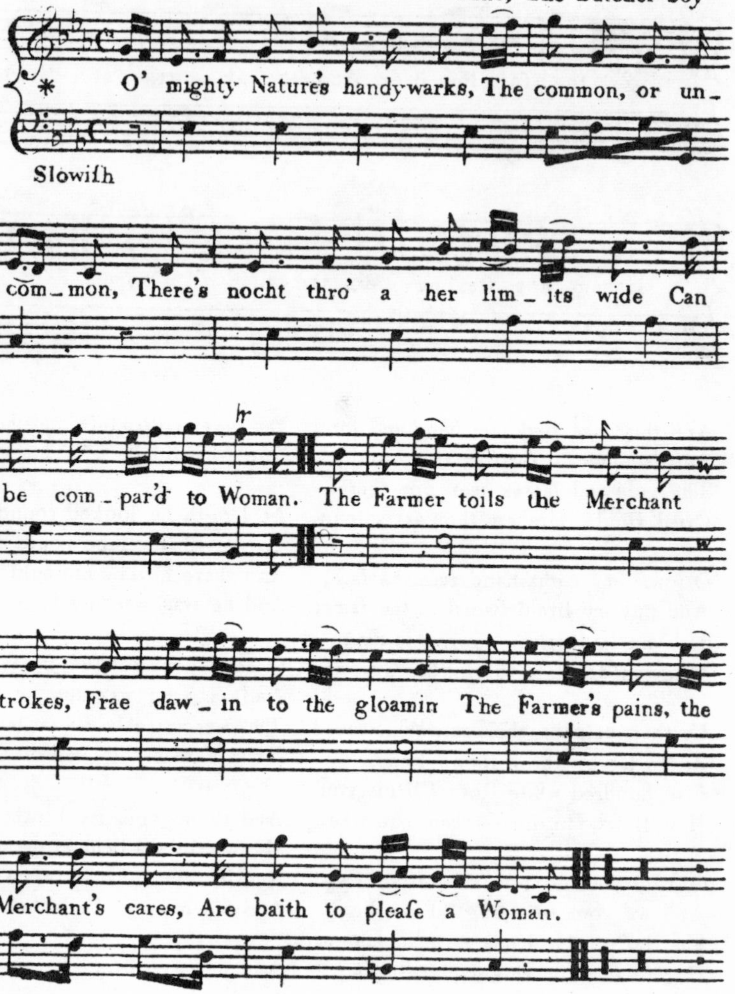
*
Slowish
O' mighty Nature's handywarks, The common, or un-
-com-mon, There's nocht thro' a her lim-its wide Can
be com-par'd to Woman. The Farmer toils the Merchant
trokes, Frae daw-in to the gloamin The Farmer's pains, the
Merchant's cares, Are baith to please a Woman.

The Sailor spreads the daring sail,
Thro' angry seas a foaming;
The jewels, gems o' foreign shores,
He gies to please a Woman.
The Sodger fights o'er crimson fields,
In distant climates roaming;
Yet lays, wi' pride, his laurels down,
Before all-conquering Woman.

A Monarch lea'es his golden throne,
Wi' other men in common,
He flings aside his crown, and kneels
A Subject to a Woman.
Tho' I had a' e'er man possess'd,
Barbarian, Greek, or Roman;
It wad nae a'-be-worth a strae,
Without my goddess, Woman.

# John come Kiſs me now.

305

O John, come kiſs me now, now, now; O
Lively
John, my luve, come kiſs me now, O John, come kiſs me by &
by, For weel ye ken the way to woo. O ſome will court and
compliment, And ither ſome will kiſs and daut; But I will mak o'
my gudeman, My ain gude _ man, it is nae faute.

O ſome will court and compliment,
And ither ſome will prie their mou,
And ſome will hauſe in ithers arms,
And that's the way I like to do.
O John &c.

# I've been Courting at a laſs.

306

*
I've been courting at a laſs, Theſe twenty days & mair; Her
Slow
father winna gi'e me her, She's ſick a gleib o' gear. But
gin I had her where I wou'd Amang, the he_ther here, I'd
ſtrive to win her kind_neſs, For a' her father's care.

For ſhe's a bonny ſonſy laſs,
An armfu' I ſwear;
I wou'd marry her without a coat,
Or e'er a plack o' gear.
For, truſt me, when I ſaw her firſt,
She gae me ſick a wound,
That a' the doctors i' the earth
Can never mak me ſound.

For when ſhe's abſent frae my ſight,
I think upon her ſtill;
And when I ſleep, or when I wake,
She does my ſenſes fill.
May Heavens guard the bonny laſs
That ſweetens a' my life;
And ſhame fa' me gin e'er I ſeek
Anither for my wife.

## Peas Strae.

307

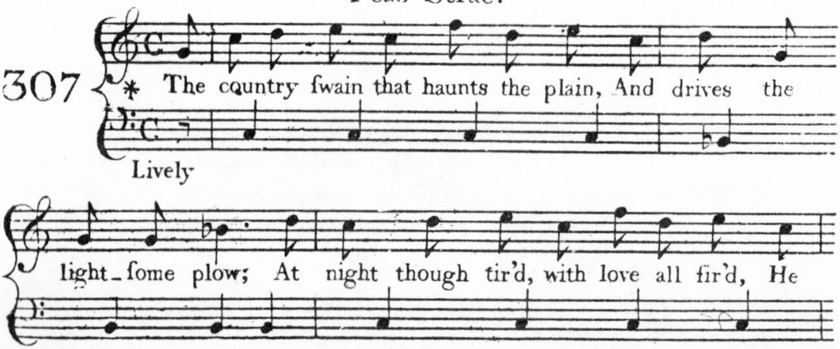
*
The country ſwain that haunts the plain, And drives the
Lively
light_ſome plow; At night though tir'd, with love all fir'd, He

## Continued.

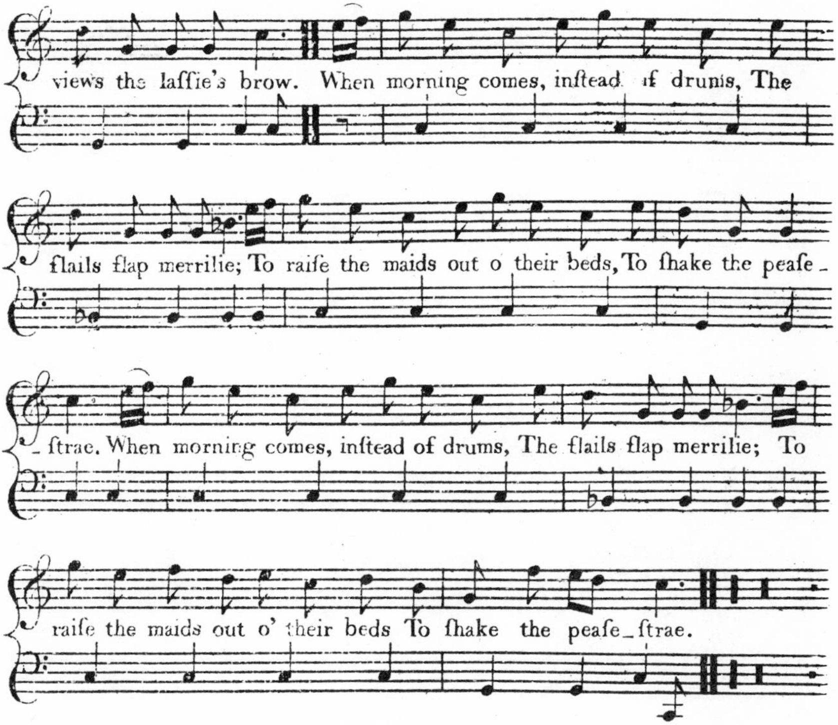
views the laſſie's brow. When morning comes, inſtead of drums, The
flails flap merrilie; To raiſe the maids out o their beds, To ſhake the peaſe_
_ſtrae. When morning comes, inſtead of drums, The flails flap merrilie; To
raiſe the maids out o' their beds To ſhake the peaſe_ſtrae.

Fair Jenny raiſe, pat on her claiſe,
Syne tuned her voice to ſing;
She ſang ſae ſweet, wi' notes compleat,
Gard a' the echoes ring;
And a' the maſes lay by their flails,
And dance moſt merrily;
And bleſs the hour that ſhe had power
To ſhake the peaſe_ſtrae.

The muſing ſwain diſturb'd in brain,
Faſt to her arms he flew,
And ſtrave a while, then wi' a ſmile,
Sweet Jenny red in hue,
She ſaid right aft, I think ye're daft,
That tempts a laſſie ſae;
Ye'll do me wrang, pray let me gang,
And ſhake the peaſe_ſtrae.

My heart, ſaid he, ſair wounded be,
For thee, my Jenny fair;
Without a jeſt, I get nae reſt,
My bed it proves a ſnare

Thy image fine, preſents me ſyne,
And takes a' reſt me frae;
And while I dream, in your eſteem
You reckon me your fae.

Which is a ſign ye will be mine,
Dear Jenny ſay nae na;
But ſoon comply, or elſe I die,
Sae tell me but a flaw,
If you can love, for none above
Thee I can fancy ſae;
I would be bleſt if I but wiſt,
That you would ſhake my ſtrae.

Then Jenny smil'd, ſaid, you're beguil'd,
I canna fancy thee;
My minny, bauld, ſhe would me ſcauld,
Sae dinna die for me.
But yet I own I am near grown,
A woman; ſince its ſae,
I'll marry thee, ſyne you'll get me
To ſhake your peaſe ſtrae.

## A Southland Jenny.

308

* A South_land Jenny that was right bo_nie, She
Slow
had for a suit_or a Nor__land John_ie But
he was sick_en a bash__full woo__er That
he could scarce ly speak un_to her.

But blinks o' her beauty and hopes o' her siller,
Forced him at last to tell his mind till her:
My Dear, quo he, we'll nae langer tarry,
Gin ye can lo'e me, let's o'er the moor and marry.

Come awa then, my Norland laddie,
Tho' we gang neat, some are mair gaudy;
Alb t I hae neither land nor money,
Come, and I'll ware my beauty on thee.

Ye lasses o' the South, ye're a' for dressin;
Lasses o' the North mind milkin and threshin:
My minnie wad be angry, and sae wad my daddie,
Should I marry ane as dink as a lady.

I maun hae a wife tnat will rise i' the mornin,
Crudle a' the milk, and keep the house a scauldin,
Tulzie wi' her neebors, and learn at my minnie,
A Norland Jockie maun hae a Norland Jenny.

My father's only dochter, wi' farms and siller ready,
Wad be ill bestowed upon sic a clownish body;
A' that I said was to try what was in thee,
Gae hame, ye Norland Jockie, and court your Norland Jenny!

## Cock up your Beaver.

309
Slowish
When first my brave Johnie lad came to this town, He
had a blue bonnet that wanted the crown, But now he has gotten a
hat and a feather, Hey, brave John_ie lad, cock up your beaver.
Cock up your beaver, and cock it fu' sprush; We'll
o_ver the bor_der and gie them a brush; There's
some_bo_dy there we'll teach better be_haviour,
Hey, brave John_ie lad, cock up your beaver.

## O Laddie I maun lo'e thee.

310

O laddie I maun lo'e thee, O lafsie lo'e na me;
O laddie I maun lo'e thee, O lafsie lo'e na me, for the
lafsie wi' the yellow cottie has ta'en away my heart frae me.

## Let me in this ae night.

311

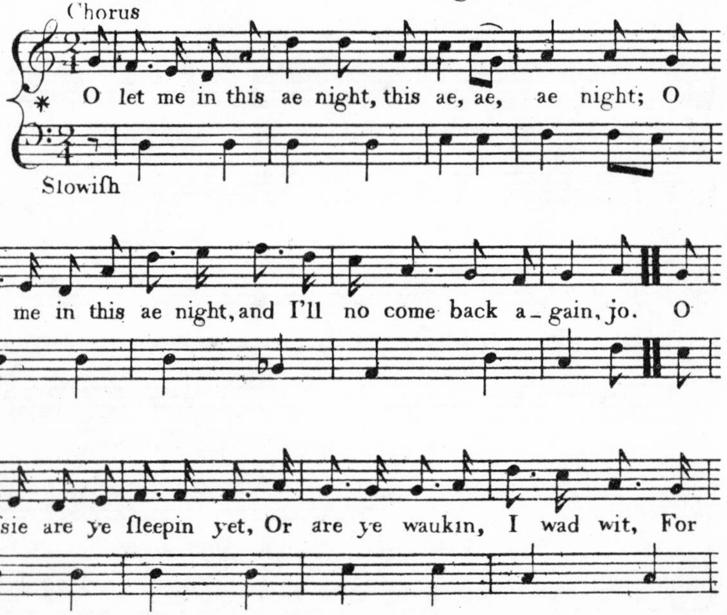
Chorus
O let me in this ae night, this ae, ae, ae night; O
Slowish
let me in this ae night, and I'll no come back a_gain, jo. O
lafsie are ye fleepin yet, Or are ye waukin, I wad wit, For

## Continued.

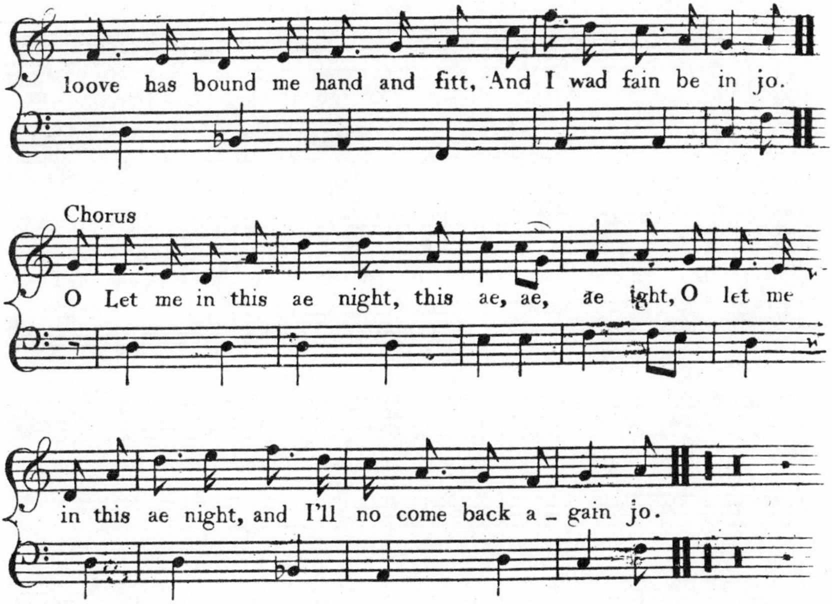
loove has bound me hand and fitt, And I wad fain be in jo.
Chorus
O Let me in this ae night, this ae, ae, ae night, O let me
in this ae night, and I'll no come back a_gain jo.

The morn it is the term_day,
I maun awa, I canna ſtay,
O pity me before I gae,
And riſe and let me in, jo.
Cho.[s] O let me in &c.

The night it is baith cauld and weet,
The morn it will be ſnaw and ſleet,
My ſhoon are frozen to my feet
In ſtanding here my lane, jo.
Cho.[s] O let me in &c.

I am the laird o' Windy_wa's,
I cam na here without a cauſe,
And I hae gotten mony fa's
In comin thro' the plain, jo.
Cho.[s] O let me in &c.

"My father's walking in the ſtreet,
"My mither the chamber keys does keep
"My chamber_door does chirp and cheep,
"I daur na let you in, jo.
Cho.[s] "O gae your ways this ae night
"This ae, ae, ae night;
"O gae your ways this ae night,
"For I daur na let you in, jo."

But I'll come ſtealing ſaftly in,
And cannily mak little din;
My fittſtep_tread there's nane can ken
For the ſughin wind and rain, jo.
Cho.[s] O let me in &c.

"Caſt up the door unto the weet,
"Caſt aff your ſhoon frae aff your feet,
"Syne to my chamber ye may creep,
"But ye maunna do't again, jo.
Cho.[s] O Leeze me on this ae night,
This ae, ae, ae night!
The joys we've had this ae night,
Your chamber was within, jo!

## My Tochers the Jewel.

Written for this Work by Robert Burns.

312

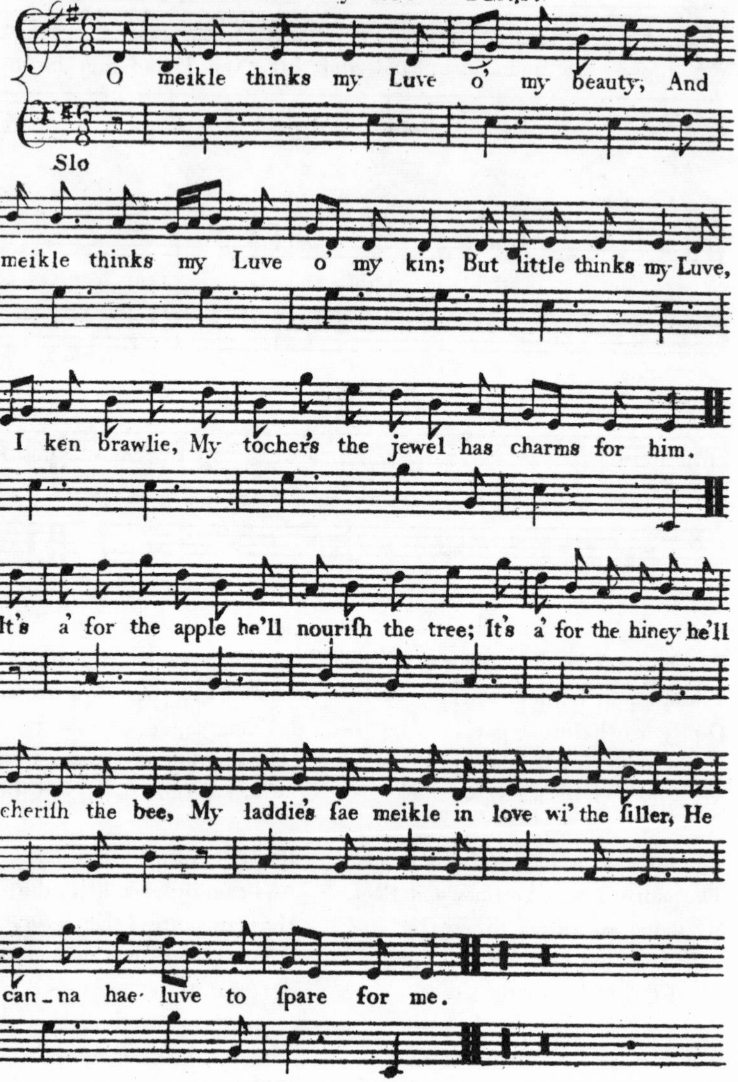
Slo
O meikle thinks my Luve o' my beauty, And
meikle thinks my Luve o' my kin; But little thinks my Luve,
I ken brawlie, My tocher's the jewel has charms for him.
It's a' for the apple he'll nourish the tree; It's a' for the hiney he'll
cherish the bee, My laddie's sae meikle in love wi' the siller, He
can_na hae luve to spare for me.

Your proffer o' luve's an airle_penny,
My tocher's the bargain ye wad buy;
But an ye be crafty, I am cunnin,
Sae ye wi' anither your fortune maun try.
Ye're like to the timmer o' yon rotten wood,
Ye're like to the bark o' yon rotten tree
Ye'll slip frae me like a knotless thread,
And ye'll crack your credit wi' mae nor me.

B

## Then Guidwife count the lawin.

Written for this Work by Robert Burns.

313

Gane is the day and mirk's the night, But we'll ne'er
Lively
stray for faute o' light, For ale and bran_dy's ſtars and moon, And
Chorus
blude red wine's the ryſin Sun. Then guid_wife count the
law_in, the law_in, the law_in, Then guidwife count the
law_in, and bring a cog_gie mair.

There's wealth and eaſe for gentlemen,
And ſemple_folk maun fecht and fen;
But here we're a' in ae accord,
For ilka man that's drunk's a lord.
Chos. Then goodwife count, &c.

My coggie is a haly pool,
That heals the wounds o' care and dool;
And pleaſure is a wanton trout,
An' ye drink it a', ye'll find him out.
Chos. Then goodwife count, &c.

## The Whiſtle.

Written for this Work by Robert Burns.

314

*
I ſing of a Whiſtle, a Whiſtle of worth, I
Slowiſh
ſing of a Whiſtle the pride of the North, Was brought to the court
of our good Scotiſh king & long with this Whiſtle all Scotland ſhall ring
Fal de dal lal lal lay & long with this Whiſtle all Scotland ſhall ring


*Old Loda ſtill rueing the arm of Fingal,
The god of the bottle ſends down from his hall _
"This Whiſtle's your challenge, to Scotland get o'er,
"And drink them to hell, Sir, or ne'er ſee me more, Fal de dal &c.

Old Poets have ſung, and old Chronicles tell,
What champions ventur'd, what champions fell:
The ſon of great Loda was conqueror ſtill,
And blew on the whiſtle their requiem ſhrill, Fal de dal &c.

Till Robert, the lord of the Cairn and the Scaur,
Unmatch'd at the bottle, unconquer'd in war,
He drank his poor godſhip as deep as the ſea,
No tide of the Baltic e'er drunker than he, Fal de dal &c.

Thus Robert, victorious, the trophy has gain'd,
Which now in his houſe has for ages remain'd,
Till three noble Chieftans, and all of his blood,
The jovial conteſt again have renew'd, Fal de dal &c.

Three joyous good fellows with hearts clear of flaw,
Craigdarroch, ſo famous for wit, worth and law;
And truſty Glenriddel ſo vers'd in old coins;
And gallant Sir Robert, deep read in old wines. Fal de dal &c.

Craigdarroch began with a tongue ſmooth as oil,
Deſiring Glenriddel to yield up the ſpoil,

* See, Oſsian's Carric thura

Continued.

Or elſe he would muſter the heads of the clan,
And once more in claret try which was the man. Fal de dal &c.

By the gods of the Ancients! Glenriddel replies,
Before I ſurrender ſo glorious a prize,
I'll conjure the ghoſt of the great Rorie More, ※
And bumper his horn with him twenty times o'er! Fal de dal &c.

Sir Robert, a Soldier, no ſpeech would pretend,
But he ne'er turn'd his back on his foe _or his friend,
Said, toſs down the Whiſtle prize of the field,
And knee-deep in claret he'd die or he'd yield. Fal de dal &c.

To the board of Glenriddel our heroes repair,
So noted for drowning of ſorrow and care;
But for wine and for welcome not more known to fame,
Than the ſenſe, wit and taſte of a ſweet lovely Dame. Fal de dal &c

A Bard was ſelected to witneſs the fray,
And tell future ages the feats of the day:
A Bard who deteſted all ſadneſs and ſpleen,
And wiſh'd that Parnaſsus a vineyard had been. Fal de dal &c

The dinner being over, the claret they ply.
And every new cork is a new ſpring of joy,
In the bands of old friendſhip and, kindred ſo ſet,
And the bands grew the tighter the more they were wet. Fal de dal &

Gay Pleaſure ran riot as bumpers ran o'er,
Bright Phebus ne'er witneſs'd ſo joyous a corps,
And vow'd that to leave them he was quite forlorn,
Till Cynthia hinted he'd find them next morn. Fal de dal &c.

Six bottles a piece had well wore out the night,
When gallant Sir Robert, to finiſh the fight,
Turn'd o'er in one bumper a bottle of red,
And ſwore 'twas the way that their Anceſtor did. Fal de dal &c

Then worthy Glenriddel ſo cautious and ſage
No longer the warfare ungodly would wage;
A high Ruling Elder to wallow in wine!
He left the foul buſineſs to folks leſs divine. Fal de dal &c.

The gallant Sir Robert fought hard to the end,
But who can with Fate and quart-bumpers contend;
Tho' Fate ſaid, a hero ſhould periſh in light,
So uproſe bright Phebus _and down fell the Knight. Fal de dal &c.

Next uproſe our Bard, like a prophet in drink,
"Craigdarroch, thou'lt ſoar when Creation ſhall ſink.
"But if thou wouldſt flouriſh immortal in rhyme,
"Come, one bottle more, and have at the ſublime... Fal de dal &c.

"Thy Line that have ſtruggled for freedom with Bruce,
"Shall Heroes and Patriots ever produce:
"So thine be the laurel, and mine be the bay,
"The field thou haſt won, by yon bright god of day!" Fal de dal &c.

※ See Johnson's tour through Scotland.

# There'll never be peace till Jamie comes hame.

315

*
By yon caſtle wa' at the cloſe of the day, I heard a man
Slowiſh
ſing tho' his head it was grey; And as he was ſinging the tears down
came, There'll never be peace till Jamie comes hame. The
Church is in ruins, the ſtate is in jars, De_luſions, oppreſsions, and
murderous wars, We dare na weel ſay't, but we ken wha's to
blame, There'll never be peace till Jamie comes hame.

My ſeven braw ſons for Jamie drew ſword,
And now I greet round their green beds in the yerd;
It brak the ſweet heart of my faithfu' auld Dame,
There'll never be peace till Jamie comes hame.
Now life is a burden that bows me down,
Sin I tint my bairns, and he tint his crown;
But till my laſt moments my words are the ſame,
There'll never be peace till Jamie comes hame.

## What can a young lafsie do wi' an auld man.

Written for this Work by Robert Burns

316
*
What can a young lafsie, what fhall a young lafsie, What
Lively but not too faft
can a young lafsie do wi' an auld man. Bad luck on the pennie that
tempted my min_nie To fell her poor Jen_ny for
filler an lan'. Bad luck on the pen_nie that tempted my
Minnie to fell her poor Jen_ny for fil_ler and lan'!

He's always compleenin frae mornin to e'enin,
He hofts and he hirpls the weary day lang:
He's doyl't and he's dozin, his blude it is frozen,
O, dreary's the night wi' a crazy auld man!

He hums and he hankers, he frets and he cankers,
I never can pleafe him, do a' that I can;
He's peevifh, and jealous of a' the young fellows,
O, dool on the day I met wi' an auld man!

My auld auntie Katie upon me taks pity,
I'll do my endeavour to follow her plan;
I'll crofs him, and wrack him untill I heart break him,
And then his auld brafs will buy me a new pan

R

## The bonie lad that's far awa.

317

* O how can I be blythe and glad, Or how can I gang
Slowish,
brisk and braw, When the bonie lad that I loe best, Is
o'er the hills and far a_wa When the bo_nie lad that
I loe best, Is o'er the hills and far a_wa.

My father pat me frae his door,
  My friends they hae disown'd me a';
But there is ane will tak my part,
  The bonie lad that's far awa.
    But there &c.

A pair o' gloves he bought to me,
  And silken snoods he gae me twa,
And I will wear them for his sake,
  The bonie lad that's far awa.
    And I will &c.

O weary winter soon will pass,
  And spring will cleed the birken shaw;
And my young babie will be born,
  And he'll be hame that's far awa.
    And my &c.

X

## The Auld Goodman.

318
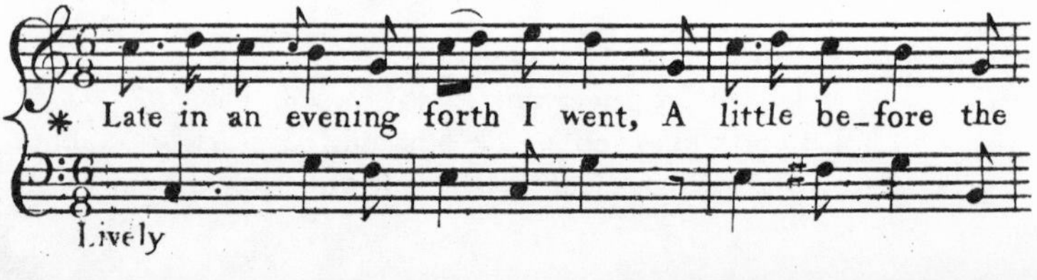
* Late in an evening forth I went, A little be_fore the
Lively

Continued.

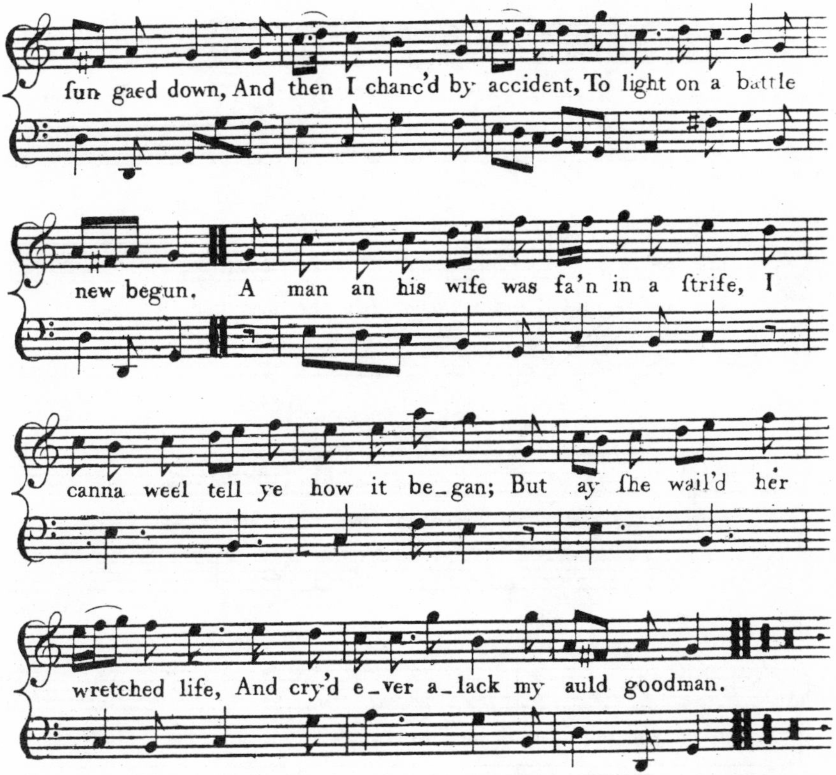
ſun gaed down, And then I chanc'd by accident, To light on a battle
new begun. A man an his wife was fa'n in a ſtrife, I
canna weel tell ye how it be_gan; But ay ſhe wail'd her
wretched life, And cry'd e_ver a_lack my auld goodman.

Thy auld goodman that thou tells of,
The country kens where he was born,
Was but a ſilly poor vagabond,
And ilka ane leugh him to ſcorn;
For he did ſpend and mak an end
Of gear that his forefathers wan,
He gart the poor ſtand frae the door,
Sae tell nae mair of thy auld goodman.

My heart, alake, is liken to break,
When I think on my winſome John,
His blinken ee, and gait ſae free,
Was naething like thee, thou dozend-drone.
His roſy face, and flaxen hair,
And a ſkin as white as ony ſwan,
Was large and tall, and comely withal,
And thou'lt never be like my auld goodman.

Why doſt thou pleen. I thee maintain,
For meal and mawt thou diſna want;
But thy wild bees I canna pleaſe,
Now when our gear 'gins to grow ſcant,
Of houſehold ſtuff thou haſt enough,
Thou wants for neither pat nor pan;
Of ſicklike ware he left thee bare,
Sae tell nae mair o' thy auld goodman.

Yes, I may tell, and fret my ſell,
To think on theſe blyth days I had,
When he and I together lay,
In arms into a weel made bed:
But now I ſigh and may be ſad,
Thy courage is cauld, thy colour wan,
Thou falds thy feet, and fa's aſleep,
And thou'lt ne'er be like my auld good-man.

Then coming was the night ſae dark,
And gane was a' the light o' day;
The carl was fear'd to miſs his mark,
And therefore wad nae langer ſtay.
Then up he gat, and he ran his way,
I trow the wife the day ſhe wan.
And ay the o'erword o' the fray
Was ever, Alake, my auld goodman.

## O as I was kist yestreen.

319

O, as I was kist ye_streen, O, as I was
Lively
kist yestreen! I'll never forget till the day that I die, Sae
mony braw kisses his Grace gae me. My Father was sleeping, my
mither was out, And I was my lane, and in came the Duke; I'll
never forget till the day that I die, Sae mony braw kisses his Grace gae me.

Kist the streen, kist the streen,
Up the Gallowgate, down the Green:
I'll never forget till the day that I die,
Sae mony braw kisses his Grace gae me.

## Fine flowers in the Valley.

320

She ſat down be_low a thorn, Fine flowers in the val_ley And there ſhe has her ſweet babe born And the green leaves they grow rare _ ly.
Very Slow

Smile na ſae ſweet, my bonie babe
  Fine flowers in the valley,
And ye ſmile ſae ſweet, ye'll ſmile me dead,
  And the green leaves they grow rarely.

She's taen out her little penknife
  Fine flowers, &c.
And twinn'd the ſweet babe o' its life.
  And the green, &c.

She's howket a grave by the light o' the moon,
  Fine flowers, &c.
And there ſhe's buried her ſweet babe in,
  And the green, &c.

As ſhe was going to the church,
  Fine flowers, &c.
She ſaw a ſweet babe in the porch.
  And the green, &c.

O ſweet babe and thou were mine,
  Fine flowers, &c.
I wad cleed thee in the ſilk ſo fine.
  And the green, &c.

O mother dear, when I was thine,
  Fine flowers, &c.
You did na prove to me ſae kind.
  And the green, &c.

× × × × × × × × × × × × × × × × × × × × × ×

## I do confeſs thou art ſae fair.

321

*
I do confeſs thou art ſae fair, I wad been o'er the
Slowiſh
lugs in luve; Had I na found the ſlighteſt prayer That lips could ſpeak thy
heart could muve. I do confeſs thee ſweet, but find, Thou art ſae thriftleſs
o' thy ſweets,.Thy favors are the ſilly wind That kiſses ilka thing it meets

See yonder roſe_bud, rich in dew,
  Amang its native briers ſae coy,
How ſune it tines its ſcent and hue
  When pu'd and worn a common toy!
Sic fate e'er lang ſhall thee betide;
  Tho' thou may gayly bloom a while,
Yet ſune thou ſhalt be thrown aſide,
  Like ony common weed and vile.

Z

## If e'er I do well 'tis a wonder.

322

*
When I was a young lad, My for _ tune was
Lively

Continued.

bad if e'er I do well 'tis a won_ _der. I
ſpent all my means On whores, bawds, and queans; Then I got a com_
_miſsion to plun_ _ der I ſpent all my means on whores, bawds, &
queans; Then I got a commiſsi_on to plun_ _der.

The hat I have on,
So greaſy is grown,
Remarkable 'tis for its ſhining;
'Tis ſtitch'd all about,
Without button or lopp,
And never a bit of a lining.

The coat I have on,
So thread-bare is grown,
So out at the armpits and elbows,
That I look as abſurd
As a ſailor on board,
That has ly'n fifteen months in the bilboes.

My ſhirt it is tore
Both behind and before,
The colour is much like a cinder;
'Tis ſo thin and ſo fine,
That it is my deſign
To preſent it to the muſes for tinder.

My blue fuſtian breeches
Is wore to the ſtitches,
My legs you may ſee what's between them;
My pockets all four,
I'm the ſon of a whore,
If there's ever one farthing within them.

I have ſtockings, 'tis true,
But the devil a ſhoe,
I'm oblig'd to wear boots in all weather,
Be damn'd the boot ſoal,
Curſe on the ſpur-roll,
Confounded be the upper leather.

Had ye then but ſeen
The ſad plight I was in,
Ye'd not ſeen ſuch a poet amongſt twenty;
I have nothing that's full,
But my ſhirt and my ſkull
For my pockets and belly are empty.

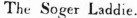

# The Soger Laddie.

323

Lively
* My ſoger laddie is over the ſea, And he'll bring gold &
money to me; And when he comes hame, he'll make me a Lady, My
bleſsings gang wi' my ſoger laddie. My dough_ty laddie is
handſome and brave, & can as a ſoger & lover behave; He's true to his
country, to love he is ſteddy, There's few to compare wi' my ſoger laddie.

O Shield him, ye angels, frae death in alarms,
Return him with laurels to my langing arms.
Syne frae all my care ye'll pleaſantly free me,
When back to my wiſhes my ſoger ye gie me.
O ſoon may his honours bloom fair on his brow,
As quickly they muſt, if he get his due:
For in noble actions his courage is ready,
Which makes me delight in my ſoger-laddie.

## Where wad bonie Annie ly

324 *

Lively

O where wad bonie Annie ly, A_lane nae mair ye
mauna ly; Wad ye a good_man try, Is that the thing ye're
lacking. O can a laſs ſae young as I, Ven_ture on the
brid_al_tye Syne down with a good_man ly I'm
flee'd he'd keep me wauk_ing.

Never judge until ye try,
Mak me your goodman, I
Shanna hinder you to ly,
And ſleep till ye be weary.

What if I ſhou'd wauking ly,
When the hoboys are gawn by,
Will ye tent me when I cry,
My dear, I'm faint and iry.

In my boſom thou ſhalt ly,
When thou wakrife art, or dry,
Healthy cordial ſtanding by,
Shall preſently revive thee.

To your will I then comply,
Join us, prieſt, and let me try,
How I'll wi' a goodman ly,
Wha can a cordial gi'e me.

## Galloway Tam.

325

O Galloway Tam came here to woo, I'd rather we'd gin him the
Lively
brawnit cow; For our lafs Befs may curfe & ban, The wanton wit o'
Galloway Tam. O Gal_loway Tam came here to fhear, I'd
rather we'd gin him the gude gray mare, He kifst the gudewife and
ftrack the gudeman, And thats the tricks o' Galloway Tam.

## As I cam down by yon caftle wa',

326

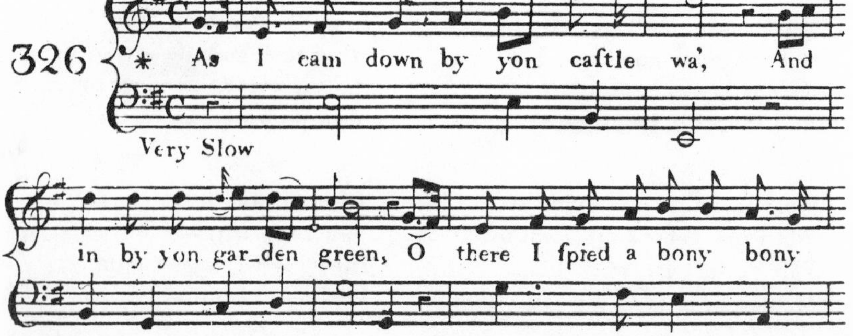
As I cam down by yon caftle wa', And
Very Slow
in by yon gar_den green, O there I fpied a bony bony

## Continued.

lafs, But the flower borders were us be_ tween.

A bony bony lafsie fhe was,
As ever mine eyes did fee:
O five hundred pounds would I give,
For to have fuch a pretty bride as thee.

To have fuch a pretty bride as me,
Young man ye are fairly miftaen;
Tho' ye were king o' fair Scotland,
I wad difdain to be your queen

Talk not fo very high bony lafs,
O talk not fo very very high:
The man at the fair that wad fell,
He maun learn at the man that wad buy.

I truft to climb a far higher tree,
And herry a far richer neft:
Tak this advice o' me bony lafs,
Humility wad fet thee beft.

## Lord Ronald my fon.

327

O where hae ye been Lord Ronald, my fon? O where hae ye

Very Slow

been, Lord Ronald my fon? I hae been wi' my fweetheart, mother, make my

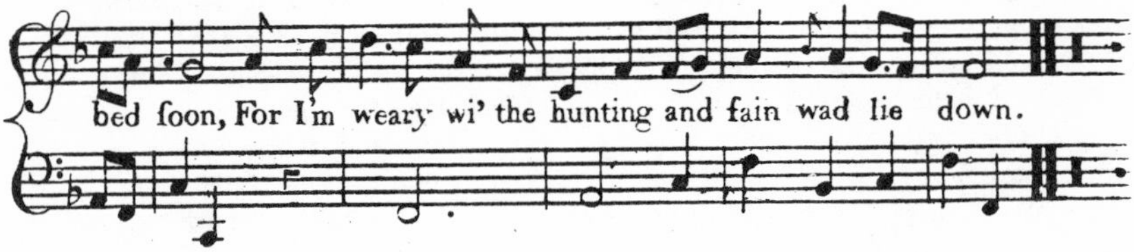
bed foon, For I'm weary wi' the hunting and fain wad lie down.

What got ye frae your fweetheart Lord Ronald, my fon.
What got ye frae your fweetheart Lord Ronald, my fon.
I hae got deadly poifon, mother, make my bed foon;
For life is a burden that foon I'll lay down.

# O'er the moor amang the heather.

328

* Comin thro' the craigs o' Kyle, A_mang - the bo_ny
Lively, but Slow.
blooming heather, There I met a bonie laſsie Keeping a' her
Chorus.
yowes the_gether O'er the moor a_mang the heather,
O'er the moor a_mang the heather, There I met a
bo_nie laſsie keeping a' her yowes the_gither.

Says I my dear whare is thy hame,
In moor, or dale, pray tell me whether,
She ſays, I tent thae fleecy flocks
That feed amang the blooming heather.
Cho.[s] O'er the moor, &c.
O'er the moor, &c.
She ſays, I tent thae fleecy flocks
That feed amang the blooming heather.

We laid us down upon a bank,
Sae warm and ſunny was the weather,
She left her flocks at large to rove,
Amang the bonie blooming heather.
Cho.[s] O'er the moor, &c.
O'er the moor, &c.
She left her flocks at large to rove,
Amang the bonie blooming heather.

While thus we lay ſhe ſang a ſang,
Till echo rang a mile and farther,
And ay the burden o' the ſang
Was, o'er the moor amang the heather.
Cho.[s] O'er the moor, &c.
O'er the moor, &c.
And ay the burden o' the ſang
Was, o'er the moor amang the heather.

She charm'd my heart, and ay ſinſyne
I could na think on ony ither:
By ſea and ſky! ſhe ſhall be mine!
The bonie laſs amang the heather.
Cho.[s] O'er the moor, &c.
O'er the moor, &c.
By ſea and ſky. ſhe ſhall be mine.
The bonie laſs amang the heather

# Senſibility how charming.

Written for this Work by Robert Burns.

329
Plaintive
Sen_ſi_bi_li_ty how charming, Deareſt Nancy, thou canſt tell, But diſtreſs with horrors arming, Thou haſt alſo known too well.
Faireſt flower, behold the li_ly, Blooming in the ſunny ray.
Let the blaſt ſweep o'er the valley, See it proſtrate on the clay.
Faireſt flower, behold the lily, Blooming in the ſunny ray;
For.
Pia.
Let the blaſt ſweep o'er the vallty, See it proſtrate on the clay.

Hear the woodlark charm the foreſt,
Telling o'er his little joys:
Hapleſs bird! a prey the ſureſt
To each pirate of the ſkies.
:S: Dearly bought the hidden treaſure,
Finer Feelings can beſtow:
Chords that vibrate ſweeteſt pleaſure,
Thrill the deepeſt notes of woe. :S:

## To the Roſe bud.

330

*
All Hail to thee thou baw_my bud, Thou charming
Slow
child O ſimmer Hail; Ilk fra_grant Thorn and lof_ty
wood Does nod thy wel_come to the Vale.

See on thy lovely faulded form
Glad Phæbus ſmiles wi' chearing eye
While on thy head the dewy morn
Has ſhed the tears o' ſilent joy.

The tuneful tribes frae yonder bower
Wi' ſangs of joy thy preſence hail,
Then haſte thou bawmy fragrant flower
And gie thy boſom to the gale.

And ſee the fair induſtrious Bee,
With airy wheel and ſoothing hum,
Flies ceaſeleſs round thy parent tree,
While gentle breezes trembling come.

If ruthleſs Liza paſs this way,
She'll pou thee frae thy thorny ſtem;
A while thou'lt grace her Virgin breaſt
But ſoon thou'lt fade my bonny gem.

Ah ſhort, too ſhort, thy rural reign,
And yield to fate alas thou muſt.
Bright emblem of the Virgin train,
Thou blooms alas, to mix wi' duſt.

Sae bonny Liza hence may learn,
Wi' every youthfu' maiden gay,
That Beauty like the ſimmer's roſe
In time ſhall wither and decay.

## Yon wild moſsy mountains.

331

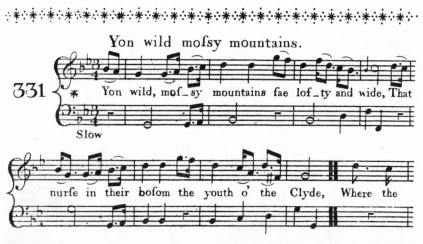

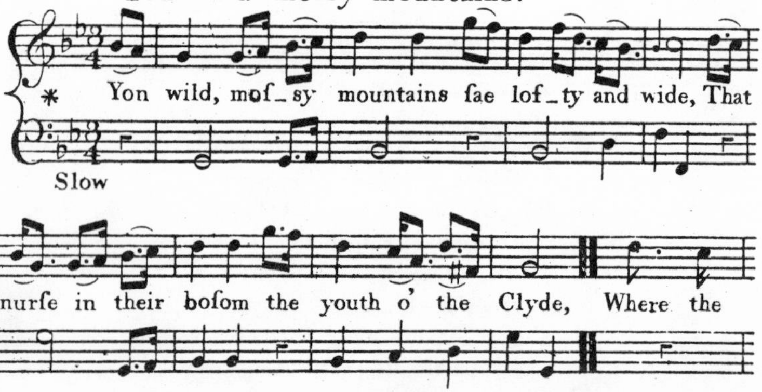
*
Yon wild, moſ_sy mountains ſae lof_ty and wide, That
Slow
nurſe in their boſom the youth o' the Clyde, Where the

Continued.

grous lead their coveys thro' the heather, to feed, And the
ſhepherd tents his flock as he pipes on his reed: Where the
grous lead their coveys thro' the heather to feed, And the
ſhepherd tents his flock as he pipes on his reed:

Not Gowrie's rich valley, nor Forth's ſunny ſhores,
To me hae the charms o' yon wild, moſsy moors;
For there, by a lanely, ſequeſtred ſtream,
Reſides a ſweet Laſsie, my thought and my dream.

Amang thae wild mountains ſhall ſtill be my path,
Ilk ſtream foaming down its ain green, narrow ſtrath,
For there, wi' my Laſsie, the day-lang I rove,
While o'er us unheeded, flie the ſwift hours o' Love.

She is not the faireſt, altho' ſhe is fair;
O' nice education but ſma' is her ſhare;
Her parentage humble as humble can be;
But I loe the dear Laſsie becauſe ſhe loes me.

To Beauty what man but maun yield him a prize,
In her armour of glances, and bluſhes, and ſighs;
And when Wit and Refinement hae poliſh'd her darts,
They dazzle our een, as they flie to our hearts.

But Kindneſs, ſweet Kindneſs, in the fond-ſparkling e'e,
Has luſtre outſhining the diamond to me;
And the heart beating love as I'm claſp'd in her arms,
O, theſe are my Laſsie's all-conquering charms.

# Bonie laddie Highland laddie.

332

I hae been at Croo_kie_den, My bon_ie lad_die
Lively
Highland laddie, Viewing Willie and his men my bonie laddie
High_land lad_die. There our faes that burnt and flew, My
bo_nie lad_die High_land lad_die There, at laſt, they
gat there due, My bonie lad_die Highland laddie.

Satan ſits in his black neuk,
 My bonie laddie, Highland laddie,
Breaking ſticks to roaſt the Duke,
 My bonie laddie, Highland laddie,
The bloody monſter gae a yell,
 My bonie laddie, Highland laddie,
And loud the laugh gaed 'round a' hell!
 My bonie laddie, Highland laddie.

# It is na, Jean, thy bonie face

Written for this Work by Robert Burns.

333
It is na, Jean, thy bonie face, Nor ſhape that
Slow
I ad_mire Al_tho' thy beau_ty and thy grace might
weel a_wauk de_ſire. Some_thing in il__ka
part o' thee To praiſe, to love, I find, But dear as
is thy form to me; Still dear_er is thy mind.

Nae mair ungen'rous wiſh I hae,
  Nor ſtronger in my breaſt,
Than, if I canna mak thee ſae,
  At leaſt to ſee thee bleſt.
Content am I, if Heaven ſhall give
  But happineſs to thee:
And as wi' thee I'd wiſh to live,
  For thee I'd bear to die.

## Donald Couper.

334

Hey Donald how Donald, Hey Donald Couper; He's
Canty
gane a_wa to feek a wife and he's come hame with_out her.
O Donald Couper and his man, Held to a Highland fair, man, And
a' to feek a bo_nie lafs, But fient a' ane was there, man.

At length he got a Carlin gray,
And fhe's come hirplin hame, man;
And fhe's fa'n o'er the buffet ftool,
And brak her rumple-bane, man.
Hey Donald &c.

## The Vain Purfuit.

335

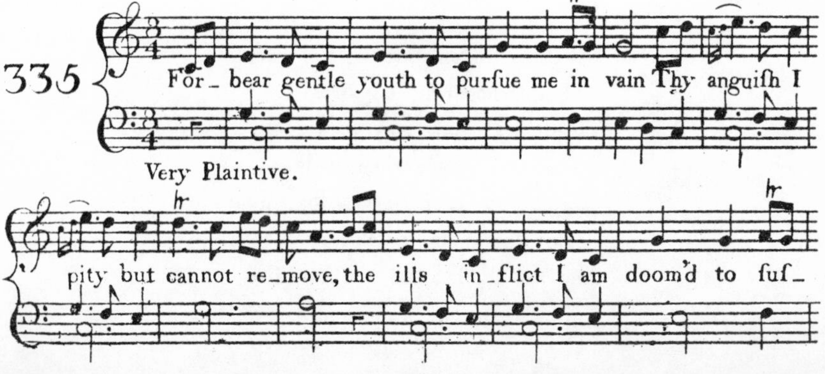
For_ bear gentle youth to purfue me in vain Thy anguifh I
Very Plaintive.
pity but cannot re_move, the ills in_flict I am doom'd to fuf_

Continued.

_tain Nor ſhalt thou a_lone be the victim of love My_Sandy was
beau_tiful happy and wiſe in ev'_ry accompliſhment deſtin'd to
ſhine He had wit for all taſtes he had charms for all eyes a_
_las the dear youth was too charming for mine.

He ſaw me he lov'd me, his paſsion confeſs'd,
The ſoft declaration ſtill ſounds in my ear;
My image, he ſaid, on his ſoul was impreſs'd,
And faithful! his flame, as his heart was ſincere.
His wiſhes tho' fond, I as fondly repaid,
For oh! a warm heart it is eaſy to gain,
Which kind profeſsions already perſuade,
Our pleaſure was mutual and mutual our pain.

Still fortune relentleſs our union denied,
In queſt of more treaſure to India he went,
But there, hapleſs youth, to my ſorrow he died,
And left me for ever his fate to lament.
Gay hopes and delightful preſages adieu,
Adieu ye ſoft whiſpers of tender deſire;
From thee my dear ſwain theſe emotions firſt grew,
In deep diſappointment with thee they expire.

# Eppie Mc Nab.

336

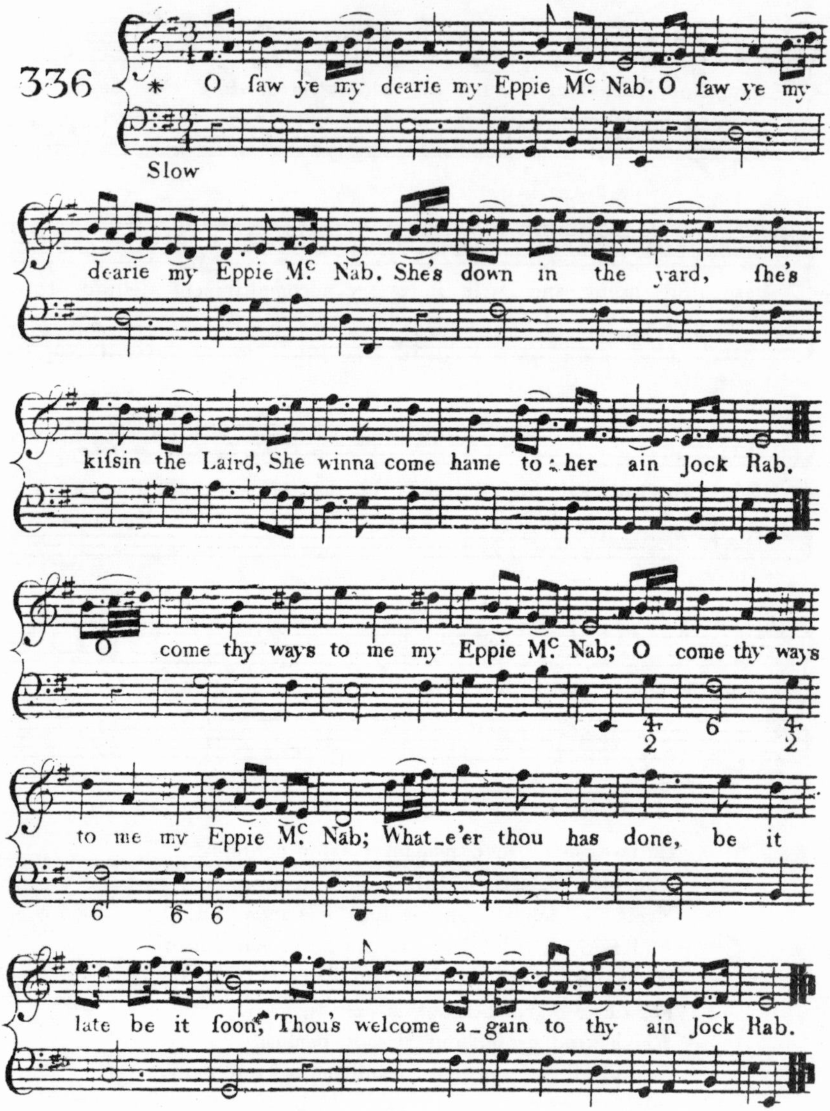

Slow
O saw ye my dearie my Eppie Mc Nab. O saw ye my dearie my Eppie Mc Nab. She's down in the yard, she's kissin the Laird, She winna come hame to her ain Jock Rab.
O come thy ways to me my Eppie Mc Nab; O come thy ways to me my Eppie Mc Nab; What_e'er thou has done, be it late be it soon, Thou's welcome a_gain to thy ain Jock Rab.


What says she, my dearie, my Eppie Mc Nab.
What says she, my dearie, my Eppie Mc Nab.
She lets thee to wit, that she has thee forgot
And for ever disowns thee, her ain Jock Rab.
O had I ne'er seen thee, my Eppie Mc Nab!
O had I ne'er seen thee, my Eppie Mc Nab!
As light as the air, and fause as thou's fair,
Thou's broken the heart o' thy ain Jock Rab.

Wha is that at my bower door–

Written for this Work bobert Burns.

337 *

Wha is that at my bower..door? O wha is it but
Lively
Find_lay Then gae your gate ye'ſe nae be here! In_
_deed maun I, quo' Findlay. What mak ye, ſae like a thief. O
come and ſee, quo' Findlay; Be_fore the morn ye'll
work miſchief; In_deed will I quo Findlay.

Gif I riſe and let you in,
Let me in, quo' Findlay;
Ye'll keep me waukin wi' your din;
Indeed will I, quo' Findlay.
In my bower if ye ſhould ſtay,
Let me ſtay, quo' Findlay;
I fear ye'll bide till break o' day;
Indeed will I, quo Findlay.

Here this night if ye remain,
I'll remain, quo' Findlay;
I dread ye'll learn the gate again
Indeed will I, quo' Findlay.
What may paſs within this bower,
Let it paſs, quo' Findlay;
Ye maun conceal till your laſt hour
Indeed will I, quo' Findlay

## Thou art gane awa.

338

Thou art gane a_wa thou art gane a_wa, Thou art
gane a_wa frae me Ma_ry, nor friends nor I could
make thee ſtay, Thou haſt chea_ted them and me Ma_ry.
Un_til this hour I ne_ver thought That ought could
al_ter thee, Ma_ry, Thou'rt ſtill the Miſtreſs of my
heart, Think what you will of me, Ma_ry.
S.
S.
S.
S.

## Thou art gane awa, New Sett.

339

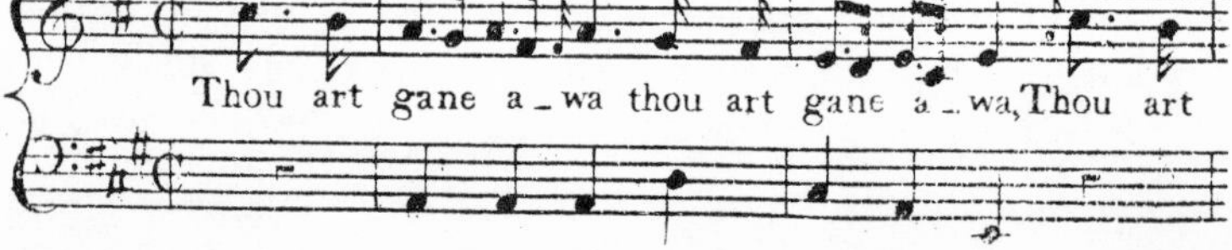
Thou art gane a_wa thou art gane a_wa, Thou art

## Continued.

gane a_way frae me, Ma_ry, nor friends nor I could
make thee ſtay, Thou haſt chea ted them and me, Ma_ry. Un_
_till this hour I ne_ver thought, That ought could
al_ter thee, Ma_ry, Thou'rt ſtill the Miſtreſs of my
heart, Think what you will of me Ma_ry.
S.
S.
S.
S.

What e'er he ſaid or might pretend,
That ſtaw that heart o' thine, Mary;
True love I'm ſure was ne'er his end,
Or nae ſic love as mine, Mary.
I ſpake ſincere nor flatter'd much,
Nae ſelfiſh thoughts in me Mary,
Ambition, wealth, nor naething ſuch;
No I, lov'd only thee, Mary.

Tho' you've been falſe, yet while I live
I'll lo'e nae maid but thee, Mary;
Let friends forget, as I forgive
Thy wrangs to them and me, Mary.
So then fareweel! of this be ſure,
Since you've been falſe to me, Mary;
For a' the world I'd not endure,
Half what I've done for thee, Mary.

## The tears I ſhed &c.

340

The tears I ſhed muſt ev_ er fall, I mourn not for an
Slow with expreſsion
ab_ ſent ſwain, For thought may paſt delights recall, And par_ ted
lovers meet a_ gain I weep not for the ſi_ lent dead, their
toils are paſt, their ſorrows o'er, And thoſe they lov'd their ſteps ſhall
tread, And death ſhall join_ and death ſhall join to part no more.

Tho' boundleſs oceans roll'd between,
If certain that his heart is near,
A conſcious tranſport glads each ſcene,
Soft is the ſigh, and ſweet the tear.
Even when by Death's cold hand remov'd,
We mourn the tenant of the tomb;
To think that even in death he lov'd,
Can gild the horrors of the gloom.

But bitter, bitter are the tears,
Of her who ſlighted love bewails;
No hope her dreary proſpect chears,
No pleaſing melancholy hails.
Her's are the pangs of wounded pride,
Of blaſted hope, of wither'd joy:
The prop ſhe lean'd on pierc'd her ſide,
The flame ſhe fed, burns to deſtroy.

Even conſcious virtue cannot cure
The pangs to every feeling due:
Ungenerous youth! thy boaſt how poor,
To ſteal a heart, and break it too!
In vain does memory renew,
The hours once ting'd in tranſport's dye;
The ſad reverſe ſoon ſtarts to view,
And turns the thought to agony.

No cold approach, no alter'd mien,
Juſt what would make ſuſpicion ſtart;
No pauſe the dire extremes between,
He made me bleſt _ and broke my heart!
From hope, the wretched's anchor torn,
Neglected, and neglecting all,
Friendleſs, forſaken, and forlorn
The tears I ſhed muſt ever fall.

# The bonny wee thing.

Written for this Work by Robert Burns.

341

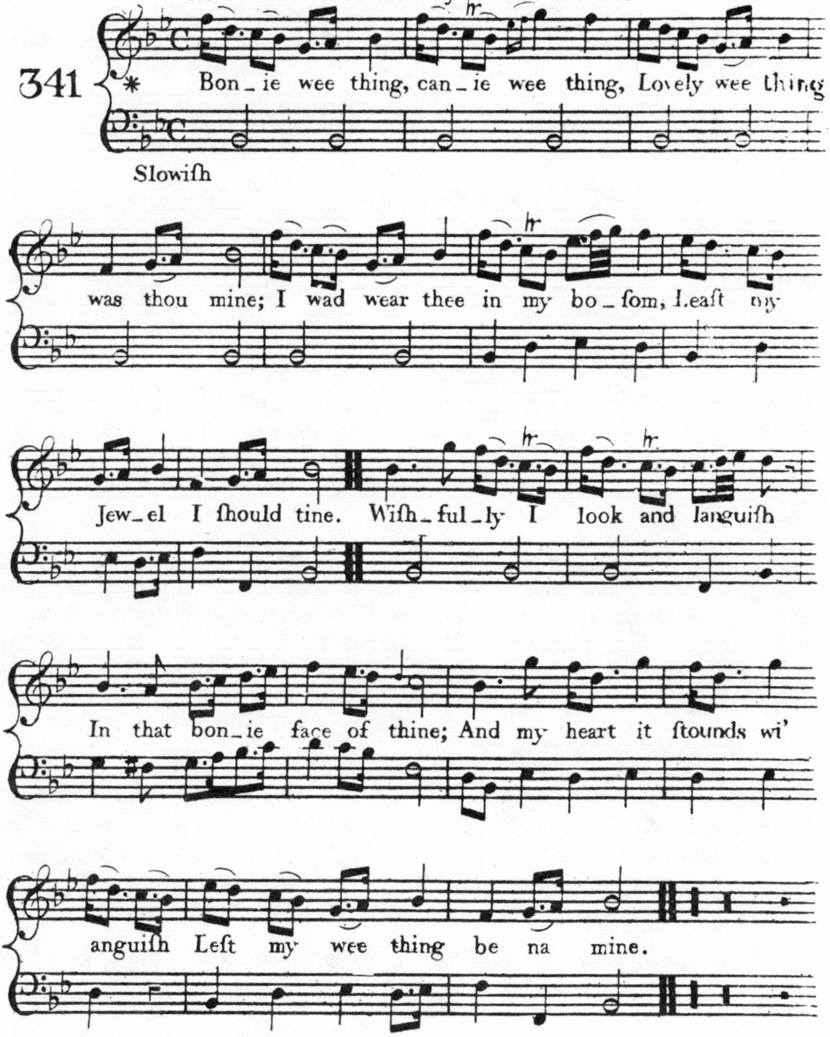
Bon_ie wee thing, can_ie wee thing, Lovely wee thing
Slowiſh
was thou mine; I wad wear thee in my bo_ſom, Leaſt my
Jew_el I ſhould tine. Wiſh_ful_ly I look and languiſh
In that bon_ie face of thine; And my heart it ſtounds wi'
anguiſh Leſt my wee thing be na mine.

Wit, and Grace, and Love, and Beauty,
In ae conſtellation ſhine;
To adore thee is my duty,
Goddeſs o' this ſoul o' mine!
Bonie wee &c.

## Roy's Wife of Alldivaloch.

342

Roy's wife of All_di_va_loch Roy's wife of Alldi_valoch
Pathetic
Wat ye how she cheated me as I came o'er the braes of Balloch.
She vow'd she swore she wad be mine She said that she lo'ed me best of
ony but oh the fickle faithless quean She's taen the Carl & left her Johnie.
Da Capo

O She was a can ty quean,
And well cou'd she dance the highland walloch,
How happy I, had she been mine
Or I'd been Roy of Alldivaloch
Roy's wife &c.

Her hair sae fair, her e'en sae cle[ar]
Her wee bit mou', so sweet and bon[ie]
To me she ever will be dear
Tho' she's forever left her Johnie
Roy's wife &c.

## Lady Randolph's Complaint.

Tune, Earl Douglas's Lament

343

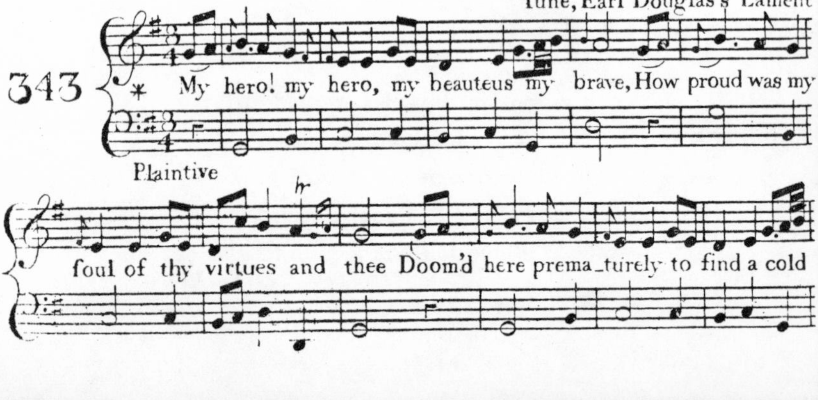
My hero! my hero, my beauteus my brave, How proud was my
Plaintive
soul of thy virtues and thee Doom'd here prema_turely to find a cold

Continued.

grave, Nor couldſt thou e _ lude what thou couldſt not fore ſee Of
gen'rous endeavours, was this thy re_ward. The Lord of this manſion
from foes to de_fend; Henceforth hoſ_pi _ ta_li _ ty who ſhall re _
_ gard; What man on the friendſhip of man ſhall de _ pend.

With tranſport this day, my fond heart overflow'd,
When keenly indulging the pleaſing preſage,
How warm with maternal affection, it glow'd,
Midſt an offspring of thine whilſt I hop'd for old age!
Whoſe prattle endearing, and innocent play
To me might the loſs of thy childhood atone;
Thoſe actions, the fame of your houſe might diſplay,
Adorn'd with a huſband's dear name, and thy own.

Thy gallant deportment, thy exquiſite bloom,
Which mercileſs foes might, with rapture, admire,
With them my dear hopes are all quench'd in the tomb,
With thee they were born, and with thee they expire.
In conjugal union how ſhort my delight!
In a mothers high rank how much ſhorter my boaſt!
With planets malignant, no more let me fight,
No longer in life's cruel tempeſt be toſt!

Forgive, gracious powers, in compaſsion my ſtate,
Whilſt by ſorrow compell'd, with reluctance I ſeize
The only ſweet moment reſerved me by fate,
The moment which renders me juſt what I pleaſe.
My Douglas, my darling, my glory, my pride!
How happy was I but to name thee, my ſon!
For thee would to heaven a fond mother had died,
Since living without thee, is living undone.

## Come here's to the nymph that I love.

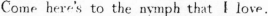

Tune, Auld Sir Symon the King

344
*
Lively
Come here's to the nymph that I love! A_way ye vain ſorrows,
away; Far, far from me ſorrows, begone; All here ſhall be pleaſant & gay
Far hence be the ſad and the penſive, Come fill up the glaſses around We'll
drink till our faces be ruddy, And all our vain ſorrows are drown'd.

'Tis done, and my fancy's exulting,
With every gay blooming deſire,
My blood with briſk ardour is glowing,
Soft pleaſures my boſom inſpire.
My ſoul now to love is diſſolving,
Oh fate! had I here my fair charmer,
I'd, claſp her, I'd claſp her ſo eager,
Of all her diſdain I'd diſarm her.

But hold, what has love to do here,
With his troops of vain cares in array.
A vaunt, idle penſive intruder,_
He triumphs, he will not away,
I'll drow him, come give me a bumper;
Young Cupid, here's to thy confuſion_
Now, now he's departing, he's vanquiſh'd,
Adieu to his anxious deluſion.

Come jolly god Bacchus, here's to thee;
Huzza, boys, huzza boys, huzza;
Sing I o, ſing I o to Bacchus —
Hence all ye dull thinkers, withdraw.

Come, what ſhould we do but be jovial.
Come tune up our voices and ſing;
What ſoul is ſo dull to be heavy,
When wine ſets our fancies on wing.

Come, Pegaſus lies in this bottle,
He'll mount us, he'll mount us on high,
Each of us a gallant young Perſeus,
Sublime we'll aſcend to the ſky.
Come mount or adieu I ariſe,
In ſeas of wide æther I'm drown'd;
The clouds far beneath me are ſailing,
I ſee the ſpheres whirling around.

What darkneſs, what rattling is this.
Thro' Chaos' dark regions I'm hurl'd,
And now, _ O my head it is knock'd
Upon ſome confounded new world.
Now, now theſe dark ſhades are retiring,
See yonder bright blazes a ſtar;
Where am I! behold the Empyreum,
With flaming light ſtreaming from far.

## The tither morn.

345
*
The tither morn, When I forlorn Aneath an aik ſat
Lively with expreſsion
moaning, I did na trow, I'd ſee my jo Be_ſide me gain the
glowning. But he ſae trig lap o'er the rig And
daw_ting_ly did chear me When I, what reck, did
leaſt expect, To ſee my lad ſae near me.

His bonnet he,
A thought ajee
Cock'd ſpruſh when firſt he claſp'd me;
And I, I wat,
Wi' fainneſs grat,
While in his grips he preſs'd me
De'il tak the war!
I late and air
Hae wiſh'd ſince Jock departed
But now as glad
I'm wi' my lad,
As ſhortſyne broken hearted.

Fu' aft at e'en
Wi' dancing keen,
When a' were blyth and merry
I car'dna by,
Sae ſad was I
In abſence o' my deary
But praiſe be bleſt,
My mind's at reſt,
I'm happy wi' my Johnny,
At kirk and fair,
I'ſe ay be there;
And be as canty's ony.

## A Country Laſs.

346

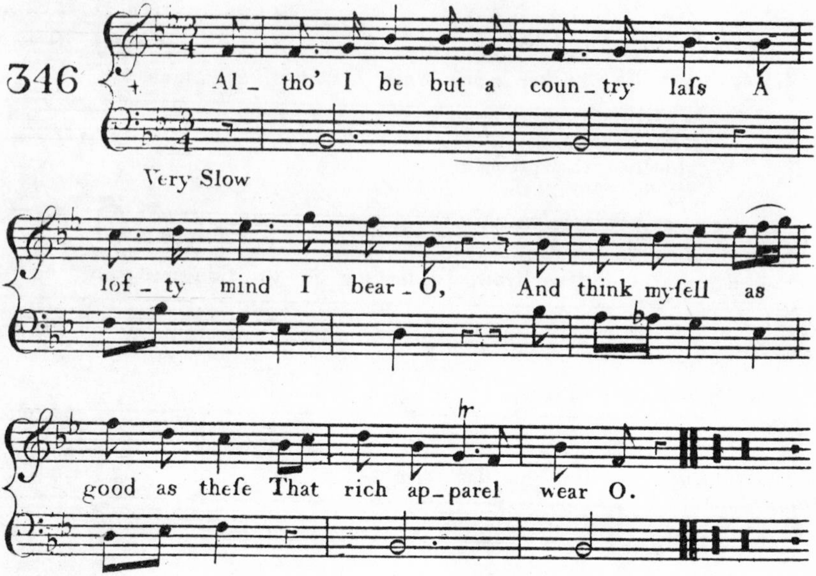
Al_ tho' I be but a coun_try laſs A
Very Slow
lof_ty mind I bear_O, And think myſell as
good as theſe That rich ap_parel wear O.

Altho' my gown be hame-ſpun grey,
My ſkin it is as ſoft _O,
As them that ſattin weeds do wear,
And carry their heads aloft_O.

What tho' I keep my father's ſheep.
The thing that muſt be done _O,
With garlands of the fineſt flow'rs
To ſhade me frae the ſun_O.

When they are feeding pleaſantly,
Where graſs and flowers do ſpring_O,
Then on a flow'ry bank at noon,
I ſet me down and ſing_O

My Peiſley piggy cork'd with ſage,
Contains my drink but thin _O.
No wines do e'er my brain enrage,
Or tempt my mind to ſin _O.

My country curds and wooden ſpoon
I think them unco fine _O,
And on a flowery bank at noon
I ſet me down and dine _O.

Altho' my parents cannot raiſe
Great bags of ſhining gold_O,
Like them whoſe daughters now a days
Like ſwine are bought and ſold_O;

Yet my fair body it ſhall keep
An honeſt heart within _O,
And for twice fifty thouſand crowns
I value not a pin_O:

I uſe nae gums upon my hair,
Nor chains about my neck_O,
Nor ſhining rings upon my hands,
My fingers ſtraight to deck_O

But for that lad to me ſhall fa',
And I have grace to wed_O,
I'll keep a jewel worth them a',
I mean my maidenhead_O.

If canny Fortune give to me
The man I dearly love _O,
Tho' we want gear I dinna care,
My hands I can improve _O.

Expecting for a bleſsing ſtill
Deſcending from above_O,
Then we'll embrace and ſweetly kiſs,
Repeating tiles of love_O.

## Geordie — An old Ballad. — Same Tune.

There was a battle in the north,
And nobles there was many,
And they hae kill'd Sir Charlie Hay,
And they laid the wyte on Geordie.

O he has written a lang letter,
He ſent it to his lady;
Ye maun cum up to Enbrugh town
To ſee what words o' Geordie.

When firſt ſhe look'd the letter on,
She was baith red and roſy;
But ſhe had na read a word but twa,
Till ſhe wallow't like a lily.

Gar get to me my gude grey ſteed,
My menzie a' gae wi' me;
For I ſhall neither eat nor drink,
Till Enbrugh town ſhall ſee me.

And ſhe has mountit her gude grey ſteed,
Her menzie a' gaed wi' her;
And ſhe did neither eat nor drink
Till Enbrugh town did ſee her.

And firſt appear'd the fatal block,
And ſyne the aix to head him;
And Geordie cumin down the ſtair,
And bands o' airn upon him.

But tho' he was chain'd in fetters ſtrang,
O' airn and ſteel ſae heavy,
There was na ane in a' the court,
Sae bra' a man as Geordie.

O ſhe's down on her bended knee
I wat ſhe's pale and weary,
O pardon, pardon, noble king
And gie me back my Dearie!

I hae born ſeven ſons to my Geordie dear,
The ſeventh ne'er ſaw his daddie:
O pardon, pardon, noble king,
Pity a waefu lady!

Gar bid the headin-man mak haſte!
Our king reply'd fu' lordly:
O noble king, tak a' that's mine,
But gie me back my Geordie.

The Gordons cam and the Gordons ran,
And they were ſtark and ſteady;
And ay the word amang them a'
Was, Gordons keep you ready.

An aged lord at the king's right hand
Says noble king, but hear me;
Gar her tell down five thouſand pound
And gie her back her Dearie.

Some gae her marks ſome gae her crowns,
Some gae her dollars many;
And ſhe's tell'd down five thouſand pound,
And ſhe's gotten again her Dearie.

She blinkit blythe in her Geordie's face.
Says, dear I've bought thee, Geordie.
But there ſud been bluidy bouks on the green,
Or I had tint my laddie.

He claſpit her by the middle ſma',
And he kiſt her lips ſae roſy:
The faireſt flower o' woman-kind
Is my ſweet, bonie Lady!

# Ae fond kiss, &c.

Written for this Work by Robert Burns. Tune, Rory Dall's Port.

347

*
Ae fond kiss, and then we sever; Ae farewell and
Slow & tender
then for ev_er! Deep in heart_wrung tears I'll pledge thee, Warring
sighs and groans I'll wage thee. Who shall say that fortune grieves him
While the star of hope she leaves him? Me, nae chear_ fu'
twinkle lights me; Dark despair a_ round benights me.

I'll ne'er blame, my partial fancy,
Naething could resist my Nancy:
But to see her, was to love her;
Love but her, and love for ever.
Had we never lov'd sae kindly,
Had we never lov'd sae blindly,
Never met _ or never parted,
We had ne'er been broken_hearted.

Fare thee weel, thou first and fairest!
Fare thee weel, thou best and dearest!
Thine be ilka joy and treasure,
Peace Enjoyment, Love and Pleasure!
Ae fond kiss, and then we sever;
Ae fareweel, Alas: for ever!
Deep in heart_wrung tears I'll pledge thee
Warring sighs and groans I'll wage thee.

# As I was a wand'ring.

Tune, Rinn m' eudial mo mhealladh. A Gaelic Air.

348

*
Plaintive
As I was a wand'ring ae midsummer e'enin The pipers & youngsters were makin their game, A _ mang them I spyed my faithless fause luver, Which bled a' the wounds o' my dolour a _ _gain. Weel, since he has left me, may pleasure gae wi' him; I may be distress'd but I winna complain: I'll flatter my fan _ cy I may get anither my heart it shall ne _ ver be broken for ane.

I could na get sleepin till dawin, for greetin;
The tears trickl'd down like the hail and the rain:
Had I na got greetin, my heart wad a broken,
For oh, luve forsaken's a tormenting pain!
Weel since he has, &c.

Although he has left me for greed o' the siller,
I dinna envy him the gains he can win:
I rather wad bear a' the lade o' my sorrow,
Than ever hae acted sae faithless to him.
Weel since he has, &c.

# Lovely Davies.

Tune, Miſs Muir.

349
* O how ſhall I, un_ſkilfu', try The Poets oc_cu_
Slow
_pa__tion, The tunefu' powers, in happy hours, That whiſ_pers
in_ſpi_ration, Even they maun dare an effort mair Than
aught they e_ver gave us, Or they re_hearſe in
e_qual verſe, The charms o' love_ly Davies. Each
eye it chears when ſhe appears, Like Phebus in the

Continued.

morning, When paſt the ſhow'r, and every flower The
gar_den is a _ dorning: As the wretch looks o'er Si_.
_beria's ſhore, When winter bound the wave is; Sae droops our
heart when we maun part Frae charming, love_ly Davies.

Her ſmile's a gift frae boon the lift,
  That maks us mair than princes;
A ſcepter'd hand, a king's command,
  Is in her darting glances:
The man in arms 'gainſt female charms,
  Even he her willing ſlave is;
He hugs his chain, and owns the reign
  Of conquering lovely Davies.
My Muſe to dream of ſuch a theme,
  Her feeble powers ſurrender;
The eagle's gaze alone ſurveys
  The ſun's meridian ſplendor:
I wad in vain eſsay the ſtrain,
  The deed too daring brave is;
I'll drap the lyre, and mute, admire.
  The charms o' lovely Davies.

# The weary Pund O' Tow.

350

*
The weary pund, the weary pund, The weary pund o'
Very Slow
tow; I think my wife will end her life, Before ſhe ſpin her tow
I bought my wife a ſtane o' lint as gude as e'er did grow; And
a' that ſhe has made o' that Is ae poor pund o' tow.
Chorus
The weary pund, the weary pund, The weary pund o' tow; I
think my wife will end her life, Before ſhe ſpin her tow.

There ſat a bottle in a bole,
Beyont the ingle low;
And ay ſhe took the tither ſouk,
To drouk the ſtourie tow.
The weary, &c.

Quoth I, for ſhame, ye dirty dame,
Gae ſpin your tap o' tow!
She took the rock, and wi' a knock,
She brak it o'er my pow.
The weary, &c.

At laſt her feet, I ſang to ſee't,
Gaed foremoſt o'er the knowe;
And or I wad anither jad,
I'll wallop in a tow.
The weary, &c.

## Now weſtlin winds.

Written for this Work by Burns. Tune, Come kiſs wi' me, come clap wi' me

351
Now weſtlin winds, and ſlaughterin guns Brings Autumn's
Slow with expreſsion
pleaſant weather; The gor -cock ſprings, on whirring wings A_
_mang the blooming heather: Now waving grain, wide o'er the
plain Delights the wea_ry Farmer, The moon ſhines bright, as I
rove by night, To muſe u_pon my charmer.

The Pairtrick lo'es the fruitfu' fells;
  The Plover lo'es the mountains;
The Woodcock haunts the lanely dells;
  The ſoaring Hern the fountains:
Thro' lofty groves the Cuſhat roves,
  The path o' Man to ſhun it;
The hazel buſh o'erhangs the Thruſh,
  The ſpreading thorn the Linnet.

Thus every kind their pleaſure find,
  The ſavage and the tender;
Some, ſocial join, and leagues combine,
  Some ſolitary wander:
Avaunt, away! the cruel ſway,
  Tyrannic Man's dominion;
The Sportsman's joy, the murdering cry,
  The fluttering gory pinion.

But Peggy dear, the evening's clear,
  Thick flies the ſkimming ſwallow;
The ſky is blue, the fields in view
  All fading-green and yellow:
Come let us ſtray our gladſome way,
  And view the charms o' Nature,
The ruſtling corn, the fruited thorn,
  And ilka happy creature.

We'll gently walk, and ſweetly talk,
  While the ſilent moon ſhines clearly:
I'll claſp thy waiſt, and fondly preſt,
  Swear how I lo'e thee dearly.
Not vernal ſhowers to budding flowers
  Not Autumn to the Farmer,
So dear can be as thou to me,
  My fair, my lovely Charmer.

## I hae a wife o' my ain.

Written for this Work by Robert Burns.

352

* I hae a wife o' my ain, I'll partake wi' nae_body
I'll tak Cuck_old frae nane; I'll gie Cuckold to nae_body
I hae a pen_ny to ſpend, There, thanks to nae_bo_dy
I hae nae_thing to lend, I'll borrow frae nae_bo_dy.

I am naebody's lord,
I'll be ſlave to naebody;
I hae a gude braid ſword,
I'll tak dunts frae naebody.

I'll be merry and free,
I'll be ſad for naebody;
Naebody cares for me,
I care for naebody. B

## When ſhe cam ben ſhe bobbed.

353

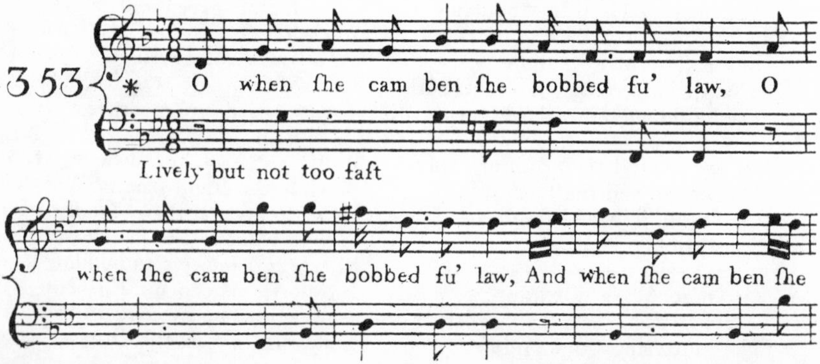
* O when ſhe cam ben ſhe bobbed fu' law, O
Lively but not too faſt
when ſhe cam ben ſhe bobbed fu' law, And when ſhe cam ben ſhe

Continued.

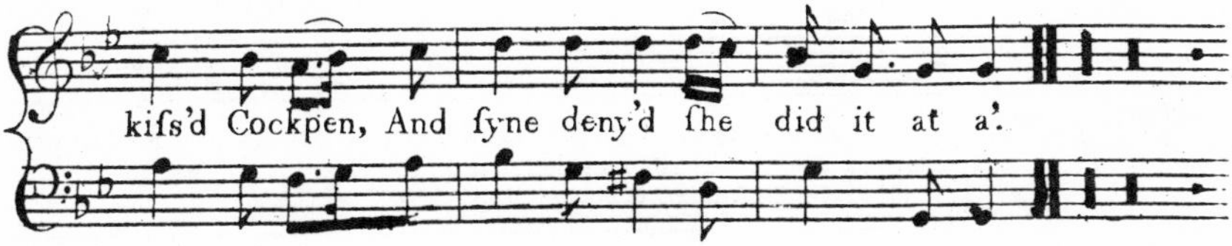
kifs'd Cockpen, And fyne deny'd fhe did it at a'.

And was na Cockpen right faucy witha',
And was na Cockpen right faucy witha',
In leaving the dochter of a lord,
And kifsin a Collier lafsie an a'.

O never look down, my lafsie at a',
O never look down, my lafsie at a',
Thy lips are as fweet and thy figure compleat,
As the fineft dame in caftle or ha'.

Tho' thou has nae filk and holland fae fma,
Tho' thou has nae filk and holland fae fma,
Thy coat and thy fark are thy ain handywark
And Lady Jean was never fae braw.

## O Fare ye weel my auld wife.

354

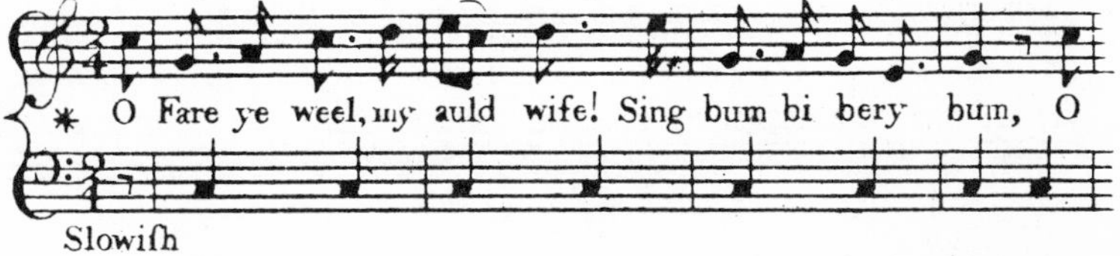
* O Fare ye weel, my auld wife! Sing bum bi bery bum, O

Slowifh

fare ye weel my auld wife fing bum O fare ye weel my

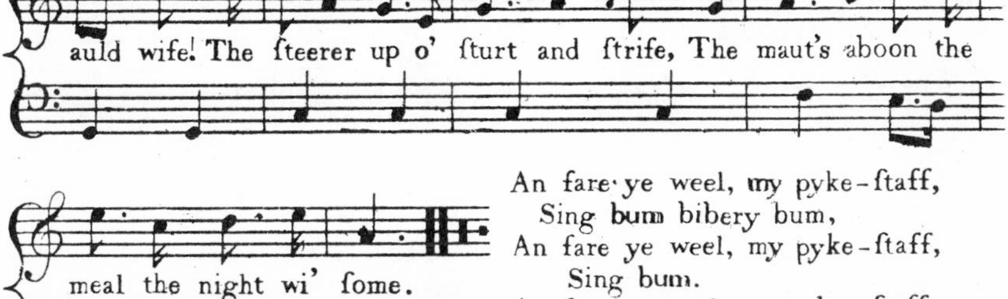
auld wife! The fteerer up o' fturt and ftrife, The maut's aboon the

meal the night wi' fome.

An fare ye weel, my pyke-ftaff,
Sing bum bibery bum,
An fare ye weel, my pyke-ftaff,
Sing bum.
An fare ye weel, my pyke-ftaff,
Nae mair wi' you my wife I'll baff,
The maut's aboon the meal the night.
Wi' fome.

## O, for ane and twenty Tam.

Written for this Work by Robert Burns. Tune, The Moudiewort.

355

*
Canty
An O, for ane and twenty Tam! An hey, sweet ane & twenty, Tam! I'll learn my kin a rattlin sang, An I saw ane and twenty Tam.
They snool me sair, & haud me down, And gar me look like bluntie, Tam; But three short years will soon wheel roun', And then comes ane & twenty Tam
Chorus
An O, for ane and twenty Tam! And hey, sweet ane & twenty, Tam! I'll learn my kin a rattlin sang, An I saw ane and twenty, Tam.

A gleib o' lan', a claut o' gear,
Was left me by my Auntie, Tam;
At kith or kin I need na spier,
An I saw ane and twenty, Tam.
An O, for &c.

They'll hae me wed a wealthy coof,
Tho' I mysel hae plenty, Tam;
But hearst thou, laddie, there's my loof,
I'm thine at ane and twenty, Tam!
An O, for &c.

# Johnie Armſtrang.

356
* Some ſpieks of lords, ſum ſpieks of lairds And ſic like
Very Slow
men of hie degree; Of a gentle_man I ſing a ſang ſum_
tyme call'd Laird of Gilnoc_kie. The king he writes a kind
letter Wi' his ain hand ſae ten_der_lie, And he has ſent it to
Johnie Armſtrang, To cum and ſpiek with him ſpeedi_lie.

The Elliots and Armſtrangs did convene;
They were a gallant companie:
We'll ryde and meit our lawful king,
And bring him ſafe to Gilnockie.
Make kinnen and capon ready then,
And veniſon in great plentie;
We'll welcum hame our royal king,
I hope he'll dyne at Gilnockie.

They ran their horſe on the Langun holm,
And brake their ſpeirs with meikle main;
The Ladies lukit frae their lofty windows
God bring our men weil back again.
Quhen Johnie came before the King,
With all his men ſae brave to ſee,
The King he movit his bonnet to him,
He weind he was king as well as he.

May I find grace, my ſovereign Liege,
Grace for my loyal men and me.
For my name it is Johnie Armſtrang,
And ſubject of zours, my Liege, ſaid he.
Away, away, thou traytor ſtrang,
Out of my ſicht thou mayſt ſune be,
I grantit nevir a traytor's lyſe,
And now I'll not begin with thee.

Grant me my lyfe, my Liege, my King,
And a bonny giſt I will gi' to thee,
Full four-and-twenty milk-whyt ſteids,
Were a' foald in a zeir to me.
I'll gie thee all theſe milk whyt ſteids,
That pranc and nicher at a ſpeir,
With as meikle gude Inglis gilt,
As four of their braid backs dow bein

# Hey how Johnie Lad.

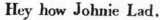

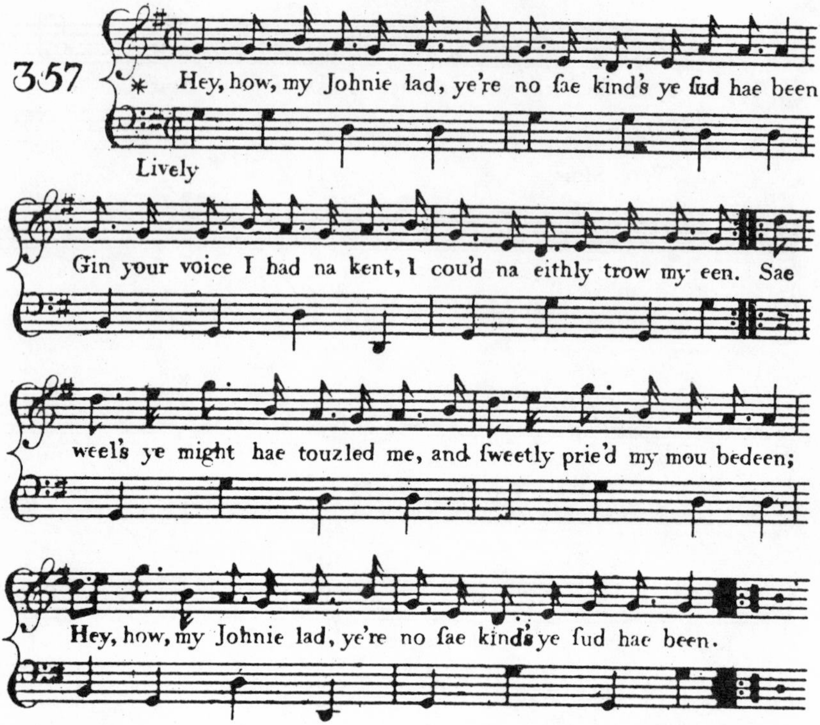
357
* Hey, how, my Johnie lad, ye're no ſae kind's ye ſud hae been
Lively
Gin your voice I had na kent, I cou'd na eithly trow my een. Sae
weel's ye might hae touzled me, and ſweetly prie'd my mou bedeen;
Hey, how, my Johnie lad, ye're no ſae kind's ye ſud hae been.

My Father he was at the pleugh, my Mither ſhe was at the mill,
My Billie he was at the moſs, and no ane near our ſport to ſpill,
The feint a Body was therein there was nae fear of being ſeen,
Hey, how, my Johnie lad, ye're no ſae kinds ye ſud hae been.

Wad ony lad wha lo'ed her weel, hae left his bonny laſs her lane,
To ſigh and greet ilk langſome hour, and think her ſweeteſt minutes gane
O, had ye been a wooer leal, we ſhu'd hae met wi' hearts mair keen,
Hey how my Johnie lad, ye're no ſae kind's ye ſud hae been.

But I maun hae anither joe, whaſe love gangs never out o' mind,
And winna let the moment paſs, when to a laſs he can be kind,
Then gang your wa's to blinken Beſs, nae mair for Johnie ſhall ſhe green,
Hey, how, my Johnie lad, ye're no ſae kind's ye ſud hae been.

# Logie o' Buchan.

358
* O Logie o' Buchan, O Logie the laird, They've
Slowiſh & tender

Continued.

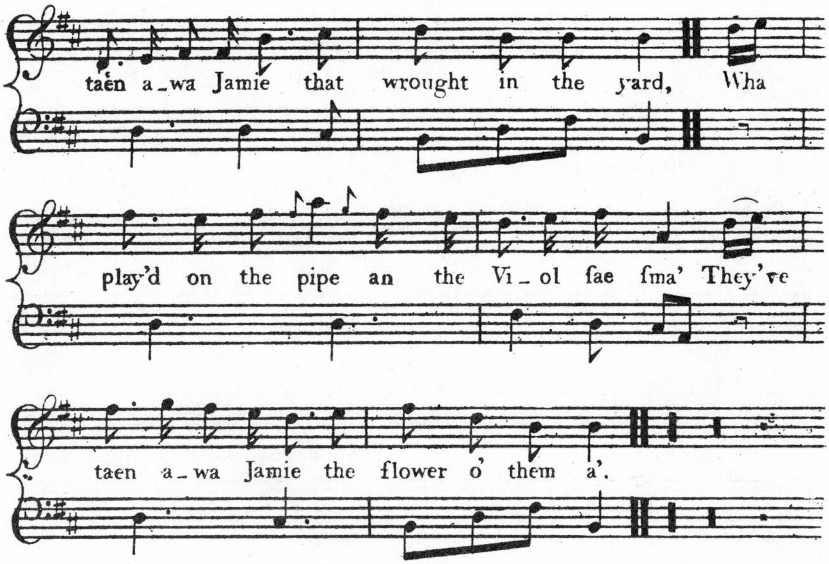
taen a_wa Jamie that wrought in the yard, Wha
play'd on the pipe an the Vi_ol ſae ſma' They're
taen a_wa Jamie the flower o' them a'.

O think na lang, laſsie, tho' I be awa,
An' think na lang, laſsie, tho' I be awa;
The ſimmer is come and the winter's awa,
And I'll come and ſee thee in ſpite o' them a'.

O Sandy has owſen, and ſiller, and kye,
A houſe and a haddin, and a' things forbye,
But I wad hae Jamie wi's bonnet in's hand,
Before I'd hae Sandy wi' houſes and land.
(The 2d. verſe ſung here,) O think na lang, &c

My daddie was ſulkie, my minnie was ſour,
They gloom'd on my Jamie becauſe he was poor;
But daddie and minnie altho' that they be,
There's nane o' them a' like my Jamie to me.
(The 2d. verſe ſung here,) O think na lang, &c.

I'll ſit on my ſunkie and ſpin at my wheel,
And ſing o my Jamie wha loes me ſae weel;
He took a white ſaxpence and brak it in twa,
And gae me the hauf o't when he gaed awa.

Sayin, think upon't laſsie when I am awa,
An' think upon't laſsie when I am awa:
The ſimmer is come, and the winter's awa,
And I'll come and ſee thee in ſpite o' them a'.

## O Kenmure's on and awa, Willie,

359

O Kenmure's on and a_wa, Willie, O Kenmure's on and a_
Slowish but with spirit
wa; An Ken_mure's Lord's the bravest Lord That
e_ver Galloway saw, _ . Success to Kenmure's band, Willie! Suc_
_cess to Ken_mure's band, There's no a heart that
fears a Whig That rides by Ken_mure's hand.

Here's Kenmure's health in wine, Willie,
  Here's Kenmure's health in wine,
There ne'er was a coward o' Kenmure's blude,
  Nor yet o' Gordon's Line

O Kenmure's lads are men, Willie,
  O Kenmure's lads are men,
Their hearts and swords are metal true,
  And that their faes shall ken

They'll live, or die wi' fame, Willie.
  They'll live, or die wi' fame,
But soon wi' sounding victorie
  May Kenmure's Lord come hame

Here's Him that's far awa, Willie,
  Here's Him that's far awa,
And here's the flower that I lo'e best,
  The rose that's like the snaw

## Befs and her Spinning Wheel.

Written for this Work by Robert Burns.

360

O Leeze me on my fpinning-wheel, And leeze me on my
Slow
rock and reel; Frae tap to tae that cleeds me bien, And haps me
fiel and warm at e'en! I'll fet me down and fing and fpin, While
laigh defcends the fimmer fun, Bleft wi' con_tent, and
milk and meal, O leeze me on my fpinnin_wheel.

On ilka hand the burnies trot,
And meet below my theekit cot;
The fcented birk and hawthorn white
Acrofs the pool their arms unite,
Alike to fcreen the birdie's neft,
And little fifhes caller reft:
The fun blinks kindly in the biel,'
Where, blythe I turn my fpinnin wheel.

On lofty aiks the cufhats wail,
And Echo cons the doolfu' tale;
The lintwhites in the hazel braes,
Delighted, rival ithers lays:

The craik amang the claver hay,
The pairtrick whirrin o'er the ley,
The fwallow jinkin round my fhiel,
Amufe me at my fpinnin wheel

Wi' fma' to fell, and lefs to buy,
Aboon diftrefs, below envy,
O wha wad leave this humble ftate,
For a' the pride of a' the great?
Amid their flairing, idle toys,
Amid their cumbrous, dinfome joys.
Can they the peace and pleafure feel
Of Befsy at her fpinnin wheel!

## My Collier Laddie.

361
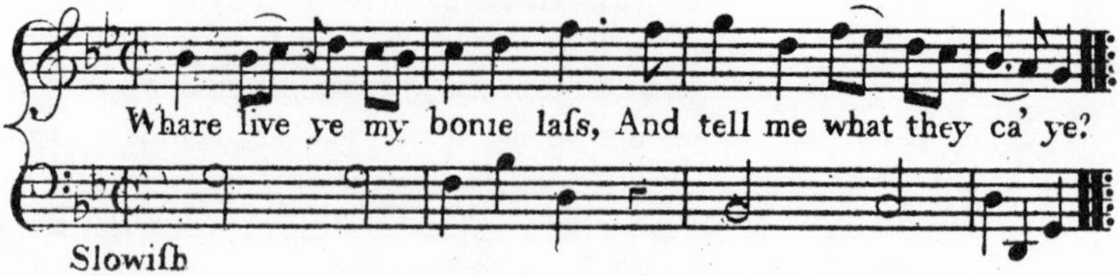
Whare live ye my bonie laſs, And tell me what they ca' ye?
Slowiſh

My name, ſhe ſays is Miſtreſs Jean, And I follow the Collier laddie.

See you not yon hills and dales
The ſun ſhines on ſae brawlie!
They a' are mine and they ſhall be thine,
Gin ye'll leave your Collier laddie.
They a' are, &c.

Ye ſhall gang in gay attire,
Weel buſkit up ſae gaudy;
And ane to wait on every hand,
Gin ye'll leave your Collier laddie.
And ane to wait, &c.

Tho' ye had a' the ſun ſhines on,
And the earth conceals ſae lowly;
I wad turn my back on you and it a',
And embrace my Collier laddie.
I wad turn, &c.

I can win my five pennies in a day,
And ſpen't at night fu' brawlie:
And make my bed in the Collier's neuk,
And lie down wi' my Collier laddie.
And make my bed, &c.

Loove for loove is the bargain for me,
Tho' the wee Cot-houſe ſhould haud me;
And the warld before me to win my bread,
And fair fa' my Collier laddie.
And the warld before me to win my bread,
And fair fa' my Collier laddie.

## The Shepherd's Wife.

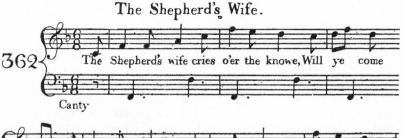

362
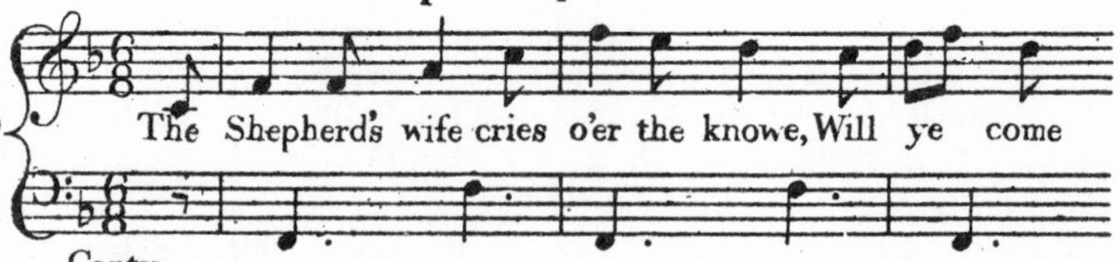
The Shepherd's wife cries o'er the knowe, Will ye come
Canty

hame will ye come hame; The Shepherd's wife cries o'er the knowe, Will

Continued.

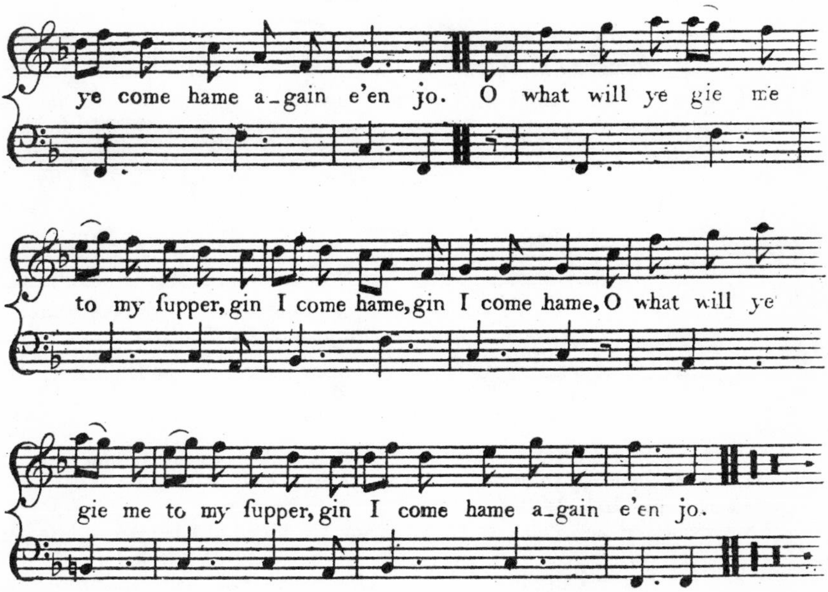
ye come hame a_gain e'en jo. O what will ye gie me
to my ſupper, gin I come hame, gin I come hame, O what will ye
gie me to my ſupper, gin I come hame a_gain e'en jo.

3 Ye'se get a panfu' o' plumpin parridge,
And butter in them, and butter in them,
Ye's get a panfu' o' plumpin parridge,
Gin ye'll come hame again een, jo!

4 Ha, ha, how! that's naething that dow,
I winna come hame, I canna come hame;
Ha, ha, how! that's naething that dow,
I winna come hame gin een, jo.

The Shepherd's wife &c.
(the 1st. & 2d. verſes ſung here)

A reekin fat hen, weel fryth'd i' the pan,
Gin ye'll come hame, gin ye'll come hame,
A reekin fat hen weel fryth'd i' the pan,
Gin ye'll come hame again een jo.

Ha, ha, how! &c.
(the 4th. verſe here)

The Shepherd's wife, &c.
(the firſt & 2d. verſes here)

A weel made bed and a pair o' clean -ſheets.
Gin ye'll come hame, gin ye'll come hame
A weel made bed & a pair o' clean ſheets,
Gin ye'll come hame again een, jo.

Ha, ha, how! &c.
(the 4th. verſe here)

The Shepherd's wife, &c.
(the 1st. & 2d. verſes here)

A luving wife in lily white linens,
Gin ye'll come hame, gin ye'll come hame
A luving wife in lily white linens,
Gin ye'll come hame again een, jo!

Ha ha how! that's ſomething that dow
I will come hame, I will come hame;
Ha ha how! that's ſomething that dow
I will come hame again een, jo

## William's Ghoſt.

363

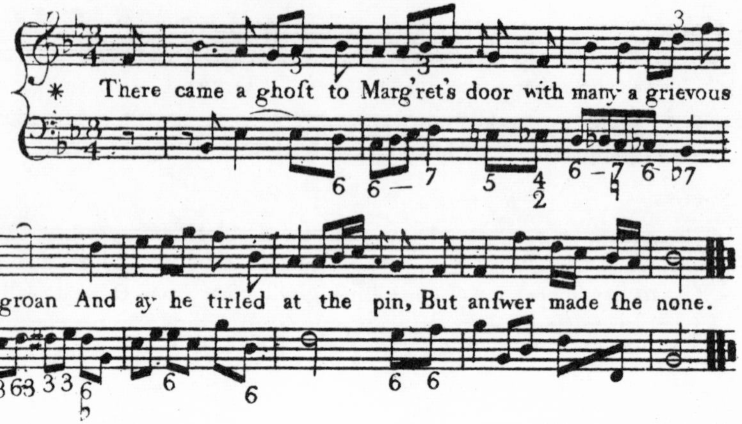
* There came a ghoſt to Marg'ret's door with many a grievous
groan And ay he tirled at the pin, But anſwer made ſhe none.

Is that my father Philip.
  Or is't my brother John.
Or is't my true love Willie
  From Scotland new come home.

'Tis not thy father Philip,
  Nor yet thy brother John;
But 'tis thy true love Willie,
  From Scotland new come home.

O ſweet Marg'ret! O dear Marg'ret!
  I pray thee ſpeak to me,
Give me my faith and troth, Marg'ret!
  As I gave it to thee.

Thy faith and troth thou's never get,
  We twa will never twin,
Till that thou come within my bower,
  And kiſs my cheek and chin.

If I ſhould come within thy bower,
  I am no earthly man;
And ſhould I kiſs thy roſy lips,
  Thy days would not be lang.

O ſweet Marg'ret! O dear Marg'ret!
  I pray thee ſpeak to me;
Give me my faith and troth, Marg'ret!
  As I gave it to thee.

Thy faith and troth thou's never get,
  We twa will never twin,
Till you take me to yon kirk-yard,
  And wed me with a ring.

My bones are buried in yon kirk-yard,
  Afar beyond the ſea;
And it is but my ſprit, Marg'ret,
  That's now ſpeaking to thee.

She ſtretched out her lily-white hand,
  And for to do her beſt;
Hae, there's your faith and troth, Willie;
  God ſend your ſaul good reſt!

Now ſhe has kilted her robes of green
  A piece below her knee,
And a' the live-lang winter-night
  The dead corpſe follow'd ſhe.

Is there any room at your head, Willie,
  Or any room at your feet,
Or any room at your ſide, Willie,
  Wherein that I may creep.

There's no room at my head, Marg'ret,
  There's no room at my feet,
There's no room at my ſide, Marg'ret,
  My coffin's made ſo meet.

Then up and crew the red cock,
  And up then crew the gray,
'Tis time, 'tis time, my dear Marg'ret,
  That you were going away.

No more the ghoſt to Marg'ret ſaid,
  But, with a grievous groan,
Evaniſh'd in a cloud of miſt,
  And left her all alone.

O ſtay, my only true-love, ſtay,
  The conſtant Marg'ret cry'd;
Wan grew her cheeks, ſhe cloſ'd her ee
  Stretch'd her ſoft limbs, and dy'd.

## Nithſdall's welcome hame.

Written for this Work by Robert Burns.

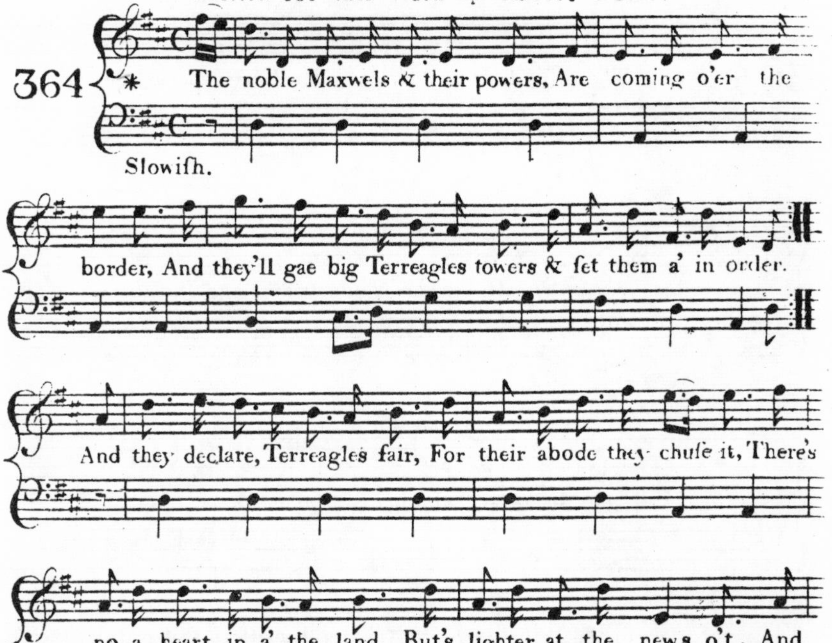
364
*
Slowiſh.
The noble Maxwels & their powers, Are coming o'er the
border, And they'll gae big Terreagles towers & ſet them a' in order.
And they declare, Terreagles fair, For their abode they chuſe it, There's
no a heart in a' the land, But's lighter at the news o't. And
they declare, Terreagles fair, For their abode they chuſe it, There's
tr
no a heart in a' the land, But's lighter at the news o't.

Tho' ſtars in ſkies may diſappear,
And angry tempeſts gather;
The happy hour may ſoon be near
That brings us pleaſant weather:
The weary night o' care and grief
May hae a joyfu' morrow,
So dawning day has brought relief,
Fareweel our night o' ſorrow. R

## Johnie Blunt.

365

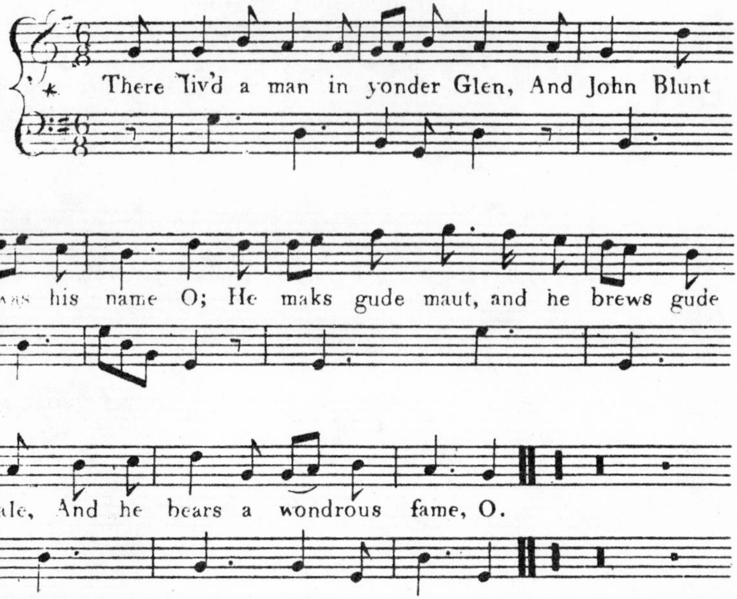
There liv'd a man in yonder Glen, And John Blunt
was his name O; He maks gude maut, and he brews gude
ale, And he bears a wondrous fame, O.

The wind blew in the hallan ae night,
Fu' ſnell out o'er the moor, O;
"Riſe up, riſe up, auld Luckie," he ſays,
"Riſe up and bar the door, O."

Three travellers that had tint their gate,
As thro' the hills they foor, O,
They airted by the line o' light
Fu' ſtraught to Johnie Blunt's door, O.

They made a paction 'tween them twa,
They made it firm and ſure, O,
Whae'er ſud ſpeak the foremoſt word,
Should riſe and bar the door, O.

They haurl'd auld Luckie out o' her bed,
And laid her on the floor, O;
But never a word auld Luckie wad ſay,
For barrin o' the door, O.

"Ye've eaten my bread, ye hae druken my ale,
"And ye'll mak my auld wife a whore, O,
A ha, Johnie Blunt! ye hae ſpoke the firſt word,
Get up and bar the door, O.

## Country Laſsie.

Written for this Work by Robert Burns.

366

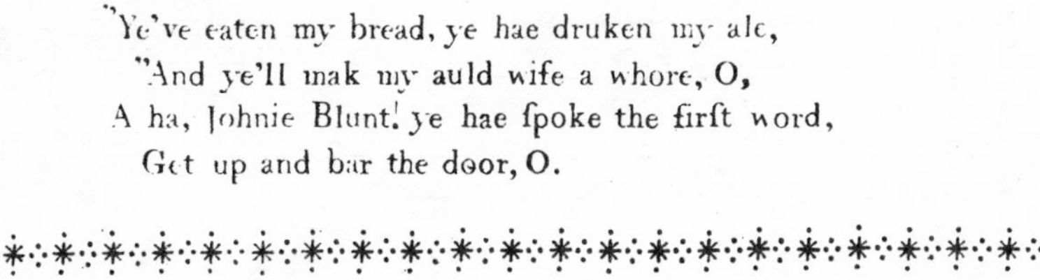
In ſimmer when the hay was mawn, And corn wav'd green in
Slowiſh

Continued.

il_ka field, While claver blooms white o'er the lea, And
roſes blaw in ilka bield; Blythe Beſsie in the milking ſhiel, Says
I'll be wed come o't what will; Out ſpak a dame in
wrinkled eild, O' gude adviſement comes nae ill.

Its ye hae wooers mony ane,
And laſsie ye're but young ye ken;
Then wait a wee, and canie wale,
A routhie butt, a routhie ben:
There's Johnie o' the Buſkie glen,
Fu' is his barn, fu' is his byre;
Tak this frae me, my bonie hen,
It's plenty beets the luver's fire.

For Johnie o' the Buſkie_glen,
I dinna care a ſingle flie;
He loes ſae weel his craps and kye,
He has nae loove to ſpare for me:
But blythe's the blink o Robie's e'e,
And weel I wat he loes me dear;
Ae blink o' him I wad na gie
For Buſkie_glen and a' his gear.

O thoughtleſs laſsie, life's a faught,
The canniest gate, the ſtrife is ſair;
But ay fit_han't is fechtin beſt,
A hungry care's an unco care:
But ſome will ſpend, and ſome will ſpare,
An' wilfu' folk maun hae their will;
Syne as ye brew, my maiden fair,
Keep mind that ye maun drink the yill.

O gear will buy me rigs o' land,
And gear will buy me ſheep and kye;
But the tender heart o' leeſome loove
The gowd and ſiller canna buy:
We may be poor, Robie and I,
Light is the burden Loove lays on;
Content and Loove brings peace & Joy
What mair hae Queens upon a throne

# Fair Eliza.

Written for this Work by Robert Burns. A Gaelic Air.

367
*
Turn a_gain thou fair E_li_za, Ae kind
Very Slow
blink be_fore we part, Rue on thy deſ_pair_ing Lover
Canſt thou break his faithfu' heart! Turn a_gain, thou fair E_
_li_za If to love thy heart de_nies, For pity hide the cruel
ſen_tence Under friend_ſhip's kind diſ_guiſe!

Thee, dear maid, hae I offended.
  The offence is loving thee:
Canſt thou wreck his peace for ever,
  Wha for thine wad gladly die!
While the life beats in my boſom,
  Thou ſhalt mix in ilka throe:
Turn again, thou lovely maiden,
  Ae ſweet ſmile on me beſtow.

Not the bee upon the bloſsom,
  In the pride o' ſinny noon;
Not the little ſporting fairy,
  All beneath the ſimmer moon;
Not the Poet in the moment
  Fancy lightens in his e'e,
Kens the pleaſure, feels the rapture,
  That thy preſence gies to me.

## Fair Eliza.

Same Song to another Gaelic Air.

368

*
Slow
Turn a_gain thou fair E_li_za Ae kind blink be_
_fore we part; Rue on thy def_pair_ing lu_ver! Canft thou
break his faith_fu' heart. Turn a_gain thou fair E
_li_za If, to luve thy heart de_nies For pity hide the cruel
fen_tence un_der friendfhip's kind difguife.


Thee, dear Maid, hae I offended.
The offence is luving thee:
Canft thou wreck his peace for ever,
Wha for thine wad gladly die!
O, while the life beats in my bofom,
Thou fhalt mix in ilka throe!
Turn again, thou lovely maiden,
Ae fweet fmile on me beftow.

Not the bee upon the blofsom,
In the pride o' finny noon;
Not the little fporting fairy,
All beneath the fimmer moon:
Not the Poet in the moment
Fancy lightens in his e'e;
Kens the pleafure, feels the rapture,
That thy prefence gies to me.

# Muirland Willie.

369

Har_ken and I will tell you how, Young Muir_land Wil_lie
Slow.
came to woo, Tho' he cou'd neither say nor do, The truth I
tell to you____ But ay he cries what__e'er be___tide,
Maggy I'se hae to be my bride, With a fall da dall la lall-
la la lall la lall la ra lall la ra lall lall_____
S.
S.
S.

2

On his gray yad as he did ride,
With durk and pistol by his side,
Ie prick'd her on wi' meikle pride,
Wi' meikle mirth and glee.
Out o'er yon moss, out o'er yon muir,
Till he came to her Dady's door.
With a fal, dal, &c.

3

Goodman, quoth he, be ye within,
I'm come your doughter's love to win,
I carena for making meikle din;
What answer gi' ye me.
Now, wooer, quoth he, will ye come in,
I'll gie ye my doughter's love to win.
With a fal, dal, &c.

## Continued.

Now, wooer, sin ye are lighted down,
Where do ye won, or in what town,
I think my doughter winna gloom;
  On sic a lad as ye.
The wooer he step'd up the house,
And vow but he was wondrous crouse.
  With a fal, dal, &c.

I hae three owsen in a pleugh,
Twa gude gaun yades, and gear enough,
The place they ca' it Cadeneugh;
  I scorn to tell a lie.
Besides, I hae frae the great laird,
A peat-pat, and a lang kail-yard.
  With a fal, dal, &c.

The maid put on her kirtle brown,
She was the brawest in a' the town,
I wat on him she did na gloom,
  But blinkit bonnilie.
The lover he stended up in haste,
And gript her hard about the waste.
  With a fal, dal, &c.

To win your love, maid, I'm come here,
I'm young, and hae enough o' gear,
And for mysell you need na fear,
  Troth try me whan you like.
He took aff his bonnet, and spat in his chow
He dighted his gab, and he prie'd her mou'
  With a fal, dal, &c.

The maiden blush'd and bing'd fu' law,
She had na will to say him na,
But to her daddy she left it a';
  As they twa cou'd agree.
The lover he ga'e her the tither kiss,
Syne ran to her daddy, and tell'd him this
  With a fal, dal, &c.

Your doughter wad na say me na,
But to yoursell she'as left it a',
As we cou'd 'gree between us twa;
  Say, what'll ye gie me wi' her.
Now, wooer, quo' he, I hae na meikle,
But sick's I hae, ye's get a pickle.
  With a fal, dal, &c

A kilufu' of corn I'll gie to thee,
Three soums of sheep, twa good milk kye,
Ye's hae the wadding dinner free,
  Troth I dow do nae mair.
Content, quo' he, a bargain be't,
I'm far frae hame, mak haste, let's gree
  With a fal, dal, &c.

The bridal-day it came to pass,
Wi' mony a blythesome lad and lass,
But sicken a day there never was,
  Sic mirth was never seen.
This winsome couple straked hands,
Mess John ty'd up the marriage bands.
  With a fal, dal, &c.

And our bride's maidens were na few,
Wi' tap-knots, lug-knots, a' in blue,
Frae tap to tae they were bra' new,
  And blinket bonnilie.
Their toys and mutches were sae clean,
They glanced in our ladses' een.
  With a fal, dal, &c.

Sick hirdum, dirdum, and sick din.
Wi' he o'er her, and she o'er him,
The minstrels they did never blin,
  Wi' meikle mirth and glee.
And ay they bobit, and ay they beck
And ay their wames together met.
  With a fal, dal, &c.

# The wee wee Man.

370

*
As I was a walking all alone, Be_tween a water
Slowiſh
and a wa', And there I ſpy'd a wee wee man, And
he was the leaſt that e'er I ſaw. His legs were ſcarce a
✠ ſhathmont's length, And thick and thimber was his thighs, Between his
brows there was a ſpan, And between his ſhoulders there was three.

He took up a meikle ſtane,
And he flang't as far as I could ſee,
Though I had been a Wallace wight,
I coudna liften't to my knee.
O wee wee man, but thou be ſtrong,
O tell me where thy dwelling be.
My dwelling's down at yon' bonny bower,
O will you go with me and ſee.

On we lap and awa we rade,
Till we came to yon bonny green;
We 'lighted down for to bait our horſe,
And out there came a lady fine.

Four and twenty at her back,
And theywere a' clad out in green,
Though the King of Scotland had been ther
The warſt o' them might ha' been his que

On we lap and awa we rade,
Till we came to yon bonny ha',
Where the roof was o' the beaten gould,
And the floor was o' the cryſtal a'.
When we came to the ſtair foot,
Ladies were dancing jimp and ſma',
But in the twinkling of an eye,
My wee wee man was clean awa'.

✠ Shathmont, in old Scotiſh, means the fiſt cloſed with the thumb extended.

## Ye Jacobites by Name.

371

*
Ye Ja_co_bites by name give an ear, give an
Slowiſh
ear; Ye Ja_co_bites by name, give an ear; Ye
Ja_co_bites by name Your fautes I will pro_claim Your
doctrines I maun blame, you ſhall hear.

What is Right, and what is Wrang, by the law, by the law?
What is Right, and what is Wrang, by the law?
What is Right, and what is Wrang?
A ſhort ſword, and a lang,
A weak arm, and a ſtrang
For to draw.

What makes heroic ſtrife, fam'd a far, fam'd a far.
What makes heroic ſtrife, fam'd a far?
What makes heroic ſtrife?
To whet th' aſsaſsin's knife,
Or hunt a Parent's life
Wi' bludie war.

Then let your ſchemes alone, in the ſtate, in the ſtate,
Then let your ſchemes alone, in the ſtate,
Then let your ſchemes alone,
Adore the riſing ſun,
And leave a man undone
To his fate.

# The poor Thresher.

372

A nobleman liv'd in a vil_lage of late, Hard
Slow
by a poor Thresh_er whose toil it was great, Who
had ma_ny children and most of them small, And
nought but his labour to keep them up all.

This poor man was seen to go early to work,
He never was known for to idle or lurk;
With his flail on his back and his bottle of beer,
As happy as those that have thousands a year.

In summer he toil'd thro' the faint, sultry heat;
Alike in the winter, the cold, and the weet:
So blythe and so merry he'd whistle and sing
As canty as ever a bird in the Spring

One evening this Nobleman, taking his walk,
Did meet the poor Thresher and freely did talk;
And many a question he ask'd him at large,
And still his discourse was concerning his charge.

You have many children I very well know,
Your labor is hard and your wages are low,
And yet you are chearful, I pray tell me how
That you do maintain them so well as you do.

I moil, and I toil, and I harrow and plough,
And sometimes a hedging and d tching I go;
No work comes me wrong for I shear and I mow,
And thus earn my bread by the sweat of my brow.

Continued.

My wife ſhe is willing to draw in the yoke,
We live like two lambs and we ſeldom provoke;
Each one loves the other, we join with the ant,
And do our endeavour to keep us from want.

I moil and I toil and I labourall day,
At night I do bring my full wages away:
What tho' it be poſsible we do live poor,
We ſtill keep the ravening wolf from the door.

And when I come home from my labourat night
To my wife and children in whom I delight,
To ſee them come round me with prattling noiſe,
O, theſe are the pleaſures the poor man enjoys!

Tho' I am as weary as weary can be,.
The youngeſt ay chiefly does dance on my knee;
I find that contentment's an abſolute feaſt,
And I never repine at my lot in the leaſt.

The Nobleman hearing him what he did ſay,
Invited him home to dine with him next day;
His wife and his children he charg'd him to bring,
And in token of favourhe gave him a ring.

He thanked his Lordſhip and taking his leave
Went home to his wife who.ſcarce could believe,
Thinking the ſtory himſelf he did raiſe,
But ſeeing the ring, then ſhe ſtood in amaze.

Early next morning the goodwife aroſe,
And dreſsed them all in the beſt of their clothes
There was he, and his wife, and his ſeven children ſmall,
They all went to dine at the Nobleman's hall.

The dinner being ended, he then let them know,
What he intended on them to beſtow;
A farm of full forty good acres of land
He gave him the rights of it all in his hand.

Becauſe thou art loving and kind to thy wife,
I'll make thy days eaſy the reſt of thy life;
I give it for ever to thee and thy heirs,
So hold thy induſtry with diligent cares.

No tongue then was able their joy to expreſs,
Their tokens of love, and their true thankfulneſs;
And many a low humble bow to the ground:
But ſuch Noblemen there's but few to be found

# The Posie.

Written for this Work by Robert Burns.

373

O luve will venture in where it daur na weel be
Slow
seen, O luve will venture in where wisdom ance has been but
I will down yon ri_ver rove, amang the wood sae green, And
a' to pu' a posie to my ain dear May.

The primrose I will pu', the firstling o' the year;
And I will pu' the pink, the emblem o' my Dear,
For she is the pink o' womankind, and blooms without a peer;
And a' to be a posie to my ain dear May.

I'll pu' the budding rose when Phebus peeps in view,
For it's like a baumy kiss o' her sweet, bonie mou;
The hyacinth's for constancy wi' its unchanging blue,
And a' to be a posie to my ain dear May.

The lily it is pure, and the lily it is fair,
And in her lovely bosom I'll place the lily there;
The daisy's for simplicity and unaffected air,
And a' to be a posie to my ain dear May.

The hawthorn I will pu', wi' it's locks o' siller grey,
Where like an aged man it stands at break o' day,
But the songster's nest within the bush I winna tak away;
And a' to be a posie to my ain dear May.

The woodbine I will pu' when the e'ening star is near,
And the diamond draps o' dew shall be her een sae clear;
The violet's for modesty which weel she fa's to wear,
And a' to be a posie to my ain dear May.

I'll tie the posie round wi' the silken band o' luve,
And I'll place it in her breast, and I'll swear by a' abuve,
That to my latest draught o' life the band shall ne'er remuve,
And this will be a posie to my ain dear May.

B

# The Banks o' Doon.

Written for this Work by Robert Burns.

374

Ye Banks and braes o' bo_nie Doon, How
can ye bloom ſae freſh and fair; How can ye chant, ye little
birds, And I ſae weary fu' o' care! Thou'll break my heart thou
warbling bird, That wantons thro' the flowering thorn: Thou minds me
o' de_par_ted joys, De_parted ne_ver to return.

Slow & tender

Oft hae I rov'd by bonie Doon,
To ſee the roſe and woodbine twine;
And ilka bird ſang o' its luve,
And fondly ſae did I o' mine.
Wi' lightſome heart I pu'd a roſe,
Fu' ſweet upon its thorny tree;
And my fauſe luver ſtaw my roſe,
But, ah! he left the thorn wi' me.

# Donocht-Head.

375

*
Keen blaws the wind o'er Donocht-head, The ſnaw drives
Slow
ſnelly thro' the dale, The Gaber-lunzie tirls my ſneck, And ſhivering
tells his waefu' tale. Cauld is the night, O let me in, And
dinna let your Minſtrel fa', And din-na let his win-din
ſheet, Be nae-thing but a wreath o' ſnaw.


Full ninety winters hae I ſeen,
And pip'd where gor-cocks whirring flew,
And mony a day ye've danc'd, I ween,
To lilts which frae my drone I blew.
My Eppie wak'd, and ſoon ſhe cry'd,
Get up, Guidman, and let him in;
For weel ye ken the winter night
Was ſhort when he began his din.

My Eppies voice, O wow it's ſweet!
E'en tho' ſhe bans and ſcaulds a wee;
But when it's tun'd to ſorrow's tale,
O haith, it's doubly dear to me.
Come in, auld Carl! I'll ſteer my fire,
I'll mak it bleeze a bonie flame;
Your blude is thin, ye've tint the gate,
Ye ſhould na ſtray ſae far frae hame.

Nae hame have I, the Minſtrel ſaid,
Sad party-ſtrife o'erturnd my ha';
And, weeping at the eve o' life,
I wander thro' a wreath o' ſnaw.

+ + + + + + + + + + + + + + + + + + +

## Sic a wife as Willie had.

Written for this Work by Robert Burns

376

*
Willie Waſtle dwalt on Tweed, The ſpot they ca'd it
Slowiſh
Linkumdoddie; Willie was a wabſter gude, Cou'd ſtown a clue wi'
o_ny bodie; He had a wife was dour and din, O
Tink_ler Maid_gie was her mith_er, Sic a wife as
Willie had I wad na gie a button for her.

She has an e'e, ſhe has but ane,
  The cat has twa the very colour;
Five ruſty teeth forbye a ſtump,
  A clapper tongue wad deave a miller;
A whiſkin beard about her mou,
  Her noſe and chin they threaten ither;
Sic a wife as Willie had,
  I wad na gie a button for her.

She's bow_hough'd, ſhe's hem ſhin'd,
  Ae limpin leg a hand breed ſhorter;
She's twiſted right ſhe's twiſted left,
  To balance fair in ilka quarter:

She has a hump upon her breaſt,
  The twin o' that upon her ſhouther;
Sic a wife as Willie had,
  I wad na gie a button for her.

Auld baudrans by the ingle ſits,
  An' wi' her loof her face a waſhin;
But Willie's wife is nae ſae trig,
  She dights her grunzie wi' a huſhion
Her walie nieves like midden_creels,
  Her face wad fyle the Logan water;
Sic a wife as Willie had,
  I wad na gie a button for her.

B

## Lady Mary Ann.

377

* O Lady Mary Ann looks o'er the caftle wa', She
Slowifh
faw three bo _ nie boys play _ ing at the ba', The
young _ eft he was the flower amang them a', My
bo _ nie lad _ dies young but he's grow _ in yet.

O Father, O Father, an ye think it fit,
We'll fend him a year to the College yet,
We'll few a green ribban round about his hat,
And that will let them ken he's to marry yet.

Lady Mary Ann was a flower in the dew,
Sweet was its fmell and bonie was its hue,
And the langer it blofsom'd, the fweeter it grew,
For the lily in the bud will be bonier yet.

Young Charlie Cochran was the fprout of an aik,
Bonie, and bloomin and ftraught was its make,
The fun took delight to fhine for its fake,
And it will be the brag o' the foreft yet.

The fimmer is gane when the leaves they were green,
And the days are awa that we hae feen,
But far better days I truft will come again,
For my bonie laddie's young but he's growin yet.

## Such a parcel of rogues in a nation.

378

Slow
Farewell to a' our Scotish fame, Fare weel our ancient glory; Fareweel even to the Scotish name, Sae fam'd in martial sto_ry. Now Sark rins o'er the Sol_way sands, And Tweed rins to the oc_ean To mark where Englands province stands, Such a parcel of rogues in a nation.

What force or guile could not subdue,
Thro' many warlike ages,
Is wrought now by a coward few,
For hireling traitors wages.
The English steel we could disdain,
Secure in valour's station;
But English gold has been our bane,
Such a parcel of rogues in a nation!

O would, or I had seen the day
That treason thus could fell us,
My auld grey head had lien in clay
Wi' Bruce and loyal Wallace!
But pith & power, till my last hour,
I'll mak this declaration;
We're bought & sold for English gold
Such a parcel of rogues in a nation.

## Kellyburnbraes.

Written for this Work by Robert Burns.

379

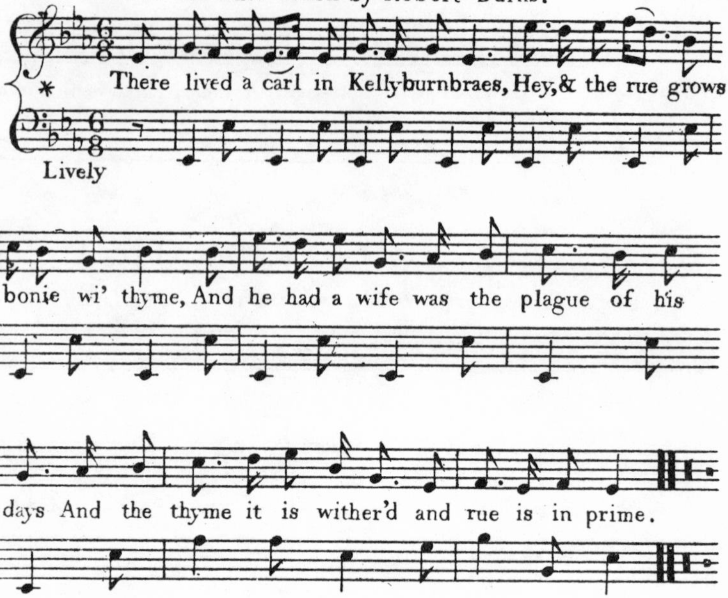
*
There lived a carl in Kellyburnbraes, Hey, & the rue grows
Lively
bonie wi' thyme, And he had a wife was the plague of his
days And the thyme it is wither'd and rue is in prime.

Ae day as the carl gaed up the lang_glen,
  Hey and the rue grows bonie wi' thyme;
He met wi' the d_v_l, ſays, how do ye ſen?
  And the thyme it is wither'd and rue is in prime.

I've got a bad wife, Sir, that's a' my complaint,
  Hey, &c.
For, ſaving your preſence, to her ye're a ſaint,
  And, &c.

It's neither your ſtot nor your ſtaig I ſhall crave,
  Hey, &c.
But gie me your wife, man, for her I muſt have,
  And, &c.

O, welcomemoſt kindly! the blythe carl ſaid;
  Hey, &c.
But if ye can match her _ ye're waur than ye're ca'd,
  And, &c.

The d_v_l has got the auld wife on his back,
  Hey, &c.
And like a poor pedlar he's carried his pack,
  And, &c.

Continued.

He's carried her hame to his ain hallan-door,
Hey, &c.
Syne bade her gae in for a b- - and a w- -
And, &c.

Then ſtraight he makes fifty, the pick o' his band,
Hey, &c.
Turn out on her guard in the clap of a hand,
And, &c.

The carlin gaed thro' them like ony wud bear,
Hey, &c.
Whae'er ſhe gat hands on, cam near her nae mair,
And, &c.

A reekit, wee deevil looks over the wa',
Hey, &c.
O help, Maſter, help! or ſhe'll ruin us a',
And, &c.

The d-v-l he ſwore by the edge o' his knife,
Hey, &c.
He pitied the man that was ty'd to a wife,
And, &c.

The d-v-l he ſwore by the kirk and the bell,
Hey, &c.
He was not in wedlock, thank Heaven, but in h -,
And, &c.

Then Satan has travell'd again wi' his pack,
Hey, &c.
And to her auld huſband he's carried her back,
And, &c.

I hae been a d-v l the feck o' my life,
Hey and the rue grows bonie wi' thyme;
But ne'er was in h-ll till I met wi' a wife,
An' the thyme it is wither'd, and rue is in prime.

## Evanthe.

380

When dear E_vanthe we were young, As genial nature
fresh and gay, To me these melting notes you fung, More
fweet than Phi_lo_mela's lay. But cruel time with en_vious
wing, Blafts every charm that decks our year, With pleafure you no
longer fing, No longer I with tranfport hear.

Tho unexprefsed by human hands
For art efsays the tafk in vain,
Deep on my foul infcribed it ftands,
And ftill I feel the potent ftrain
Should fancy lofe the enchanting found,
Your heavenly voice fo fweet & clear,
Alone could chain the echoes round,
And give it to my lift'ning ear

From nerve to nerve thro' all my frame,
With more than magic force, it darts,
And all the power of youthful flame,
To frozen age at once imparts
But tho' lifes winter now fevere,
To hurt us all it's plagues may bring
Once more with tranfport I fhall hear
Whilft you once more with pleafure fing

# Jocky fou, and Jenny fain.

381
Joc_ky fou, and Jen_ny fain, Jen_ny was nae
Lively
ill to gain, She was cou_thy, he was kind, Thus the
wo_oer tell'd his mind: Jen_ny I'll nae mair be nice
Gi'e me love at o_ny price, I'll ne'er. prig for
red or white, Love alane can gi'e delight.

Ithers ſeek they kenna what,
Features, carriage, and a' that;
Gie me loove in her I court;
Loove to loove maks a' the ſport.

Colours mingl'd unco fine,
Common motives lang ſinſyne,
Never can engage my loove;
Let my fancy firſt approve.

Let loove ſparkle in her e'e;
Let her loe nae man but me;
That's the tocher gude I prize,
There the Luver's treaſure lies.

Nae the meat, but appetite
Maks our eating a delyt:
Beauty is at beſt deceit
Fancy only kens nae cheat.

## Ay Waking oh.

See another set of this Tune Vol: 3d Page 222.

382

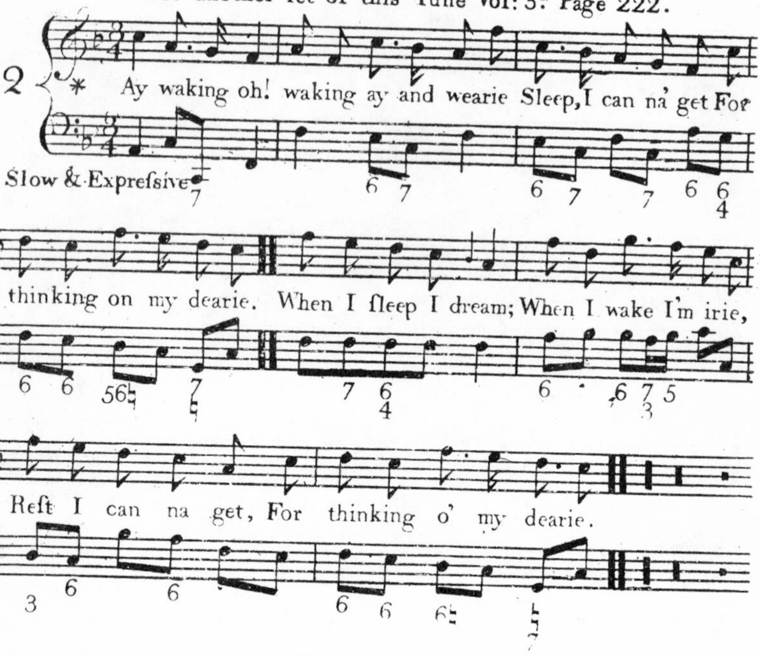

* Ay waking oh! waking ay and wearie Sleep, I can na' get For
Slow & Expressive
thinking on my dearie. When I sleep I dream; When I wake I'm irie,
Rest I can na get, For thinking o' my dearie.


## Patie's Wedding.

383

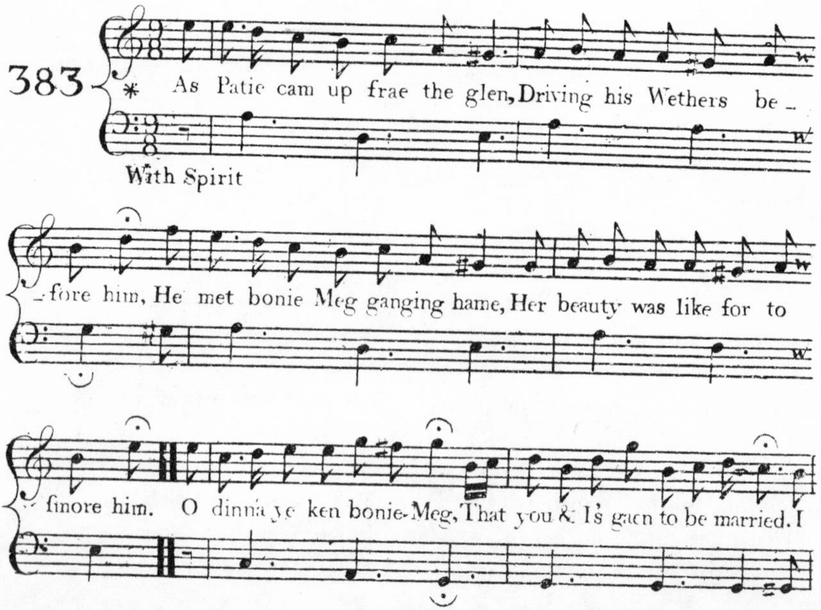

* As Patie cam up frae the glen, Driving his Wethers be-
With Spirit
-fore him, He met bonie Meg ganging hame, Her beauty was like for to
smore him. O dinna ye ken bonie Meg, That you & I's gaen to be married. I

Continued.

rather had broken my leg, Be_fore ſic a bargain miſcarried.

Na Patie_O wha's tell'd you that
  I think that of news they've been ſcanty,
That I ſhould be married ſo ſoon,
  Or yet ſhould hae been ſae flantly:
I winna be married the year,
  Suppoſe I were courted by twenty;
Sae, Patie, ye need nae mair ſpear,
  For weel a wat I dinna want ye.

Now, Meggie, what maks ye ſae ſweer,
  Is't cauſe that I henna a maillin,
The lad that has plenty o' gear
  Need ne'er want a half or a hail ane.
My dad has a good gray mare,
  And yours has twa cows and a filly:
And that will be plenty o' gear,
  Sae Maggie, be no ſae ill_willy.

Indeed, Patie, I dinna ken,
  But firſt ye maun ſpeir at my daddy
You're as well born as Ben,
  And I canna ſay but I'm ready.
There's plenty o' yarn in clues,
  To make me a coat and a jimpy,
And plaiden enough to be trews,
  Gif ye get it, I ſhanna ſcrimp ye.

Now fair fa' ye, my bonny Meg,
  I's let a wee ſmacky fa' on you,
May my neck be as lang as my leg,
  If I be an ill huſband unto you.
Sae gang your way hame e'now,
  Make ready gin this day fifteen days,
And tell your father the news,
  That I'll be his ſon in great kindneſs.

It was nae lang after that,
  Wha came to our bigging but Patie,
Weel dreſt in a braw new coat,
  And wow but he thought himſelf pretty.
His bannet was little frae new,
  In it was a loop and a ſlitty,
To tie in a ribbon ſae blue,
  To bab at the neck o' his coaty.

Then Patie came in wi' a ſtend,
  Said, peace be here to the bigging,
You're welcome, quo' William, come ben,
  Or I wiſh it may rive frae the rigging.
Now draw in your ſeat and ſit down,
  And tell's a' your news in a hurry;
And haſte ye, Meg, and be done,
  And hing on the pan wi' the berry.

Quoth Patie, My news is nae thrang;
  Yeſtreen I was wi' his Honour;
I've taen three riggs of bra' land,
  And hae bound myſel under a bonour.
And now my errant to you
  Is for Meggy to help me to labour
I think you maun gie's the beſt cow,
  Becauſe that our haddin's but ſober

Well, now for to help you through,
  I'll be at the coſt of the bridal;
I'ſe cut the craig of the ewe
  That had amaiſt deid of the ſide.il.
And that 'ill be plenty of bree
  Sae lang as our well is nae reiſted;
To all the good neighbours and we,
  And I think we'll no be that ill feaſted

Quoth Patie, O that'il do well,
  And I'll gie you your broſe in the (morning,
O'kail that was made yeſtreen
  For I like them beſt in the forenoon.
Sae Tam the piper did play,
  And ilka ane danc'd that was willing.
And a' the lave they ranked through,
  And they held the ſtoupy ay filing.

The auld wives ſat and they chew'd,
  And when that the carles grew nappy,
They danc'd as weel as they dow'd,
  Wi' a crack o' their thumbs & a kappie.
The lad that wore the white band,
  I think they cau'd him Jamie Mather,
And he took the bride by the hand,
  And cry'd to play up Maggie Lauder.

# The Slaves Lament.

384

Slow
It was in sweet Se_ne_gal that my foes did me en_thral, For the lands of Vir_ginia ginia O: Torn from that lovely shore and must never see it more; And a_las I am weary weary O! Torn from that lovely shore, and must never see it more, And a_las I am weary weary O!

All on that charming coast is no bitter snow and frost,
Like the lands of Virginia_ginia O;
There streams forever flow, and there flowers for ever blow,
And alas! I am weary, weary O!
There streams &c.

The burden I must bear, while the cruel scourge I fear,
In the lands of Virginia_ginia O;
And I think on friends most dear with the bitter, bitter tear,
And alas! I am weary, weary O!
And I think &c.

## Orananaoig or, The Song of death.

Written for this Work by Robert Burns. A Gaelic Air.

385

Very Slow
Farewell, thou fair day; thou green earth; and ye ſkies, Now
gay with the broad ſetting ſun! Farewell, loves and friendſhips, ye
dear ten_der ties! Our race of ex_iſ_tence is run.
Thou grim king of terrors, Thou life's gloomy foe, Go frighten the
coward and ſlave! Go teach them to tremble, fell tyrant!, but
know, No terrors haſt thou to the Brave.

Thou ſtrik'st the dull peaſant, he ſinks in the dark,
  Nor ſaves e'en the wreck of a name:
Thou ſtrik'st the young hero, a glorious mark.
  He falls in the blaze of his fame.
In the field of proud honor, our ſwords in our hands,
  Our King and our Country to ſave,
While victory ſhines on life's laſt ebbing ſands,
  O, who would not die with the Brave!

## Afton Water.

Written for this Work by Robert Burns.

386

* Flow gently ſweet Afton a_mong thy green braes,
Slow & tender
Flow gently, I'll ſing thee a ſong in thy praiſe; My
Mary's a_ſleep by thy mur_mur_ing ſtream, Flow
gently, ſweet Af_ton, diſ_turb not her dream.

Thou ſtock dove whoſe echo reſounds thro' the glen,
Ye wild whiſtling blackbirds in yon thorny den,
Thou green creſted lapwing thy ſcreaming forbear,
I charge you diſturb not my ſlumbering Fair.

How lofty, ſweet Afton, thy neighbouring hills,
Far mark'd with the courſes of clear, winding rills;
There daily I wander as noon riſes high,
My flocks and my Mary's ſweet Cot in my eye.

How pleaſant thy banks and green vallies below,
Where wild in the woodlands the primroſes blow;
There oft as mild ev'ning weeps over the lea,
The ſweet ſcented birk ſhades my Mary and me.

Thy chryſtal ſtream, Afton, how lovely it glides,
And winds by the cot where my Mary reſides;
How wanton thy waters her ſnowy feet lave,
As gathering ſweet flowerets ſhe ſtems thy clear wave.

Flow gently, ſweet Afton, among thy green braes,
Flow gently, ſweet River, the theme of my lays;
My Mary's aſleep by thy murmuring ſtream,
Flow gently, ſweet Afton, diſturb not her dream. B.

# Bonie Bell.

Written for this Work by Robert Burns.

387

*
The ſmiling ſpring comes in re_joicing, And ſurly winter
Slow
grimly flies; Now cryſtal clear are the falling waters, And bonny
blue are the ſunny ſkies. Freſh o'er the mountains breaks forth the
morning, The ev'ning gilds the Ocean's ſwell; All Creatures joy in the
ſun's returning, And I rejoice in my Bonie Bell.

The flowery Spring leads ſunny Summer,
And yellow Autumn preſses near,
Then in his turn comes gloomy Winter,
Till ſmiling Spring again appear.
Thus ſeaſons dancing, life advancing,
Old Time and Nature their changes tell,
But never ranging, ſtill unchanging,
I adore my Bonie Bell.

## Green Sleeves.

388

* Ye watchful guardians of the fair, Who ſkiff on wings of
Lively
ambient air, of my dear Delia take a care, And repreſent her
lover. With all the gai_e_ty of youth, With
hon_our juſt_ice, love and truth; Till I return, her
paſsions ſoothe, For me in whiſpers move her.

Be careful no baſe ſordid ſlave,
With ſoul ſunk in a golden grave,
Who knows no virtue but to ſave,
With glaring gold bewitch her.
Tell her, for me ſhe was deſign'd,
For me who know how to be kind,
And have mair plenty in my mind,
Than ane who's ten times richer.

Let all the warld turn upſide down,
And fools run an eternal round,
In queſt of what can ne'er be found,
To pleaſe their vain ambition;
Let little minds great charms eſpy,
In ſhadows which at diſtance ly,
Whoſe hop'd-for pleaſure when come nigh,
Proves nothing in fruition:

But caſt into a mold divine,
Fair Delia does with luſtre ſhine,
Her virtuous ſoul's an ample mine,
Which yields a conſtant treaſure.
Let poets in ſublimeſt lays,
Employ their ſkill her fame to raiſe;
Let ſons of muſic paſs whole days,
With well-tun'd reeds to pleaſe her.

# The Gallant Weaver.

Written for this Work by Robert Burns.

389
*
Slowifh.
Where Cart rins rowin to the fea, By mony a flow'r and
fpreading tree, There lives a lad, the lad for me, He is a
gallant Weaver. Oh I had woo_ers aught or nine, They
gied me rings and ribbons fine; And I was fear'd my
heart would tine, And I gied it to the Weaver.

My daddie fign'd my tocher_band
To gie the lad that has the land,
But to my heart I'll add my hand,
And give it to the Weaver.
While birds rejoice in leafy bowers;
While bees delight in opening flowers;
While corn grows green in fimmer fhowers,
I love my gallant Weaver.

## Sleepy Body.

390

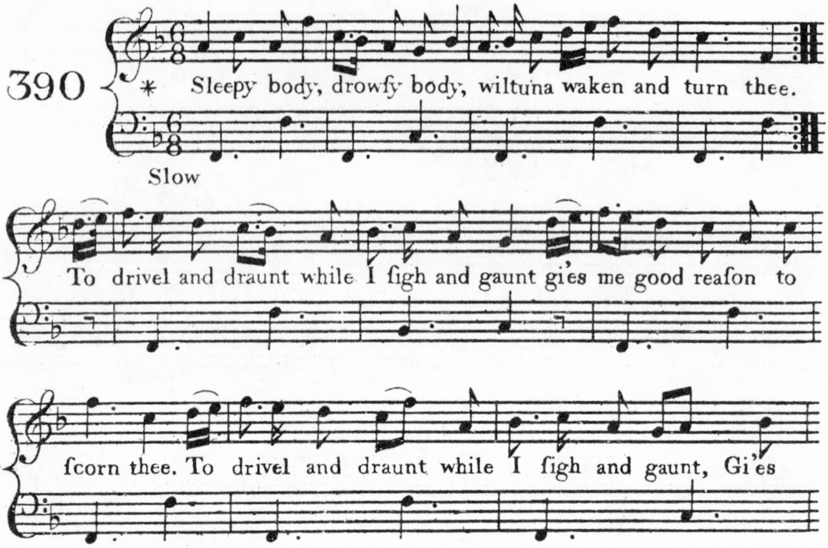
* Sleepy body, drowfy body, wiltuna waken and turn thee.
Slow
To drivel and draunt while I figh and gaunt gies me good reafon to
fcorn thee. To drivel and draunt while I figh and gaunt, Gi'es

me good reafon to fcorn thee.

When thou fhouldft be kind,
Thou turns fleepy and blind,
And fnoters and fnores far frae me.
Wae light on thy face,
Thy drowfy embrace
Is enough to gar me betray thee.

## I love my Jovial Sailor.

391

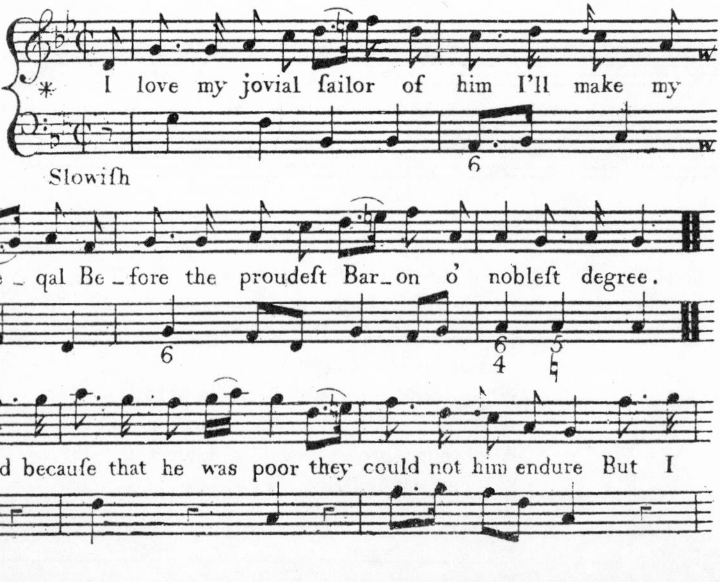
* I love my jovial failor of him I'll make my
Slowifh
e _ qal Be _ fore the proudeft Bar _ on o' nobleft degree.
And becaufe that he was poor they could not him endure But I

Continued.

love him mair and mair he's a dear boy to me.

Tho' he maun face the cannon amid the line o' battle,
Forby the mony dangers upon the roaring ſea
Yet I truſt the Heavenly Power will ſhield him in that hour,
And ſafe and ſound return him, my dear boy, to me.

## Hey Ca' thro'.

392
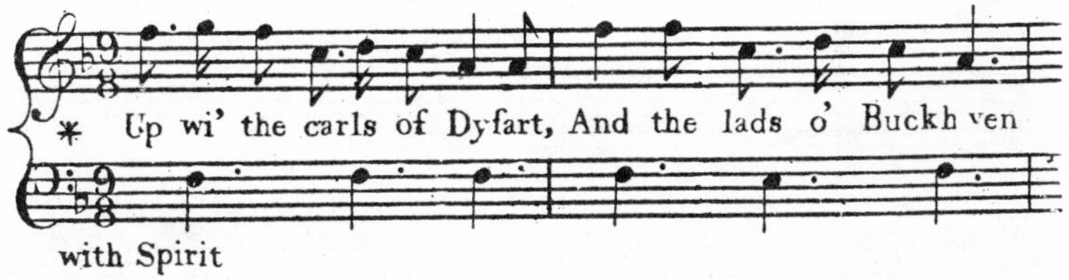
* Up wi' the carls of Dyſart, And the lads o' Buckh ven
with Spirit

And the Kim_mers o' Lar_go, And the laſses o' Leven.
Hey ca' thro' ca' thro' For we hae mic_kle a do,
Hey ca' thro' ca' thro' for we hae mickle a do.

We hae tales to tell,
And we hae ſangs to ſing;
We hae pennies to ſpend,
And we hae pints to bring.
Hey ca' thro', &c.

We'll live a' our days,
And them that comes behin',
Let them do the like,
And ſpend the gear they win.
Hey ca thro', &c.

## While hopeless, &c.

393
While hopeless and al_most re_duc'd to despair, Yet
even in my anguish some comfort I find; Tho' remov'd from the
smiles of the maid I ad_mire, Her i_de_a alone can give
ease to my mind. Why then should I pine, and in_dulge thus
my grief, Tho' Fortune at present seems rather to frown. with
calm re_sig_nation I'll wait for re__lief, She
yet with success all my wishes may crown.

## O can ye labor lea, young man.

394

Slow
O can ye labor lea, young man, O can ye labor lea; Gae
back the gate ye came a_gain, ye'se ne_ver ſcorn me. I
feed a man at martin_mas, Wi' airle_pen_nies three; But
a' the faute I had to him, He could na labor lea. O
Chos
can ye labor lea, young man, O can ye labor lea; Gae
back the gate ye came a_gain ye'se never ſcorn me.

O clappin's gude in Febarwar,
An kiſsin's ſweet in May;
But what ſignifies a young man's love,
An't dinna laſt for ay.
O can ye, &c.

O kiſsin is the key o luve,
An clappin is the lock,
An makin_of's the beſt thing,
That e'er a young Thing got.
O can ye, &c.

# On the Death of Delia's Linnet.

395
*
O, all ye loves and groves lament, And you of hearts hu-
Slow
-mane, Our dar-ling lin-nets breath is ſpent, And all our
tears are vain. Its' ſweet-ly var-ied voice no
more, Shall ſtrike my Del-ia's ear, It viſits now the
Stygian ſhore, Whence no re-turns are here.

Sweet bird! whoſe quick inſtinctive ſenſe,
As well my Delia knew,
As ſhe her mother. far from hence
You prematurely flew
No more ſhalt thou expecting ſtand,
From her a boon to wait;
No more pick ſugar from her hand,
Detaind by cruel fate.

No more when danger threatens nigh,
Shall thou aſcend the wind,
To Delia's gentle boſom fly,
There ſweet aſylum find. -

For ever ſtopt thy buſy-wing
Thy tongue in ſilence lies,
No kind return of grateful ſpring
Again ſhall bid thee riſe.

Torpid and cold, thy beauteous frame,
Our ſight no more ſhall charm;
Thy loſs the deepeſt woe ſhall claim,
The brighteſt eyes diſarm.
Long ſhall my Delia mourn thy doom
With undiſſembl'd woe,
Before her clouded charms reſume;
Their animating glow.

## The Deuks dang o'er my daddie.

Written for this Work by Robert Burns.

396

* The bairns gat out wi' an un_co fhout, The deuks dang
Lively
o'er my daddie O! The fien_ma_care, quo' the feirrie auld wife,. He
was but a paidlin body, O! He paidles out, and he paidles in, An he
paidles late and ear_ly, O! This feven lang years I hae
lien by his fide, An' he is but a fufionlefs car_lie, O.


O had your tongue, my feirrie auld wife
  O had your tongue, now Nanfie, O:
I've feen the day, and fae hae ye,
  Ye wad na been fae donfie, O.
I've feen the day ye butter'd my brofe,
  And cuddled me late and early, O;
But downa do's come o'er me now,
  And, Oh, I find it fairly, O.

## As I went out ae May morning.

397

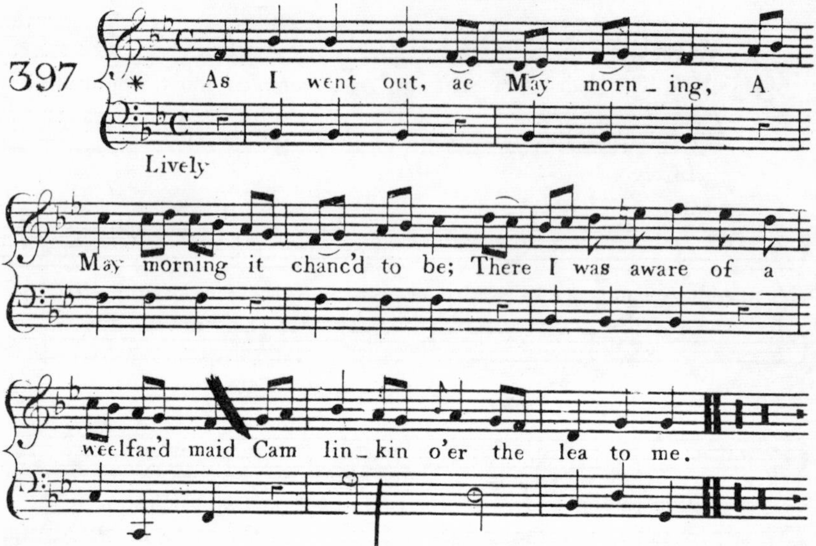
As I went out, ae May morn_ing, A
Lively
May morning it chanc'd to be; There I was aware of a
weelfard maid Cam lin_kin o'er the lea to me.

O but ſhe was a weelfar'd maid,
  The bonieſt laſs that's under the ſun;
I ſpier'd gin ſhe could fancy me,
  But her anſwer was, I am too young.

To be your bride I am too young,
  To be your loun wad ſhame my kin,
So therefore pray young man begone,
  For you never, never ſhall my favour win.

But amang yon birks and hawthorns green,
  Where roſes blaw and woodbines hing,
O there I learn'd my bonie laſs,
  That ſhe was not a ſingle hour too young.

The laſsie bluſh'd, the laſsie ſigh'd,
  And the tear ſtood twinklin in her e'e;
O kind Sir, ſince ye hae done me this wrang,
  It's pray when will ye marry me.

It's of that day tak ye nae heed,
  For that's a day ye ne'er ſhall ſee;
For ought that paſs'd between us twa,
  Ye had your ſhare as weel as me.

She wrang her hands, ſhe tore her hair,
  She cried out moſt bitterlie,
O what will I ſay to my mammie
  When I gae hame wi' my big bellie!

O as ye maut, ſo maun ye brew,
  And as ye brew, ſo maun ye tun;
But come to my arms, my ae bonie laſs,
  For ye never ſhall rue what ye now hae done!

# She's fair and fause, &c.

Written for this Work by Robert Burns.

398
*
Slowish
She's fair and fause that causes my smart, I lo'ed her
meikle and lang; She's broken her vow, She's broken my heart, And
I may e'en gae hang. A coof cam in wi' routh o'
gear, And I hae tint my dearest dear, But women is but
warld's gear, Sae let the bo_nie lass gang.

Whae'er ye be that woman love,
To this be never blind,
Nae ferlie 'tis tho' fickle she prove,
A woman has't by kind:
O woman, lovely woman fair!
An angel form's faun to thy share.
'Twad been o'er meikle to gien thee mair,
I mean an angel mind.

R

# The Deil's awa wi' th' Exciseman.

Written for this Work by Robert Burns.

399

* The deil cam fiddlin thro' the town, And danc'd awa wi' th' Ex_
With Spirit
_cise_man; And il_ka wife cries, auld Ma_houn, I
Chorus
wish you luck o' the prize, man, The deil's a_wa the
deil's awa The deil's awa wi' th' Exciseman, He's danc'd awa he's
danc'd a_wa He's danc'd a_wa wi' th' Ex_cise_man.

We'll mak our maut and we'll brew our drink,
We'll laugh, sing, and rejoice, man;
And mony braw thanks to the meikle black deil,
That danc'd awa wi' th' Exciseman.
The deil's awa, &c.

There's threesome reels, there's foursome reels,
There's hornpipes and strathspeys, man,
But the ae best dance e'er cam to the Land
Was, the deil's awa wi' th' Exciseman.
The deil's awa &c.

## Miſs Weir.

400

O love, thou delights in man's ruin, Thy conqueſts they
Slow
coſt us full dear! Maun I forfeit my life for the viewing The
charms o' that lovely Miſs Weir. Tho' ſometimes thou bid me aſ-
-pire; A-gain thou diſ-tracts me wi' fear, And En-vy o
ane that is higher, Wha's even'd to the charming Miſs Weir.

As down in yon valley a walking,
Whare nae chriſten'd creature was near,
The birds all around me were talking
O' naething but charming Miſs Weir
That ſweet, little bird ca'd the linnet,
In accents delightfully dear,
Declar'd to the world, that in it
Was nought like the lovely Miſs Weir.

O, Cupid, my head it is muddy,
I wiſh it may ever be clear!
For ay when I ſit down to ſtudy,
My mind rins on charming Miſs Weir.
Im toſt like a ſhip on the ocean,
That kens na what courſe for to ſteer,
Yet at times I'm as vain in my notion
As hope for the lovely Miſs Weir.

END OF VOLUME FOURTH.

# THE SCOTS Musical Museum

Consisting of Six hundred Scots Songs

with proper Basses for the

PIANO FORTE &c.

Humbly Dedicated

To the Society

of

Antiquaries of Scotland

BY JAMES JOHNSON

*In this publication the original simplicity of our Ancient National Airs is retained unincumbered with useless Accompaniments & graces depriving the hearers of the sweet simplicity of their native melodies.*

Volume 5 Pr. 7s

Butterworth Scripsit

Printed & Sold by JAMES JOHNSON Music Seller EDINBURGH to be had at T. PRESTON N.º 97 Strand LONDON. M.c FADYEN GLASGOW. & at all the principal Music Sellers.

# PREFACE.

AT the time the Editor publiſhed the $4^{th}$ Volume of this Work, he had every reaſon to believe that five Volumes would be ſufficient to contain all thoſe Scots Songs the merit of which called for publication; But, owing to the exertions of the late celebrated Scottiſh Bard, the Work has been enlarged far beyond what was originally expected. To attempt to deſcribe the taſte and abilities of Mr. Burns in his Native Poetry, would be abſurd. The Public are in poſseſsion of his productions which loudly proclaim his merit. —To him is the preſent Collection indebted for almoſt all of theſe excellent pieces which it contains. He has not only enriched it with a variety of beautiful and original Songs compoſed by himſelf, but his zeal for the ſucceſs of the Scots Muſical Muſeum prompted him to collect and write out accurate Copies of many others in their genuine ſimplicity —Prior to his deceaſe, he furniſhed the Editor with a number, in addition to thoſe already publiſhed, greater than can be included in one Volume —To withhold theſe from the public eye, would be moſt improper. And the Editor therefore at the ſolicitation of many of the Subſcribers, has agreed to publiſh them in a Sixth Volume, which moſt certainly will conclude the preſent work. As theſe however will not fill up a Volume, the Editor means to inſert a number of tunes adapted to the Flute, which he is confident many of the Subſcribers will approve of. Thoſe Ladies who Sing and perform upon the Piano Forte, ſhall be furniſhed with the Songs and Muſic for their uſe, at a reduced price, upon application to the Editor.

To ſhew the Public with what extreme anxiety Mr. Burns wiſhed for the ſucceſs of this Work, the Editor cannot refrain from inſerting an Extract of a letter which he received from that admirable Poet a few weeks before his death —In this letter tho' written under the preſsure of affliction, are alone ſeen the fervent ſentiment and poetical language of Burns. The original the Editor will chearfully ſhew to his ſubſcribers

"How are you, my Dear Friend? and how comes on your Fifth Volume?
"You may probably think that for ſome time paſt I have neglected you &
"your work; but, alas, the hand of pain, and ſorrow, and care has theſe
"many months lain heavy on me! Perſonal and domeſtic affliction have
"almoſt entirely baniſhed that alacrity and life with which I uſed to woo
"the rural Muſe of Scotia. —In the mean time, let us finiſh what we have
"ſo well begun. —The gentleman, Mr. L——s, a particular friend of mine,
"will bring out any proofs (if they are ready) or any meſsage you may
"have. "Farewel!

"R. BURNS."

"You ſhould have had this when Mr. L—s called on you, but his ſaddle-
"bags miſcarried. —I am extremely anxious for your work, as indeed I
"am for every thing concerning you and your welfare, - - - - - - -
" - - - - - - - - - - - - - - - - - - - - - -
"Many a merry meeting this Publication has given us, and poſsibly it may
"give us more, though alas! I fear it —This protracting, ſlow, conſuming
"illneſs which hangs over me, will, I doubt much, my ever dear friend,
"arreſt my ſun before he has well reached his middle carreer, and will

"turn

"turn over the Poet to far other and more important concerns then ſtu-"-dying the brilliancy of Wit, or the pathos of Sentiment. _However, "Hope is the cordial of the human heart, and I endeavour to cheriſh it "as well as I can _Let me hear from you as ſoon as convenient. _ "Your work is a great one; and though, now that it is near finiſhed, I "ſee if we were to begin again, two or three things that might be mend-"ed, yet I will venture to propheſy that to future ages your Publication "will be the text book and ſtandard of Scotiſh Song and Muſic.
" - - - - - - - - "Yours ever - - _R. BURNS."

Note. The Songs in the four preceding Volumes marked B. R. X. and Z. and the Authors' names, cannot be inſerted in this Index, as the Editor does not know the names of thoſe Gentlemen who have favoured the Public and him with their Productions. There are a number marked B. and R. which the Editor is certain are Burns's compoſition.

# INDEX TO VOLUME FIFTH.

First line of each Song. Page

# INDEX.

# INDEX.

# The Lovely Lass of Inverness.

Written for this Work by Robert Burns.

No 401

*
Slow
The love_ly lass o' In_ver_ness Nae joy nor pleasure can she see; For e'en and morn she cries, A_las! And ay the saut tear blins her e'e. Drum_os_sie moor, Drum_os_sie day, A waefu' day it was to me; For there I lost my father dear, My fa_ther dear and brethren three.

Their winding sheet the bludy clay,
  Their graves are growing green to see;
And by them lies the dearest lad
  That ever blest a woman's e'e!
Now wae to thee thou cruel lord,
  A bludy man I trow thou be;
For mony a heart thou has made fair
  That ne'er did wrang to thine or thee!

# A red red Rose.

Written for this Work by Robert Burns.

402

*
Slow
O my Luve's like a red, red rose, That's
new_ly sprung in June; O My Luve's like the
me_lo_die That's sweet_ly play'd in tune. As
fair art thou, my bon_ie lass, So deep in luve am
I; And I will luve thee still, my dear, Till
a' the seas gang dry. Till a' the seas, gang dry, my
Dear, And the rocks melt wi' the sun: O I will love thee

## Continued

ſtill my dear, While the ſands o' life ſhall run.

## Old Set, _Red red Roſe.

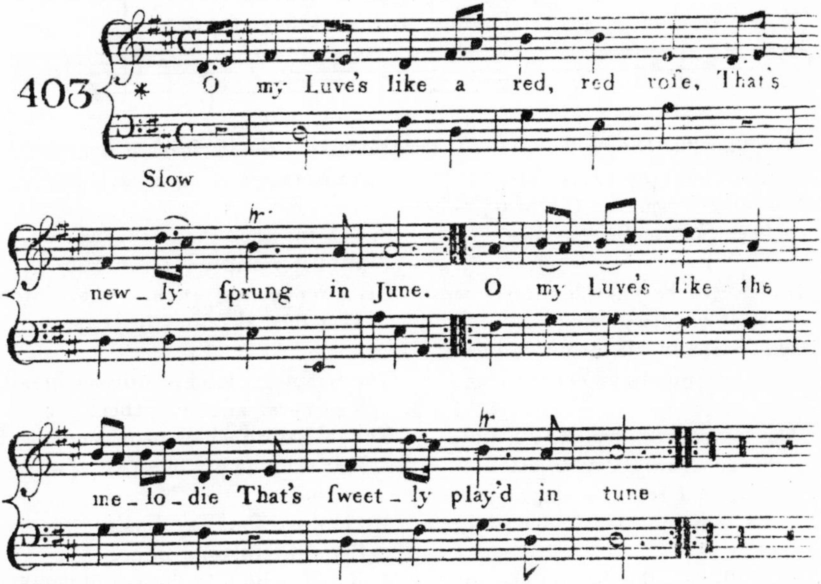
403
O my Luve's like a red, red roſe, That's
Slow
new _ ly ſprung in June. O my Luve's like the
me _ lo _ die That's ſweet _ ly play'd in tune

As fair art thou, my bonie laſs,
So deep in luve am I;
And I will love thee ſtill, my Dear,
Till a' the ſeas gang dry.

Till a' the ſeas gang dry, my Dear,
And the rocks melt wi' the ſun:
I will love thee ſtill, my Dear,
While the ſands o' life ſhall run:

And fare thee weel, my only Luve!
And fare thee weel, a while!
And I will come again, my Luve,
Tho' it wa'e ten thouſand mile!

# Mary Queen of Scots Lament.

Written for this Work by Robert Burns.

404

Now nature hangs her mantle green On ilka blooming
Slow
tree, And ſpreads her ſheets o' daiſies white Out o'er the graſsy lea.

Now Phoebus chears the cryſtal ſtreams,
And glads the azure ſkies;
But nought can glad the weary wight
That faſt in durance lies

Now laverocks wake the merry morn,
Aloft on dewy wing;
The merle, in his noontide bow'r,
Makes woodland echoes ring

The mavis mild wi' many a note,
Sings drowſy day to reſt:
In love and freedom they rejoice,
Wi' care nor thrall oppreſt.

Now blooms the lily by the bank,
The primroſe down the brae;
The haw horn's budding in the glen,
And milk-white is the ſlae:

The meaneſt hind in fair Scotland
May rove their ſweets amang;
But I, the Queen of a' Scotland,
Maun lie in priſon ſtrang.

I was the Queen o' bonie France,
Where happy I hae been;
Fu' lightly raſe I in the morn,
As blythe lay down at e'en:

And I'm the ſov'reign of Scotland,
And mony a traitor there;
Yet here I lie in foreign bands,
And never ending care.

But as for thee, thou falſe woman,
My ſiſter and my fae,
Grim vengeance, yet, ſhall whet a ſword
That thro' thy ſoul ſhall gae:

The weeping blood in womans breaſt
Was never known to thee;
Nor th' balm that draps on wounds of woe
Frae woman's pitying e'e.

My ſon! my ſon! may kinder ſtars
Upon thy fortune ſhine:
And may thoſe pleaſures gild thy reign,
That ne'er wad blink on mine!

God keep thee frae thy mother's faes,
Or turn their hearts to thee:
And where thou meet'ſt thy mother's friend,
Remember him for me!

O! ſoon, to me, may ſummer-ſuns
Nae mair light up the morn!
Nae mair, to me, the autumn winds,
Wave o'er the yellow corn!

And in the narrow houſe o' death
Let winter round me rave;
And the next flow'rs, that deck the ſpring,
Bloom on my peaceful grave.

# A Laſsie all alone.

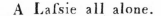

Recitative, Written by Robt. Burns. Tune, Cumnock Pſalms

405

* As I ſtood by yon roofleſs tower, Where the wa' flower ſcents the
in time, very Slow
dewy air, Where the houlet mourns in her i_vy bower, And tells the
Chorus
midnight moon her care. A laſsie all alone was making her moan, La
_menting our lads, beyond the ſea; In the bluidy wars they fa' and our
in time very Slow.
honor's gane and a', And broken-hearted we maun die.

The winds were laid, the air was ſtill,
The ſtars they ſhot alang the ſky;
The tod was howling on the hill,
And the diſtant-echoing glens reply.
A laſsie, &c.

The burn, adown its hazelly path,
Was ruſhing by the ruin'd wa's,
Haſting to join the ſweeping Nith
Whaſe roarings ſeem'd to riſe and fa'.
A laſsie, &c.

The cauld blae north was ſtreaming forth
Her lights, wi' hiſsing, eerie din;
Athort the lift they ſtart and ſhift,
Like Fortune's favors, tint as win.
A laſsie, &c.

Now, looking over firth and fauld,
Her horn the pale-fac'd Cynthia rear'd,
When, lo, in form of Minſtrel auld,
A ſtern and ſtalwart ghaiſt appear'd.
A laſsie, &c.

And frae his harp ſic ſtrains did flow,
Might rous'd the ſlumbering Dead to hear;
But oh, it was a tale of woe,
As ever met a Briton's ear.
A laſsie, &c.

He ſang wi' joy his former day,
He weeping wail'd his latter times;
But what he ſaid it was nae play,
I winna ventur't in my rhymes
A laſsie, &c.

## The Wren's Nest.

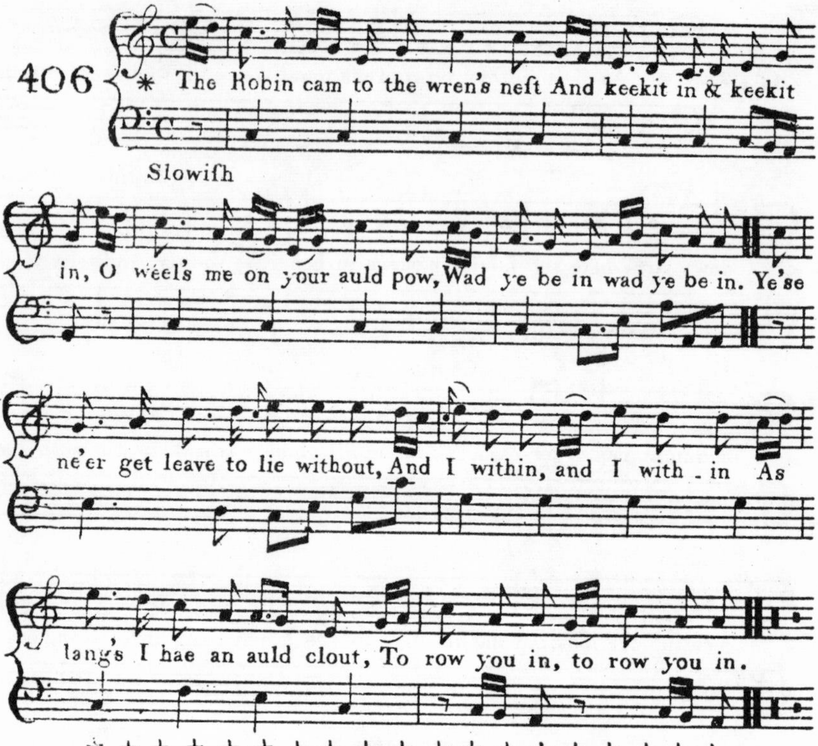
406
* The Robin cam to the wren's neſt And keekit in & keekit
Slowiſh
in, O weel's me on your auld pow, Wad ye be in wad ye be in. Ye'se
ne'er get leave to lie without, And I within, and I with - in As
langs I hae an auld clout, To row you in, to row you in.

## Peggy in Devotion.

407
* Sweet Nymph of my de votion Let thy ſmile my hours be -
Slow
- guile; For care's an idle notion, Then let love be free. Since
nature gave thee beauty, Grant the kiſs, The higheſt bliſs, For

Continued

know it is thy du _ ty Lif _ ten girl to me.

## Jamie o' the glen.

408

Auld Rob the laird o' muckle land, to woo me was nae very
blate, But fpite o' a' his gear he fand, He came to woo, a day o'er late.
A lad fae blyth, fae full o' glee, My heart did never never ken, &c.
nane can gie fic joy to me, as Jamie o' the glen.

My minny grat like daft and rar'd,
To gar me wi' her will comply.
But ftill I wadna hae the laird
Wi'a' his oufen, fheep, and kye
A lad fae blyth, &c.

Ah what are filks and fattins bra
What's a' his warldly gear to me.
They're daft that caft themfelves awa
Where nae content or luve can be.
A lad fae blyth &c.

I cou'd na bide the filly clafh
Cam hourly frae the gawky laird.
And fae to ftop his gab and fafh
Wi Jamie to the kirk repair'd.
A lad fae blyth, &c.

Now ilka fimmer's day fae lang,
And winter's clad wi' froft and fnaw
A tunefu' lilt and bonny fang
Ay keep dull care and ftrife awa.
A lad fae blyth, &c.

# O gin ye were dead Gudeman.

409

*
O an ye were dead Gudeman A green turf on your
Lively
head gudeman, I wad beſtow my widowhood up_on a ranton Highland-
-man. There's ſax eggs in the pan gudeman, There's ſax eggs in the pan
gudeman There's ane to you, and twa to me, & three to our John Highland
Chorus
man. O an ye were dead gudeman, A green turf on your head gude_
_man, I wad beſtow my widowhood up_on a ranton Highlandman.

A ſheep-head's in the pot, gudeman,
A ſheep-head's in the pot, gudeman;
The fleſh to him the broo to me,
An the horns become your brow, gudeman.
Cho^s. Sing round about the fire wi' a rung ſhe ran,
An round about the fire wi' a rung ſhe ran:
Your horns ſhall tie you to the ſtaw,
And I ſhall bang your hide, gudeman.

## My Wife has taen the gee.

410
* A friend o' mine came here yeſ_ treen, And
he wad hae me down, To drink a pot of ale wi' him, In
the nieſt borrows town; But oh, alake! it was the waur, And
ſair the waur for me; For lang or e'er that I came
hame, My wife had taen the gee.

We ſat ſae late, and drank ſae ſtout,
The truth I tell to you,
That lang or ever midnight came,
We were a' roaring fou.
My wife ſits at the fire-ſide;
And the tear blinds ay her ee,
The ne'er a bed will ſhe gae to;
But ſit and tak the gee.

In the morning ſoon, when I came down,
The ne'er a word ſhe ſpake;
But mony a ſad and ſour look,
And ay her head ſhe'd ſhake.

My dear, quoth I, what aileth thee,
To look ſae ſour on me?
I'll never do the like again,
If you'll ne'er tak the gee.

When that ſhe heard, ſhe ran, ſhe flang
Her arms about my neck
And twenty kiſses in a crack,
And, poor wee thing, ſhe grat.
If you'll neer do the like again,
But bide at hame wi me
I'll lay my life Iſe be the wife
That's never tak the gee.

## Tam Lin.

411

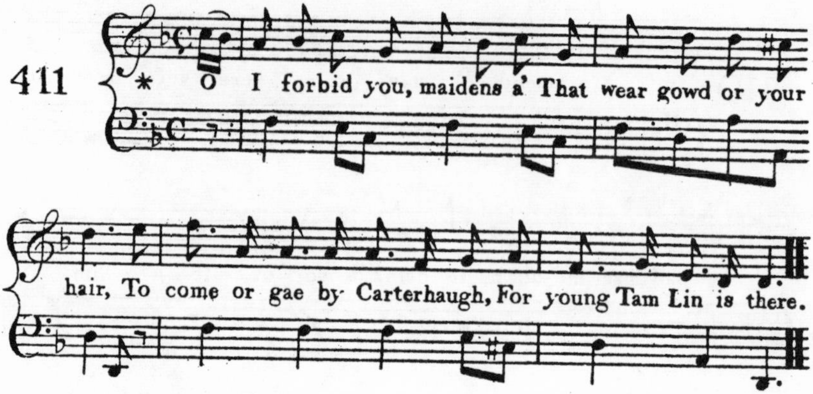
*
O I forbid you, maidens a' That wear gowd or your
hair, To come or gae by Carterhaugh, For young Tam Lin is there.

There's nane that gaes by Carterhaugh
  But they leave him a wad;
Either their rings, or green mantles,
  Or elſe their maidenhead.

Janet has belted her green kirtle,
  A little aboon her knee,
And ſhe has broded her yellow hair
  A little aboon her bree;

And ſhe's awa to Carterhaugh
  As faſt as ſhe can hie,
When ſhe came to Carterhaugh
  Tom-Lin was at the well,

And there ſhe fand his ſteed ſtanding
  But away was himſel.
She had na pu'd a double roſe
  A roſe but only twa,

Till up then ſtarted young Tam-Lin,
  Says, Lady, thou's pu' nae mae.
Why pu's thou the roſe, Janet,
  And why breaks thou the wand!

Or why comes thou to Carterhaugh
  Withoutten my command?
Carterhaugh it is my ain,
  My daddie gave it me;

I'll come and gang by Carterhaugh
  And aſk nae leave at thee.
Janet has kilted her green kirtle,
  A little aboon her knee,

And ſhe has ſnooded her yellow hair,
  A little aboon her bree,
And ſhe is to her father's ha,
  As faſt as ſhe can hie.

Four and twenty ladies fair,
  Were playing at the ba,
And out then cam the fair Janet,
  Ance the flower amang them a',

Four and twenty ladies fair,
  Were playing at the cheſs,
And out then cam the fair Janet,
  As green as onie glaſs.

Out then ſpak an auld grey knight,
  Lay o'er the caſtle wa',
And ſays, Alas, fair Janet for thee,
  But we'll be blamed a'.

Haud your tongue, ye auld fac'd knight
  Some ill death may ye die,
Father my bairn on whom I will,
  I'll father nane on thee.

Out then ſpak her father dear,
  And he ſpak meek and mild,
And ever alas, ſweet Janet, he ſays,
  I think thou gaes wi' child.

If that I gae wi' child, father,
  Myſel maun bear the blame;
There's ne'er a laird about your ha,
  Shall get the bairn's name.

If my Love were an earthly knight,
  As he's an elfin grey;
I wad na gie my ain true-love
  For nae lord that ye hae.

The ſteed that my true-love rides on,
  Is lighter than the wind;
Wi' ſiller he is ſhod before,
  Wi' burning gowd behind.

## Continued.

Jenet has kilted her green kirtle
A little aboon her knee;
And ſhe has ſnooded her yellow hair
A little aboon her brie;

And ſhe's awa to Carterhaugh
As faſt as ſhe can hie
When ſhe cam to Carterhaugh,
Tam-Lin was at the well;

And there ſhe fand his ſteed ſtanding,
But away was himſel.
She had na pu'd a double roſe,
A roſe but only twa,

Till up then ſtarted young Tam-Lin,
Says, Lady thou pu's nae mae.
Why pu's thou the roſe Janet,
Amang the groves ſae green,

And a' to kill the bonie babe
That we gat us between.
O tell me, tell me, Tam-Lin ſhe ſays,
For's ſake that died on tree,

If e'er ye was in holy chapel,
Or Chriſtendom did ſee.
Roxbrugh he was my grandfather,
Took me with him to bide

And ance it fell upon a day
That wae did me betide.
And ance it fell upon a day,
A cauld day and a ſnell.

When we were frae the hunting come
That frae my horſe I fell.
The queen o' Fairies ſhe caught me,
In yon green hill to dwell,

And pleaſant is the fairy-land;
But, an eerie tale to tell!
Ay at the end of ſeven years
We pay a tiend to hell,

I am ſae fair and fu' o' fleſh
I'm fear'd it be myſel.
But the night is Halloween, lady,
The morn is Hallowday;

Then win me, win me, an ye will,
For weel I wat ye may.
Juſt at the mirk and midnight hour
The fairy folk will ride;

And they that wad their truelove win,
At Mileſcroſs they maun bide.
But how ſhall I thee ken Tam-Lin,
Or how my true love know.

Amang ſae mony unco knights,
The like I never ſaw.
O firſt let paſs the black Lady,
And ſyne let paſs the brown;

But quickly run to the milk white-
Pu ye his rider down. (ſteed,
For I'll ride on the milk-white ſteed,
And ay neareſt the town.

Becauſe I was an earthly knight
They gie me that renown.
My right hand will be glov'd lady,
My left hand will be bare

Cockt up ſhall my bonnet be,
And kaim'd down ſhall my hair,
And thae's the takens I gie thee,
Nae doubt I will be there.

They'll turn me in your arms lady,
Into an eſk and adder,
But hald me faſt and fear me not,
I am your bairn's father.

They'll turn me to a bear ſae grim,
And then a lion bold,
But hold me faſt and feal me not,
As ye ſhall love your child.

Again they'll turn me in your arms,
To a red het gaud of airn.
But hold me faſt and fear me not,
I'll do to you nae harm.

And laſt they'll turn me in your arms,
Into the burning lead;
Then throw me into well water,
O throw me in wi' ſpeed.

And then I'll be your ain true love,
I'll turn a naked knight.
Then cover me wi' your green mantle,
And cover me out o' ſight,

Gloomy, gloomy was the night,
And eerie was the way,
As fair Jenny in her green mantle
To Mileſcroſs ſhe did gae.

About

## Continued.

About the middle o' the night,
She heard the bridles ring;
This lady was as glad at that
As any earthly thing.

Firſt ſhe let the black paſs by,
And ſyne ſhe let the brown;
But quickly ſhe ran to the milk white-ſteed,
And pu'd the rider down.

Sae weel ſhe minded what he did ſay
And young Tam Lin did win;
Syne cover'd him wi' her green mantle
As blythe's a bird in ſpring.

Out then ſpak the queen o' fairies,
Out of a buſh o broom;
Them that has gotten young Tam Lin,
Has gotten a ſtately groom.

Out then ſpak the queen o' fairies,
And an angry queen was ſhe;
Shame betide her ill-far'd face,
And an ill death may ſhe die,

For ſhe's ta'en awa the boniest knight
In a' my companie,
But had I kend Tam Lin, ſhe ſays,
What now this night I ſee.

I wad hae taen out thy twa grey een,
And put in twa een o' tree.

## Here's a Health to them that's awa.

412

Heres a health to them that's a wa here's a health to them that's a _ wa, Here's a health to them that were here ſhort ſyne But can _ a be here the day. Its gude to be merry and wiſe, Its gude to be honeſt & true, Its gude to be aff wi' the auld love be fore ye be on wi' the new.

## Auld lang syne.

413

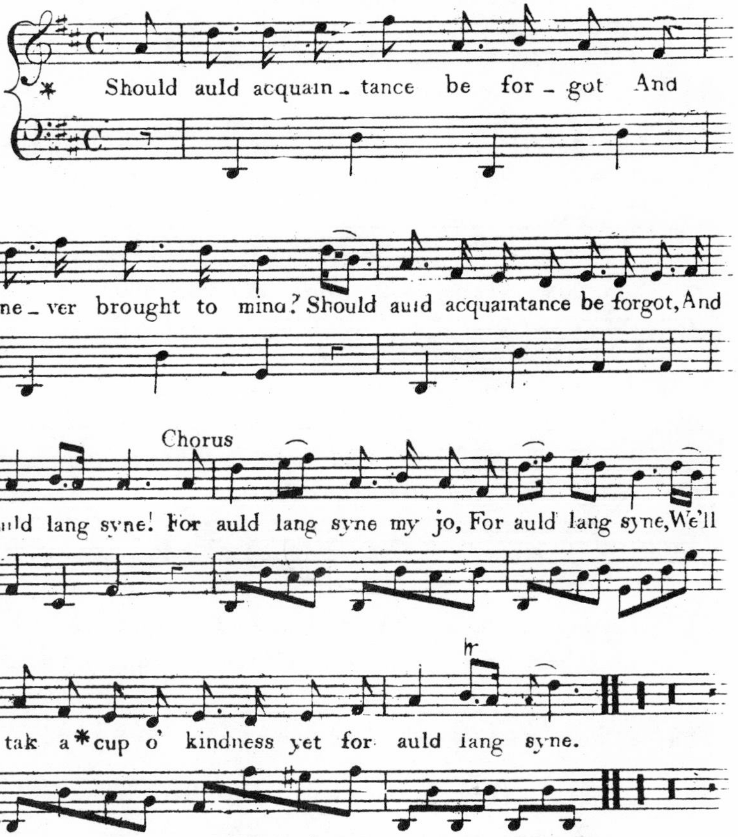
* Should auld acquain_tance be for_got And
ne_ver brought to mind? Should auld acquaintance be forgot, And
Chorus
auld lang syne! For auld lang syne my jo, For auld lang syne, We'll
tak a*cup o' kindness yet for auld lang syne.
tr

And surely ye'll be your pint stowp!
And surely I'll be mine!
And we'll tak a cup o' kindness yet,
For auld lang syne.
For auld, &c.

We twa hae run about the braes,
And pou'd the gowans fine;
But we've wander'd mony a weary fitt,
Sin auld lang syne.
For auld, &c.

We twa hae paidl'd in the burn,
Frae morning sun till dine;
But seas between us braid hae roar'd.
Sin auld lang syne.
For auld, &c.

And there's a hand, my trust fiere!
And gie's a hand o' thine.
And we'll tak a right gude_willie-
For auld lang syne. (waught,
For auld, &c.

* Some Sing, Kifs, in plaee of Cup.

## Louis what reck I by thee.

Written for this Work by Robert Burns.

414

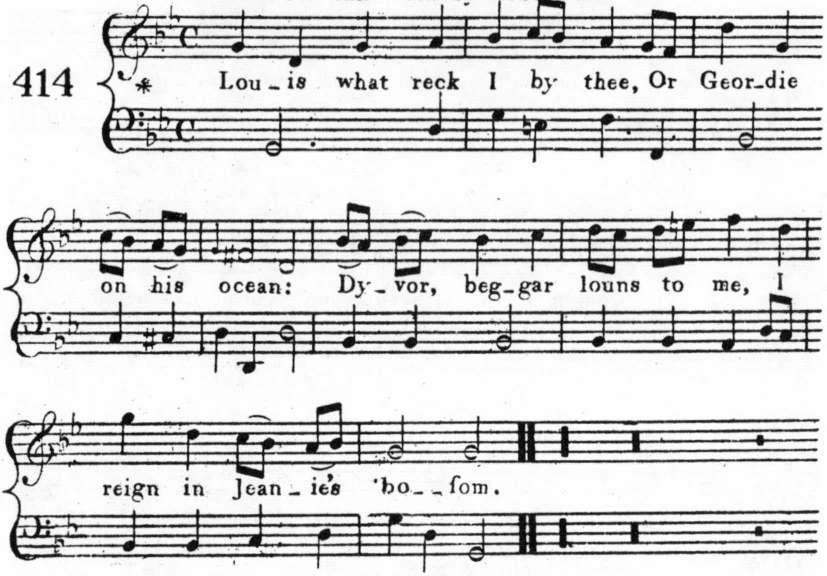
*
Lou_is what reck I by thee, Or Geor_die
on his ocean: Dy_vor, beg_gar louns to me, I
reign in Jean_ies bo__ſom.

Let her crown my love her law, And in her breaſt enthrons me:.
Kings and nations, ſwith awa! Reif randies I diſown ye! _+ + +

R

*·*·*·*·*·*·*·*·*·*·*·*·*·*·*·*·*·*·*·*·*·*·*·*

## Had I the wyte ſhe bad me.

415

*
Had I the wyte, had I the wyte, Had I the wyte, ſhe
Lively
bade me had I the wyte, had I the wyte, had I the wyte ſhe
bad me Had I the wyte, had I the wyte, had I the wyte ſhe

Continued.

bade me she watch'd me by the hie-gate-side, & up the loan she shaw'd me.
And when I wad na ven_ture in, A coward loon she ca'd me: And
when I wad na' ven_ture in, A cow_ard loon she ca'd me: And
when I wad na' ven_ture in A coward loon she ca'd me, Had
Kirk and State been in the gate, I lighted when she bade me.

Sae craftilie she took me ben,
 And bade me mak nae clatter;
"For our ramgunshoch, glum goodman
 "Is o'er ayont the water:"
Whae'er shall say I wanted grace,
 When I did kiss and dawte her,
Let him be planted in my place,
 Syne, say, I was a fautor.

Could I for shame, could I for shame,
 Could I for shame refus'd her,
And wad na Manhood been to blame,
 Had I unkindly us'd her:
He claw'd her wi' the tipplin-kame,
 And blae and bluidy bruis'd her;
When sic a husband was frae hame,
 What wife but wad excus'd her!

I dighted ay her een sae blue,
 And bann'd the cruel randy,
And weel I wat her willin mou
 Was e'en like succarcandle.
At glomin-shote it was, I wat,
 I lighted on the Monday;
But I cam thro' the Tiseday's dew
 To wanton Willie's brandy.

## The Auld man, &c.

416

*
The auld man he came o_ver the lea, Ha, ha,
ha, but I'll no hae him; He cam on purpose
for tc court me wi' his auld beard newlin shaven.

My mither she bad me gie him a stool,
Ha, ha, ha, but I'll no hae him;
I gae him a stool, and he look'd like a fool,
Wi' his auld beard newlin shaven.

My mither she bade me gie him some pye,
Ha, ha, &c,
I gae him some pye, and he laid the crust by,
Wi' his, &c.

My mither she bade me gie him a dram,
Ha, ha, &c.
I gae him a dram o' the brand sae strang,
Wi' his, &c.

My mither she bade me put him to bed,
Ha, ha, &c.
I put him to bed, and he swore he wad wed,
Wi' his, &c.

## Comin thro' the rye. 1st Sett.

Written for this Work by Robert Burns.

417
Comin thro' the rye, poor body Comin thro' the rye She
Very Slow
draigl't a' her pet_ti_coatie Comin thro' the rye. Oh
The last part repeated in Chorus
Jenny's a' weet poor body, Jenny's sel.dom dry She
draigl't a' her pet_ti_coatie Comin thro the rye.

Gin a body meet a body
  Comin thro' the rye,
Gin a body kiſs a body
  Need a body cry
    Chos. Oh Jenny's a' weet, &c.

Gin a body meet a body
  Comin thro' the glen;
Gin a body kiſs a body
  Need the warld ken!
    Chos. Oh Jenny's a' weet, &c.

## Comin thro' the rye. 2d Sett.

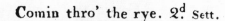

418

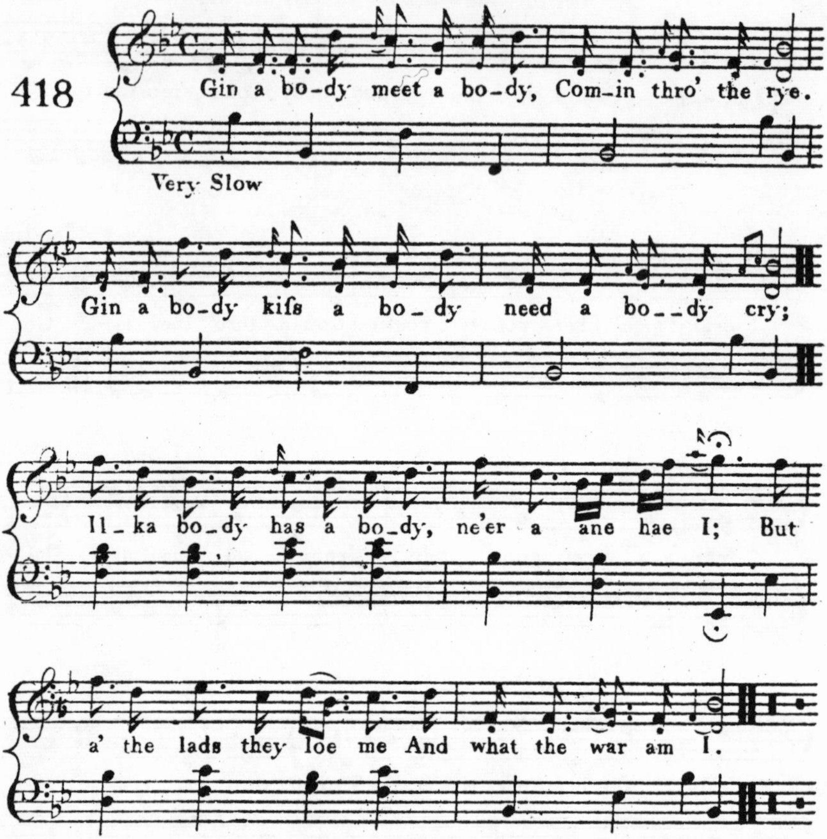
Gin a bo-dy meet a bo-dy, Com-in thro' the rye.
Very Slow
Gin a bo-dy kifs a bo-dy need a bo--dy cry;
Il-ka bo-dy has a bo-dy, ne'er a ane hae I; But
a' the lads they loe me And what the war am I.

Gin a body meet a body, comin frae the well
Gin a body kifs a body, need a body tell;
Ilka body has a body, ne'er a ane hae I,
But a' the lads they loe me, and what the war am I.

Gin a body meet a body, comin frae the town
Gin a body kifs a body, need a body gloom;
Ilka Jenny has her Jockey, ne'er a ane hae I,
But a' the lads they loe me, and what the war am I.

## The Duke of Gordon has three daughters.

419

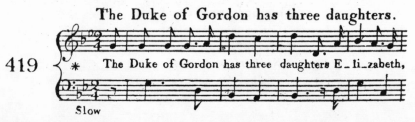

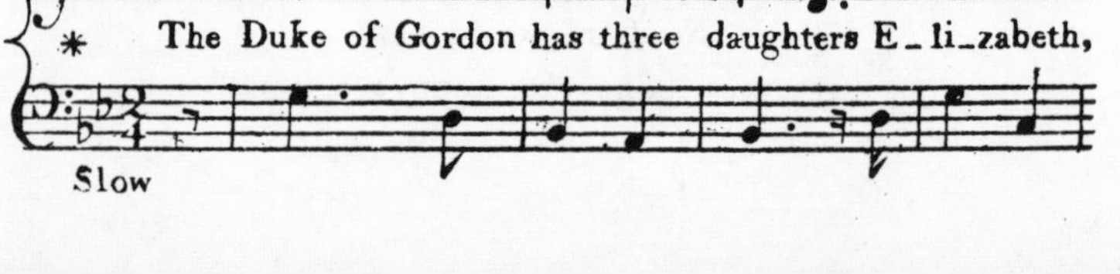
*
The Duke of Gordon has three daughters E-li-zabeth,
Slow

## Continued.

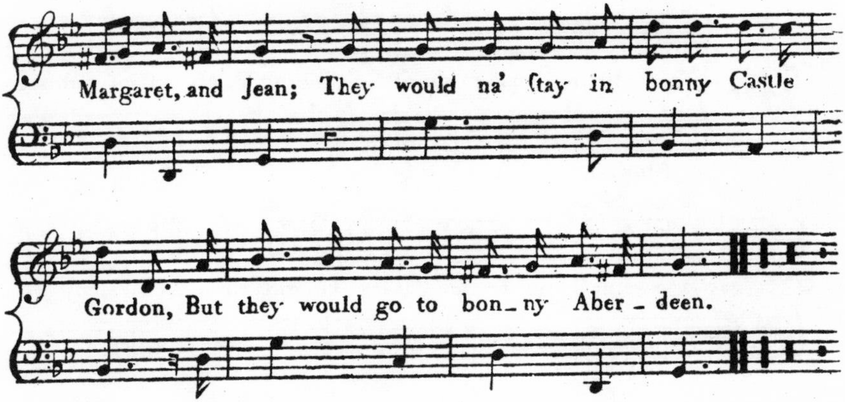
Margaret, and Jean; They would na' ſtay in bonny Caſtle
Gordon, But they would go to bon_ny Aber_deen.

They had not been in Aberdeen
 A twelvemonth and a day,
Till lady Jean fell in love with capt. Ogilvie,
 And away with him ſhe would gae.

Word came to the duke of Gordon,
 In the chamber where he lay,
Lady Jean has fell in love with capt. Ogilvie,
 And away with him ſhe would gae.

"Go ſaddle me the black horſe,
 And you'll ride on the grey;
And I will ride to bonny Aberdeen,
 Where I have been many a day."

They were not a mile from Aberdeen,
 A mile but only three,
Till he met with his two daughters walking,
 But away was lady Jean.

"Where is your ſiſter, maidens?
 Where is your ſiſter, now?
Where is your ſiſter, maidens,
 That ſhe is not walking with you?"

"O pardon us, honoured father,
 O pardon us, they did ſay;
Lady Jean is with captain Ogilvie,
 And away with him ſhe will gae."

And when he came to Aberdeen,
 And down upon the green,
There did he ſee captain Ogilvie,
 Training up his men.

"O wo to you, captain Ogilvie,
 And an ill death thou ſhalt die;
For taking to my daughter,
 Hanged thou ſhalt be."

Duke Gordon has wrote a broad letter,
 And ſent it to the king,
To cauſe hang captain Ogilvie,
 If ever he hanged a man.

"I will not hang captain Ogilvie,
 For no lord that I ſee;
But I'll cauſe him to put off the lace & ſcarlet,
 And put on the ſingle livery."

Word came to captain Ogilvie,
 In the chamber where he lay,
To caſt off the gold lace and ſcarlet;
 And put on the ſingle livery.

"If this be for bonny Jeany Gordon,
 This pennance I'll take wi';
If this be for bonny Jeany Gordon,
 All this I will dree."

Lady Jean had not been married,
 Not a year ut three,
Till ſhe had a babe in every arm,
 Another upon her knee.

"O but I'm weary of wandering!
 O but my fortune is bad!
It ſets not the duke of Gordon's daughter
 To follow a ſoldier lad. &c. &c. &c.

# Young Jamie pride of a the plain.

Tune The carlin of the glen.

420

Young Jamie pride of a' the plain, sae galant.and sae
Slowish
gay a swain, Thro' a' our lasses he did rove, And reign'd re_
sistless king of love. But now wi' sighs and starting tears He
strays a_mang the woods and briers Or in the glens and
rocky caves, His sad complain_ing dowie raves.

I wha sae late did range and rove,
And chang'd with every moon my love,
I little thought the time was near
Repentance I should buy sae dear:
The slighted maids my torments see,
And laugh at a' the pangs I dree;
While she, my cruel, scornfu' Fair,
Forbids me e'er to see her mair.

## Out over the Forth, &c.

421
Slow
* Out o_ver the Forth, I look to the North, But what is the North and its High_lands to me; The South nor the Eaſt, gie eaſe to my breaſt, The far foreign land, or the wide rolling ſea: But I look to the Weſt when I gae to reſt, That hap_py my dreams and my ſlumbers may be. For far in the Weſt lives he I lo'e beſt, The man that is dear to my ba_bie and me.

## Wantonneſs for ever mair.

422

* Wantonneſs for ever mair, Wantonneſs has been my
Slow
ru_in; Yet, for a' my dool and care, Its wantonneſs for ever.
I hae lo'ed the Black, the Brown; I hae lo'ed the Fair, the Gowden:
A' the colours in the town I hae won their wanton favour.

+ + + + + + + + + + + +

## The Humble Beggar.

423

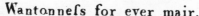

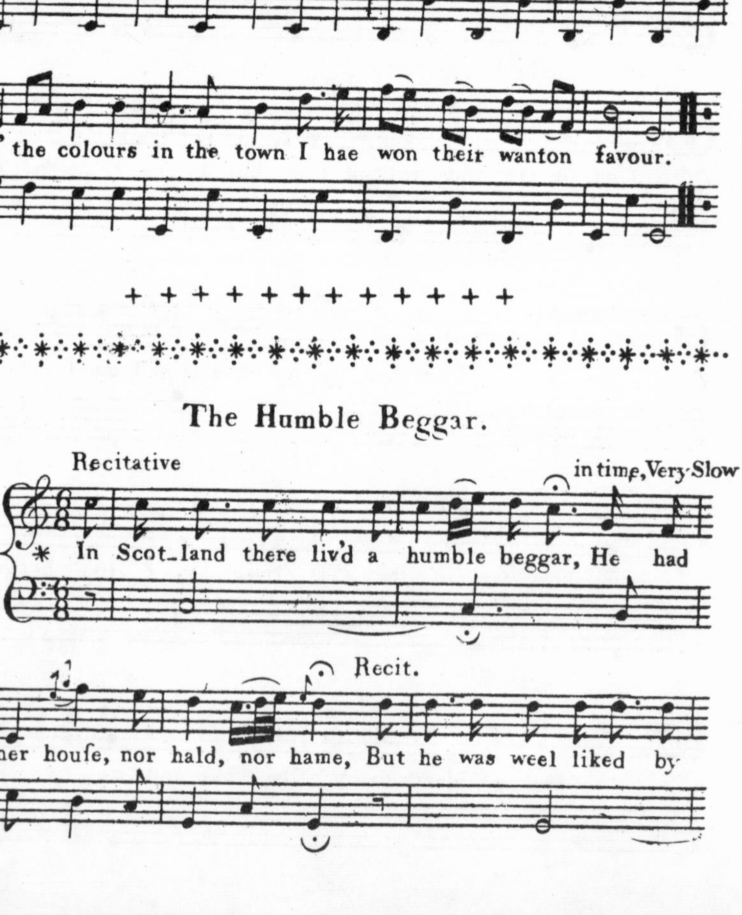
Recitative
in time, Very Slow
* In Scot_land there liv'd a humble beggar, He had
Recit.
neither houſe, nor hald, nor hame, But he was weel liked by

## Continued

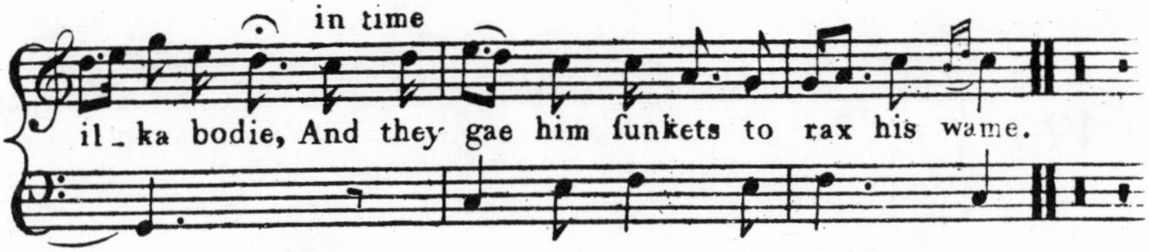
in time
il _ ka bodie, And they gae him ſunkets to rax his wame.

A nivefow of meal, and handfow of groats,
A daad of a bannock or herring brie,
Cauld parradge, or the lickings of plates,
Wad mak him as blyth as a beggar could b

This beggar he was a humble beggar,
The feint a bit of pride had he,
He wad a ta'en his a'ms in a bikker
Frae gentleman or poor bodie.

His wallets ahint and afore did hang,
In as good order as wallets could be;
A lang kail-gooly hang down by his ſide,
And a meikle now't horn to rout on had he.

It happen'd ill, it happen'd warſe,
It happen'd ſae that he did die;
And wha do ye think was at his late-wak?
But lads and laſſes of a high degree?

Some were blyth, and ſome were ſad,
And ſome they play'd at blind Harrie;
But ſuddenly up-ſtarted the auld carle,
I redd you, good folks, tak tent o' me.

Up gat Kate that ſat i' the nook,
Vow kimmer and how do ye?
Up he gat and ca'd her limmer,
And ruggit and tuggit her cockernonie.

They houkit his grave in Duket's kirk-yard,
E'en fair fa' the companie;
But when they were gaun to lay him i' th' yird,
The feint a dead, nor dead was he.

And when they brought him to Duket's kirk-yard
He dunted on the kiſt, the boards did flie;
And when they were gaun to put him i' the yird,
In fell the kiſt, and out lap he.

He cry'd, I'm cald, I'm unco cald,
Fu' faſt ran the folk, and fu' faſt ran he;
But he was firſt hame at his ain ingle-ſide,
And he helped to drink his ain dirgie.

# The rowin't in her apron.

424

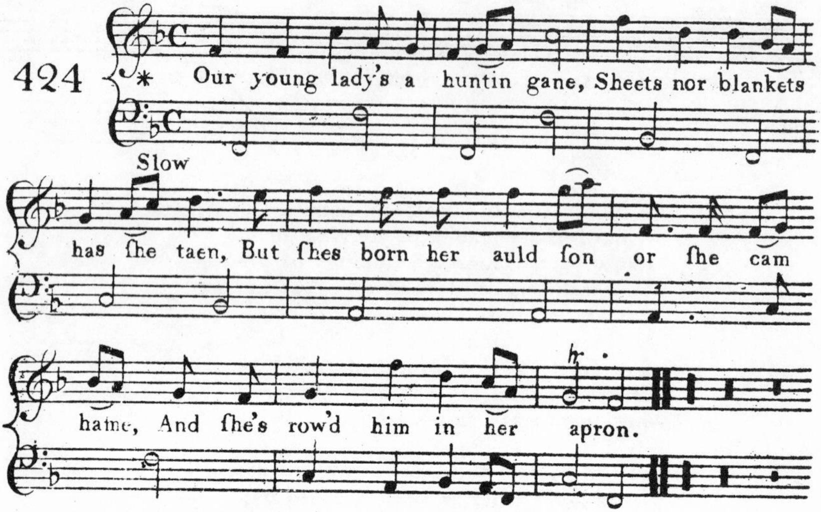
*
Our young lady's a huntin gane, Sheets nor blankets
Slow
has fhe taen, But fhes born her auld fon or fhe cam
hame, And fhe's row'd him in her apron.

Her apron was o' the hollan fine
Laid about wi' laces nine;
She thought it a pity her babie fhould tyne,
And fhe's row'd him in her apron.

Her apron was o' the hollan fma,
Laid about wi' laces a',
She thought it a pity her babe to let fa,
And fhe row'd him in her apron.
\+ + + + + + + + + + + + + +
Her father fays within the ha',
Amang the knights and nobles a',
I think I hear a babie ca,
In the chamber amang our young ladies.

O father dear it is a bairn,
I hope it will do you nae harm,
For the daddie I lo ed, and he'll lo'e me again,
For the rowin't in my apron.

O is he a gentleman, or is he a clown,
That has brought thy fair body down,
I would not for a' this town
The rowin't in thy apron.

Young Terreagles he's nae clown,
He is the tofs of Edinborrow town,
And he'll buy me a braw new gown
For the rowin't in my apron
\+ + + + + + + + + + + + + +
Its I hae caftles, I hae towers,
I hae barns, and I hae bowers,
A' that is mine it fhall be thine,
For the rowin't in thy apron.

## The Boatie rows, First Sett.

425

* O weel may the boat_ie row, And better
Slowish
may the speed; O lee_some may the boat_ie row. That
wins the bairns bread. The boatie rows, The boatie
rows, the boatie rows in_deed And hap_py be the
lot o' a' wha wish_es her to speed.

## The Boatie rows. Second Sett.

426

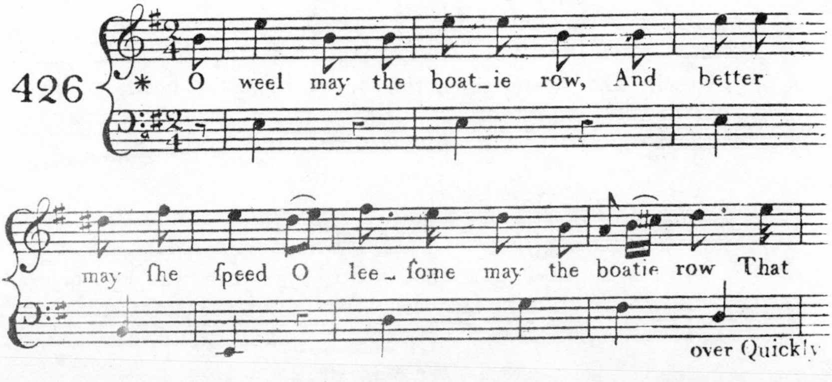
* O weel may the boat_ie row, And better
may she speed O lee_some may the boatie row That
over Quickly

## Continued.

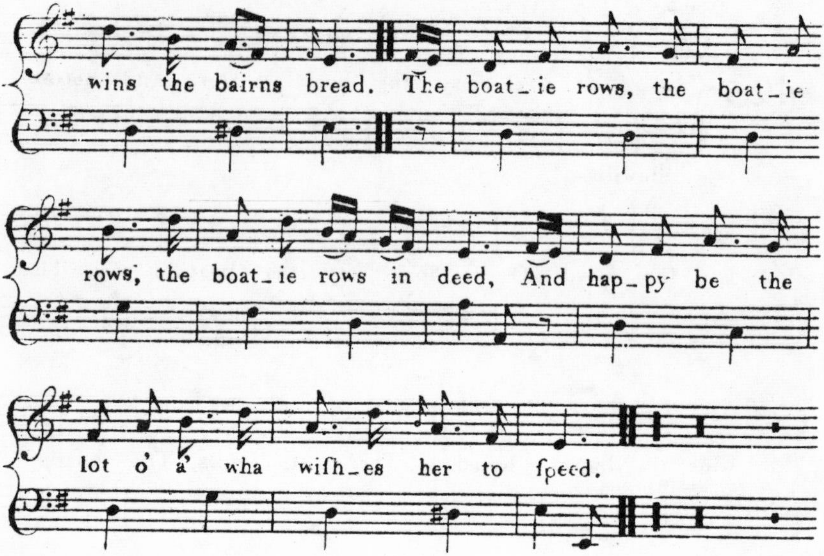
wins the bairns bread. The boat_ie rows, the boat_ie
rows, the boat_ie rows in deed, And hap_py be the
lot o' a' wha wiſh_es her to ſpeed.

## The Boatie rows. Third Sett.

427

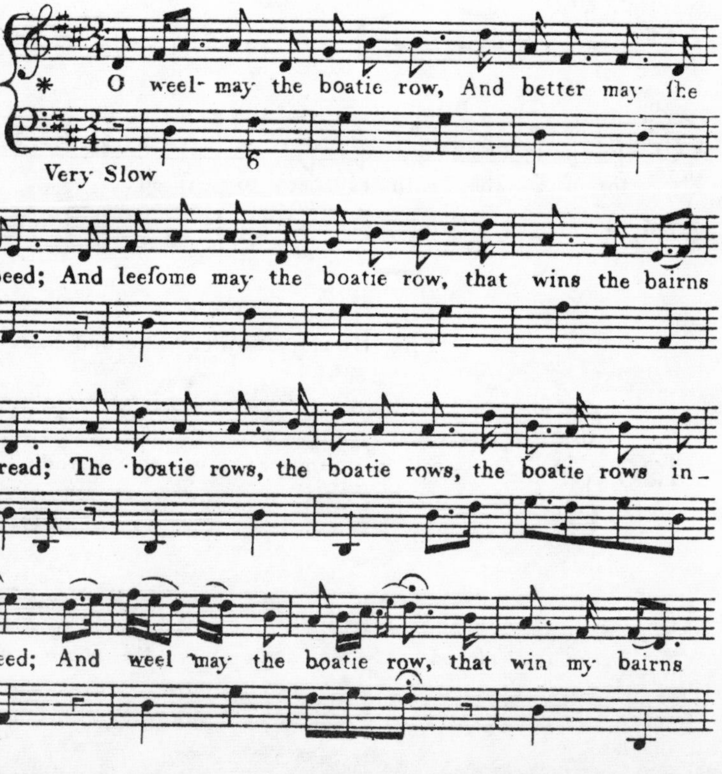
* O weel- may the boatie row, And better may ſhe
Very Slow
ſpeed; And leeſome may the boatie row, that wins the bairns
bread; The boatie rows, the boatie rows, the boatie rows in_
deed; And weel may the boatie row, that win my bairns

## Continued.

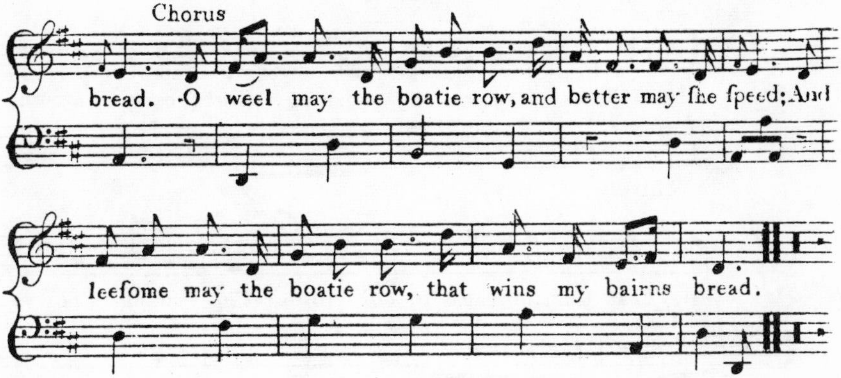
Chorus
bread. O weel may the boatie row, and better may ſhe ſpeed; And
leeſome may the boatie row, that wins my bairns bread.

I caſt my line in Largo bay,
And fiſhes I catch'd nine,
There was three to boil, & three to fry,
And three to bait the line.
.S. The boatie rows, the boatie rows,
The boatie rows indeed,
And happy be the lot o' a',
Who wiſhes her to ſpeed .S.

O weel may the boatie row,
That fills a heavy creel,
And cleads us a' frae head to feet,
And buys our pottage meal;
.S. The boaty rows, the boatie rows,
The boatie rows indeed,
And happy be the lot of a',
That wiſh the boatie ſpeed. .S.

When Jamie vow'd he wou'd be mine,
And wan frae me my heart,
O muckle lighter grew my creel,
He ſwore we'd never part:
S. The boaty rows, the boatie rows,
The boatie rows fu' weel,
And muckle lighter is the load,
When love bears up the creel.

My kurtch I put upo' my head,
And dreſs'd myſel' fu' braw,
I true my heart was douf an' wae,
When Jamie gaed awa',
.S. But weel may the boatie row,
And lucky be her part;
And lightſome be the laſsie's care,
That yields an honeſt heart. .S.

When Sawney, Jock, an Janetie,
Are up and gotten lear;
They'll help to gar the boatie row,
And lighten a' our care.
.S. The boatie rows, the boatie rows,
The boatie rows fu' weel,
And lightſome be her heart that bears,
The Murlain, and the creel. .S.

And when wi' age we're worn down,
And hirpling round the door,
They'll row to keep us dry and warm,
As we did them before;
.S. Then weel may the boatie row,
She wins the bairn's bread;
And happy be the lot o' a',
That wiſh the boat to ſpeed. .S.

## Charlie he's my darling.

428

* 'Twas on a monday morning, Right early in the
Lively
year, That Charlie came to our town, The young Che_va_
_lier. An' Charlie he's my darling, my dar_ling, my dar_ling,
Charlie he's my dar_ling the young Chevalier.

As he was walking up the ſtreet,
 The city for to view,
O there he ſpied a bonie laſs
 The window looking thro'. _ An' Charlie &c.

Sae light's he jimped up the ſtair,
 And tirled at the pin;
And wha ſae ready as herſel,
 To let the laddie in. ___ An' Charlie &c.

He ſet his Jenny on his knee,
 All in his Highland dreſs;
For brawlie weel he ken'd the way
 To pleaſe a bonie laſs. ____ An' Charlie &c.

It's up yon hethery mountain,
 And down yon ſcroggy glen,
We daur na gang a milking,
 For Charlie and his men. ___ An' Charlie &c.

## As Sylvia in a forest lay.

429

As Sylvia in a for_est lay, To vent her woe a_
_lone; Her swain Syl_van_der came that way, And
heard her dy_ing moan. Ah! is my love, she said to
you So worthless and so vain? Why is your won_ted
fond ness now Con_ver_ted to dis__dain?

You vow'd the light shou'd darkness turn,
 E'er you'd exchange your love;
In shades may now creation mourn,
 Since you unfaithful prove.
Was it for this I credit gave
 To ev'ry oath you swore?
But ah! it seems they most deceive,
 Who most our charms adore.

'Tis plain your drift was all deceit,
 The practice of mankind:
Alas! I see it, but too late,
 My love had made me blind

For you delighted, I should die;
 But oh! with grief I'm fill'd,
To think that credulous constant I
 Shou'd by yourself be kill'd.

This said —all breathless, sick & pale,
 Her head upon her hand,
She found her vital spirits fail.
 And senses at a stand.
Sylvander then began to melt;
 But e'er the word was given,
The heavy hand of death she felt,
 And sigh'd her soul to Heaven.

## The Lass of Ecclefechan.

430

* Gat ye me, O gat ye me, O gat ye me wi' naething,
Lively
Rock and reel and ſpinnin wheel A mickle quarter baſon.
Bye attour, my Gutcher has a hich houſe and a laigh ane
a' for bye, my bonnie ſel, The toſs of Eccle_fech_an.

O had your tongue now Luckie Laing,
O had your tongue and jauner;
I held the gate till you I met,
Syne I began to wander:

I tint my whiſtle and my ſang,
I tint my peace and pleaſure;
But your green graff, now Luckie Laing,
Wad airt me to my treaſure.

## The Couper o' Cuddy.

431

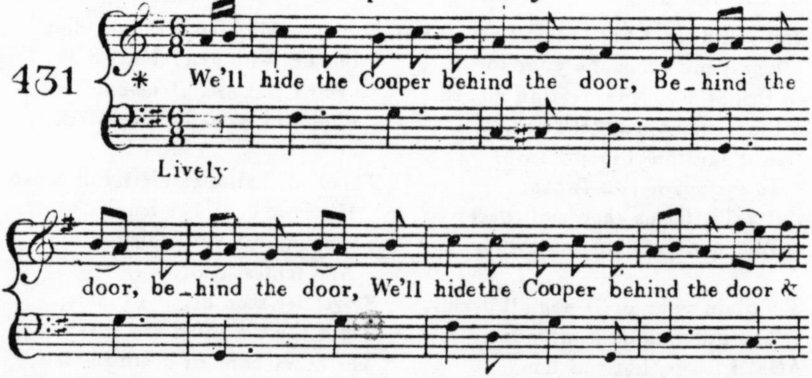
* We'll hide the Couper behind the door, Be_hind the
Lively
door, be_hind the door, We'll hide the Couper behind the door &

Continued.

cover him under a mawn O, The Cooper o' cuddy cam here awa, He
ca'd the girrs out o'er us a'; And our gudewife has gotten a ca', That
Chorus
anger'd the filly gude_man O. We'll hide the Cooper behind the
door, Be_hind the door, be_hind the door We'll hide the Cooper be
_hind the door, And cover him un_der a maun O.

He fought them out, he fought them in,
Wi' deil hae her! and deil hae him!
But the body he was fae doited and blin,
He wift na whare he was gaun O.
We'll hide, &c.

They couper'd at e'en, they couper'd at morn,
Till our gudeman has gotten the fcorn;
On ilka brow fhe's planted a horn,
And fwears that there they fhall ftan' O
We'll hide, &c.

## Widow, are ye waking?

432
*
Slowish
Wha's is that at my chamber door? "Fair wi_dow
are ye wa_king?" Auld carl, your suit give o'er, Your
love lies a' in tawking. Gi'e me a lad that's young and
tight, Sweet like an A_pril meadow; 'Tis sick as he can
bless the sight, And bo_som of a wi_dow.

"O widow, wilt thou let me in?
"I'm pawky, wise, and thrifty,
"And come of a right gentle kin;
"I'm little mair than fifty."
Daft carle, dit your mouth,
Wha. signifies how pawky,
Or gentle-born ye be,-but youth
In love ye're but a gawky.

"Then, widow, let these guineas speak,
"That powerfully plead clinkan;
"And if they fail, my mouth I'll steek,
"And nae mair love will think on".
These court indeed, I maun confess,
I think they mak you young, Sir,
And ten times better can express
Affection, than your tongue, Sir.

# The Maltman.

433

* The malt_man_comes on Munanday, He craves wonderous
ſair, Cries dame, come gi'e me my fil_ler, Or
malt ye'll ne'er get mair. I took him in_to the pantry, And
gave him ſome good cock-broo, Syne paid him upon a
gan_tree As hoſt_ler wives ſhould do.

When maltmen come for ſiller,
And gaugers wi' wands o'er ſoon,
Wives, tak them a' down to the cellar,
And clear them as I have done.
This bewith, when cunzie is ſcanty,
Will keep them frae making din,
The knack I learn'd frae an auld aunty,
The ſnackeſt of a' my kin.

The maltman is right cunning,
But I can be as ſlee,
And he may crack of his winning,
When he clears-ſcores with me:
For come when he likes, I'm ready,
But if frae hame I be,
Let him wait on our kind lady,
She'll anſwer a bill for me.

## Leezie Lindſay

434

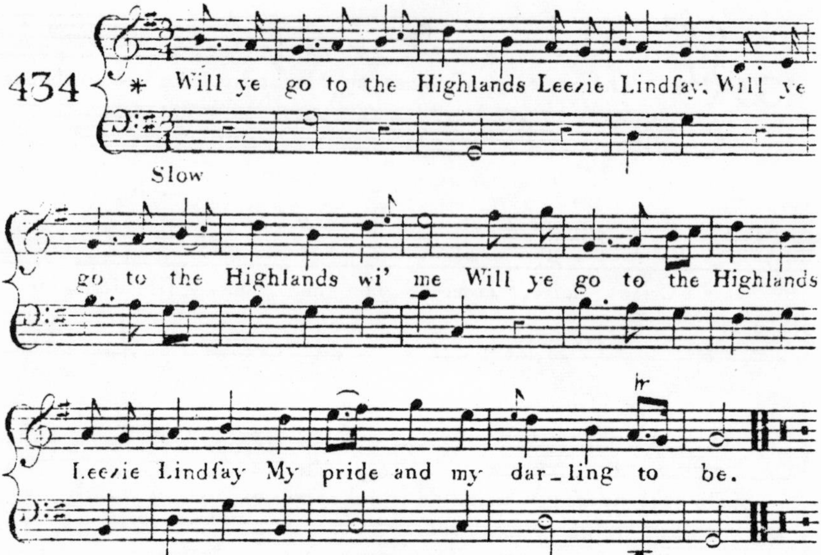
* Will ye go to the Highlands Leezie Lindſay, Will ye
Slow
go to the Highlands wi' me Will ye go to the Highlands
Leezie Lindſay My pride and my dar_ling to be.

## The Auld Wife ayont the Fire.

435

* The auld wife beyond the fire, The auld wife a_
Lively
_neiſt the fire The auld wife ayont the fire She died for
lack o' ſniſhing There was a wife won'd in a glen, And
ſhe had dochters nine or ten, That ſought the houſe baith

## Continued.

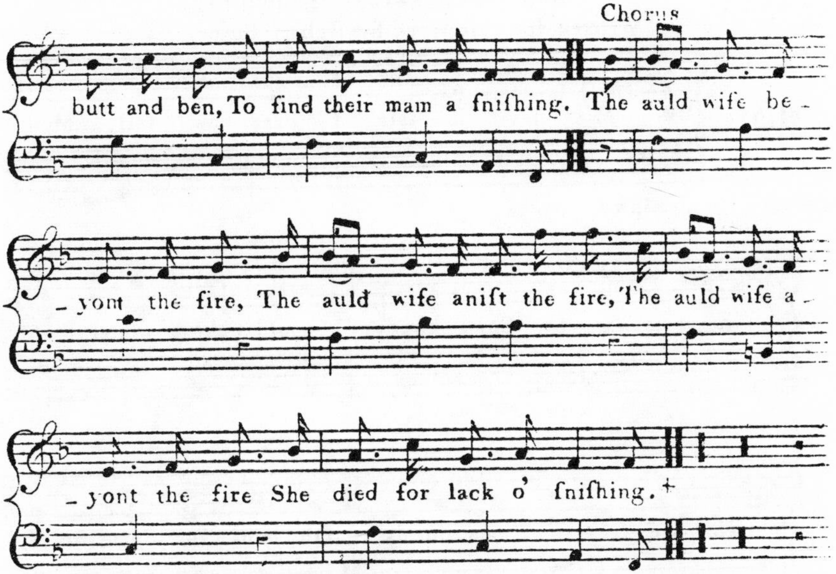
Chorus
butt and ben, To find their mam a ſniſhing. The auld wife be-
-yont the fire, The auld wife aniſt the fire, The auld wife a-
-yont the fire She died for lack o' ſniſhing. *

Her mill into ſome hole had fawn,
Whatrecks, quoth ſhe, let it be gawn,
For I maun hae a young goodman
Shall furniſh me with ſniſhing.
The auld wife, &c.

Her eldeſt dochter ſaid right bauld,
Fy, mother, mind that now ye're auld,
And if ye with a younker wald,
He'll waſte away your ſniſhing.
The auld wife, &c.

The youngeſt dochter gae a ſhout,
O mother dear! your teeth's a' out,
Beſides ha'f blind, you hae the gout,
Your mill can had nae ſniſhing.
The auld wife, &c.

Ye lied, ye limmers, cried auld mump,
For I hae baith a tooth and ſtump,
And will nae langer live in dump,
By wanting o' my ſniſhing.
The auld wife, &c.

Thole ye, ſays Peg, that pauky ſlut,
Mother, if you can crack a nut,
Then we will a' conſent to it,
That you ſhall have a ſniſhing.
The auld wife, &c.

The auld ane did agree to that,
And they a piſtol-bullet gat;
She powerfully began to crack,
To win herſelf a ſniſhing.
The auld wife, &c.

Braw ſport it was to ſee her chow't
And'tween her gums ſae ſqueeze & row't
While frae her jaws the ſlaver flow't,
And ay ſhe curs'd poor ſtumpy.
The auld wife, &c.

At laſt ſhe gae a deſperate ſqueeze
Which brak the auld tooth by the neez
And ſyne poor ſtumpy was at eaſe,
But ſhe tint hopes of ſniſhing.
The auld wife, &c.

She of the taſk began to tire,
And frae her dochters did retire,
Syne lean'd her down ayont the fire,
And died for lack of ſniſhing.
The auld wife, &c.

Ye auld wives, notice weel this truth,
Aſſoon as ye're paſt mark of mouth,
Ne'er do what's only fit for youth,
And leave aff thoughts of ſniſhing:
Elſe like this wife beyont the fire,
Your bairns againſt you will conſpire
Nor will ye get, unleſs ye hire,
A young man with your ſniſhing

* Sniſhing, in its literal meaning, is ſnuff made of tobacco; but in this ſong it means ſometimes contentment, a huſband, love, money, &c.

# For the ſake o Somebody.

Written for this Work by Robert Burns.

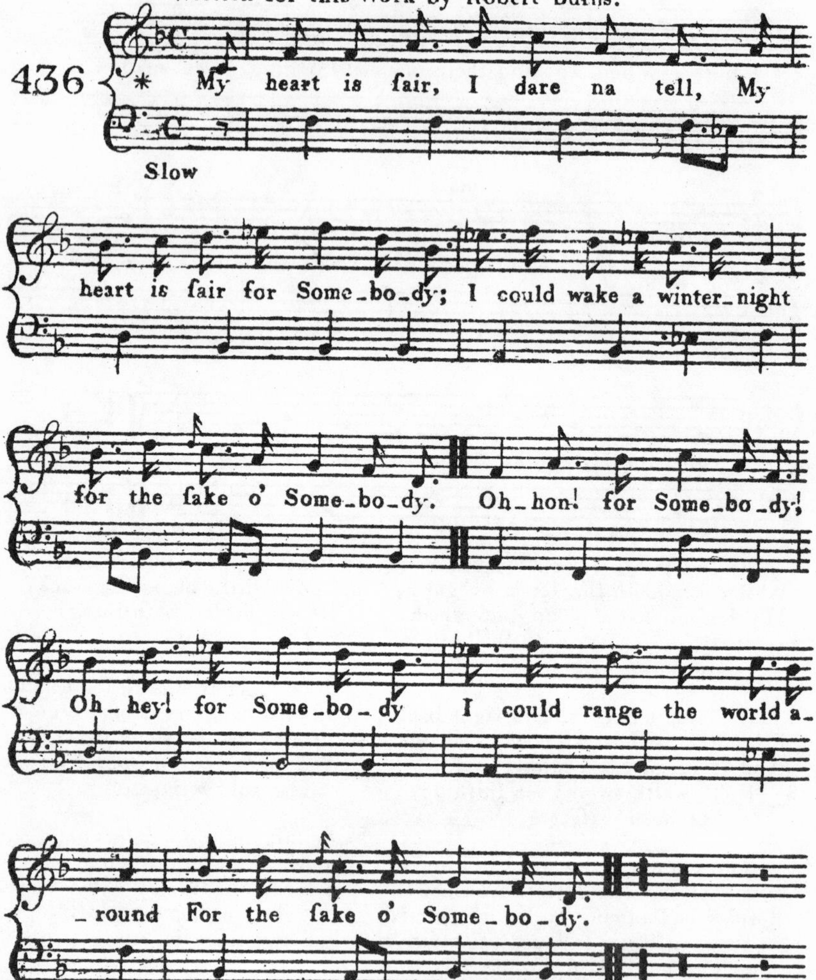
436
* My heart is ſair, I dare na tell, My
Slow
heart is ſair for Some_bo_dy; I could wake a winter_night
for the ſake o' Some_bo_dy. Oh_hon! for Some_bo_dy!
Oh_hey! for Some_bo_dy I could range the world a_
_round For the ſake o' Some_bo_dy.

Ye Powers that ſmile on virtuous love,
O, ſweetly ſmile on Somebody!
Frae ilka danger keep him free,
And ſend me ſafe my Somebody.
Oh_hon! for Somebody!
Oh_hey! for Somebody!
I wad do ——— what wad I not
For the ſake o' Somebody!

B

## The Cardin o't, &c.

437

* I coſt a ſtane o' haſlock woo, To mak a wat to
Johnie o't; For John_ie is my on_ly jo, I lo'e him
Chorus
beſt of onie yet. The cardin o't the ſpin_nin o't The
war_pin o't the win_nin o't when il_ka ell coſt
me a groat, The tay_lor ſtaw the lyn_in o't.

For-though his locks be lyart gray,
And though his brow be beld aboon,
Yet I hae ſeen him on a day
The pride of a' the pariſhen.
The cardin, &c.

## The Souters o' Selkirk.

438

* Its up wi' the Souters o' Selkirk, And down wi' the Earl of
Slowish, & Lively
Hume, And here is to a' the braw laddies That wear the single soal'd shoon:
Its up wi' the souters o' Selkirk, For they are baith trusty and leal; And
up wi' the lads o' the Forest, And down wi' the merse to the deil.

## Rock and wee pickle Tow.

439

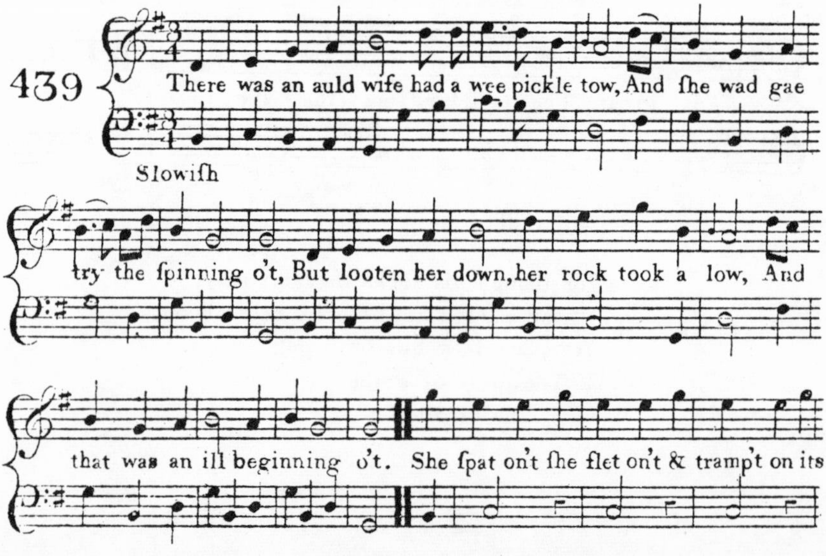
There was an auld wife had a wee pickle tow, And she wad gae
Slowish
try the spinning o't, But looten her down, her rock took a low, And
that was an ill beginning o't. She spat on't she flet on't & tramp't on its

Continued.

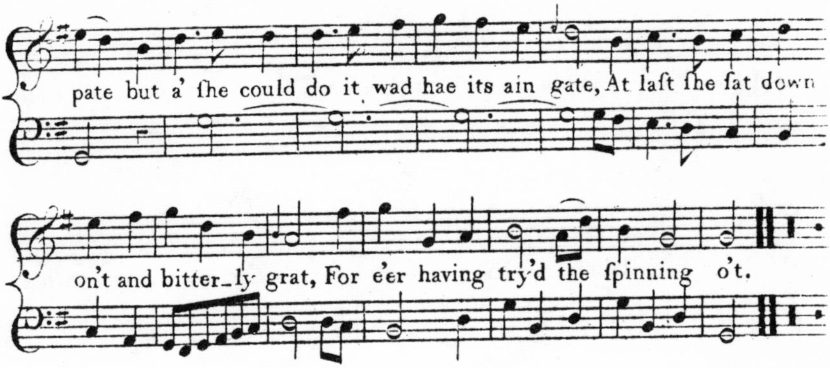
pate but a' ſhe could do it wad hae its ain gate, At laſt ſhe ſat down
on't and bitter_ly grat, For e'er having try'd the ſpinning o't.

I hae been a wife theſe three ſcore of years,
And never did try the ſpinning o't,
But how I was ſarked foul fa' them that ſpeirs
To mind me o' the beginning o't.
The women are now a days turned ſae bra'
That ilk ane maun hae a ſark, ſome maun hae twa
But better the warld was when ſint ane ava
To hinder the firſt beginning o't.

Foul fa' them that e'er adviſ'd me to ſpin
It minds me o' the beginning o't,
I well might have ended as I had begun
And never have try'd the ſpinning o't
But ſhes a wiſe wife wha kens her ain weird
I thought anes a day it wad never be ſpier'd
How let you the low tack the rock by the beard
When you gaed to try the ſpinning o't.

The ſpinning the ſpinning, it gars my heart ſab
To think on the ill beginning o't
I took't in my head to make me a wab
And this was the firſt beginning o't
But had I nine Daughters as I hae but three
The ſafeſt and ſoundeſt advice I wad gie
That they wad frae ſpinning ſtill keep their hands free
For fear of an ill beginning o't.

But if they in ſpite of my counſel wad run
The dreary ſad taſk o' the ſpinning o't.
Let them find a loun ſeat light up by the ſun
Syne venture on the beginning o't:
For wha's done as I've done alake and avow
To buſk up a rock at the cheek of a low,
They'll ſay that I had little wit in my pow.
The meikle Deil tak the ſpinning o't.

## Tibbie Fowler.

440

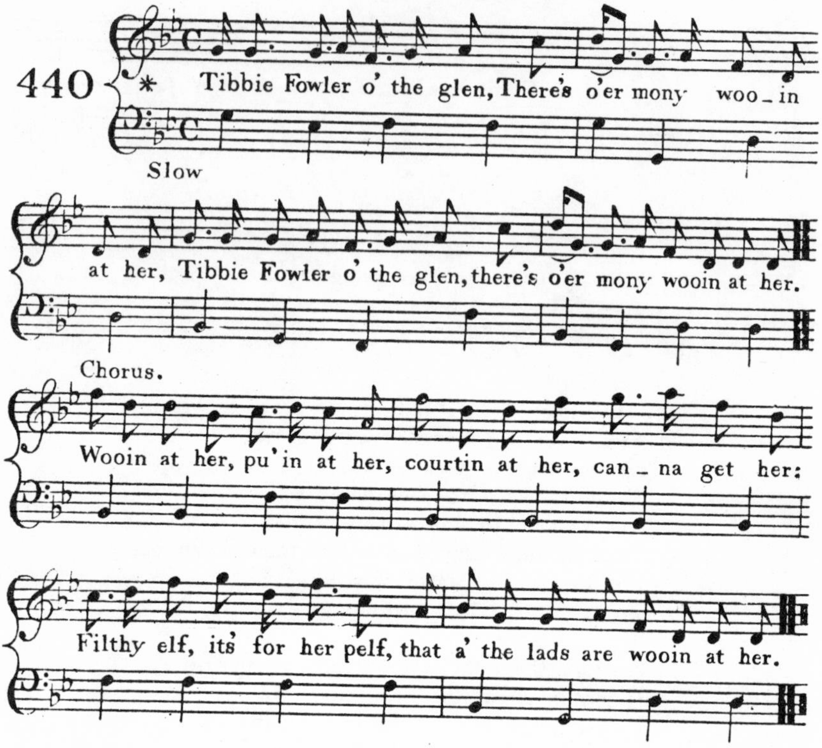
* Tibbie Fowler o' the glen, There's o'er mony woo _ in
Slow
at her, Tibbie Fowler o' the glen, there's o'er mony wooin at her.
Chorus.
Wooin at her, pu'in at her, courtin at her, can _ na get her:
Filthy elf, its' for her pelf, that a' the lads are wooin at her.

Ten cam eaſt, and ten came weſt, ten came rowin o'er the water;
Twa came down the lang dyke ſide, there's twa and thirty wooin at her.
Wooin at her, &c.

There's ſeven but, and ſeven ben, ſeven in the pantry wi' her;
Twenty head about the door, There's ane and forty wooin at her.
Wooin at her, &c.

She's got pendles in her lugs, Cockle-ſhells wad ſet her better;
High-heel'd ſhoon and ſiller tags, And a' the lads are wooin at her.
Wooin at her, &c.

Be a laſsie e'er ſae black, An ſhe hae the name o' ſiller,
Set her upo' Tintock-tap, The wind will blaw a man till her.
Wooin at her, &c.

Be a laſsie e'er ſae fair, An ſhe want the pennie ſiller;
A flie may fell her in the air, Before a man be even till her.
Wooin at her, &c.

## On hearing a young Lady Sing.

441

*
Bleſt are the mortals above all, Who hear the
Slow
charming Jackie ſing; Her notes pathe_tic riſe and fall ſweet
as the mu_ſic of the ſpring. The grace_ful ac_cents
of her ſong, With raptures fill the youthful breaſt; E'en age re_
vives, grows gay_ly young, And blithly joins the vocal feaſt

Go, on ſweet maid, improve the lay
Attun'd to ſtrains of plaintive woe;
They always bear reſiſtleſs ſway
When ſung by charming Jackie O.
Long may ſhe bleſs her parents ear,
And always prove their mutual joy,
May no beguilers artful ſnare,
The peace of innocence annoy.

# There's three gude fellow ayont yon glen.

442

*
There's three true gude fellows, There's three true gude
Lively
Solo
fellows; There's three true gude fellows down ayont yon glen. Its
now the day is dawin, But or night to fain, Whase cock's beft at crawin,
Chorus
Willie thou fall ken. There's three true gude fellows, There's three true
gude fellows, There's three true gude fellows down ayont yon glen.

## The wee thing: or Mary of Caftle Cary.

443

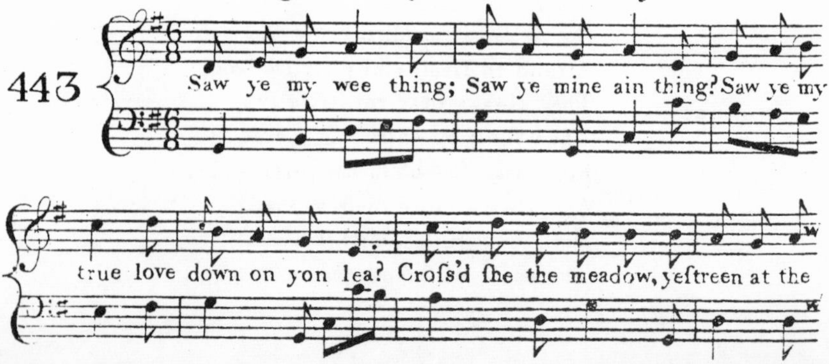
Saw ye my wee thing; Saw ye mine ain thing? Saw ye my
true love down on yon lea? Crofs'd fhe the meadow, yeftreen at the

Continued

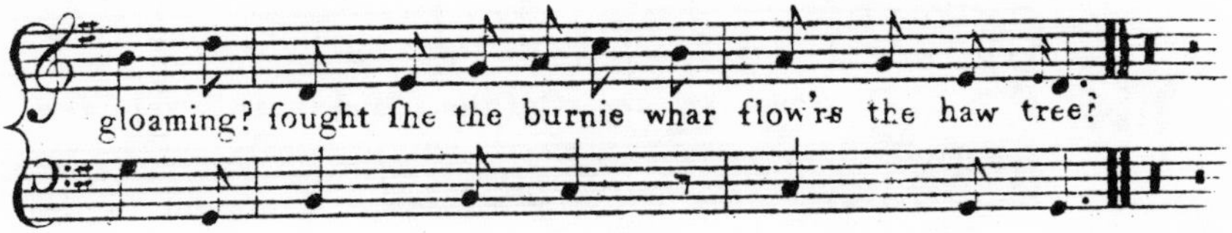
gloaming? ſought ſhe the burnie whar flow'rs the haw tree?

"Her hair it is lint white! her ſkin it is milk white!
"Dark is the blue o' her ſaft rolling ee!
"Red red her ripe lips, and ſweeter than roſes. —
"Whar could my wee thing wander frae me?

'I ſaw na your wee thing, I ſaw na your ain thing,
'Nor ſaw I your true love down by yon lea;
'But I met my bonny thing late in the gloaming,
'Down by the burnie whar flow'rs the haw tree.

'Her hair it was lint white, her ſkin it was milk white,
'Dark was the blue o' her ſaft rolling ee!
'Red war her ripe lips, and ſweeter than roſes.
'Sweet war the kiſses that ſhe gae to me!

"It was na my wee thing! It was na my ain thing!
"It was na my true love ye met by the tree!
"Proud is her leil heart; modeſt her nature,
"She never lo'od ony till ance ſhe lo'od me.

'Her name it is Mary, ſhe's frae Caſtle Cary,
'Aft has ſhe ſat, when a bairn, on my knee!
'Fair as your face is, wart fifty times fairer,
'Young bragger! ſhe ne'er would gie kiſses to thee."

'It was then your Mary, ſhe's frae Caſtle Cary,
'It was then your true love I met by the tree!
'Proud as her heart is, and modeſt her nature,
'Sweet war the kiſses that ſhe gae to me!

Sair gloom'd his dark brow, blood red his Cheek grew,
Wild flach'd the fire, frae his red rolling ee; —
"Ye's rue ſair this morning, your boaſts and your ſcorning —
"Defend ye fauſe traitor; fu' loudly ye lie!

"Awa wi' beguiling, cried the youth ſmiling;
Aff went the bonnet; the lint-white locks flee;
The belted plaid fa'ing, her white boſom ſhawing,
Fair ſtood the lov'd maid wi' the dark rolling ee!

"Is it my wee thing! is it mine ain thing?
"Is it my true love here that I ſee?
'O Jamie! forgie me, your heart's conſtant to me;
'I'll never mair wander, my true love, frae thee!

## O can ye ſew Cuſhions.

444

O can ye ſew Cuſhions and can ye ſew
Slow
Sheets and can ye ſing bal_lu_loo when the bairn
greets. And hee and baw bir_die and hee and baw
lamb and hee and baw bir_die my bon_nie wee lamb.
Lively
Hee O wee O what wou'd I do wi' you black's the
life that I lead wi' you monny O you little for to gie you
Slow
hee O wee O what would I do wi' you.

## The glancing of her Apron.

445

In lovely August last, On Monondаy at morn As
thro' the fields I past, To view the yellow corn I
look-ed me behind, And saw come o'er the know, And
glancing in her ap_ron, With a bonnie brent brow.

I said, good morrow, fair maid;
And she, right courteoslie,
Return'd a back, and kindly said
"Good day, sweet sir to thee."
I speir'd, my dear, how far awa
Do ye intend to gae,
Quoth she, I mean a mile or twa
And o'er yon broomy brae.

Fair maid, I'm thankfu' to my fate
To have sic company;
For Iam ganging straight that gate,
Where ye intend to be.
When we had gane a mile or twain,
I said to her, my dow.
May we not lean us on this plain,
And kiss your bonny mou!

## Waly, Waly. _A different set _see Volume 2d. Page 166

446

* O Waly, waly up yon bank, And waly waly down yon
brae, And waly by yon river side, Where I and my love wont to gae!
O waly waly love is bonny, A little while when it is new, But
when its auld it waxes cauld, And wears a_wa' like the morning dew!

## She says she lo'es me best of a'.

Written for this Work by Robert Burns. An Irish Air.

447

*. Sae flax_en were her ringlets, Her eyebrows of a
dark_er hue, Be witchingly o'er arch_ing Twa laughing een o'
bon_ie blue Her smil_ing sae wyl_ing. Wad make a

## Continued.

wretch for_get his woe; What pleaſure, what treaſure, un_
_to theſe ro_ſy lips to grow: Such was my Chloris bo_nie
face, When firſt her bonie face I ſaw; And _ay my Chloris
deareſt charm, She ſays ſhe lo'es me beſt of a'.

Like harmony her motion;
Her pretty ancle is a ſpy,
Betraying fair proportion,
Wad make a ſaint forget the ſky.
Sae warming, ſae charming,
Her fauteleſs form and gracefu' air;
Ilk feature __auld Nature
Declar'd that ſhe could do nae mair:
Her's are the willing chains o' love,
By conquering Beauty's ſovereign law;
And ay my Chloris deareſt charm,
She ſays, ſhe lo'es me beſt of a'.

Let others love the city,
And gaudy ſhew at ſunny noon;
Gie me the lonely valley,
The dewy eve, and riſing moon
Fair beaming, & ſtreaming
Her ſilver light the boughs amang;
While falling, recalling,
The amorous thruſh concludes his ſang;
There, dearest Chloris, wilt thou rove
By wimpling burn & leafy ſhaw,
And hear my vows o' truth and love
And ſay, thou lo'es me beſt of a'.

## The bonie laſs made the bed to me.

Written for this Work by Robert Burns.

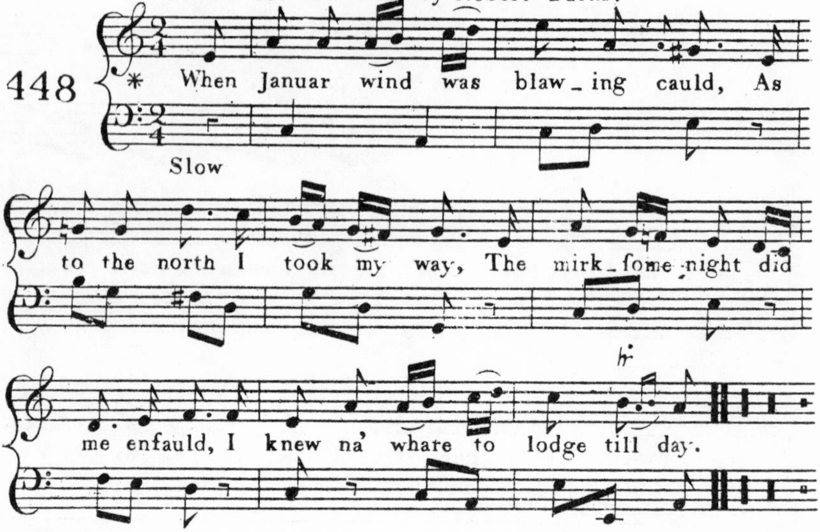
448
*
When Januar wind was blaw_ing cauld, As
Slow
to the north I took my way, The mirk_ſome night did
me enfauld, I knew na' whare to lodge till day.

By my gude luck a maid I met,
Juſt in the middle o' my care;
And kindly ſhe did me invite
To walk into a chamber fair.

I bow'd fu' low unto this maid,
And thank'd her for her courteſie;
I bow'd fu' low unto this maid,
And bad her mak a bed for me.

She made the bed baith large and wide,
Wi' twa white hands ſhe ſpread it down;
She put the cup to her roſy lips
And drank," Young man now ſleep ye ſound."

She ſnatch'd the candle in her hand,
And frae my chamber went wi' ſpeed;
But I call'd her quickly back again
To lay ſome mair below my head.

A cod ſhe laid below my head,
And ſerved me wi' due reſpect;
And to ſalute her wi' a kiſs,
I put my arms about her neck.

Haud aff your hands young man, ſhe ſays,
And dinna ſae uncivil be:
Gif ye hae ony luve for me,
O wrang na my virginitie!

Her hair was like the links o' gowd,
Her teeth were like the ivorie.
Her cheeks like lilies dipt in wine,
The laſs that made the bed to me.

Her boſom was the driven ſnaw,
Twa drifted heaps ſae fair to ſee,
Her limbs the poliſh'd marble ſtane
The laſs that made the bed to me.

I kiſs'd her o'er and o'er again,
And ay ſhe wiſt na what to ſay;
I laid her between me and the wa'
The laſsie thought na lang till day.

Upon the morrow when we raſe,
I thank'd her for her courteſie:
But ay ſhe bluſh'd & ay ſhe ſigh'd,
And ſaid, Alas ye've ruin'd me.

I claſp'd her waiſt & kiſs'd her ſyne,
While the tear ſtood twinklin in her e'
I ſaid, my laſsie dinna cry,
For ye ay ſhall mak the bed to me.

She took her mither's holland ſheets
And made them a' in ſarks to me:
Blythe and merry may ſhe be,
The laſs that made the bed to me.

The bonie laſs made the bed to me,
The braw laſs made the bed to me.
I'll ne'er forget till the day that I d
The laſs that made the bed to me.

## Sae far Awa.

Written for this Work by Robert Burns.

449

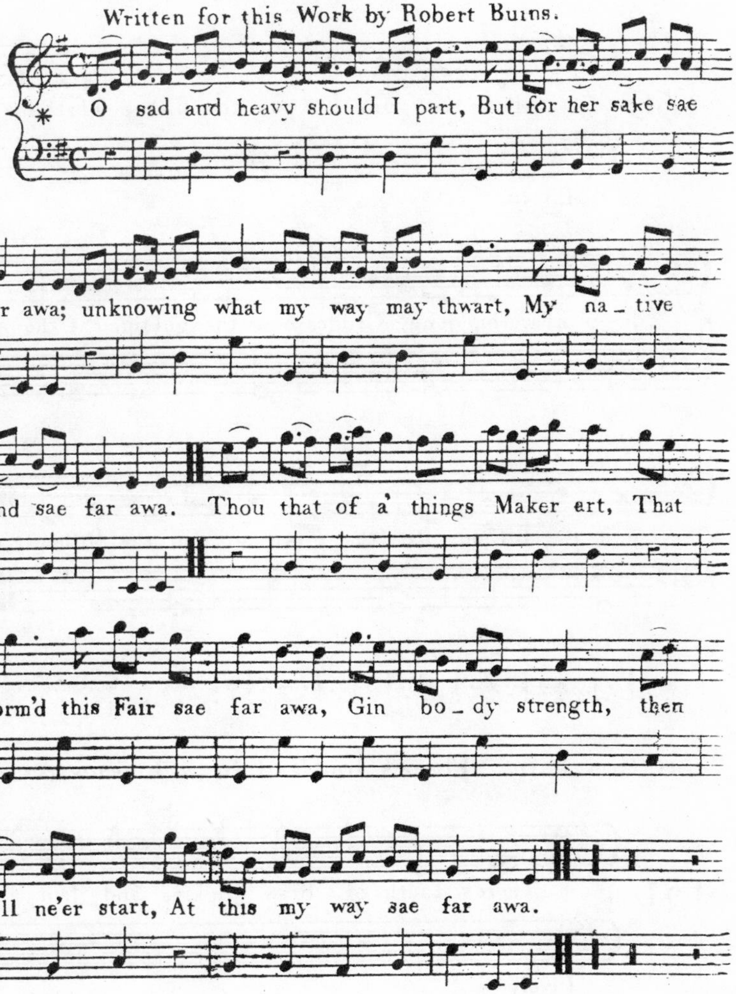
*
O sad and heavy should I part, But for her sake sae
far awa; unknowing what my way may thwart, My na _ tive
land sae far awa. Thou that of a' things Maker art, That
form'd this Fair sae far awa, Gin bo _ dy strength, then
I'll ne'er start, At this my way sae far awa.

How true is love to pure desert,
So love to her, sae far awa:
And nocht can-heal my bosom's smart,
While, Oh, she is sae far awa.
Nane other love, nane other dart,
I feel, but her's sae far awa;
But fairer never touch'd a heart
Than her's, the Fair sae far awa.

## Put the gown upon the Bishop.

450

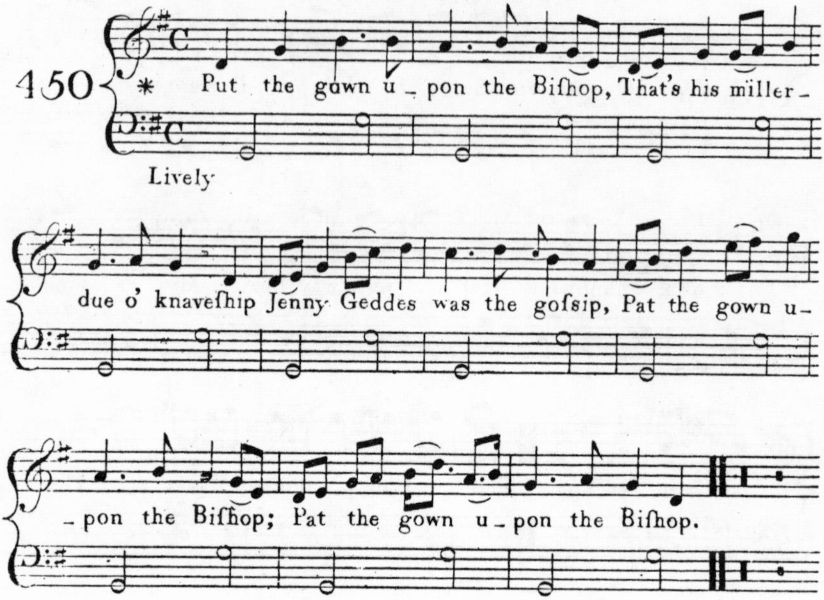
* Put the gown u_pon the Bishop, That's his miller_
Lively
due o' knaveship Jenny Geddes was the gossip, Pat the gown u_
_pon the Bishop; Pat the gown u_pon the Bishop.

## Hallow Fair. _There's fouth of braw Jockies, &c.

451

There's fouth of braw Jockies and Jenny's Comes
Lively
weel_busked into the fair, With ribbons on their cocker_no_
_nies, And fouth o' fine flour on their hair Oh Maggie she was

Continued.

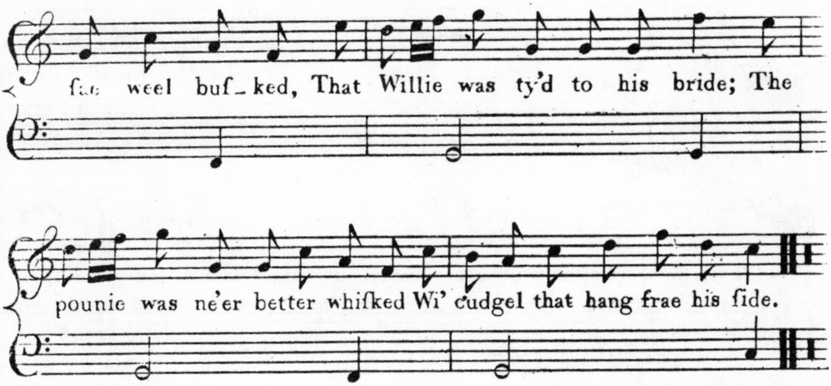
ſae weel buſ_ked, That Willie was ty'd to his bride; The
pounie was ne'er better whiſked Wi' cudgel that hang frae his ſide.

But Maggie was wondrous jealous
To ſee Willie buſked ſae braw;
And Sawney he ſat in the alehouſe,
And hard at the liquor did caw-sie,
There was Geordy that well lov'd his las
He touk the pint-ſtoup in his arms,
And hugg'd it, and ſaid, Trouth they're ſaucy
That loos nae a good father's bairn.

There was Wattie the muirland laddie,
That rides on the bonny grey cout,
With ſword by his ſide like a cadie,
To drive in the ſheep and the knout.
His doublet ſae weel it did fit him,
It ſcarcely came down to mid thigh,
With hair pouther'd, hat and a feather,
And houſing at courpon and tee.

But bruckie play'd boo to bauſie,
And aff ſcour'd the cout like the win':
Poor Wattie he fell in the cauſie,
And birs'd a the bains in his ſkin.
His piſtols fell out of the hulſters,
And were a' bedaubed with dirt;
The folks they came round him in cluſters,
Some leugh, and cry'd, Lad, was you hurt?

But cout wad let nae body ſteer him,
He was ay ſae wanton and ſkeegh;
The packmans ſtands he o'erturn'd them,
And gard a' the Jocks ſtand a-beech;
Wi' ſniring behind and before him,
For ſic is the metal of brutes:
Poor Wattie, and wae's me for him,
Was fain to gang hame in his boots.

Now it was late in the ev'ning,
And boughting time was drawing near:
The laſses had ſtench'd their greening
With fouth of braw apples and beer.
There was Lillie, and Tibbie, and Sibbie,
And Ceicy on the ſpinnell could ſpin,
Stood glowring at ſigns & glaſs winnocks,
But deil a ane bade them come in.

God guide's! ſaw you ever the like o' it?
See yonder's a bonny black ſwan;
It glowrs as't wad fain be at us;
What's yon that it hads in its hand?
Awa, daft gouk, cries Wattie,
They're a' but a rickle of ſticks:
See there is Bill, Jock, and auld Hackis,
And yonder's Meſs John & auld Nick.

Quoth Maggie, Come buy us our fairing:
And Wattie right ſleely cou'd tell
I think thou're the flowr of the clach'en
In trouth now I'ſe gie you my ſell.
But wha wou'd e'er thought it o him,
That e'er he had rippled the lint?
Sae proud was he o' his Maggie,
Tho' ſhe did baith ſcalie and ſquint.

# I'll never love thee more.

452

×
My dear and only love I pray, This lit_tle world of
Very Slow
thee, Be govern'd by no other sway, But purest monar_chy: For
if confusion have a part, Which virtuous souls ab hor, I'll
call a synod in my heart, And never love thee more.

As Alexander I will reign,
And I will reign alone,
My thoughts did evermore disdain
A rival on my throne.
He either fears his fate too much,
Or his deserts are small,
Who dares not put it to the touch,
To gain or lose it all.

But I will reign and govern still,
And always give the law;
And have each subject at my will,
And all to stand in awe;
But gainst my batt'ries if I find
Thou storm or vex me sore,
And if thou set me as a blind,
I'll never love thee more.

And in the empire of thy heart,
Where I should solely be,
If others do pretend a part,
Or dare to share with me;
Or committees if thou erect,
Or go on such a score,
I'll, smiling, mock at the neglect,
And never love thee more.

But if no faithless action stain
Thy love and constant word,
I'll make thee famous by my pen,
And glorious by my sword.
I'll serve thee in such noble ways,
As ne'er was known before;
I'll deck and crown thy head with bays,
And love thee more and more.

## My father has forty good ſhillings.

453

* My father has forty good ſhillings, Ha. ha! good
ſhillings! And never a daughter but I; My mother ſhe is right willing,
Ha! ha! right willing! That I ſhall have all when they die. And I
wonder when I'll be marry'd Ha! ha! be marry'd! My beauty begins to
decay; It's time to catch ha'd o' ſomebody Ha! ha! ſomebody! Be_
_fore it be a' run away. And I wonder when I'll be marry'd.

My ſhoes they are at the mending,
My buckles they are in the cheſt;
My ſtockings are ready for ſending
Then I'll be as braw as the reſt.
And I wonder, &c.

My father will buy me a ladle,
At my wedding we'll hae a good ſang;
For my uncle will buy me a cradle,
To rock my child in when it's young.
And I wonder, &c.

## Our Goodman came hame at e'en, &c.

454

Recit.
in time
Recit.
Our goodman came hame at e'en, And hame came he; And
Slowish.
in time
there he saw a saddle-horse, Where nae horse should be. O how
Recit.
in time
came this horse here? Or how can it be O how came this horse here, With
Recit.
in time
-out the leave o' me? A horse, quo' she: Ay a horse, quo' he. Ye
Recit.
auld blind dotard carl, And blinder mat ye be 'Tis but a dain-ty
in time
Recit.
milk cow, My minny sent to me. A milk cow! quo' he; Ay a
in time
milk cow, quo' she. O far hae I ridden, And meikle hae I
Recit.
in time
seen, But a saddle on a milk cow a-fore I ne'er saw nane.

## Continued.

Our goodman came hame at e'en,
And hame came he;
He spy'd a pair of jackboots,
Where nae boots should be.
What's this now goodwife?
What's this I see?
How came these boots there
Without the leave o' me!
Boots! quo' she:
Ay, boots quo' he.
Shame fa' your cuckold face,
And ill mat ye see,
It's but a pair of water stoups
The cooper sent to me.
Water stoups! quo' he:
Ay, water stoups, quo' she.
Far hae I ridden,
And farer hae I gane,
But siller spurs on water stoups
Saw I never nane.

Our goodman came hame at e'en,
And hame came he;
And then he saw a (siller) sword,
Where a sword should not be:
What's this now goodwife?
What's this I see?
O how came this sword here,
Without the leave o' me?
A sword! quo' she:
Ay, a sword, quo' he.
Shame fa' your cuckold face,
And ill mat you see,
It's but a parridge spurtle
My minnie sent to me.
(A parridge spurtle! quo' he:
Ay, a parridge spurtle quo' she.)
Weil, far hae I ridden,
And muckle hae I seen;
But siller handed (parridge) spurtles
Saw I never nane.

Our goodman came hame at e'en,
And hame came he;
There he spy'd a powder'd wig,
Where nae wig should be.
What's this now goodwife?
What's this I see?
How came this wig here,
Without the leave o' me.
A wig! quo' she:
Ay, a wig, quo' he.
Shame fa' your cuckold face,
And ill mat you see,
'Tis naething but a clocken hen
My minnie sent to me.
A clocken hen! quo' he:
Ay, a clocken hen, quo' she.
Far hae I ridden,
And muckle hae I seen,
But powder on a clocken-hen,
Saw I never nane.

Our goodman came hame at e'en,
And hame came he;
And there he saw a muckle coat,
Where nae coat should be.
O how came this coat here?
How can this be?
How came this coat here
Without the leave o' me?
A coat! quo' she:
Ay, a coat, quo' he.
Ye auld blind dotard carl,
Blind mat ye be,
It's but a pair of blankets
My minnie sent to me.
Blankets! quo' he:
Ay, blankets, quo' she.
Far hae I ridden,
And muckle hae I seen,
But buttons upon blankets
Saw I never nane

Ben went our goodman,
And ben went he;
And there he spy'd a sturdy man,
Where nae man should be.
How came this man here.
How can this be?
How came this man here,
Without the leave o' me?
A man! quo' she:
Ay, a man, quo' he.
Poor blind body,
And blinder mat ye be,
It's a new milking maid,
My mither sent to me.
A maid! quo' he:
Ay, a maid, quo' she,
Far hae I ridden,
And muckle hae I seen,
But lang-bearded maidens
Saw I never nane.

## Sir John Malcolm.

455

* O keep ye weel frae Sir John Malcolm, I_go and
Slow
a_go, If he's a wife man I miftak him, Iram coram dago.
O keep ye weel frae San_die Don, I_go and a_go He's
ten times daf_ter than Sir John, Iram coram da_go.

To hear them of their travels talk, Igo and ago,
To gae to London's but a walk: Iram coram dago.
I hae been at Amfterdam, &c.
Where I faw mony a braw madam.

To fee the wonders of the deep,
Wad gar a man baith wail and weep;
To fee the Leviathans fkip,
And wi' their tail ding o'er a fhip.

Was ye e'er in Crail town?
Did ye fee Clark Difhingtoun?
His wig was like a drouket hen,
And the tail o't hang down,
like a meikle maan lang draket gray goofe-pen.

But for to make ye mair enamour'd,
He has a glafs in his beft chamber;
But forth he ftept unto the door,
For he took pills the night before.

## Lizae Baillie.

456

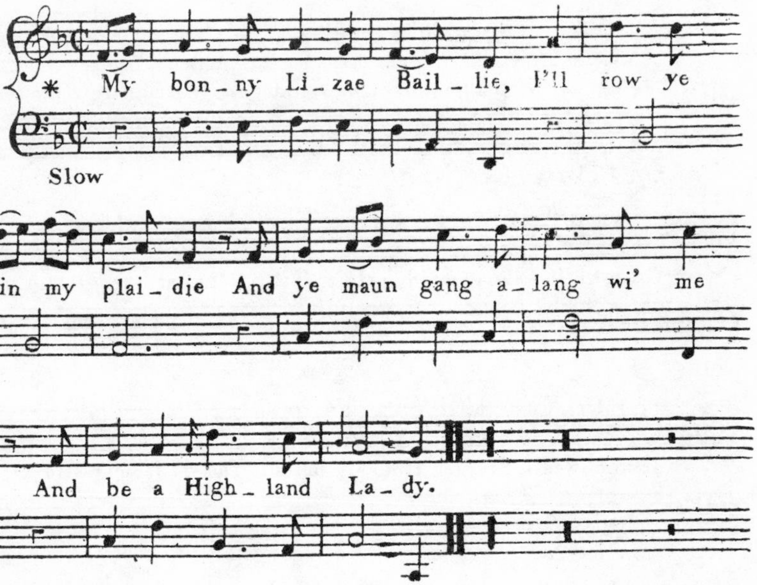
* My bon_ny Li_zae Bail_lie, I'll row ye
Slow
in my plai_die And ye maun gang a_lang wi' me
And be a High_land La_dy.

"I am ſure they wad nae ca' me wife,
Gin I wad gang wi' you, Sir;
For I can neither card nor ſpin,
Nor yet milk ewe or cow, Sir."

"My bonny Lizae Baillie,
Let nane o' theſe things daunt ye·
Ye'll hae nae need to card or ſpin,
Your mither weel can want ye."

Now ſhe's caſt aff her bonny ſhoen,
Made o' the gilded leather,
And ſhe's put on her highland brogues,
To ſkip amang the heather:

And ſhe's caſt aff her bonny gown,
Made o' the ſilk and ſattin,
And ſhe's put on a tartan plaid,
To row amang the braken:

She wad nae hae a Lawland laird,
Nor be an Engliſh lady;
But ſhe wad gang wi' Duncan Græme
And row her in his plaidie.

She was nae ten miles frae the town,
When ſhe began to weary;
She aften looked back, and ſaid,
"Farewell to Caſtlecarry.

"The firſt place I ſaw my Duncan Græme
Was near yon holland buſh.
My father took frae me my rings,
My rings but and my purſe.

"But I wad nae gie my Duncan Græme
For a' my father's land,
Though it were ten times ten times mair
And a' at my command."

\+ + + + + + + +

Now wae be to you, logger-heads,
That dwell near Caſtlecarry,
To let awa ſic a bonny laſs,
A Highlandman to marry.

## The Reel o' Stumpie.

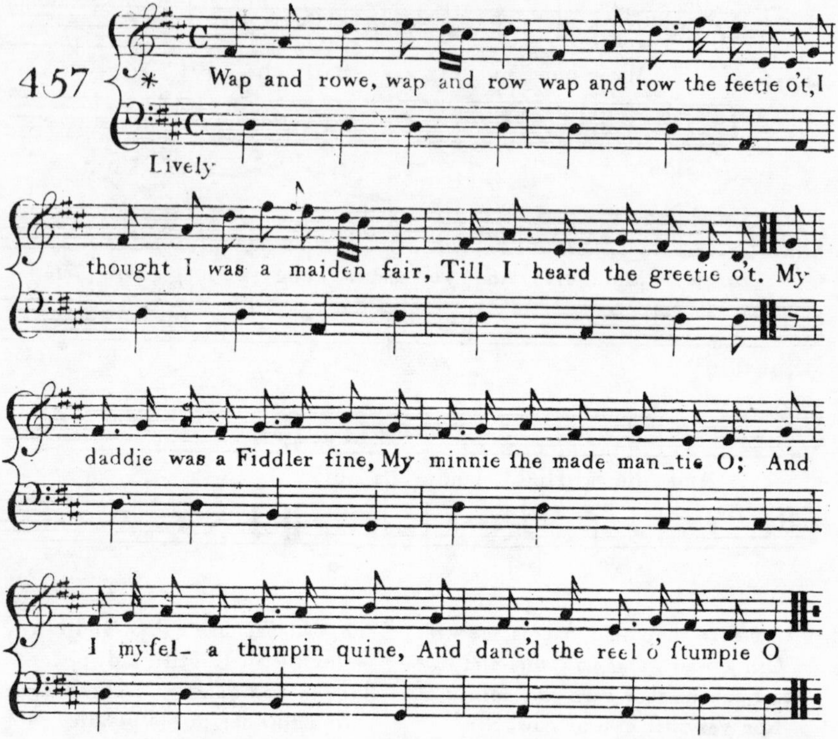
457
*
Wap and rowe, wap and row wap and row the feetie o't, I
Lively
thought I was a maiden fair, Till I heard the greetie o't. My
daddie was a Fiddler fine, My minnie ſhe made man_tie O; And
I myſel_ a thumpin quine, And danc'd the reel o' ſtumpie O

## I'll ay ca' in by yon Town.

458
*
I'll ay ca' in by yon town, And by yon garden
Lively
green, a_gain; I'll ay ca' in by yon town, And ſee my
bonie Jean a_gain. There's nane ſall ken there's nane ſall

Continued.

gueſs, What brings me back the gate again, But ſhe my faireſt
faithfu' laſs, And ſtow'nlins we ſall meet again.

She'll wander by the aiken tree,
When tryſtin time draws near again;
And when her lovely form I ſee,
O haith, ſhe's doubly dear again!
I'll ay ca', &c.

---

## To the foregoing Tune.
### Written for this Work by Robert Burns.

O wat ye wha's in yon town,
Ye ſee the e'enin Sun upon,
The deareſt maid's in yon town,
That e'enin Sun is ſhining on.
Now haply down yon gay green ſhaw;
She wanders by yon ſpreading tree,
How bleſt ye flowr's that round her blaw,
Ye catch the glances o' her e'e.
O wat ye wha's, &c.

How bleſt ye birds that round her ſing,
And welcome in the blooming year,
And doubly welcome be the ſpring,
The ſeaſon to my Jeanie dear.
O wat ye wha's, &c.

The ſun blinks blyth on yon town,
Amang the broomy braes ſae green;
But my delight's in yon town,
And deareſt pleaſure is my Jean:
O wat ye wha's, &c.

Without my fair, not a' the charms,
O' Paradiſe could yeild me joy;
But gie me Jeanie in my arms,
And welcome Lapland's dreary ſky;
O wat ye wha's, &c.

My cave wad be a lovers bow'r,
Tho' raging winter rent the air;
And ſhe a lovely little flower,
That I wad tent and ſhelter there.
O wat ye wha's, &c.

O ſweet is ſhe in yon town,
The ſinkin Sun's gane down upon;
A fairer than's in yon town,
His ſetting beam ne'er ſhone upon.
O wat ye wha's, &c.

If angry fate is ſworn my foe,
And ſuffering I am doom'd to bear;
I careleſs quit aught elſe below,
But, ſpare me ſpare me Jeanie dear.
O wat ye wha's, &c.

For while life's deareſt blood is warm,
Ae thought frae her ſhall ne'er depart,
And ſhe as faireſt is her form,
She has the trueſt kindeſt heart.
O wat ye wha's, &c. B.

# Will ye go and marry Katie.

159

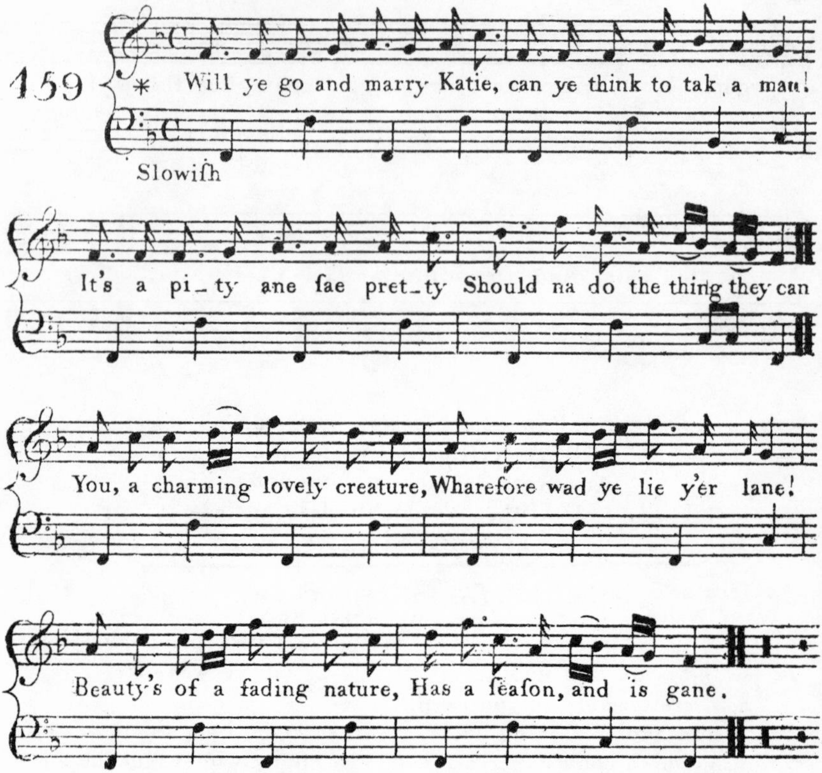

* Will ye go and marry Katie, can ye think to tak a man!
Slowish
It's a pi_ty ane ſae pret_ty Should na do the thing they can
You, a charming lovely creature, Wharefore wad ye lie y'er lane!
Beauty's of a fading nature, Has a ſeaſon, and is gane.


Therefore while ye're blooming Katie,
  Liſten to a loving ſwain;
Tak a mark by auntie Betty,
  Ance the darling o' the men:
She, wi' coy and fickle nature,
  Trifled aff till ſhe's grown auld,
Now ſhe's left by ilka creature;
  Let na this o' thee be tauld.

But, my dear and lovely Katie,
  This ae thing I hae to tell,
I could wiſh nae man to get ye,
  Save it were my very ſel.
Tak me, Katie, at my offer,
  Or be-had, and I'll tak you:
We's mak nae din about your tocher;
  Marry, Katie, then we'll woo.

Mony words are needleſs, Katie,
  Ye're a wanter, ſae am I;
If ye wad a man ſhould get ye,
  Then I can that want ſupply:
Say then, Katie, ſay ye'll take me,
  As the very wale o' men,
Never after to forſake me,
  And the Prieſt ſhall ſay, Amen.

Then, O! then, my charming Katie
  When we're married what comes the
Then nae ither man can get ye,
  But ye'll be my very ain:
Then we'll kiſs and clap at pleaſure,
  Nor wi' envy troubled be;
If ance I had my lovely treaſure
  Let the reſt admire and die.

## Blue Bonnets

460

* Wherefore ſighing art thou Phillis? Has thy Prime un-
-head-ed paſt haſt thou found that beauty's li-lies Were not
made for aye to laſt. Know thy form was once a treaſure;
Then it was thy hour of ſcorn Since thou then de-ny'st the
pleaſure Now 'tis fit that thou ſhouldſt mourn.


## Same Tune.

POWERS celeſtial, whoſe protection
Ever guards the virtuous Fair,
While in diſtant climes I wander,
Let my Mary be your care:
Let her form ſo fair and faultleſs,
Fair and faultleſs as your own;
Let my Mary's kindred ſpirit,
Draw your choiceſt influence down.

Make the gales you waft around her
Soft and peaceful as her breaſt;
Breathing in the breeze that fans her,
Sooth her boſom into reſt:
Guardian angels, O protect her,
When in diſtant lands I roam,
To realms unknown while fate exiles me
Make her boſom ſtill my home.

## The broom blooms bonie,

461

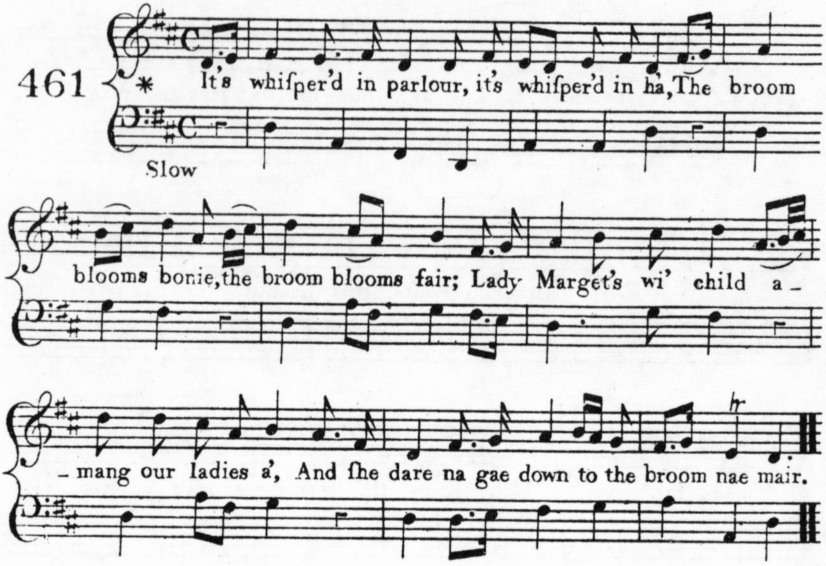
* It's whiſper'd in parlour, it's whiſper'd in ha, The broom
Slow
blooms bonie, the broom blooms fair; Lady Marget's wi' child a-
-mang our ladies a', And ſhe dare na gae down to the broom nae mair.

One lady whiſper'd unto another,
The broom blooms bonie, the broom blooms fair;
Lady Marget's wi' child to Sir Richard her brother,
And ſhe dare na gae down to the broom nae mair.

+ + + + + + + + + + + + + + + + + + + + + +

O when that you hear my loud loud cry,
The broom blooms &c.
Then bend your bow and let your arrows fly,
For I dare na gae down &c.

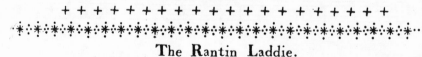

+ + + + + + + + + + + + + + + + + + + + + +

## The Rantin Laddie.

462

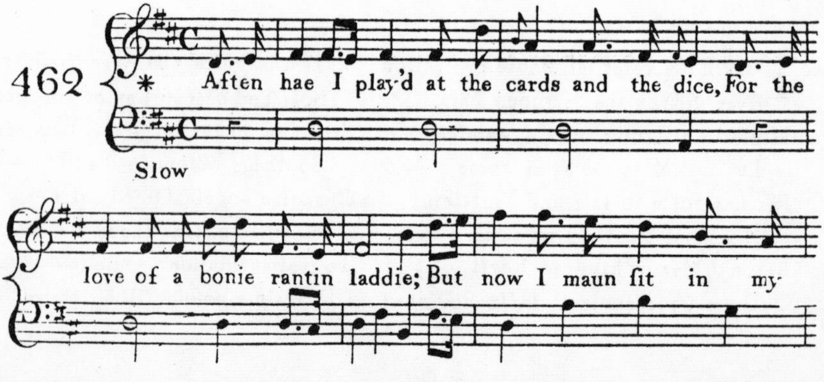
* Aften hae I play'd at the cards and the dice, For the
Slow
love of a bonie rantin laddie; But now I maun ſit in my

Continued.

fathers kitchen neuk and Be_low a baſtard babie.

For my father he will not me own,
And my mother ſhe neglects me,
And a' my friends hae lightlyed me,
And their ſervants they do ſlight me.
But had I a ſervant at my command,
As aft times I've had many,
That wad rin wi' a letter to bonie Glenſwood,
Wi' a letter to my rantin laddie.
Oh, is he either a laird, or a lord,
Or is he but a cadie,
That ye do him ca' ſae aften by name,
Your bonie, bonie rantin laddie.
Indeed he is baith a laird and a lord,
And he never was a cadie;
But he is the Earl o' bonie Aboyne,
And he is my rantin laddie.
O ye'se get a ſervant at your command,
As aft times ye've had many,
That ſall rin wi' a letter to bonie Glenſwood,
A letter to your rantin laddie.
When lord Aboyne did the letter get,
O but he blinket bonie;
But or he had read three lines of it,
I think his heart was ſorry.
O wha is daur be ſae bauld,
Sae cruelly to uſe my laſsie?
\+ + + + + + + + + + +
\+ + + + + + + + +
For her father he will not her know,
And her mother ſhe does ſlight her;
And a' her friends hae lightlied her,
And their ſervants they neglect her.
Go raiſe to me my five hundred men,
Make haſte and make them ready;
With a milkwhite ſteed under every ane,
For to bring hame my lady.
As they cam in thro' Buchan-ſhire,
They were a company bonie,
With a gude claymor in every hand,
And O, but they ſhin'd bonie.

# The Lass that winna sit down.

463

*
What think ye o' the scornfu' quine 'ill no sit-down by
Slowish
me I'll see the day that she'll repine un_less she does agree. O
she did hoot, and toot and flout 'cause I bad her sit down; But
the next time that e'er I do't I'll be whip't like a loon. wi' a
Tirry &c.

And yet she is a charming quine,
She's just o'er meikle spice
I'll see the day that she'll be mine,
For I'm nae very nice.
I loot the lassie tak' her will,
An' stand upo' her shanks,
The day may come whan I will spoil,
Her bonny saucy pranks.
Wi' my Tirry, &c.

I laid my head upo' my loof,
I did na' care a strae,
I ken'd fow weel that in a joof
Stand lang she wad na sae.
At last a blythsome lass did cry,
Come Sandy gie's a sang,
O now meg dorts I'll fairly try
Your heart strings for to twang.
Wi' a Tirry, &c.

The lassie's pride it cou'd na' last,
I sang wi' meikle glee,
Until at last she fairly cast,
Upo' me a sheeps ee.
A ha! thinks I, my bonnie lass,
Hae ye laid by your pride.
You're bonnier now than e'er you was,
And ye sall be my bride.
Wi' your Tirry, &c.

I ga'e the lass a lovin' squint,
That made her blush sae red,
I saw she fairly took the hint,
Which made my heart fou glad
The bonnie lass is a' mine ain:
For we twa did agree,
Now ilka night she's unco fain,
For to lie doun wi' me.
We' her Tirry, &c.

## O May thy morn.

Written for this Work by Robert Burns.

464

O May thy morn was ne'er sae sweet, As the
Slowish
mirk night o' December, For sparkling was the rosy wine, And
private was the chamber: And dear was she, I dare na
name, But I will ay remember. And dear was she I
dare na name, But I will ay remember.

And here's to them, that, like oursel,
Can push about the jorum,
And here's to them that wish us weel,
May a' that's gude watch o'er them:
And here's to them, we dare na tell,
The dearest o' the quorum.
And here's to them, we dare na tell,
The dearest o' the quorum.

B

## My Minnie says I manna.

465

*
Fu' fain wad I be Jamie's lass, My Minnie says I
manna. My daddie curs'd, my minnie grat, And I wi' Jamie's
love sud quat, But in my heart I'll tell you what, I said in
sooth I canna I canna I said in sooth I can_na.

## The Cherry and the Slae.

Tune, the banks of Helicon.

466

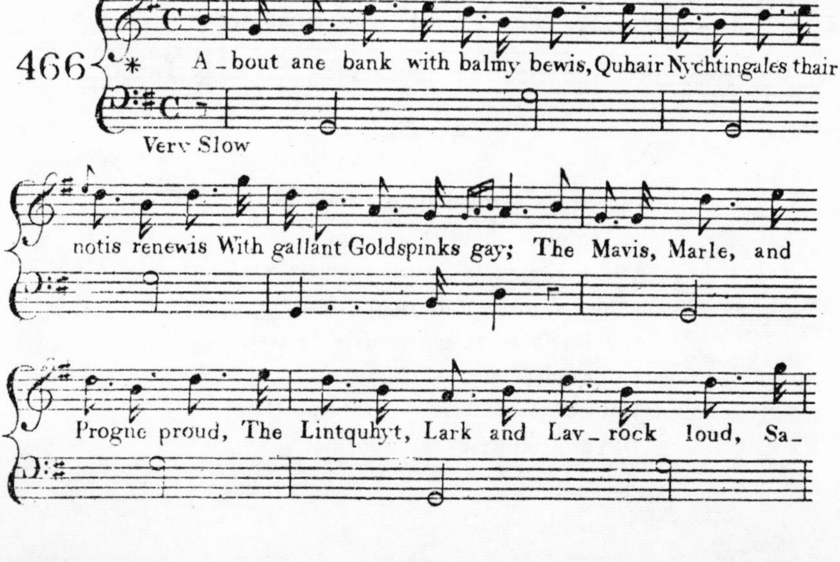
*
A_bout ane bank with balmy bewis, Quhair Nychtingales thair
Very Slow
notis renewis With gallant Goldspinks gay; The Mavis, Marle, and
Progne proud, The Lintquhyt, Lark and Lav_rock loud, Sa_

## Continued.

_lutet mirthful May. Quhen Philo_mel had sweetly sung, To
Progne scho deplord, How Tereus cut out her tung, And
falsly her deflourd; Quhilk sto_ry so sor_ie To schaw her self
scho seimt, To heir her, so neir her, I doutit if I dreimt.

The Cushat crouds, the Corbie crys,
The Coukow couks, the prattling Pyes,
To geck hir they begin:
The jargoun of the jangling Jayes,
The craiking Craws, and keckling Kays,
They deavt me with their din.
The painted Pawn with Argos eyis,
Can on his May-ock call,
The Turtle wails on witherit tries,
An Echo answers all,
Repeting with greiting,
How fair Narcissus fell,
By lying and spying
His schadow in the well.

I saw the Hurcheon and the Hare
In hidlings hirpling heir and thair,
To mak thair morning mang:
The Con, the Cuning and the Cat,
Quhais dainty downs with dew were wat,
With stif mustachis strange.
The Hart, the Hynd, the Dae, the Rae,
The Fulmert and false Fox;
The beardit Buck clam up the brae,
With birssy Bairs and Brocks
Sum feiding, sum dreiding
The Hunters subtile snairs,
With skipping and tripping,
They playit them all in pairs.

The air was sobir, saft and sweet,
Nae misty vapours, wind nor weit,
But quyit, calm and clear,
To foster Flora fragrant flowris,
Quhairon Apollos paramouris,
Had trinklit mony a teir; (-shyned
The quhilk lyke silver schaikers
Embroydering Bewties bed
Quhairwith their heavy heids declyned
In Mayis collouris cled,
Sum knoping, sum droping,
Of balmy liquor sweit,
Excelling and smilling
Throw Phebus hailsum heit.
&c. &c. &c. &c. &c. &c. &c.

## As I came o'er the Cairney mount.

467

As I came o'er the Cairney mount, And down amang the
Slow
blooming heather, Kindly stood the milking-shiel, To shelter
frae the stormy weather. O my bonie Highland lad, My
win - some, weel-far'd Highland laddie; Wha wad mind the
wind and rain, Sae weel row'd in his tartan plaidie.

× × × × × × × × × × × × × × × × ×

Now Phebus blinkit on the bent,  
And o'er the know's the lambs were bleating:  
But he wan my heart's consent,  
To be his ain at the neist meeting.  
O my bonie Highland lad,  
My winsome, weelfar d Highland laddie:  
Wha wad mind the wind and rain,  
Sae weel row'd in his tartan plaidie.

Z

# Highland Laddie.

468
*
The bon_niest lad that e'er I saw,
Slowish, but Chearful.
Bonie laddie, highland laddie Wore a plaid and was fu' braw
Bo_nie High_land laddie. On his head a bonnet blue,
Bo_nie lad_die, High_land laddie, His royal heart was
firm and true Bo_nie High_land lad_die.

Trumpets sound and cannons roar,
  Bonie lassie, Lawland lassie,
And a' the hills wi' echoes roar,
  Bonie Lawland lassie
Glory, Honour, now invite.
  Bonie lassie, Lawland lassie.
For freedom and my King to fight,
  Bonie Lawland lassie.

The sun a backward course shall take
  Bonie laddie, Highland laddie,
Ere ought thy manly courage shake;
  Bonie, Highland laddie.
Go, for yoursel procure renown,
  Bonie laddie, Highland laddie,
And for your lawful king his crown,
  Bonie, Highland laddie

## Chronicle of the heart.

Tune Gingling Geordie.

469

* How often my heart has by love been o'erthrown, what
grand revolutions its mpire has known, you aſk my dear friend then at-
-tend the ſad ſtrain, ſince you bid me relate ſuch ineffable pain. For
who that has got e'er an eye in his pate ſo diſmal a tale without tears can re-
-late, or who ſuch dire annals recall to his mind, without burſting in tears
both before & behind.
Chorus
O Love thy viciſsitudes who can deſcribe, How
fiercely they threaten how highly they bribe, How ſweetly they tickle! how
keenly they ſmart and how dreadful the havock they make in my heart.

## Continued.

This kingdom as Authors impartial have told,
At firſt was elective, but afterwards sold,
For experience will shew whoe'er pleases to try,
That kingdoms are venal, when subjects can buy,
Lovely Peggy, the first in succession and name,
Was early invested with honour supreme,
But a bold son of Mars grew fond of her form
Swore himself into grace and surpris'd her by storm. O Love, &c.

Maria succeeded in honour and place
By laughing and squeezing and song and grimace.
But her favours alas! like her carriage, were free,
Bestow'd on the whole male creation but me.
Next Margret the second attempted the chace,
Tho' the small Pox and age had enamell'd her face,
She sustain'd her pretence, sans merite and sans love,
And carried her point by a Je ne ſai ſai quoi. O Love, &c.

The heart which so tamely acknowledged her sway,
Still suffer'd in silence, and kept her at bay,
Till old Time at last so much mellow'd her charms,
That she dropt with a breeze in a Livery-mans arms.
The most easy conquest Belinda was thine
Obtaind by the musical tinkle of coin
But she more enamour'd of sport than of prey,
Had a fish in her hook which she wanted to play. O Love, &c.

High hopes were her baits; but if truth were confess'd,
A good still in prospect is not good possess'd;
For the fool found too late he had taken a tartar
Retreated with wounds and begg'd stoutly for quarter.
Uranea came next, and with subtile address,
Discover'd no open attempts to possess;
But when fairly admitted, of conquest secure,
She acknowledg'd no law, but her will and her power. O Love, &c.

For seven tedious years to get rid of her chain,
All force prov'd abortive all stratagem vain,
Till a youth with much fatness and gravity bless'd,
Her person detain'd by a lawful arrest.
To a reign so despotic tho' guiltless of blood,
No wonder a long interregnum ensu'd,
For an ass tho' the patientest brute of the plain,
Once saded and gull'd, will beware of the rein. O Love, &c.

O Nancy, dear Nancy, my fate I deplore,
No magic thy beauty and youth can restore,
By thee had this cordial dominion been sway'd,
Thou hadst then been a queen, but art now an old maid,
Now the kingdom stands doubtful it-self to surrender,
To Chloe the sprightly or Celia the slender,
But if once it were out of this pitiful case,
No law, but the Salic henceforth shall take place.
O Love, &c.

## Wilt thou be my Dearie.

Written for this Work by Robert Burns.

470

Wilt thou be my Dear_ie; When sorrow
Very. Slow
wrings thy gentle heart, O wilt thou let me chear thee:
By the treasure of my soul, That's the love I bear thee! I
swear and vow, that only thou shall ev_er be my dearie.
Only thou I swear and vow, Shall ever be my Dearie.

Lassie, say thou lo'es me;
Or if thou wilt na be my ain,
Say na thou'lt refuse me:
If it winna, canna be,
Thou for thine may chuse me,
Let me, Lassie, quickly die,
Trusting that thou lo'es me
Lassie, let me quickly die,
Trusting that thou lo'es me.

B

# Lovely Polly Stewart.

Tune Ye're welcome Charlie Stewart.

Chorus.
471
*
Lively
O Lovely Polly Stewart, O charming Polly Stewart There's
ne'er a flower that blooms in May That's half so fair as
thou art. The flower it blaws, it fades, it fa's, And
art can ne'er re_new it; But worth and truth e_
_ternal youth will gie to Polly Stewart.

May he, whase arms shall fauld thy charms,
Possess a leal and true heart.
To him be given, to ken the Heaven,
He grasps in Polly Stewart.
O lovely, &c.

Written for this Work by Robert Burns.

## The Highland balou.

472

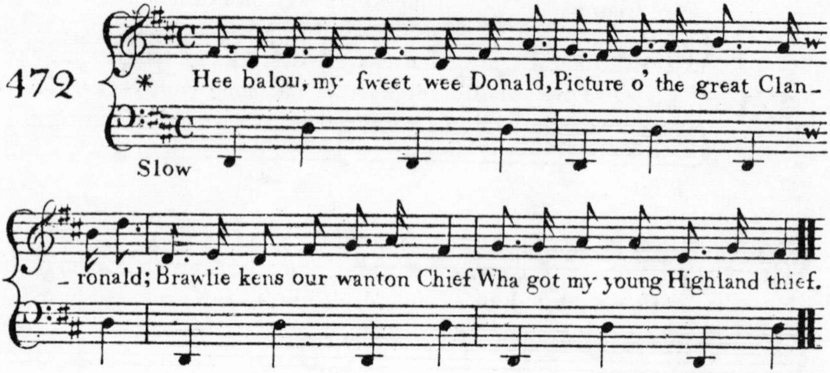
Hee balou, my sweet wee Donald, Picture o' the great Clan-
-ronald; Brawlie kens our wanton Chief Wha got my young Highland thief.
Slow

Leez me on thy bonie craigie,
And thou live, thou'll steal a naigie.
Travel the country thro' and thro',
And bring hame a Carlisle cow.

Thro' the Lawlands, o'er the Border,
Weel, my babie, may thou furder:
Herry the louns o' the laigh Countrie,
Syne to the Highlands hame to me.

+ + + + + + + + + + + + + + + + + +

## Auld king Coul.

473

* Our auld king Coul was a jol-ly auld soul, And a
Lively
jolly auld soul was he; Our auld king Coul fill'd a jolly brown
bowl, And he ca'd for his fid--lers three:
Ad. Lib.
Fidell-didell, fidell-didell, quo' the fid-dlers three; There's

* This must be repeated to the additional lines.

## Continued.

no a laſs in a Scotland Like our ſweet Mar-jo - rie.

Our auld king Coul was a jolly auld ſoul,
  And a jolly auld ſoul was he;
Our auld king Coul fill'd a jolly brown bowl,
  And he ca'd for his pipers three:
Ha didell, ho didell, quo' the pipers;
  Fidell, didell, fidell, didell, quo' the fiddlers three;
There's no a laſs in a' Scotland
  Like our ſweet Marjorie.

Our auld king Coul was a jolly auld ſoul,
  And a jolly auld ſoul was he;
Our auld king Coul fill'd a jolly brown bowl
  And he ca'd for his harpers three:
Twingle-twangle, twingle-twangle, quo' the harpers;
  Ha-didell, ho didell, quo' the pipers;
Fidell didell, fidell-didell, quo' the fiddlers three;
  There's no a laſs in a' Scotland
Like our ſweet Marjorie.

Our auld king Coul was a jolly auld ſoul,
  And a jolly auld ſoul was he;
Our auld king Coul fill'd a jolly brown bowl
  And he ca'd for his trumpeters three:
Twara-rang, twara-rang, quo' the trumpeters;
  Twingle twangle, twingle-twangle, quo the harpers;
Ha didel, ho didell, quo' the pipers;
  Fidell-didell, fidell-didell, quo' the fiddlers three;
There's no a laſs in a' Scotland
  Like our ſweet Marjorie.

Our auld king Coul was a jolly auld ſoul,
  And a jolly auld ſoul was he;
Our auld king Coul fill'd a jolly brown bowl,
  And he c'ad for his drummers three:
Rub-a-dub, rub-a-dub, quo' the drummers;
  Twara-rang, twara-rang, quo' the trumpeters;
Twingle-twangle, twingle-twangle, quo' the harpers;
  Ha-didell, ho-didell, quo' the pipers;
Fidell-didell, fidell-didell, quo' the fiddlers three:
  There's no a laſs in a' Scotland
Like our ſweet Marjorie.

## The Rinaway Bride.

474

*
A Laddie and a Lassie Dwelt in the South countrie, And they hae cassen their claiths thegither, And
married they wad be: On Tyseday was the bri_dal
day Appointed for to be. Then hey play up the
rin_away Bride, For she has taen the gee.

She had nae run a mile or twa,
  When she began to consider,
The angering of her father dear,
  The displeasing o' her mither;
The slighting of the silly bridegroom,
  The weel warst o' the three;
Then hey play up the rinawa' bride,
  For she has taen the gee.

Her father and her mither
  Ran after her wi' speed,
And av they ran until they came
  Unto the water of Tweed,
And when they came to Kelso town,
  They gart the clap gae thro'
    Then hey, &c.

Saw ye a lass wi' a hood and a mantle
  The face o't lin'd up wi' blue;
The face o't lin'd up wi' blue,
  And the tail lin'd up wi' green,
Saw ye a lass wi' a hood and a mantle,
  Was married on Tyseday 'teen.
    Then hey, &c.

Now wally fu' fa' the silly bridegroom,
  He was as saft as butter;
For had she play'd the like to me,
  I had nae sae easily quit her;
I'd gi'en her a tune o' my hoboy,
  And set my fancy free,
And syne play'd up the rinaway bride,
  And lutten her tak the gee.

## Bannocks o' oear meal.

475

Ban_nocks o' bear meal Ban_nocks o' bar_ley
Here's to the High_land_man's bannocks o' bar_ley.
Wha, in a brul_zie, will first cry a par_-ley?
Ne_ver the lads wi' the ban_-nocks o' bar_-ley
Chorus.
Bannocks o' bear meal Bannocks o' barley Here's to the
High_land_man's ban_nocks o' bar_ley.

Wha in his wae days, were loyal to Charlie?
Wha but the lads wi' the bannocks o' barley
Cho.s Bannocks o', &c.

+ + + + + + + + + + + + + + + + + + + +

## Wae is my heart.

476

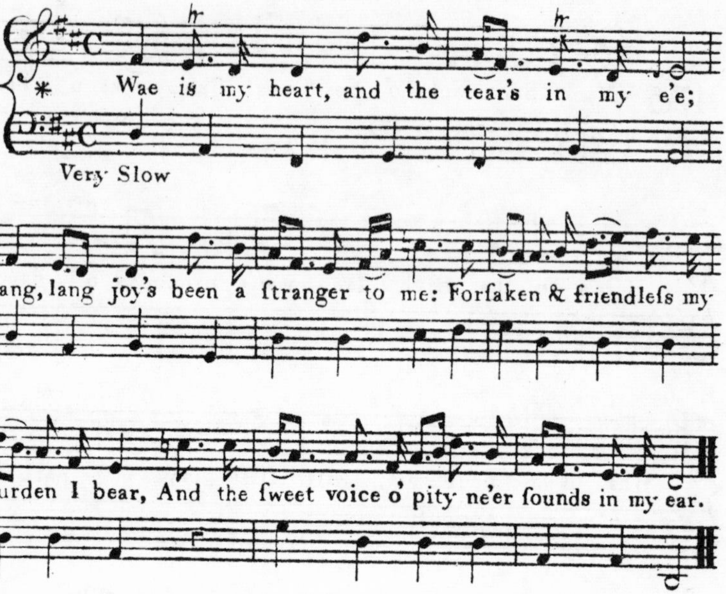
* Wae is my heart, and the tear's in my e'e;
Very Slow
Lang, lang joy's been a ſtranger to me: Forſaken & friendleſs my
burden I bear, And the ſweet voice o' pity ne'er ſounds in my ear.

Love, thou haſt pleaſures, and deep hae I loved;
Love thou haſt ſorrows, and ſair hae I proved:
But this bruiſed heart that now bleeds in my breaſt,
I can feel by its throbbings will ſoon be at reſt.

O, if I were, where happy I hae been;
Down by yon ſtream and yon bonie-caſtle-green:
For there he is wandring, and muſing on me,
Wha wad ſoon dry the tear frae his Phillis's e'e.

## There was a ſilly Shepherd Swain.

477

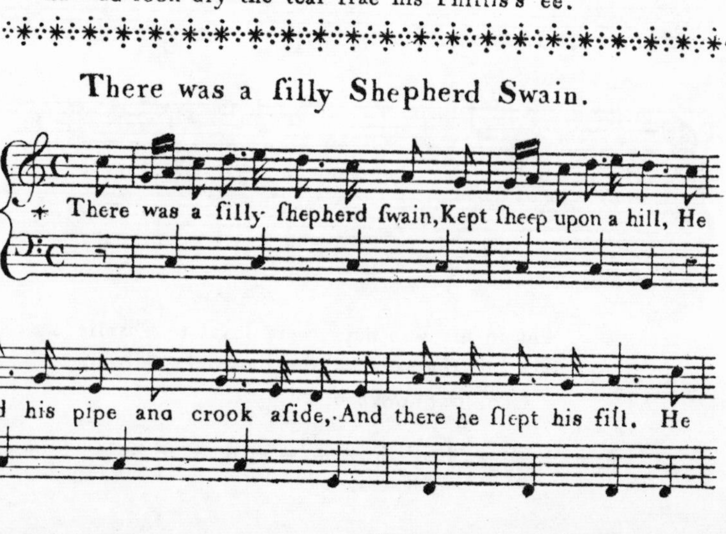
+ There was a ſilly ſhepherd ſwain, Kept ſheep upon a hill, He
laid his pipe and crook aſide, And there he ſlept his fill. He

## Continued.

laid his pipe and crook aſide, And there he ſlept his fill.

He looked eaſt, he looked weſt,
Then gave an under-look,
And there he ſpied a lady fair,
Swimming in a brook,
And there,&c.

He rais'd his head frae his green bed,
And then approach'd the maid,
Put on yourclaiths, my dear, he ſays,
And be ye not afraid.
Put on,&c.

'Tis fitter for a lady fair,
To ſew her ſilken ſeam,
Than to get up in a May morning,
And ſtrive againſt the ſtream.
Than to get,&c.

If you'll not touch my mantle,
And let my claiths alane;
Then I'll give you as much money,
As you can carry hame.
Then I'll,&c.

O! I'll not touch your mantle,
And I'll let your claiths alane;
But I'll tak you out of the clear water,
My dear, to be my ain,
But I'll tak,&c.

And when ſhe out of the water came,
He took her in his arms;
Put on your claiths, my dear, he ſays,
And hide thoſe lovely charms.
Put on your,&c.

Hemounted her on a milk-white ſteed,
Himſelf upon anither;
And all along the way they rode,
Like ſiſter and like brither.
And all along,&c.

When ſhe came to her father's yate,
She tirled at the pin;
And ready ſtood the porter there,
To let this fair maid in.
And ready,&c.

And when the gate was opened,
So nimbly's ſhe whipt in;
Pough! you're a fool without, ſhe ſays,
And I'm a maid within.
Pough! you're,&c.

Then fare ye well, my modeſt boy,
I thank you for your care;
But had you done what you ſhould do,
I ne'er had left you there.
But had you,&c.

Oh! I'll caſt aff my hoſe and ſhoon,
And let my feet gae bare,
And gin I meet a bonny laſs,
Hang me, if her I ſpare.
And gin I,&c.

In that do as you pleaſe, ſhe ſays,
But you ſhall never more
Have the ſame opportunity;
With that ſhe ſhut the door.
Have the,&c.

There is a gude auld proverb,
I've often heard it told,
He that would not when he might,
He ſhould not when he would.
He that,&c.

# Kind Robin looes me.

478

Ro_bin is my on_ly joe, For Robin has the
Andante
art to loo', So to his ſuit I mean to bow Be_cauſe I
ken he looes me. Hap_py happy was the ſhow'r, That
led me to his bir_ken bow'r, Whare firſt of love I
fand the pow'r, And kend that Robin loo'd me.

They ſpeak of napkins, ſpeak of rings,
Speak of gloves and kiſsing ſtrings,
And name a thouſand bonny things,
And ca' them ſigns he loes me.
But I'd prefer a ſmack of Rob,
Spo ting on the velvet fog,
To gifts as lang's a plaiden wabb,
Becauſe I ken he looes me.

He's tall and ſonſy, frank and free,
Lood by a' and dear to me,
Wi' him I'd live, wi' him I'd die,
Becauſe my Robin looes me.
My titty Mary ſaid to me,
Our courtſhip but a joke wad be,
And I, or lang, be made to ſee,
That Robin did na looe me.

But little kens ſhe what has been,
Me and my honeſt Rob between,
And in his wooing, O ſo keen,
Kind Robin is that looes me.
Then fly ye lazy hours away,
And haſten on the happy day
When join'd our hands Meſs John ſhall-ſay,
And mak him mine that looes me.

'Till then let every chance unite,
To weigh our love and fix delight,
And I'll look down on ſuch wi' ſpite,
Wha doubt that Robin looes me.
O hey Robin quo' ſhe,
O hey Robin quo' ſhe,
O hey Robin quo' ſhe,
Kind Robin looes me.

# We'll put the ſheep head in the Pat

479

* We'll put the ſheep head in the Pat, Horns an'
a' the gither, And that will mak dainty fine broth & we'll
a' ſup the gither. We'll a' ſup the gither We'll
a' lye the gither We'll hae nae mae beds but
ane Un_til it be warm_er weather.

The woo will lyith the kail,
The Horns will ſerve for bread,
By that ye will ſee the vertu
Of a gude ſheep head.
    We'll a' ſup &c.

Some will lie at the head,
Some will lie at the feet,
John Cuddie will lie in the midſt,
For he wou'd hae a' the heat.
    We'll a' lie &c.

## Here's his health in water

480

*
Altho' my back be at the wa', And though he be the
Lively
fautor, Although my back be at the wa', Yet here's his health in
water. O wae gae by his wanton ſides, Sae brawly's he could flatter; till
for his ſake I'm ſlighted fair, And dree the kintra clat_ter: But
though my back be at the wa', Yet here's his health in water.
Z

## The maid gaed to the Mill.

481

*
The maid's gane to the mill by night; Hech hey, ſae
wan_ton; The maid's gane to the mill by night, Hech

## Continued.

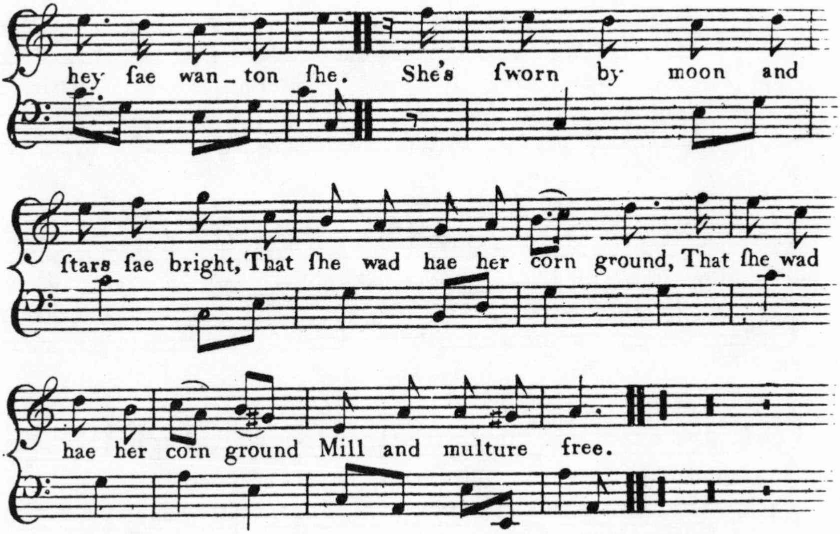
hey ſae wan_ton ſhe. She's ſworn by moon and
ſtars ſae bright, That ſhe wad hae her corn ground, That ſhe wad
hae her corn ground Mill and multure free.

Out then came the miller's man,
  Hech hey, ſae wanton;
Out then came the miller's man,
  Hech hey, ſae wanton he;
He ſware he'd do the beſt he can,
For to get her corn ground,
For to get her corn ground,
  Mill and multure free.

He put his hand about her neck,
  Hech hey, ſae wanton;
He put his hand about her neck,
  Hech hey, ſae wanton he;
He dang her down upon a ſack,
And there ſhe got her corn ground,
And there ſhe got her corn ground,
  Mill and multure free.

When other maids gaed out to play,
  Hech hey, ſae wanton;
When other maids gaed out to play,
  Hech hey, ſae wantonlie;
She ſigh'd and ſobb'd, and wadnae ſtay,
Becauſe ſhe'd got her corn ground,
Becauſe ſhe'd got her corn ground,
  Mill and multure free.

When forty weeks were paſt and gane,
  Hech hey, ſae wanton;
When forty weeks were paſt and gane,
  Hech hey, ſae wantonlie;
This maiden had a braw lad bairn,
Becauſe ſhe'd got her corn ground,
Becauſe ſhe'd got her corn ground,
  Mill and multure free.

Her mither bade her caſt it out,
  Hech hey, ſae wanton;
Her mither bade her caſt it out,
  Hech hey, ſae wantonlie;
It was the miller's duſty clout,
For getting of her corn ground,
For getting of her corn ground,
  Mill and multure free.

Her father bade her keep it in,
  Hech hey, ſae wanton;
Her father bade her keep it in,
  Hech hey, ſae wantonlie;
It was the chief of a' her kin,
Becauſe ſhe'd got her corn ground,
Becauſe ſhe'd got her corn ground,
  Mill and multure free.

# Sir Patrick Spence.

482

* The King ſits in Dumfermline toune, Drink_
_ing the blude-rid wine O quhar wull I get a
guid ſai_lor to ſail this ſchip of mine.

Up and ſpak an eldern knicht,
Sat at the king's richt kne:
Sir Patrick Spence is the beſt ſailor,
That ſails upon the ſea

The King has written a braid letter,
And ſignd it wi' his hand;
And ſent it to Sir Patrick Spence,
Was walking on the ſand.

The firſt line that Sir Patrick red,
A loud lauch lauched he:
The next line that Sir Patrick red,
The teir blinded his ee.

O quha is this has don this deid,
This ill deid don to me;
To ſend me out this time o' the zeir,
To ſail upon the ſea?

Mak haſte, mak haſte, my mirry men all,
Our guid ſchip ſails the morne.
O ſay na ſae, my maſter deir,
For I feir a deadlie ſtorme.

Late late yeſtreen I ſaw the new moone
Wi' the auld moone in her arme;
And I feir, I feir, my deir maſter,
That we wull cum to harme.

O our Scots nobles wer richt laith
To weet their cork-heild ſhoone;
Bot lang or a' the play were playd,
They wat thair heads aboone.

O lang, lang, may thair ladies ſit
Wi' thair fans into their hand,
Or eir they ſe Sir Patrick Spence
Cum ſailing to the land.

O lang, lang, may thair ladies ſtand
Wi' thair gold kems in their hair,
Waiting for thair ain deir lordes,
For they'll ſe thame na mair.

Haff owre, haff owre to Aberdour,
It's fiftie fadom deip:
And thair lies guid Sir Patrick Spence,
Wi' the Scots lordes at his feit.

## The Wren, or Lennox's love to Blantyre

483

*
Slowish
The Wren soho lyes in care's bed, In care's bed, in care's bed The Wren soho lyes in care's bed, In meikle dule and pyne _ _ O! Quhen in came Ro _ _ bin Red _ breast, Quhen in came Robin Red breast, Quhen in came Robin Red _ breast, Wi' succar _ saps and wyne _ O.

Now, maiden, will ye taste o' this,
Taste o' this, taste o' this;
Now, maiden, will ye taste o' this?
It's succar-saps and wyne_O.
Na, ne'er a drap, Robin,
Robin, Robin;
Na, ne'er a drap, Robin,
Gin it was ne'er so fine_O.

\+ + + + + + + + + + +

And quhere's the ring that I gied ze,
That I gied ze, that I gied ze;
And quhere's the ring that I gied ze,
Ze little cutty quean_O.
I gied it till a soger,
A soger, a soger,
I gied it till a soger,
A kynd sweet-heart o yne_O

## Gude Wallace.

484

O for my ain king, quo gude Wal_lace, The
Slowiſh
right_fu' king of fair Scotland. Be_tween me and my
ſoverign blude I think I ſee ſome ill ſeed ſawn.

Wallace out over yon river he lap,
And he has lighted low down on yon plain
And he was aware of a gay ladie,
As ſhe was at the well waſhing.

What tydins, what tydins, fair lady, he ſays,
What tydins haſt thou to tell unto me
What tydins, what tydins, fair lady, he ſays,
What tydins hae ye in the ſouth Countrie.

Low down in yon wee Oſtler houſe,
There is fyfteen Engliſhmen,
And they are ſeekin for gude Wallace,
It's him to take and him to hang.

There's nocht in my purſe, quo gude Wallace,
There's nocht, not even a bare pennie,
But I will down to yon wee Oſtler houſe
Thir fyfteen Engliſhmen to ſee.

## Continued.

And when he cam to yon wee Ostler house,
He bad bendicite be there;
+ + + + + + + + + + +
+ + + + + + + + + +

Where was ye born, auld crookt Carl,
Where was ye born in what countrie,
I am a true Scot born and bred,
And an auld crookit carl just sic as ye see.

I wad gie fifteen shillings to onie crookit carl,
To onie crookit carl just sic as ye,
If ye will get me gude Wallace,
For he is the man I wad very fain see.

He hit the proud Captain alang the chafft blade,
That never a bit o' meal he ate mair;
And he sticket the rest at the table where they sat,
And he left them a' lyin sprawlin there.

Get up, get up, gudewife, he says,
And get to me some dinner in haste;
For it will soon be three lang days
Sin I a bit o' meat did taste.

The dinner was na weel readie,
Nor was it on the table set,
Till other fyfteen Englishmen
Were a' lighted about the yett.

Come out, come out, now gude Wallace
This is the day that thou maun die;
I lippen nae sae little to God, he says,
Altho' I be but ill wordie.

The gudewife had an auld gudeman,
By gude Wallace he stiffly stood,
Till ten o' the fyfteen, Englishmen,
Before the door lay in their blude.

The other five to the greenwood ran,
And he hang'd these five upon a grssn,
And on the morn wi' his merry men a'
He sat at dine in Lochmaben town.

# The auld man's mare's dead.

485

*
The auld man's mare's dead, The poor man's mare's dead, The
Slowish
auld man's mare's dead A mile a_boon Dun_dee. She was
cut_luggit, paich_lip-pit, Steel waimit, Stain_cher_fit_tit,
Chorus
Chan_ler_chaftit, lang_neckit, Yet the brute did die. The
auld man's mare's dead, The poor man's mare's dead, The
auld man's mare's dead A mile a_boon Dundee.

Hen Iwnzie_banes were knaggs & neuks,
She had the cleeks, the cauld, the crooks.
The jawpish and the wanton yeuks,
And the howks aboon her e'e
The auld man's &c.

My Mafter rade me to the town,
He ty'd me to a ftaincher round;
He toch a chappin till himfel.
But fient a drap gae me.
The auld man's &c.

The auld man's mare's dead,
The poor man's mare's dead.
The peats and tours and a' to lead
And yet the jad did die.

# The winter of life.

Written for this Work by Robert Burns.

486

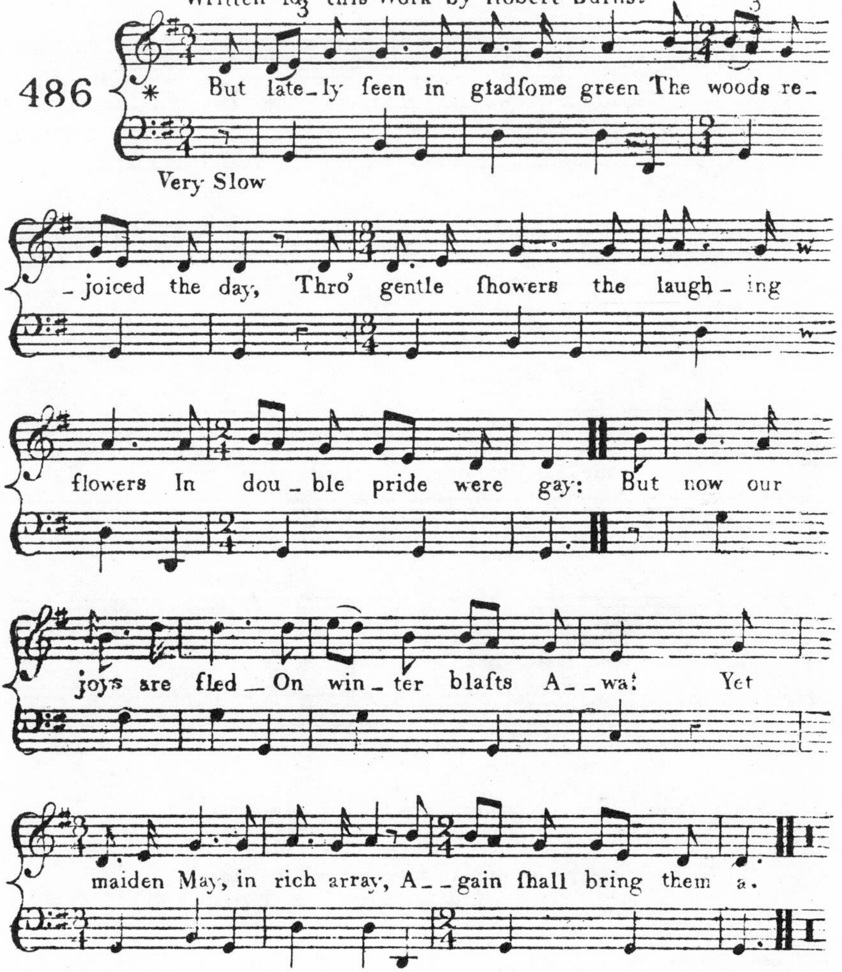
But late_ly feen in gladfome green The woods re_
Very Slow
_joiced the day, Thro' gentle fhowers the laugh_ing
flowers In dou_ble pride were gay: But now our
joys are fled _ On win_ter blafts A_ _wa! Yet
maiden May, in rich array, A_ _gain fhall bring them a.

But my white pow-nae kindly thows
  Shall melt the fnaws of Age;
My trunk of eild, but bufs or beild,
  Sinks in Time's wintry rage
Oh, Age has weary days.
  And nights o' fleeplefs pain.
Thou golden time o' Youthfu' prime,
  Why comes thou not again!

## Good morrow, fair mistress.

487 
Good morrow fair mistress the be gin _ ner of strife, I took ye frae the begging, and made ye my wife. It was your fair outside, that first took my ee, But this is the last time my face ye sall see
Slow

Fye on ye, ill woman, the bringer o' shame,
The abuser o' love, the disgrace o' my name;
The betrayer o' him that so trusted in thee:
But this is the last time my face ye sall see.

To the ground shall be razed these halls and these bowers,
Defil'd by your lusts and your wanton amours:
I'll find out a lady of higher degree;
And this is the last time my face ye sall see.

## The Haws of Cromdale.

488 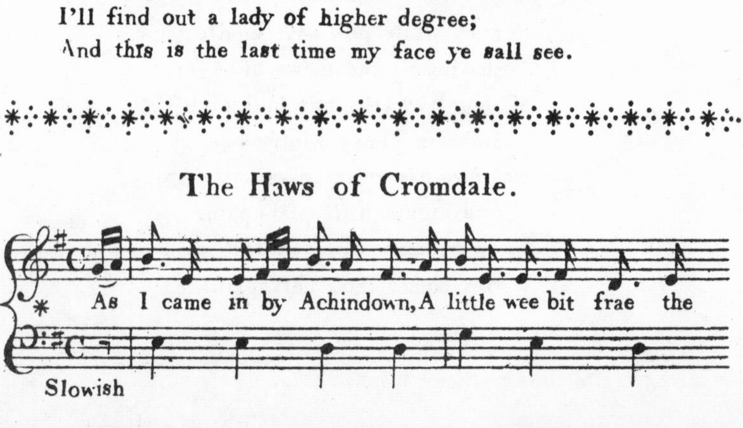
As I came in by Achindown, A little wee bit frae the
Slowish

## Continued.

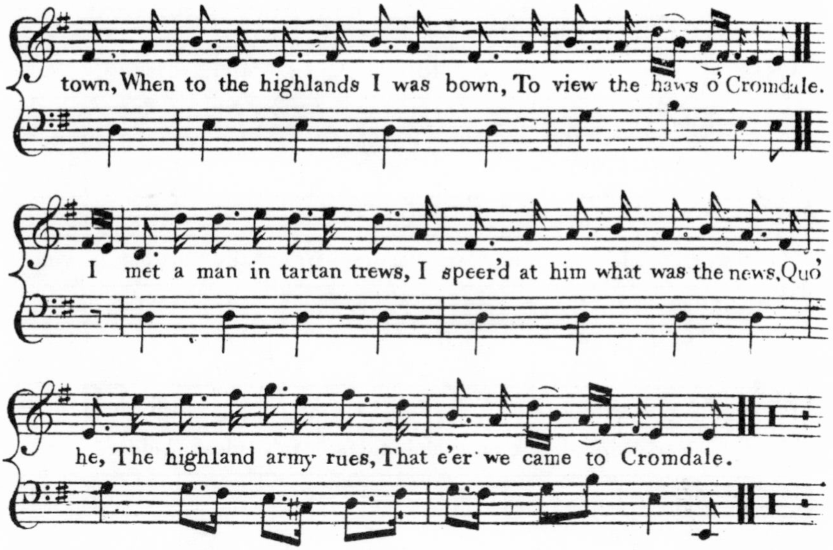
town, When to the highlands I was bown, To view the haws o' Cromdale.
I met a man in tartan trews, I speer'd at him what was the news, Quo'
he, The highland army rues, That e'er we came to Cromdale.

We were in bed, sir, every man,
When the English host upon us came;
A bloody battle then began,
Upon the haws of Cromdale.
The English horse they were so rude,
They bath'd their hoofs in highland blood,
But our brave clans they boldly stood,
Upon the haws of Cromdale.

But alas we could no longer stay,
For o'er the hills we came away,
And sore we do lament the day
That e'er we came to Cromdale.
Thus the great Montrose did say,
Can you direct the nearest way.
For I will o'er the hills this day,
Ano view the haws of Cromdale.

Alas, my lord, you're not so strong,
You scarcely have two thousand men,
And there's twenty thousand on the plain,
Stand rank and file on Cromdale.
'Thus the great Montrose did say,
I say, direct the nearest way,
For I will o'er the hills this day,
And see the haws of Cromdale.

They were at dinner, every man,
When great Montrose upon them came,
A second battle then began,
Upon the haws of Cromdale.

The Grants, Mackenzies, and M'kys,
Soon as Montrose they did espy,
O then they fought most vehemently,
Upon the haws of Cromdale.

The M^c. Donalds they return'd again,
The Camerons did their standard join,
M^c. Intosh play'd a bonny game,
Upon the haws of Cromdale.
The M^c. Gregors faught like lyons bold,
M^c. Phersons, none could them controul,
M^c. Lauchlins faught like loyal souls,
Upon the haws of Cromdale.

(M^c. Leans, M^c. Dougals, and M^c. Neals,
So boldly as they took the field,
And made their enemies to yield,
Upon the haws of Cromdale.)
The Gordons boldly did advance,
The Fraziers fought with sword & lance,
The Grahams they made their heads to dance,
Upon the haws of Cromdale.

The loyal Stewarts, with Montrose
So boldly set upon their foes,
And brought them down with highland blows
Upon the haws of Cromdale.
Of twenty thousand Cromwell's men,
Five hundred went to Aberdeen,
The rest of them lyes on the plain,
Upon the haws of Cromdale.

# No Dominies for me, laddie.

489

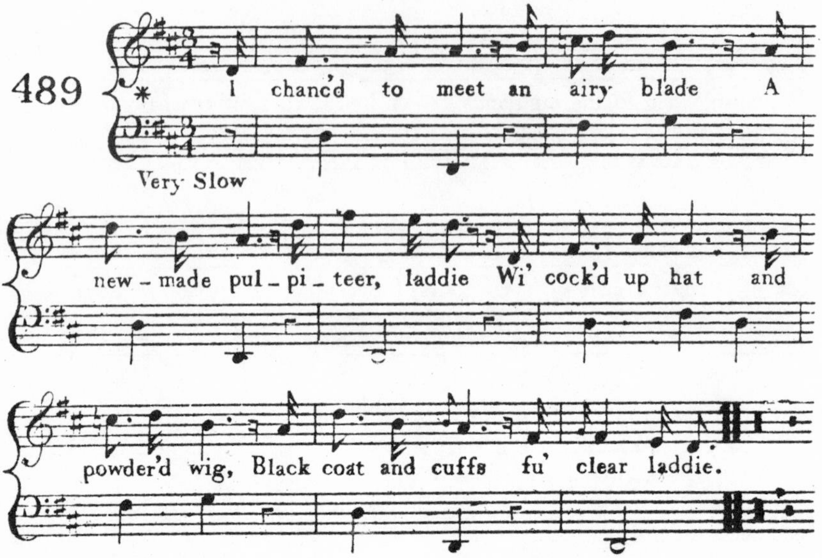

I chanc'd to meet an airy blade A
Very Slow
new-made pul-pi-teer, laddie Wi' cock'd up hat and
powder'd wig, Black coat and cuffs fu' clear laddie.


A lang cravat at him did wag,
And buckles at his knee, laddie;
Says he, My heart, by Cupid's dart,
Is captivate to thee laſſie.

I'll rather chuſe to thole grim death;
So ceaſe and let me be, laddie:
For what? ſays he; Good troth, ſaid I,
No dominies for me, laddie.

Miniſter's ſtipends are uncertain rents
For ladies conjunct-fee, laddie;
When books & gowns are a' cried down,
No dominies for me, laddie.

But for your ſake I'll fleece the flock,
Grow rich as I grow auld, laſſie;
If I be ſpar'd I'll be a laird,
And thou's be Madam call'd, laſſie.

But what if ye ſhou'd chance to die,
Leave bairns, ane or twa, laddie?
Neathing wad be reſerv'd for them
But hair moul'd books to gnaw, laddie.

At this he angry was, I wat,
He gloom'd & look'd fu' high, laddie:
When I perceved this in haſte
I left my dominie, laddie.

Fare ye well, my charming maid,
This leſſon learn of me, laſſie,
At the next offer hold him faſt,
That firſt makes love to thee, laſſie.

Then I returning hame again,
And coming down the town, laddie,
By my good luck I chanc'd to meet
A gentleman dragoon, laddie;

And he took me by baith the hands,
'Twas help in time of need, laddie.
Fools on ceremonies ſtand,
At twa words we agreed, laddie.

He led me to his quarter-houſe,
Where we exchang'd a word, laddie:
We had nae uſe for black gowns there,
We married o'er the ſword, laddie.

Martial drums is muſic fine,
Compar'd wi' tinkling bells, laddie;
Gold, red and blue, is more divine
Than black, the hue of hell, laddie.

Kings, queens, and princes, crave the aid
Of my brave ſtout dragoon, laddie;
While dominies are much employ'd,
'Bout whores and ſackloth gowns, laddie.

Away wi' a' theſe whining loons;
They look like, Let me be, laddie:
I've more delight in roaring guns;
No dominies for me, laddie.

# The Taylor

490
* For weel he kend the way O, The way O, the way O. For
Slowish
weel he kend the way O, The lass_ie's heart to win O! The
Taylor he cam here to sew, And weel he kend the way to woo, For
ay he pree'd the lass_ie's mou As he gade but and ben O!
Chorus
For weel he kend the way O, The way O, the way O, For weel he
kend the way O, The lass_ie's heart to win O.

The Taylor rase and sheuk his duds,
The flaes they flew awa in cluds,
And them that stay'd gat fearfu' thuds,
The Taylor prov'd a man O.

Cho.[s] For now it was the gloamin,
The gloamin, the gloamin,
For now it was the gloamin,
When a' to rest are gaun O.

+ + + + + + + + + + + + + + + + + + + + + + +

# There was a wee bit Wiffikie.

491

Slowish
There was a wee bit wiffikie And ſhe held to the fair; She
got a little drappikie, that coſt her meikle care; It gaed about the
wiffie's heart, and ſhe began to ſpeu; O quo' the wee bit wiffikie I
Chorus
wiſh I be na fu'. I wiſh I be na fu' quo' ſhe, I wiſh I be na
fu' Oh! quo' the wee bit wiffikie I wiſh I be na fou'.

If Johnnie find me Barrel-ſick, I'm ſure he'll claw my ſkin;
But I'll lye down and tak a Nap before that I gae in —
Sitting at the Dyke-ſide, and taking at her Nap,
By came a merchant wi' a little Pack
Wi' a little pack, quo' ſhe, wi' a little pack,
By came a merchant wi' a little pack.

He's clippit a' her Gowden locks ſae bonnie and ſae lang;
He's ta'en her purſe & a' her placks, and faſt away did gang,
And when the wiffie waken'd her head was like a bee
Oh! quoth the wee wiffekie this is nae me,
This is nae me, quoth ſhe, this is nae me,
Somebody has been felling me, and this is nae me.

## Continued.

I met with kindly company, and birl'd my Babee;
And ſtill, if this be Beſsikie, three placks remain with me
But I will look the Purſie nooks, ſee gin the Cunzie be
There's neither Purſe nor Plack about me, _ this is nae me
This is nae me, quoth ſhe, this is nae me
Some-body has been felling me, and this is nae me.

But I have a little houſekie, but and a kindly man;
A Dog, they call him Douſsekie, if this be me he'll faun,
And Johnnie, he'll come to the door and kindly welcome gie,
And a' the Bairns on the floor will dance if this be me.
This is nae me, quoth ſhe, this is nae me
Some-body has been felling me and this is nae·me.

The night was late and dang'out weet, and oh but it was dark,
The Doggie heard a bodie's foot, and he began to bark.
Oh when ſhe heard the Doggie bark and kenning it was he,
Oh well ken ye Douſsie, quoth ſhe, this is nae me,
This is nae me, quoth ſhe, this is nae me
Some-body has been felling me and this is nae me.

When Johnnie heard his Beſsie's word, faſt to the door he ran
Is that you Beſsikie. Wow na Man __
Be kind to the Bairns, and well mat ye be. __
And farewell Johnnie, quoth ſhe, this is nae me,
This is nae me, quoth ſhe, this is nae me
Some-body has been felling me, and this is nae me.

John ran to the Miniſter, his hair ſtood a' on end,
I've gotten ſuch a fright Sir, I'll ne'er be well again
My wife's come hame without a head, crying out moſt piteouſly,
Oh! Farewell Johnnie quoth ſhe, this is nae me,
This is nae me, quoth ſhe, this is nae me
Some-body has been felling me, and this is nae me.

The tale you tell, The Parſon ſaid, is wonderful to me,
How that a wife without a head could ſpeak, or hear, or ſee!
But things that happen hereabout ſo ſtrangely alter'd be
That I could almoſt with Beſsie ſay that this is nae me,
This is nae me quoth ſhe, this is nae me
Wow na. Johnnie ſaid, 'tis neither you nor me.

Now Johnnie he came hame again, and oh! but he was fain
To ſee his Little Beſsikie come to herſelf again
He got her ſitting on a ſtool with Tibbek on her knee
Oh come awa Johnnie, quoth ſhe, come awa to me.
For I've got a Nap with Tibbekie and this is now me
This is now me, quoth ſhe, this is now me. _
I've got a Nap with Tibbeki and this is now me.

# There grows a bonie brier bush &c.

492

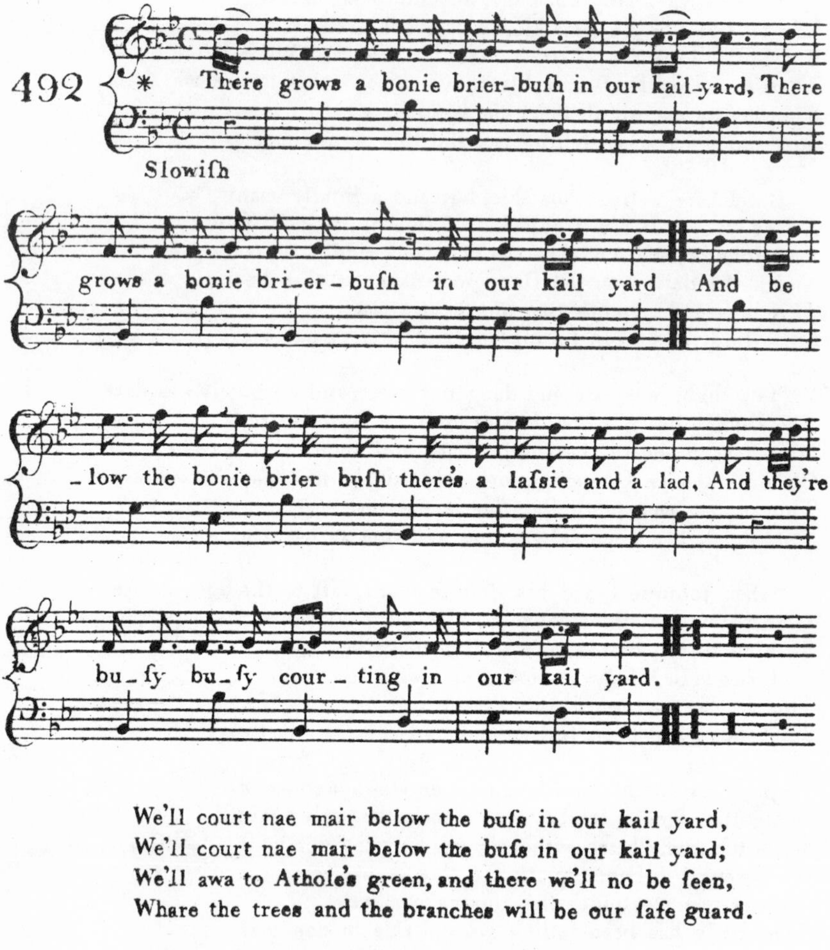
* There grows a bonie brier-bush in our kail-yard, There
Slowish
grows a bonie bri-er-bush in our kail yard And be
-low the bonie brier bush there's a lassie and a lad, And they're
bu-sy bu-sy cour-ting in our kail yard.

We'll court nae mair below the buss in our kail yard,
We'll court nae mair below the buss in our kail yard;
We'll awa to Athole's green, and there we'll no be seen,
Whare the trees and the branches will be our safe guard.

Will ye go to the dancin in Carlyle's ha',
Will ye go to the dancin in Carlyle's ha';
Whare Sandy and Nancy I'm sure will ding them a'?
I winna gang to the dance in Carlyle-ha'.

What will I do for a lad, when Sandy gangs awa?
What will I do for a lad, when Sandy gangs awa?
I will awa to Edinburgh and win a pennie fee,
And see an onie bonie lad will fancy me.

He's comin frae the North that's to fancy me,
He's comin frae the North that's to fancy me;
A feather in his bonnet and a ribbon at his knee,
He's a bonie, bonie laddie and yon be he.

# Could aught of Song.

Written for this Work by Robert Burns.

493
* Could aught of ſong de_clare my pains, Could artful
Andante
numbers move thee, The muſe ſhould tell in labor'd ſtrains, O
Mary how I love thee. They who but feign a wound_ed
heart, May teach the lyre to languiſh; But what avails the
pride of art, When waſtes the ſoul with anguiſh.

Then let the ſudden burſting ſigh
The heart-felt pang diſcover;
And in the keen, yet tender eye,
O read th' imploring lover.
For well I know thy gentle mind
Diſdains art's gay diſguiſing;
Beyond what Fancy e'er refin'd
The voice of Nature prizing.

## O! dear what can the matter be.

494

O! dear what can the matter be O! what can the
matter be dear! what can the matter be Johnny's ſae lang at the
fair. He promis'd he'd buy me a fairing ſhould pleaſe me and
then, for a kiſs O! he vow'd he would teaze me he promis'd he'd
bring me a bunch of blue ribbons to tie up my bonny brown hair.

O! dear what can the matter be
Dear! dear! what can the matter be
O! dear what can the matter be
Johnny's ſae lang at the fair.
He promis'd to buy me a pair of ſleeve buttons
A pair of new garters that coſt him but two pence
He promis'd he'd bring me a bunch of blue ribbons
To tye up my bonny brown hair.

O! dear what can the matter be
Dear! dear! what can the matter be
O! dear what can the matter be
Johnny's ſae lang at the fair.
He promis'd he'd bring me a baſket of poſies
A garland of lilies a garland of roſes
A little ſtraw hat to ſet off the blue ribbons
To tye up my bonny brown hair.

# Heres to thy health my bonie laſs.

Written for this Work by Rob[t] Burns. Tune, Loggan burn

495

Here's to thy health, my bon_ie laſs, Gude
Slowiſh
night and joy be wi' thee: I'll come nae mair to thy bower-
-door, To tell thee that I loe thee. O dinna think my
pretty pink, But I can live with_out thee: I vow and
ſwear, I dinna care, How lang ye look a_bout ye.


Thou'rt ay ſae free informing
Thou haſt nae mind to marry.
I'll be as free informing thee,
Nae time hae I to tarry.
I ken thy friends try ilka means
Frae wedlock to delay thee;
Depending on ſome higher chance,
But fortune may betray thee.

I ken they ſcorn my low eſtate,
But that does never grieve me;
For I'm as free as any he,
Sma' ſiller will relieve me.

I'll count my health my greateſt weal-(th
Sae lang as I'll enjoy it:
I'll fear nae ſcant, I'll bode nae want,
As lang's I get employment.

But far off fowls hae feathers fair,
And ay until ye try them:
Tho' they ſeem fair, ſtill have a care,
They may prove as bad as I am.
But at twel at night, when the moon ſhines
My dear, I'll come & ſee thee;(bright,
For the man that loves his miſtreſs weel
Nae travel makes him weary.

## Jenny's Bawbie.

496

* And a' that e'er my Jenny had, My Jenny had, my
Lively
Jenny had And a' that e'er my Jenny had was ae baw_bie.
There's your plack, and my plack, And your plack and my
plack, And my plack and your plack, And Jenny's baw _ bie.
Chorus
And a' that e'er my Jenny had, My Jenny had, my Jenny had: And
a' that eer my Jenny had, Was ae baw_ _ bie.

We'll put it a' in the pint-ſtoup,
The pint-ſtoup, the pint-ſtoup,
We'll put it in the pint-ſtoup,
And birle t a' three.

And a' that e'er, &c.

## It was a' for our rightfu king.

497

It was a' for our right_fu king We
left fair Scot_land's ſtrand; It was a' for our
right_fu' king, We e'er ſaw I_riſh land my dear, We
e'er ſaw I_ _riſh land.

Now a' is done that men can do,
And a' is done in vain:
My Love and Native Land fareweel,
For I maun croſs the main, my dear,
For I maun, &c.

He turn'd him right and round about,
Upon the Iriſh ſhore,
And gae his bridle reins a ſhake,
With, adieu for evermore, my dear
With, adieu, &c.

The ſoger frae the wars returns,
The ſailor frae the main,
But I hae parted frae my Love,
Never to meet again, my dear,
Never to meet, &c.

When day is gane, and night is come,
And a' folk bound to ſleep;
I think on him that's far awa,
The lee-lang night & weep my dear
The lee-lang, &c.

## The Highland widow's lament.

498

Oh I am come to the low coun _ trie Och
_ on, Och _ on, Och _ rie! With _ out a pen _ ny
in my purſe to buy a meal to me.
Very Slow

It was na ſae in the Highland hills,
Ochon, Ochon, Ochrie!
Nae woman in he Country wide
Sae happy was as me.

For then I had a ſcore o' kye,
Ochon, &c.
Feeding on yon hill ſae high,
And giving milk to me.

And there I had three ſcore o' yowes,
Ochon, &c.
Skipping on yon bonie knowes,
And caſting woo to me.

I was the happieſt of a' the Clan,
Sair, ſair may I repine;
For Donald was the braweſt man,
And Donald he was mine.

Till Charlie Stewart cam at laſt,
Sae far to ſet us free;
My Donald's arm was wanted then
For Scotland and for me.

Their waefu' fate what need I tell,
Right to the wrang did yield;
My Donald and his Country fell,
Upon Culloden field.

Ochon, O. Donald, Oh!
Ochon, Ochon, Ochrie!
Nae woman in the warld wide,
Sae wretched now as me.

# Gloomy December

Written for this Work by Robert Burns.

499

*
Ance mair I hail thee, thou gloomy De_cem_ber!
Slow
Ance mair I hail thee wi' forrow and care; fad was the
parting thou makes me remember, Parting wi' Nancy, Oh! ne'er. to
meet mair. Fond lovers parting is fweet pain-ful pleafure, Hope beam
_ing mild on the foft parting hour But the dire feeling, O
farewell for e__ver. Anguifh un_mingl'd and a_go_ny pure.

Wild as the winter now tearing the foreft,
Till the laft leaf o' the fummer is flown,
Such is the tempeft has fhaken my bofom,
Till my laft hope and laft comfort is gone:
Still as I hail thee, thou gloomy December,
Still fhall I hail thee wi' forrow and care;
For fad was the parting thou makes me remember,
Parting wi' Nancy, Oh, ne'er to meet mair.

## Evan Banks.

Written for this Work by Robert Burns.

500

*
Slow ſpreads the gloom my ſoul deſires, The ſun from
India's ſhore retires; To E_van_banks, with temp'rate ray, Home
of my youth, he leads the day. Oh! banks to me for
e_ver dear! Oh! ſtream whoſe murmurs ſtill I hear! All, all my
hopes of bliſs re_ſide Where E_van mingles with the Clyde.

And ſhe, in ſimple beauty dreſt,
Whoſe image lives within my breaſt;
Who trembling heard my parting ſigh,
And long purſued me with her eye;
Does ſhe with, heart unchang'd as mine,
Oft in the vocal bowers recline?
Or where yon grot o'erhangs the tide,
Muſe while the Evan ſeeks the Clyde?

Ye lofty banks that Evan bound!
Ye laviſh woods that wave around,
And o'er the ſtream your ſhadows throw,
Which ſweetly winds ſo far below;
What ſecret charm to mem'ry brings,
All that on Evan's border ſprings,
Sweet banks! ye bloom by Mary's ſide:
Bleſt ſtream! ſhe views thee haſte to Clyde

Can all the wealth of India's coaſt
Alone for years in abſence loſt?
Return, ye moments of delight,
With richer treaſures bleſs my ſight.
Swift from this deſart let me part,
And fly to meet a kindred heart!
Nor more may aught my ſteps divide
From that dear ſtream which flows to Clyd

END OF VOLUME FIFTH

# THE SCOTS Musical Museum

Consisting of Six hundred Scots Songs

with proper Basses for the

PIANO FORTE &c.

Humbly Dedicated

To the Society

of

Antiquaries of Scotland

BY JAMES JOHNSON

*In this publication the original simplicity of our Ancient National Airs is retained unincumbered with useless Accompaniments & graces depriving the hearers of the sweet simplicity of their native melodies.*

Volume 7 Pr. 7s

Butterworth Scripsit

*Printed & Sold by JAMES JOHNSON Music Seller EDINBURGH to be had at T. PRESTON N.º 97 Strand LONDON, M.ᶜFADYEN GLASGOW, & at all the principal* Music Sellers.

# PREFACE

THE Editor now presents to the Public the Sixth Volume of the Scots Musical Museum; which in all probability will be the last.

These Volumes contain every Scotish Air and Song, which the exertions of the Editor, and those of his friends and numerous correspondents, have been able to procure during a period of sixteen years. He is therefore inclined to think that the Scots Musical Museum now contains almost every Scotish Song extant. However, as he wishes to make it as complete as possible, he will spare no pains in endeavouring to procure any which may hitherto have escaped his research; and if successful, they will be published at some future period.

Without wishing to over rate this publication, the Editor may be permitted to observe, that it unquestionably contains the greatest Collection of Scotish Vocal Music ever published, including many excellent Songs written for it by BURNS; He therefore flatters himself with the hope that the prediction of our celebrated BARD respecting it will be verified; and that "To future ages the Scots Musical Museum "will be the Text Book and Standard of Scotish Song and Music."*

* See extract from BURNS'S Letter in the Preface to Volume 5th

Edin.r June 4th 1803.

Entered in Stationers Hall.

# I N D E X.

Nota, The Songs in the 5 preceding Volumes marked R. and B. the Editor is now at liberty to say are the production of Mr. BURNS ___ The Originals of Mr. BURNS'S writing are in his possession ___ They were written for this work, but being often sent the Editor on the spur of the moment, Mr. BURNS requested these marks only, and not his name should be added to them.

V

# INDEX.

# I N D E X.

# My Peggy's face,

Written for this Work by Robert Burns.

No. 501

Slowish
My Peggy's face, my Peggy's form, The frost of hermit
age might warm; My Peggy's worth, my Peg_gy's mind, Might
charm the first of human kind. I love my Peg_gy's angel
air, Her face so truly heav'nly fair, Her na_tive grace so
void of art, But I a_dore my Peg_gy's heart.

The lily's hue, the rose's die,
The kindling lustre of an eye;
Who but owns their magic sway,
Who but knows they all decay!
The tender thrill, the pitying tear.
The generous purpose nobly dear,
The gentle look that Rage disarms,
These are all Immortal charms.

Dear Mr. Publisher,

I hope against I return, you will be able to tell me from Mr. CLARKE if these words will suit the tune. _ If they don't suit, I must think on some other Air; as I have a very strong private reason for wishing them in the 2d. Volume. ___ Don't forget to transcribe me the list of the Antiquarian Music. Farewel!

R. BURNS.

# My boy Tammy

502

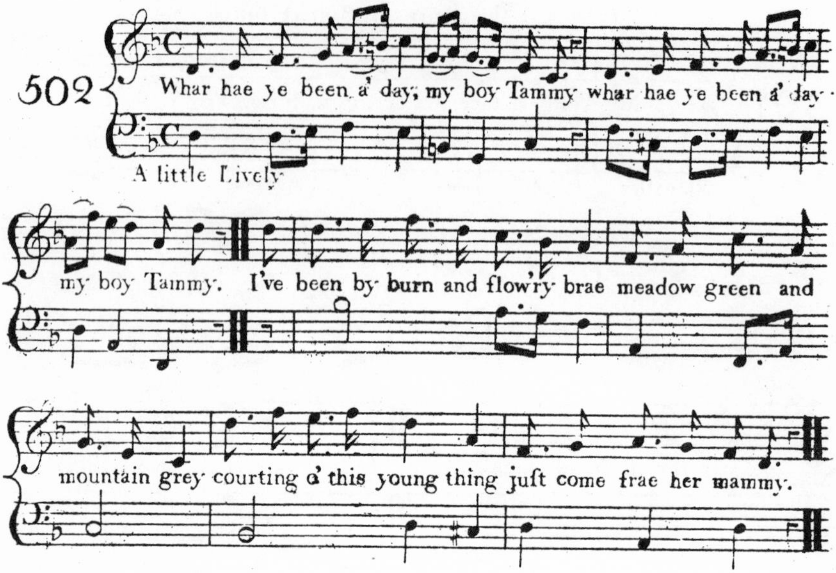
Whar hae ye been a' day, my boy Tammy whar hae ye been a' day
A little Lively
my boy Tammy. I've been by burn and flow'ry brae meadow green and
mountain grey courting o' this young thing just come frae her mammy.

And whar gat ye that young thing my boy Tammy?
I gat her down in yonder how,
Smiling on a broomy know,
Herding ae wee Lamb and Ewe for her poor Mammy.

What said ye to the bonny bairn my boy Tammy?
I prais'd her een sae lovely blue,
Her dimpled cheek, and cherry mou; —
I pree'd it aft as ye may true — She said, she'd tell her Mammy.

I held her to my beating heart "— my young my smiling Lammy!
"I hae a house — it cost me dear,
"I've walth o' plenishan and geer;
"Ye'se get it a' war't ten times mair, gin ye will leave your Mammy."

The smile gade aff her bonny face — "I manna leave my Mammy.
"She's ge'en me meat; she's geen me claise;
"She's been my comfort a' my days —
"My Father's death brought mony wae's — I canna leave my Mammy.

"We'll tak her hame and mak her fain, my ain kind hearted Lammy!
"We'll gee her meat; we'll gee her claise,
"We'll be her comfort a' her days;" —
The wee thing gi'es her hand and says "There! gang and ask my Mammy"

Has she been to Kirk wi' thee my boy Tammy?
She has been to Kirk wi' me,
And the tear was in her ee, —
But Oh! she's but a young thing just come frae her Mammy!

## Red gleams the ſun.

503

* Red gleams the ſun on yon hill tap the dew ſits on the gowan; Deep murmurs thro' her glens the Spey, A_round Kin_ra_ra rowan. Where art thou faireſt, kindeſt laſs! A_las wert thou but near me, Thy gen_tle ſoul, thy mel_ting eye would ever ever cheer me.
Lively

The Lavrock ſings amang the clouds,
  The Lambs they ſport ſo cheery,
And I ſit weeping by the birk;
  O where art thou my dearie!
Aft may I meet the morning dew;
  Lang greet till I be weary
Thou canna, winna, gentle maid!
  Thou canna be my deary.

## O ſteer her up and had her gaun.

Written for this Work by Robert Burns.

504

Briſk
* O ſteer her up and had her gaun, her mither's at the mill, jo; An' gin ſhe win_na tak a man E'en let her tak her will, jo. Firſt ſhore her wi' a kind_ly kiſs and ca' anither gill, jo; An' gin ſhe tak the thing a_miſs E'en let her flyte her fill, jo.


O ſteer her up and be na blate,
An' gin ſhe tak it ill, jo,
Then lea'e the laſsie till her fate,
And time nae langer ſpill, jo.
Ne'er break your heart for ay rebute,
But think upon it ſtill, jo,
That gin the laſsie winna do't,
Ye'll fin' anither will, jo.

## When I gaed to the mill.

505
* When I gaed to the mill my lane, A' for to grind my
Lively
maut The-mill_er lad__die kiſt me I thought it
was nae faut. What tho' the lad_die kiſt
me When I was at the mill, A kiſs is but a
touch and a touch can do nae ill.

O I loo the miller laddie!
And my laddie loes me;
He has ſic a blyth look,
And a bonnie blinking ee.
What though the laddie kiſt me,
When I was at the mill!
A kiſs is but a touch
And a touch can do nae ill.

## Whar' Esk its silver stream

506
Whar' Esk its silver current leads 'mang greenwoods gay wi'
Slow
mony a flower I hied me aft to dewy meads in hap_py days and
built my bower. I call'd upon the birds to sing An' nestle in ilk
fragrant flower, While in the liv'ry of the spring I deck'd my sweet en

_chanted bow'r.

'Twas there I found ah! happy time,
The sweetest flower, and sic a flower
I crop't it in its virgin prime
To deck my sweet, my shady bower
But soon the blast houl'd in the air
That robb'd me of this matchless flower
An' sorrow since and mony a care
Ha'e stript and withered a' my bower.

## Tho' for seven years.

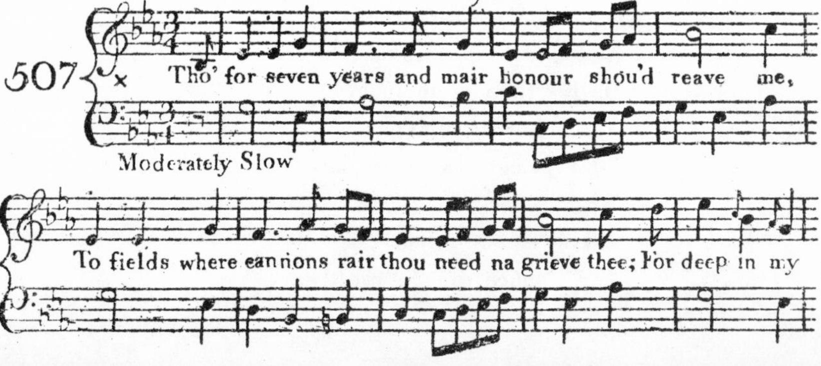
507
Tho' for seven years and mair honour shou'd reave me,
Moderately Slow
To fields where cannons rair thou need na grieve thee; For deep in my

Continued.

spirits thy sweets are indented, And love shall preserve ay what love has
Chorus
imprinted, Leave thee leave thee I'll never leave thee gang the warld
as it will dear _ est be _ lieve me.

## NELLY.

O Johny! I'm jealous whene'er ye discover
My sentiments yielding, ye'll turn a loose rover;
And nought i' the warld wad vex my heart sairer
If you prove unconstant, and fancy ane fairer.
Grieve me, grieve me, oh it wad grieve me!
A' the lang night and day, if you deceive me.

## JOHNY.

My Nelly, let never sick fancies oppress ye,
For while my blood's warm I'll kindly caress ye:
Your blooming saft beauties first beeted Love's fire,
Your virtue and wit make it ay flame the higher,
Leave thee, leave thee, I'll never leave thee,
Gang the warld as it will, dearest, believe me.

## NELLY.

Then, Johny, I frankly this minute allow ye
To think me your mistress, for love gars me trow ye;
And gin you prove fa'se, to ye'rsell be it said then;
Ye'll win but sma' honour to wrang a kind maiden.
Reave me, reave me, Heav'ns' it wad reave me
Of my rest night and day, if ye deceive me.

## JOHNY.

Bid iceshogles hammer red gads on the studdy,
And fair simmer mornings nae mair appear ruddy;
Bid Britons think ae gait, and when they obey ye,
But never till that time believe I'll betray ye.
Leave thee, leave thee, I'll never leave thee;
The starns shall gang withershins e'er I deceive thee.

## Row saftly, thou stream,

508

* Row saftly, thou stream, thro' the wild spangl'd valley, O green be thy
Slow
banks e_ver bonny an' fair, Sing sweetly ye birds as ye wanton fu' gaily yet
strangers to sorrow an' strangers to care. The weary day lang I list to your
sang, An' waste ilka moment sad cheerless alane; Each sweet little treasure o'
heart-cheering pleasure, Far fled frae my bosom wi' Captain O'Kaine.

Fu' aft on thy banks hae we pu'd the wild gowan,
An' twisted a ringlet beneath the haw thorn!
Ah! then each fond moment wi' pleasure was glowin!
Sweet days o' delight which can never return!
  Now ever, wae's me
  The tear fills mine e'e!
An' sair is my heart wi' the rigour o' pain!
  Nae prospect returning
  To gladden life's morning,
For green waves the willow o'er Captain O'Kaine!

## As I went o'er &c.

509

As I went o'er the highland hills to a farmer's house I came The
A little Slow
night being dark and something wet, I ventur'd into the same. Where
I was kind_ly treated and a pret_ty maid I spy'd, Who
ask'd me if I had a wife but marriage I de_ny'd.

I courted her the lea long night,
Till near the dawning day
When frankly she to me did say,
Alang with you I'll gae;
For Ireland is a fine country,
An' the Scots to you are kin',
So I will gae alang with you,
My fortune to begin.

Day being come, an' breakfast o'er,
To parlour I was ta'en,
The goodman kindly ask'd me,
If I'd marry his daughter Jean;
Five hundred marks I'll give to thee,
Besides a piece of land,
But scarcely had he spoke the word,
Till I thought on Peggy Bawn.

Your offer Sir! is very good,
An' I thank you too: said I,
But I cannot be your son in law,
I'll tell you the reason why;
My business calleth me in haste
I'm the King's servant bound,
An' I must gae away this day,
Straight on, to Edinburgh town.

O! Peggy Bawn thou art my own,
My heart lys in thy breast,
An' tho' we at a distance are,
Yet still I love thee best;
Altho' we at a distance be,
An' seas between us roar,
Yet I'll be constant, Peggy Bawn,
To thee, for ever more.

## O Cherub Content.

510

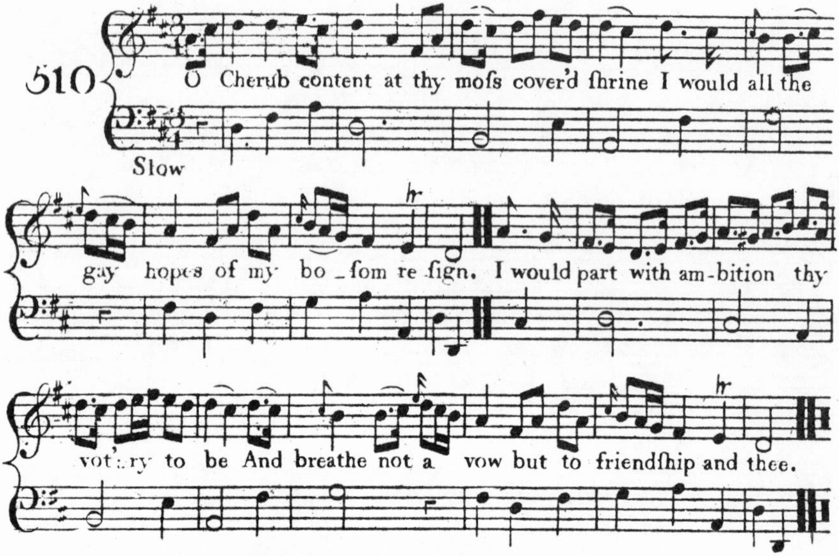
O Cherub content at thy moss cover'd shrine I would all the
Slow
gay hopes of my bo _ som re sign. I would part with am-bition thy
vot'ary to be And breathe not a vow but to friendship and thee.

But thy presence appears from my pursuit to fly,
Like the gold colour'd cloud on the verge of the sky;
No lustre that hangs on the green willow tree
Is so short as the smile of thy favour to me.

In the pulse of my heart I have nourish'd a care
That forbids me thy sweet inspiration to share;
The noon of my youth slow departing I see;
But its years as they pass bring no tidings of thee.

O Cherub content! at thy moss-cover'd shrine
I would offer my vows if Matilda were mine;
Could I call her my own whom enraptur'd I see,
I would breathe not a vow but to friendship and thee.

*∴*∴*∴*∴*∴*∴*∴*∴*∴*∴*∴*∴*∴*∴*∴*∴*∴*∴*∴*∴*∴*∴*∴*∴*

## As walking forth.

511

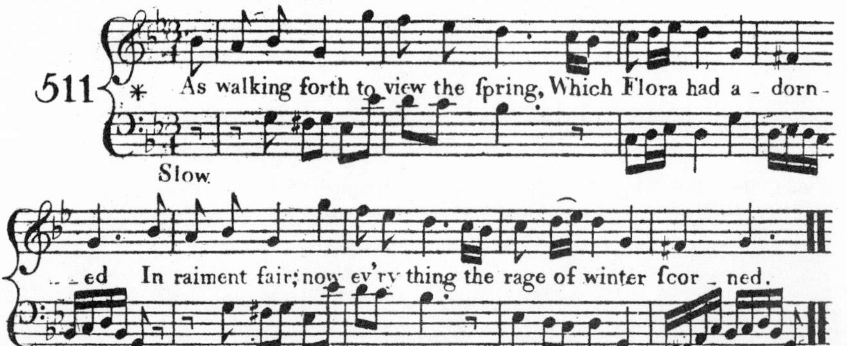
* As walking forth to view the spring, Which Flora had a - dorn-
Slow
- - ed In raiment fair; now ev'ry thing the rage of winter scor - ned.

## Continued.

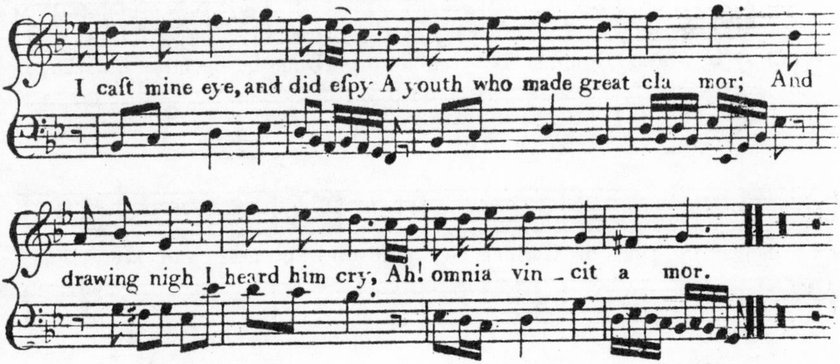
I caſt mine eye, and did eſpy A youth who made great cla mor; And
drawing nigh I heard him cry, Ah! omnia vin - cit a mor.

Upon his breaſt he lay along,
Hard by a murm'ring river,
And mournfully his doleful ſong
With ſighs he did deliver;
Ah! Jeany's face has comely grace,
Her locks that ſhine like lammer,
With burning rays have cut my days;
For omnia vincit amor.

Her glancy een like comets ſheen,
The morning-ſun outſhining,
Have caught my heart in Cupid's net,
And make me die with pining.
Durſt I complain, nature's to blamé,
So curiouſly to frame her,
Whoſe beauties rare make me with care
Cry, omnia vincit amor.

Ye cryſtal ſtreams that ſwiftly glide,
Be partners of my mourning,
Ye fragrant fields and meadows wild,
Condemn her for her ſcorning:
Let every tree a witneſs be,
How juſtly I may blame her;
Ye chanting birds, note theſe my words,
Ah! omnia vincit amor.

Had ſhe been kind as ſhe was fair,
She long had been admired,
And been ador'd for virtues rare,
Wh' of life now makes me tired.

Thus ſaid, his breath began to fail
He could not ſpeak, but ſtammer;
He ſigh'd full ſore, and ſaid no more,
But omnia vincit amor.

When I obſerv'd him near to death,
I run in haſt to ſave him,
But quickly he reſign'd his breath,
So deep the wound love gave him.
Now for her ſake this vow I'll make,
My tongue ſhall ay defame her,
While on his hearſe I'll write this verſe,
Ah! omnia vincit amor.

Straight I conſider'd in my mind
Upon the matter rightly,
And found tho' Cupid he be blind,
He proves in pith moſt mighty.
For warlike Mars, and thund'ring Jove,
And Vulcan with his Hammer,
Did ever prove the ſlaves of love
For omnia vincit amor

Hence we may ſee th' effects of love.
Which gods and men keep under,
That nothing can his bonds remove,
Or torments break aſunder:
Nor wiſe nor fool, need go to ſchool,
To learn this from his grammar;
His heart's the book where he's to look,
For omnia vincit amor.

# The Battle of Harlaw.✫

512
Slow
✱ Frae Dunidier as I cam through, Doun by the hill o' Banochie, A_langst the lands of Garioch: Grit pitie 'twas to hear and see. The noys and dulesum harmonie, That e'er that dreiry day did daw. Cry_and the Cory_noch on hie, A_las! alas! for the Harlaw.

I marvlit quhat the matter meint,
All folks war in a fiery fairy:
I wist nocht qua was fae or friend;
Zit quietly I did me carrie.
But sen the days of auld king Hairie,
Sic slaughter was not herde nor sene,
And thair I had nae tyme to tairy,
For bissiness in Aberdene.

Thus as I walkit on the way,
To Inverury as I went,
I met a man, and bad him stay,
Requeisting him to make me quaint.
Of the beginning and the event,
That happenit thair at the Harlaw;
Then he entrited me tak tent,
And he the truth sould to me chaw.

Grit Donald of the Yles did claim,
Unto the lands of Ross sum richt,
And to the Governour ✫ he came,
Thaim for to haif gif that he micht;
Quha saw his interest was but slicht:
And thairfore answert with disdain;
He hastit hame baith day and nicht,
And sent nae bodward back again.

But Donald richt impatient
Of that answer Duke Robert gaif,
He vowed to God omnipotent,
All the hale lands of Ross to haif,
Or ells be graithed in his graif.
He wald not quat his richt for nocht,
Nor be abusit lyk a slaif,
That bargin sould be deirly bocht. &c.
&c. &c.

✫ Fought upon Friday, July 24, 1411, against Donald of the Isles.

✫ Robert Duke of Albany, uncle to King James I. The account of this famous battle may be seen in our Scots histories.

# O Bothwell bank.

513
O Bothwell bank thou bloomeſt fair, But ah thou
Slow
mak'st my heart fu' ſair, For a beneath thy woods ſae green
w
w
My love and I wad ſit at een While daiſies and primroſes
mixt wi' blue bells in my locks he fixt, O Both_well
bank thou bloomeſt fair But ah thou mak'st my heart fu' ſair.

Sad he left me ae dreary day,
And haplie now ſleeps in the clay
Without ae ſigh his death to moan,
Without ae flow'r his grave to crown.
O whither is my lover gone,
Alas I fear he'll ne'er return
O Bothwell bank thou bloomeſt fair,
But ah thou mak st my heart fu' ſair.

## Wee Willie Gray.

Written for this Work by R. Burns.

514

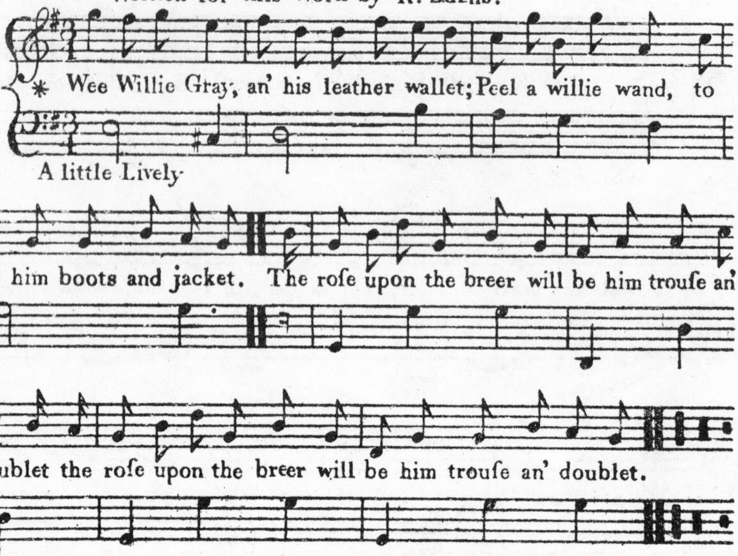
* Wee Willie Gray, an' his leather wallet; Peel a willie wand, to
A little Lively
be him boots and jacket. The rose upon the breer will be him trouse an'
doublet the rose upon the breer will be him trouse an' doublet.

Wee Willy Gray, and his leather wallet;
Twice a lily-flower will be him sark and cravat;
Feathers of a flee wad feather up his bonnet,
Feathers of a flee wad feather up his bonnet.

## When the days they are lang.

515

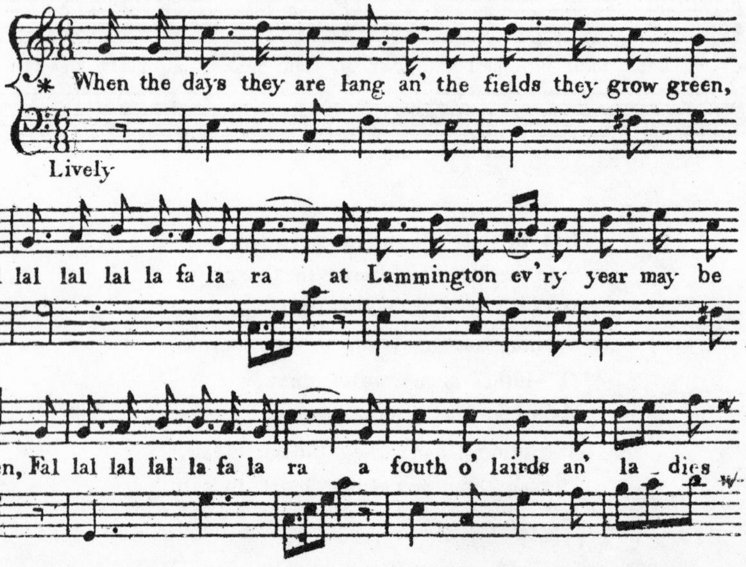
* When the days they are lang an' the fields they grow green,
Lively
Fal lal lal lal la fa la ra at Lammington ev'ry year may be
seen, Fal lal lal lal la fa la ra a routh o' lairds an' la - dies

Continued.

too Wi- lads an' laſses nae that few, An' O! the ſport is
rare to view, Fal lal lal lal la fa la ra.

There's mony a filly come in on the ſcore, Fal lal, &c.
Wi' galloping graith, clad ahint an' afore, Fal lal, &c.
Our ancient Wager for to win,
The Prize nae leſs than forty pun';
To ſee them is the beſt o' fun, Fal lal, &c.

The rout the town officers held at command, Fal lal, &c.
An' Baillies wi' halberts weel ſcour'd, in their hand, Fal lal, &c.
To clear the courſe, the cauſe was gude,
An' guide the rabble, wild an' rude,
For ilka ane on tip-tae ſtood, Fal lal, &c.

Now Kirkfield frae braw Leſmahago came, Fal lal, &c.
Our ſiller, nae doubt, for to tak wi' him hame Fal lal &c.
But tho' he cam wi' noiſe an' din,
The beaſt was unco laith to rin;
In ſhort the lad was ahin, Fal lal &c.

An' Glentowin's horſe, he was ſairly out-worn, Fal lal &c.
That morning he gat a haill firlet o' corn, Fal lal &c.
His groom kept him but careleſsly·
Tho', had he fed him ſoberly
'Twas thought he wad hae won the gree, Fal lal &c.

But Kingledore's mare, ſhe brak aff at the firſt, Fal lal &c.
Sax paces an' mair afore a' the reſt, Fal lal &c.
She was ſae ſupple an' ſae ſtout,
She led the lave a' round about,
An' cam in firſt — as ſhe gade out, Fal lal &c.

Now Glentowin's horſe, he could do nae mair, Fal lal &c.
An' Kirkfiel's, o'er heavy to hae ony ſhare, Fal lal &c.
Sae Kingledore's brown bonny mare,
Set aff wi' a' our dainty gear,
An' caper'd crouſly thro' the fair Fal lal &c.

# The banks of the Dee.

516
'Twas summer and softly the breezes were blowing & sweetly
Slow
the nightingale sung from the tree at the foot of a rock where the river was
flowing I set myself down on the banks of the Dee. Flow on lovely Dee flow on thou
sweet river thy banks purest stream shall be dear to me ever for there I first
gain'd the affection and favour of Jamie the glory & pride of the Dee.

But now he's gone from me and left me thus mourning,
To quell the proud rebels, for valiant is he,
And ah there's no hope of his speedy returning,
To wander again on the banks of the Dee.
He's gone, hapless youth, o'er the loud roaring billows
The kindest and sweetest of all the gay fellows,
And left me to stray mong'st these once loved willows,
The loneliest maid on the banks of the Dee.

But time and my prayers may perhaps yet restore him,
Blest peace may restore my dear shepherd to me,
And when he returns with such care I'll watch o'er him,
He never shall leave the sweet banks of the Dee.
The Dee then shall flow, all its beauties displaying,
The lambs on its banks shall again be seen playing,
While I with my Jamie am carelessly straying,
And tasting again all the sweets of the Dee

# Scenes of woe and scenes of pleasure,

Written by R. Burns.

517
Scenes of woe and scenes of plea_sure, Scenes that
Very Slow
for_mer thoughts re_new; scenes of woe and scenes of pleasure,
now a sad and last adieu. Bon_ny Doon, sae, sweet at
gloaming, Fare thee weel be_fore I gang Bon_ny Doon whare
ear_ly roam_ing, First I weav'd the rus_tic sang.

Bowers adieu! where love decoying,
First enthrall'd this heart o' mine,
There the saftest sweets enjoying,
Sweets that mem'ry ne'er shall tine.
Friends so near my bosom ever,
Ye hae render'd moments dear;
But alas! when forc'd to sever,
Then the stroke, O how severe!

Friends, that parting tear reserve it,
Tho' 'tis doubly dear to me;
Could I think I did deserve it,
How much happier wou'd I be.
Scenes of woe and Scenes of pleasure
Scenes that former thought renew;
Scenes of woe and Scenes of pleasure
Now a sad and last adieu!

## Go to Berwick Johnny.

518

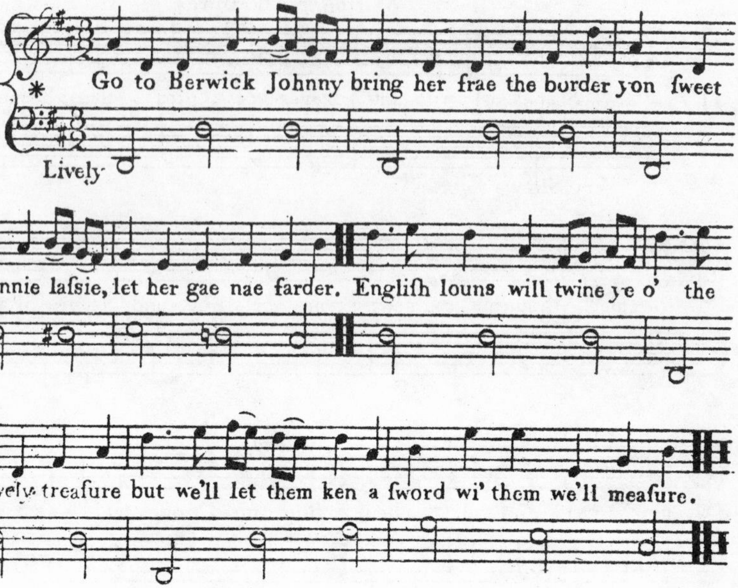
Go to Berwick Johnny bring her frae the border yon sweet
Lively
bonnie lassie, let her gae nae farder. English louns will twine ye o' the
lovely treasure but we'll let them ken a sword wi' them we'll measure.

Go to Berwick Johnny,
An' regain your honour
Drive them o'er the Tweed,
An' shaw our Scottish banner.
I am Rab the King,
An' ye are Jock my brither,
But before we lose her,
We'll a' there the gither.

## 'Twas at the shining mid-day hour.

519

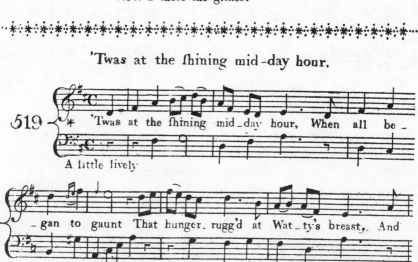

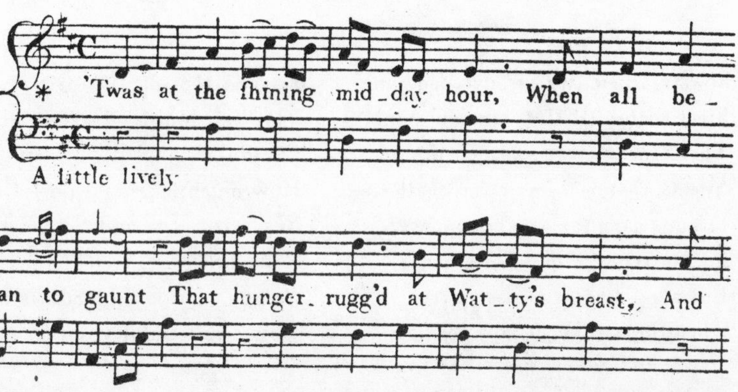
'Twas at the shining mid-day hour, When all be-
A little lively
-gan to gaunt That hunger rugg'd at Wat-ty's breast, And

## Continued.

the poor lad grew faint. His face was like a bacon
ham, That lang in reek had hung and horn hard was his
tawny hand That held the ha_zel rung.

So wad the ſofteſt face appear
  Of the maiſt dreſsy ſpark
Anc ſuch the hands that lords wad hae,
  Were they kept cloſe at wark.
His head was like a heathery buſh
  Beneath his bonnet blue,
On his braid cheeks frae lug to lug,
  His bairdy briſtles grew.
But hunger, like a gnawing worm,
  Gade rumbling thro' his kyte,
And nothing now but ſolid gear
  Could give his heart delyte.
He to the kitchen ran with ſpeed,
  To his lov'd Madge he ran,
Sunk down into the chimney nook
  With viſage ſour and wan,
Get up, he cries, my criſhy love,
  Support my ſinking ſaul
With ſomething that is fit to chew,
  Be't either het or caul.
This is the how and hungry hour,
  When the beſt cures for grief
Are cogue-fous of thy lythy kail,
  And a good junt of beef:
Oh Watty, Watty, Madge replies,
  I but o'er juſtly trow'd
Your love was thowleſs and that ye
  For cakes and pudding woo'd.
Bethink thee, Watty on that night,
  Whan all were faſt aſleep,
How ye kiſs'd me frae cheek to cheek
  Now leave theſe cheeks to dreep,
How cou'd ye ca' my hurdies fat,
  And comfort of your ſight?
How cou'd ye rooſe my dimpled hand
  Now all my dimples ſlight?
Why did you promiſe me a ſnood,
  To bind my locks ſae brown?
Why did you me fine garters height,
  Yet let my hoſe fa' down!
O faithleſs Watty think how aft
  I mend your ſarks and hoſe!
For you how many bannocks ſtown,
  How many cogues of broſe!
But hark! —the kail bell rings and I
  Maun gae link aff the pot;
Come ſee, ye haſh, how ſair I ſweat,
  To ſtegh your guts, ye ſot,
The grace was ſaid, the Maſter ſerv'd,
  Fat Madge return'd again,
Blyth Watty raiſe and rax'd himſell,
  And fidg'd he was ſae fain.
He hy'd him to the ſavoury bench,
  Where a warm haggies ſtood,
And gart his gooly thro' the bag
  Let out its fat heart's blood.
And thrice he cry'd, come eat, dear Madge
  Of this delicious fare;
Syne claw'd it aff moſt cleverly.
  Till he could eat nae mair

# Have you any Pots or Pans,

See another set of this Tune Vol. 1st Page 24

520

Have you any pots or pans, Or any bro_ken chandlers? I
Lively
am a tinker to my trade And new_ly come frae Flanders. As
scant of siller as of grace, Dis_banded, we've a bad run; Gang
tell the lady of the place, I'm come to clout her caldron.

Madam, if you have wark for me,
I'll do't to your contentment,
And dinna care a single flie
For any man's resentment;
For lady fair, though I appear
To ev'ry ane a tinker,
Yet to yoursell I'm bauld to tell,
I am a gentle jinker.

Love Jupiter into a swan
Turn'd for his lovely Leda;
He like a bull o'er meadows ran,
To carry aff Europa.

Then may not I, as well as he,
To cheat your Argus blinker,
And win your love like mighty Jove,
Thus hide me in a tinkler.

Sir, ye appear a cunningman,
But this fine plot you'll fail in,
For there is neither pot nor pan
Of mine you'll drive a nail in.
Then bind your budget on your back,
And nails up in your apron,
For I've a tinkler under tack
That's us'd to clout my caldron.

## Now bank an' brae.

521

Now bank an' brae are claith'd in green an ſcatter'd
Slow
cowſ_lips ſweet_ly ſpring by Gir_van's fai ry haun ted
ſtream the birdies flit on wanton wing To Caſſillis banks when
e'ening fa's there wi' my Ma_ry let me flee there catch her
il_ka glance of love the bonnie blink o' Ma_ry's ee.

The chield wha boaſts o' warld's walth,
Is aften laird o' meikle care;
But Mary she is a' mine ain,
Ah! Fortune canna gie me mair!
Then let me range by Caſſillis banks,
Wi' her the laſſie dear to me,
And catch her ilka glance o' love,
The bonny blink o' Mary's ee.

# Ae day a braw wooer, &c.

By Burns.

522

Ae day a braw wooer came down the lang glen, And sair wi' his
Lively
love he did deave me; But I said there was naething I hated like
men, The deuce gae wi' him to be_lieve me believe me, The
deuce gae wi' him to be__lieve me.

A weel stocket mailen himsel o't the laird,
An bridal aff han' was the proffer,
I never loot on, that I ken'd or I car'd,
But thought I might get a waur offer.

He spake o' the darts o' my bonny black een,
An' o for my love he was diein';
I said, he might die when he liket for Jean,
The gude forgie me for liein'.

But what do ye think, in a fortnight or less,
(The diel's in his taste to gae near her)
He's down to the castle to black cousin Bess,
Think how the jade I cou'd endure her.

An' a' the niest ouk as I freted wi' care,
I gade to the tryst o' Dulgarlock;
An' wha but my bra' fickle wooer was there,
Wha glowr'd as if he'd seen a warlock.

## Continued.

Out owre my left shouther I gie'd him a blink,
Lest neighbour shou'd think I was saucy;
My wooer he caper'd as he'd been in drink,
An' vow'd that I was a dear lassie.

I spier'd for my cousin, fu' couthie an' sweet,
An' if she'd recover'd her hearin;
An' how my auld ✰ shoon fitted her shachel'd feet
Gude saf' us how he fell a swearin'.

He begg'd me for gudesake that I'd be his wife,
Or else I wad kill him wi' sorrow;
An' just to preserve the poor bodie in life,
I think I will wed him to morrow.

✰ An old lover.

## To the Foregoing Tune.

THE Queen o' the Lothians cam cruisin to Fife
Fal de ral, lal de ral, lairo,
To see gin a wooer wad tak her for life,
Sing hey, fal lal de ral, lal de ral, lal de ral,
Hey, fal lal de ral, lairo.
She had na been lang at the brow o' the hill, Fal &c.
Till Jockie cam down for to visit Lochnell, Sing hey, fal &c.
He took the aunt to the neuk o' the ha', — Fal &c.
Whare naebody heard, and whare nae body saw, — Sing hey fal &c.
Madam, he says, I've thought on your advice — Fal &c.
I wad marry your niece, but I'm fley'd she'll be nice, — Sing hey fal
Jockie, she says, the wark's done to your hand, — Fal &c.
I've spoke to my niece, and she's at your command, — Sing hey fal &
But troth, Madam, I canna woo, — Fal &c.
For aft I hae tried it, and ay I fa' thro' — Sing hey fal &c.
But, O dear Madam, and ye wad begin — Fal &c.
For I'm as fley'd to do it, as it were a sin, — Sing hey fal &c.
Jenny cam in, and Jockie ran out, — Fal &c.
Madam, she says, what hae ye been about, — Sing hey fal &c.
Jenny, she says, I've been workin for you, — Fal &c.
For what do ye think, Jockie's come here to woo, — Sing hey fal &c.
Now Jenny tak care, and dash na the lad, — Fal &c.
For offers like him are na ay to be had, — Sing hey fal &c.
Madam, I'll tak the advice o' the wise, — Fal &c.
I ken the lad's worth, and I own he's a prize, — Sing hey fal &c.
Then she cries but the house, Jockie come here, — Fal &c.
Ye've neathing to do but the question to spier, — Sing hey fal &c.
The question was spier'd, and the bargain was struck, — Fal &c.
The neebors cam in, and wish'd them gude luck, — Sing hey fal &c.

# Gudeen to you kimmer.

Corrected by Burns.

523

* Gud_een to you kim_mer and how de ye do?
Canty
Hiccup, quo' kim mer, The bet_ter that I'm fou.
Chorus.
We're a' nod_din, nid nid nod_din we're a' nod_din at
our houfe at hame, We're a' nod_din nid nid nod_din
we're a' nod_din at our houfe at hame.

Kate fits i' the neuk,
  Suppin hen-broo;
Deil tak Kate
  An' fhe be na noddin too!
    We're a' noddin &c.

How's a' wi' you, Kimmer,
  And how do ye fare?
A pint o' the beft o't,
  And twa pints mair.
    We're a' noddin &c.

How's a' wi' you, kimmer,
  And how do ye thrive;
How mony bairns hae ye?
  Quo' kimmer, I hae five.
    We're a' noddin &

Are they a' Johny's?
  Eh! atweel no:
Twa o' them were gotten
  When Johny was awa.
    We're a' noddin &c.

Cats like milk
  And dogs like broo;
Lads like lafses weel,
  And lafses lads too.
    We're a' noddin &c.

## In Brechin did a wabster dwell

524

*
In Brechin did a wabster dwell, Who was a man o fame o, He
Rather Slow
was the deacon o' his trade John Steinon was his name o. A
mare he had a lus_ty jade, Baith sturdy, stark, and strang o, A
lusty trusty skiegh young yad, An' he had spar'd her lang o.

The wabster bade his mare go work,
Quoth she, I am not able,
For neither get I corn nor hay,
Nor stand I in a stable;
But hunts me, and dunts me,
And dings me from the town,
And fells me, and tells me,
I am not worth my room.

The wabster swore a bloody oath,
And out he drew a knife,
If one word come out of thy head,
I vow I'll take thy life.
The mare ay, for fear ay,
Fell fainting to the ground
And groaning and moaning.
Fell in a deadly swoon.

They clipped her, and nipped her,
They took from her the skin;
The haunches, and the paunches,
They quickly brought them in:
Make haste, dame, said he,
And wash this grease, and dry't,
For I will hazard on my life,
The doctor's wife will buy't.

They tumbl'd her, they tumbl'd her,
They shot her o'er the brae;
With rumbling, and tumbling,
She to the ground did gae.
But the night being cauld,
And the mare wanting her skin,
And darkness came out o'er the land,
And fain wou'd she been in. &c.

&c. &c.

## Willy's rare, and Willy's fair.

525
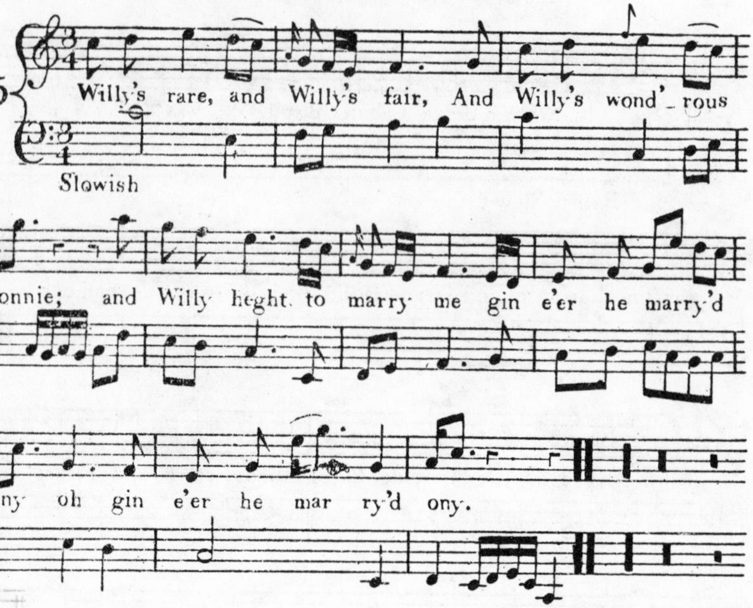
Willy's rare, and Willy's fair, And Willy's wond_rous
Slowish
bonnie; and Willy hegh, to marry me gin e'er he marry'd
ony oh gin e'er he mar ry'd ony.

Yestreen I made my bed fu' brade,
The night I'll make it narrow;
For a' the live lang winter's night,
I lie twin'd of my marrow.

O came you by yon water side,
Pu'd you the rose or lily;
Or came you by yon meadow green,
Or saw you my sweet Willy?

She sought him east, she sought him west,
She sought him brad and narrow;
Sine in the clifting of a craig,
She found him drown'd in Yarrow.

✿✿✿✿✿✿✿✿✿✿✿✿✿✿✿✿✿✿✿✿✿✿✿✿✿✿✿✿✿✿✿✿✿✿✿✿✿✿✿✿

## My Daddy left me &c.

526
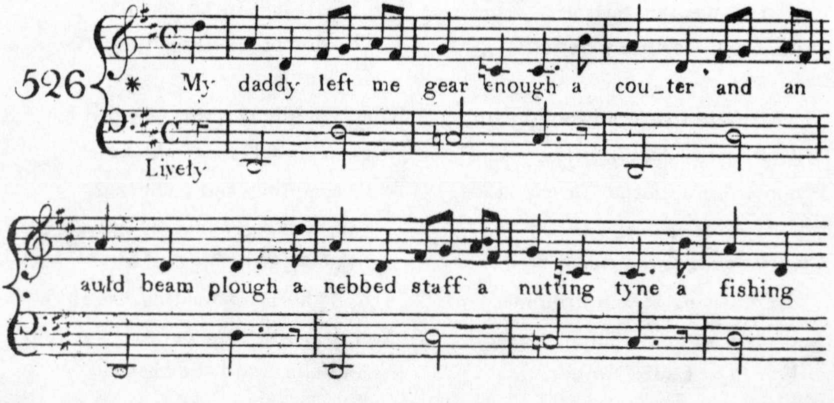
* My daddy left me gear enough a cou_ter and an
Lively
auld beam plough a nebbed staff a nutting tyne a fishing

## Continued.

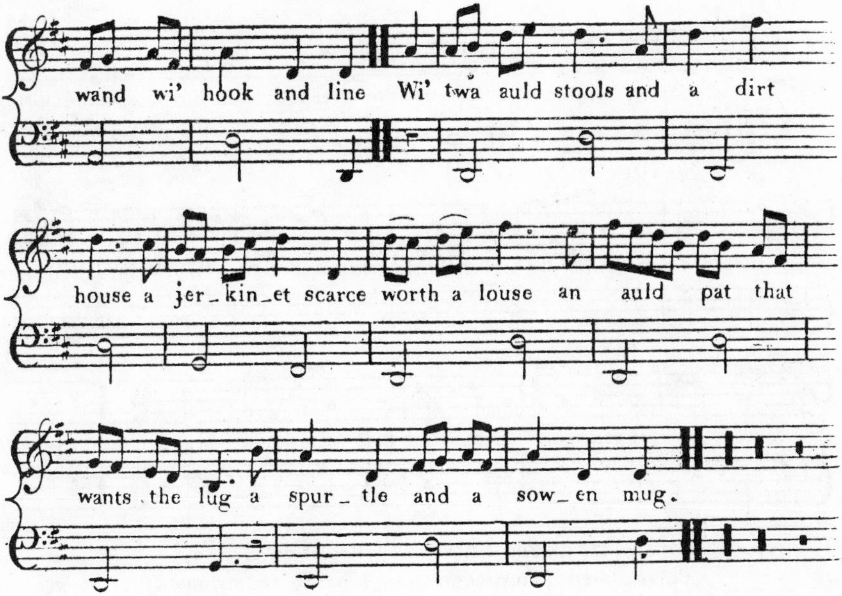
wand wi' hook and line Wi' twa auld stools and a dirt
house a jer_kin_et scarce worth a louse an auld pat that
wants the lug a spur_tle and a sow_en mug.

A hempken heckle, and a mell,
A tar horn, and a weather's bell,
A muck fork, and an auld peet creel,
The spakes of our auld spinning wheel.
A pair of branks, yea, and a saddle,
With our auld brunt and broken laddle,
A whang-bit, and a sniffle-bit;
Chear up, my bairns, and dance a fit.

A flailing staff and a timmer spit,
An auld kirn and a hole in it,
Yarn-winnles, and a reel,
A fetter-lock, a trump of steel,
A whistle, and a tup-horn spoon,
With an auld pair of clouted shoon,
A timmer spade, and a gleg shear,
A bonnet for my bairns to wear.

A timmer tong, a broken cradle,
The pillions of an auld car-saddle,
A gullie-knife and a horse-wand,
A mitten for the left hand,
With an auld broken pan of brass,
With an auld sark that wants the arse,
An auld-band, and a hoodling how,
I hope, my bairns, ye're a weil now.

Aft have I borne ye on my back,
With a' this riff-raff in my pack;
And it was a' for want of gear,
That gart me steal Mess John's grey mare
But now, my bairns, what ails ye now
For ye ha'e naigs enough to plow;
And hose and shoon fit for your feet,
Chear up, my bairns, and dinna greet.

Then with mysel I did advise,
My daddy's gear for to comprize;
Some neighbours I ca'd in to see
What gear my daddy left to me.
They sat three quarters of a year,
Comprizing of my daddy's gear;
And when they had gi'en a' their votes,
'Twas scarcely a' worth four pounds scots

## Stern winter has left us

527

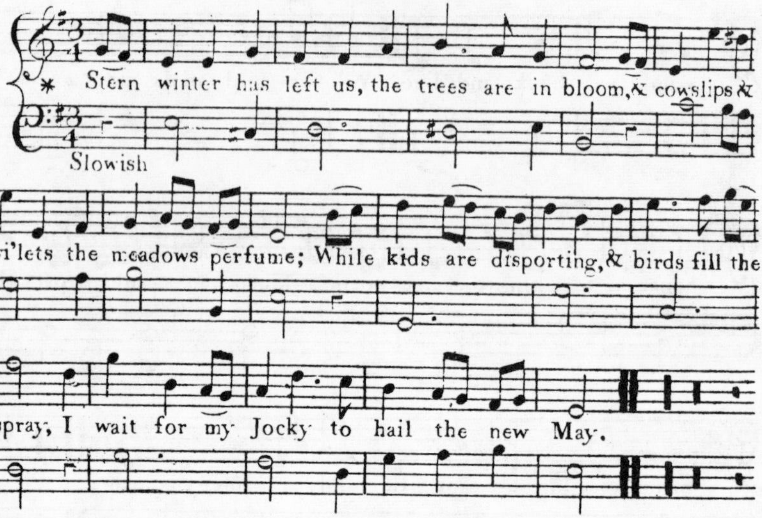
*
Stern winter has left us, the trees are in bloom, & cowslips & vi'lets the meadows perfume; While kids are disporting, & birds fill the spray, I wait for my Jocky to hail the new May.
Slowish

Jocky Among the young lilies, my Jenny, I've stray'd,
Pinks, daisies, and woodbines I bring to my maid;
Here's thyme sweetly smelling, and lavender gay,
A posy to form for my Queen of the May.

Jenny Ah! Jocky, I fear you intend to beguile,
When seated with Molly last night on a stile,
You swore that you'd love her for ever and ay,
Forgetting poor Jenny, your Queen of the May.

Jocky Young Willy is handsome in shepherds green dress,
He gave you these ribbons that hang at your breast,
Besides three sweet kisses upon the new hay;
Was that done like Jenny, the Queen of the May?

Jenny This garland of roses no longer I prize,
Since Jocky, false hearted, his passion denies:
Ye flowers so blooming, this instant decay,
For Jenny's no longer the Queen of the May.

Jocky Believe me, dear maiden, your lover you wrong,
Your name is for ever the theme of my song;
From the dews of pale eve' to the dawning of day,
I sing but of Jenny, my Queen of the May.

Jenny Again, balmy comfort with transport I view,
My fears are all vanish'd since Jocky is true;
Then to our blyth shepherds the news I'll convey,
That Jenny alone you've crown'd Queen of the May.

Jocky Come all ye young lovers, I pray you draw near,
Avoid all suspicion, whate're may appear;
Believe not your eyes, lest your peace they betray,
Then come, my dear Jenny, and hail the new May.

Stern winter has left us. Second Sett.

Jenny.
528
Slowish
Stern winter has left us, the trees are in bloom, And cowslips and vi'lets the meadows per_fume; While kids are dis_porting, and birds fill the spray I wait for my Jocky to hail the new May.
Jocky.
A_mong the young lil'_ies my Jen_ny I've stray'd, Pinks, daisies, and woodbines I bring to my maid; Here's thyme sweet_ly smelling, and la_ven_der gay A po_sy to form for my Queen of the May.

# Ah Mary sweetest maid.

529

He
Slow
Ah Mary sweetest maid farewell, My hopes are flown for
as to wreck! Heaven guard you love and heal your heart, tho' mine a_
_las maun break,
She
Dearest lad what ills betide? Is Willie to his love untrue?
Pledg'd the morn to be your bride! Ah hae ye, hae ye ta'en the rue.
He
Ye canna wear a ragged gown, O beggar wed wi' nought a_va My
kye are drown'd my house is down my last sheep lies a neath the snaw.
She
Tell na me o storm or flood or sheep a' smoor'd ayont the hill, For

Continued.

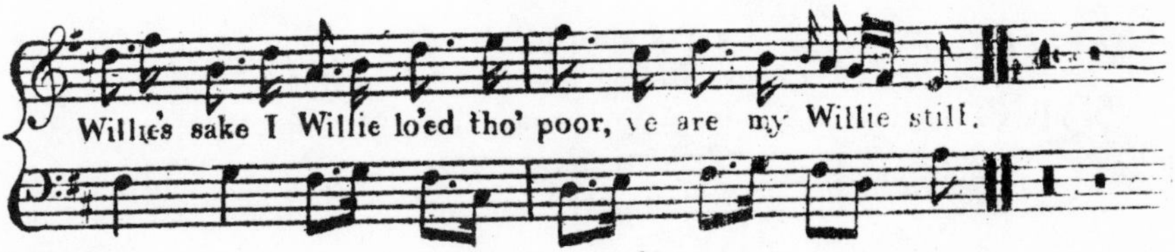
Willie's sake I Willie lo'ed tho' poor, ye are my Willie still.

He
Ye canna thole the wind and rain,
Nor wander friendless far frae hame:
Cheer cheer your heart some richer swain,
Will soon blot out lost Willie's name.

She
I'll tak my bundle in my hand
And wipe the dew_drap frae my ee;
I'll wander wi' ye o'er the land,
I'll venture wi' ye o'er the sea.

He
Pardon love. 'twas a' a snare
The flocks are safe _ we needna part:
I'd forfeit them and ten times mair,
To clasp thee, Mary, to my heart.

She
Could ye wi' my feelings sport,
Or doubt a heart sae warm and true?
I should wish mischief on ye for't,
But canna wish ought ill to you.

✩✩✩✩✩✩✩✩✩✩✩✩✩✩✩✩✩✩✩✩✩✩✩✩✩✩✩✩✩✩✩✩✩✩✩✩✩✩

## Anna, thy Charms my bosom fire.

530

Anna thy charms my bosom fire, And press my soul with
Slow
care But ah, how bootless to admire, When fat_ed to des_pair.
Yet in thy presence, lovely Fair, To hope may be for_giv'n: For
sure 'twere impious to despair, So much in sight of Heaven.

Written for this Work by Robert Burns.

## Thy cheek is o' the rose's hue,

531

Thy cheek is o' the roses hue, My on_ly joe and
Slow
dear_ie O, Thy neck is like the sil_ler dew up_on the
bark sae brier_ie O; Thy teeth are o' the i_vo_ry, O
sweets the twink_le o' thine e'e, Nae joy nae pleasure
blinks on me, My on_ly joe and dear_ie O.

The birdie sings upon the thorn
It's sang o' joy fu' cheerie, O!
Rejoicing in the simmer morn,
Nae care to mak' it eerie O!
But little kens the sangster sweet
Aught o' the care I hae to meet,
That gars my restles bosom beat,
My only joe and dearie, O!

Whan we wer bairnies on yon brae,
And youth was blinkin' bony O!
Aft we wad daff the leelang day,
Our joys fu' sweet and monie O.

Aft I wad chace thee o'er the lee,
And round about the thornie tree,
Or pu' the wild_flowers a' for thee,
My only joe and dearie O!

I hae' a wish I canna tine
'Mang a' the cares that grieve me O!
A wish that thou wert ever mine,
And never mair to leave me O.
Then I wad daut thee night and day,
Nor ither war'ly care wad hae'
Till life's warm stream forgot to play,
My only joe and dearie O.

## O ay my wife she dang me.

Written for this Work by Robert Burns.

532

Chorus
A little lively
O ay my wife she dang me, An' aft my wife she bang'd me, If ye gie a' wo_man a' her will Gude faith she'll soon o'er_gang ye. On peace and rest my mind was bent, And fool I was I marry'd; But never honest man's in_tent, As cur_sed_ly mis_car_ry'd.

Some sairie comfort still at last,
When a' thir days are done, man,
My pains o' hell on earth is past
I'm sure o' bliss aboon man
O ay my wife she &c.

## Come under my plaidy.

533

Come under my plaidy, the night's ga'en to fa'; Come
Lively
in frae the cauld blast, the drift and the snaw; Come
under my plaidy, and lye down beside me; There's room in't
dear lassie, believe me for twa Come under my plaidy, and
lye down beside me I'll hap ye frae ev'ry cauld blast that will
blaw O come under my plaidy, and lye down beside me there's
room in't dear lassie be _ lieve me for twa.

## Continued.

'Gae 'wa wi' your plaidy! auld Donald gae' wa!
'I fear na the cauld blaſt, the driſt, nor the ſnaw.
'Gae 'wa wi' your plaidy! I'll no lye beſide ye,
'Ye may be my gutchard, auld Donald gae 'wa.
'I'm ga'en to meet Johnny, he's young and he's bonny,
'He's been at Meg's bridal, fou trig and fou braw!
'O there's nane dance ſae lightly, ſae gracefu', ſae tightly,
'His cheek's like the new roſe, his brow's like the ſnaw

"Dear Marion let that flee ſtick faſt to the wa,
"Your Jock's but a gowk, and has naething ava,
"The haill o' his pack he has now on his back,
"He's thretty, and I'm but threeſcore and twa.
"Be frank now and kindly, I'll buſk you aye finely;
"At kirk or at market they'll few gang ſae braw;
"A bein houſe to bide in, a chaiſe for to ride in,
"And flunkies to tend ye as aft as ye ca'.

'My father's ay tell'd me, my mither and a',
'Ye'd mak' a gude huſband, and keep me ay braw,
'It's true I loo Johnny he's gude and he's bonny,
'But waes me! ye ken he has naething ava.
'I hae little tocher, you've made a gude offer,
'I'm now mair than twenty, my time is but ſma'
'Sae gie me your plaidie, I'll creep in beſide ye,
'I thought ye'd been aulder than threeſcore and twa.

She crap in ayont him, beſide the ſtane wa'
Whar Johnny was liſt'ning and heard her tell a',
The day was appointed, his proud heart it dunted,
And ſtrack 'gainſt his ſide as if burſting in twa.
He wander'd hame weary, the night it was dreary.
And thowleſs, he tint his gate deep 'mang the ſnaw,
The Howlet was ſcreaming, while Johnny cried, "Women
"Wa'd marry auld nick if he'd keep them ay bra'.

"O the deel's in the laſses! they gang now ſae bra',
"They'll ly down wi' auld men o' fourſcore and twa,
"The haill o' their marriage, is gowd and a carriage,
"Plain love is the cauldeſt blaſt now that can blaw.
"But lo'e them I canna nor marry I winna
"Wi' ony daft laſsie! tho' fair as a Queen,
"Till love ha'e a ſhare o't, the never a hair o't
"Shall gang in my wallet at morning or e'en"

# Come follow, follow me.

534
Come follow, follow me, Ye fairy elves that be, Come
Lively
follow me your Queen And trip it o'er the green; Hand in
hand we'll dance around because this place is fairy ground hand in
hand we'll dance around, Because this place is fairy ground.

When mortals are at rest,
And snoring in their nest;
Unheed, and unespy'd,
Through key holes we do glide,
Over tables, stools and shelves,
We trip it with our Fairy elves.

And if the house be foul,
With platter, dish or bowl,
Up stairs we nimbly creep,
And find the sluts asleep;
Then we pinch their arms and thighs:
None us hears, and none us spies.

But if the house be swept,
And from uncleanness kept,
We praise the household maid,
And surely she is paid:
Every night before we go,
We drop a tester in her shoe.

Then o'er w mushroom's head
Our table-cloth we spread,
A grain of rye or wheat,
The diet that we eat;
Pearly drops of dew we drink,
In acorn cups fill'd to the brink.

The brain of nightingales,
With unctious fat of snails,
Between twocockles stew'd,
Is meat that's eas'ly chew'd,
And brains of worms & marrow of mice
Do make a feast that's wondrous nice.

The grasshopper, gnat and fly,
Serve for our minstrelsy,
Grace said, we dance a while,
And so the time beguile;
But if the moon doth hide her head,
The glow-worm lights us home to bed.

O'er tops of dewy grass
So nimbly we do pass,
The young and tender stalk;
Ne'er bends where we do walk;
Yet in the morning may be seen,
Where we the Night before have been.

## Lord Thomas and fair Annet.

535

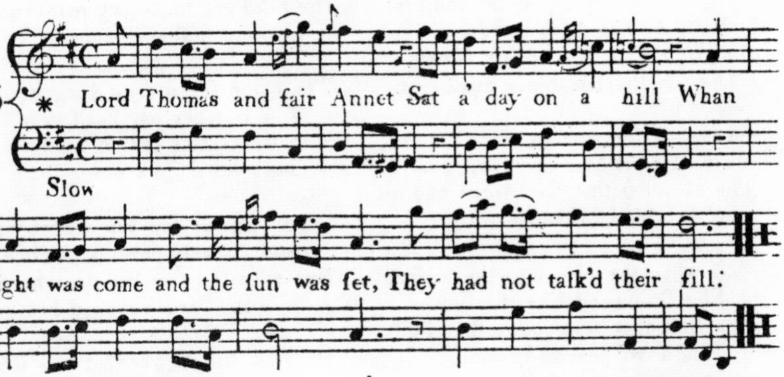

* Lord Thomas and fair Annet Sat a' day on a hill Whan
Slow
night was come and the ſun was ſet, They had not talk'd their fill.


Lord Thomas ſaid a word in jeſt,
  Fair Annet took it ill;
A. I will never wed a wife
  Againſt my ain friends will.

Gif ye will never wed a wife,
  A wife will ne'er wed yee.
Sae he is hame to tell his mither,
  An' kneld upon his knee:

O rede, O rede, mither, he ſays,
  A gude rede gie to me.
O ſall I tak the nut-browne bride,
  And let fair Annet be?

The nut-browne bride has gowd & gear,
  Fair Annet ſhe's gat nane,
And the little bewtie fair Annet has,
  O it will ſoon be gane.

And he has to his brither gane,
  Now, brither, rede ye me,
A! ſall I marrie the nut-browne bride,
  And let fair Annet be?

The nut-browne bride has oxen, brother,
  The nut-browne bride has kye,
I wad hae ye marrie the nut-browne bride,
  And caſt fair Annet by.

Her oxen may dye i' the houſe, Billie,
  And her kye into the byre,
And I ſall hae naething to myſell
  But a fat fadge by the fyre.

And he has till his ſiſter gane:
  Now, ſiſter, rede ye me,
O ſall I marrie the nut-browne bride,
  And ſet fair Annet free?

Iſe rede ye tak fair Annet, Thomas,
  And let the browne bride alane,
Leſt ye ſould ſigh, and ſay, Alas
  What is this we brought hame?

No, I will tak my mither's counſel,
  And marrie me out o' hand,
And I will tak the nut-browne bride,
  Fair Annet may leave the land.

Up then roſe fair Annet's father
  Twa hours or it wereday,
And he is gane into the bower
  Wherein fair Annet lay

Riſe up, riſe up, fair Annet, he ſays,
  Put on your ſilken ſheene,
Let us gae to St Marie's kirk,
  And ſee that rich wedden.

My maids gae to my dreſſing-room,
  And dreſs to me my hair,
Whair-ere ye laid a plait before,
  See ye lay ten times mair.

My maids, gae to my dreſſing-room
  And dreſs to me my ſmock,
The one half is o' the holland fine,
  The other o' needle-work.

The horſe fair Annet rade upon,
  He amblit like the wind,
Wi' ſiller he was ſhod before,
  Wi' burning gowd behind.

Four-and-twenty ſiller bells
  Were a' tied till his mane,
Wi' yae tift o' the norland wind,
  They tinkled ane by ane.

Over

## Continued.

Four-and-twenty gay gude knights
  Rade by fair Annet's ſide,
And four and twenty fair ladies,
  As gin ſhe had bin a bride.

And whan ſhe cam to Maries kirke,
  She ſat on Marie's ſtean,
The cleading that fair Annet had on
  It ſkinkled in their een.

And whan ſhe cam into the kirke,
  She ſkimmer'd like the ſun,
The belt that was aboute her waiſt
  Was a' wi' pearles bedone.

She ſat her by the nut-browne bride,
  And her een they wer ſae clear,
Lord Thomas he clear forgat the bride,
  When fair Annet drew near.

He had a roſe into his hand,
  He gae it kiſſes three,
And reaching by the nut-browne bride,
  Laid it on fair Annet's knee.

Up then ſpak the nut browne bride,
  She ſpak wi' meikle ſpite,
And whair gat ye that roſe-water
  That does mak yee ſae white?

O I did get the roſe-water
  Whair ye wull neir get nane,
For I did get that very roſe-water
  Into my mither's wame.

The bride ſhe drew a long bodkin
  Frae out her gay head gear,
And ſtrake fair Annet unto the heart,
  That word ſpak never mair.

Lord Thomas ſaw fair Annet wax pale,
  And marvelit what mote bee,
But whan he ſaw her dear hearts blude,
  A' wood wroth wexed hee.

He drew his dagger that was ſae ſharp,
  That was ſae ſharp and meet,
And drave it in to the nut broune bride,
  That fell deid at his feit.

Now ſtay for me, dear Annet, he ſaid,
  Now ſtay, my dear, he cry'd;
Then ſtrake the dagger until his heart,
  And fell deid by hir ſide.

Lord Thomas was bury'd without kirk-wa',
  Fair Annet within the quiere;
And o' the tane thair grew a birk,
  The other a bonny briere.

And ay they grew, and ay they threw,
  As they wad faine be neare,
And by this ye may ken right weil,
  They wer twa luvers deare.

************************

## William and Margaret.

536

'Twas at the ſilent ſolemn hour when night and morn - ing
Slow
meet; In glided Marg'rets grimly ghoſt and ſtood at Williams feet Her

Continued.

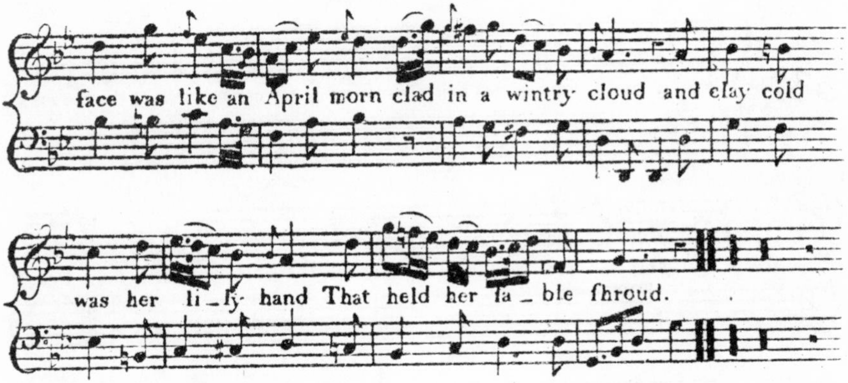
face was like an April morn clad in a wintry cloud and clay cold
was her li_ly hand That held her ſa_ble ſhroud.

So ſhall the faireſt face appear
When youth and years are flown;
Such is the robe that Kings muſt wear
When Death has reft their crown.
Her bloom was like the ſpringing flow'r
That ſ ps the ſilver dew;
The roſe was budded in her cheek,
Juſt op'ning to the view.

But love had, like a canker_worm,
Conſum'd her early prime.
The roſe grew pale, and left her cheek;
She dy'd before her time.
"Awake!" ſhe cry'd, "thy true love calls,
"Come from her midnight grave:
"Now let thy pity hear the maid
"Thy love refus'd to ſave.

"This is the dumb and dreary hour
"When injur'd ghoſts complain,
"When yawning graves give up their dead
"To haunt the faithleſs ſwain.
"Bethink thee, William! of thy fault,
"Thy pledge and broken oath,
"And give me back my maiden vow,
"And give me back my troth.

"Why did you promiſe love to me,
"And not that promiſe keep?
"Why did you ſwear my eyes were bright,
"Yet leave thoſe eyes to weep?
"How could you ſay my face was fair,
"And yet that face forſake?
"How could you win my virgin heart,
"Yet leave that heart to break.

"Why did you ſay my lips was ſweet,
"And made the ſcarlet pale?
"And why did I, young witleſs maid!
"Believe the flattering tale?
"That face, alas. no more is fair,
"Thoſe lips no longer red:
"Dark are my eyes, now clos'd in death,
"And every charm is fled.

"The hungry worm my ſiſter is;
"This winding ſheet I wear;
"And cold and weary laſts our night,
"Till that laſt morn appear.
"But, hark! the cock has warn'd me (hence;
"A long and late adieu!
"Come ſee, falſe man. how low ſhe lies
"Who dy'd for love of you"

The lark ſung loud, the morning ſmil'd
With beams of roſy red;
Pale William quak'd in every limb,
And raving left his bed.
He hy'd him to the fatal place
Where Marg'ret's body lay, (turf
And ſtretch'd him on the green graſs
That wrapp'd her breathleſs clay.

And thrice he call'd on Marg'rets name,
And thrice he wept full ſore,
Then laid his cheek o her cold grave
And word ſpoke never more.
Such be the fate of vows unpaid,
And pledge of ſacred love!
Tho' they may tempt the yielding maid,
They're regiſter'd above!

## What ails the lafses at me.

537

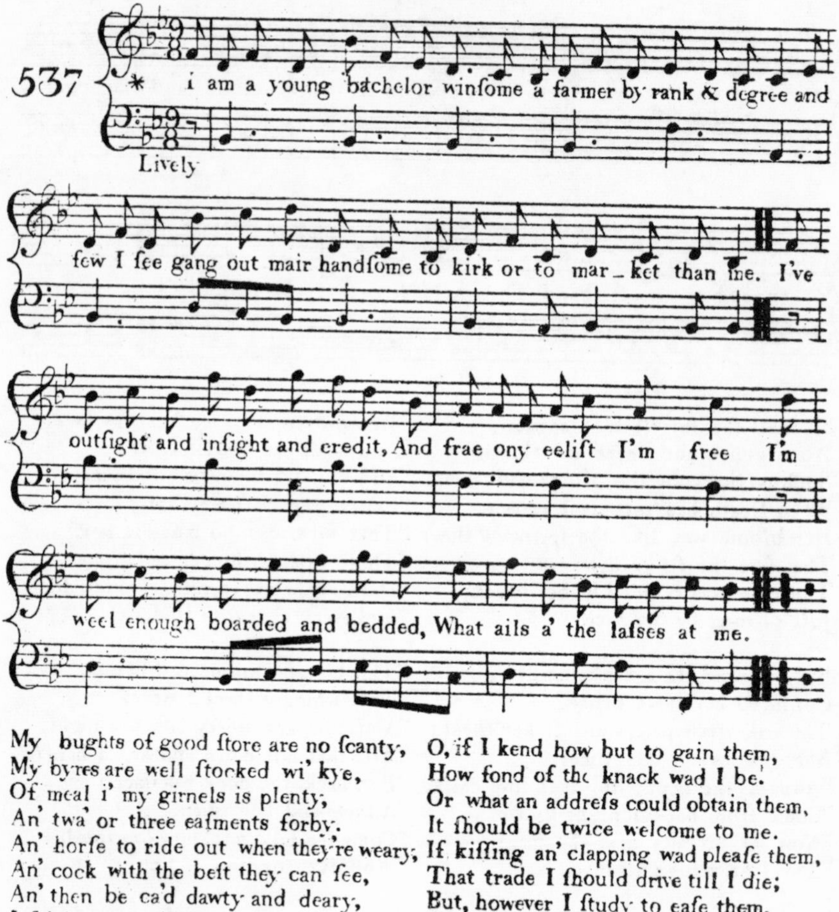
*
I am a young batchelor winfome a farmer by rank & degree and
Lively
few I fee gang out mair handfome to kirk or to mar_ket than me. I've
outfight and infight and credit, And frae ony eelift I'm free I'm
weel enough boarded and bedded, What ails a' the lafses at me.

My bughts of good ftore are no fcanty,
My byres are well ftocked wi' kye,
Of meal i' my girnels is plenty,
An' twa or three eafments forby.
An' horfe to ride out when they're weary,
An' cock with the beft they can fee,
An' then be ca'd dawty and deary,
I feirly what ails them at me.

Behind backs, afore fouk I've woo'd them,
An' a' the gates o't that I ken,
An' when they leugh o' me I trow'd them,
An' thought I had won, but what then;
When I fpeak of matters they grumble,
Nor are condefcending and free,
But at my propofals ay ftumble,
I wonder what ails them at me.

I've try'd them baith highland & lowland,
Where I a good bargain coud fee,
But nane o' them fand I wad fall in,
Or fay they wad buckle wi' me.
With jooks an' wi' fcraps I've addrefs'd them,
Been with them baith modeft and free,
But whatever way I carefs'd them,
There's fomething ftill ails them at me.

O, if I kend how but to gain them,
How fond of the knack wad I be!
Or what an addrefs could obtain them,
It fhould be twice welcome to me.
If kiffing an' clapping wad pleafe them,
That trade I fhould drive till I die;
But, however I ftudy to eafe them,
They've ftill an exception at me.

There's wratacks, an' cripples, an' cranfhaks,
An' a' the wandoghts that I ken,
No fooner they fpeak to the wenches,
But they are ta'en far enough ben;
But when I fpeak to them, that's ftately
I find them ay ta'en with the gee,
An' get the denial right flatly;
What, think ye, can ail them at me.

I have yet but ae offer to make them,
If they wad but hearken to me,
And that is, I'm willing to tak them,
If they their confent wad but gee;
Let her that's content write a billet,
An' get it tranfmitted to me,
I hereby engage to fulfil it,
Tho' cripple, tho' blind fhe fud be.

## The ſun in the weſt.

538

*
The ſun in the weſt fa's to reſt in the e'en_in' ilk
Slow
morning blinks cheerfu' u_pon the green lee, But ah on the pillow o'
ſorrow ay leanin' Nae morning, nae e'enin brings pleaſure to me O
waefu' the parting when ſmiling at danger young Allan left Scotia to
meet wi' the fae cauld cauld now he lies in a land a_mang
ſtrangers frae friends and frae Helen for e_ver a_way.

As the aik on the mountain reſiſts the blaſt rain,
Sae did he the brunt o' the battle ſuſtain,
Till treach'ry arreſted his courage ſae darin,
And laid him pale, lifeleſs upon the drear plain.
Cauld winter the flower diveſts o' its cleidin',
In ſimmer again it blooms bonny to ſee;
But naething, alas! can hale my heart bleidin,
Drear winter remaining for ever wi' me.

## Scroggam

Written for this Work by Robert Burns.

539

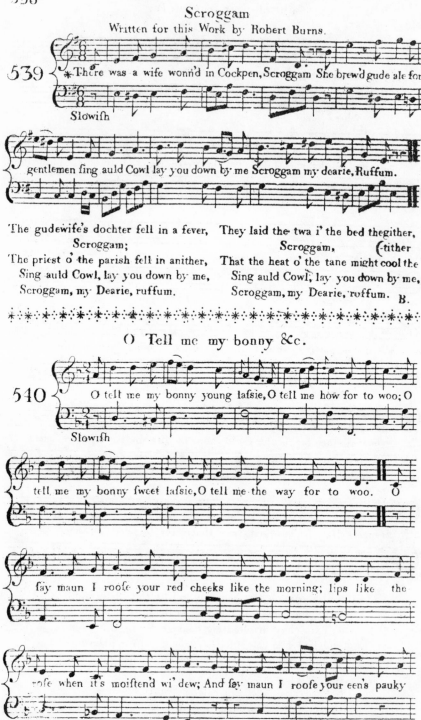

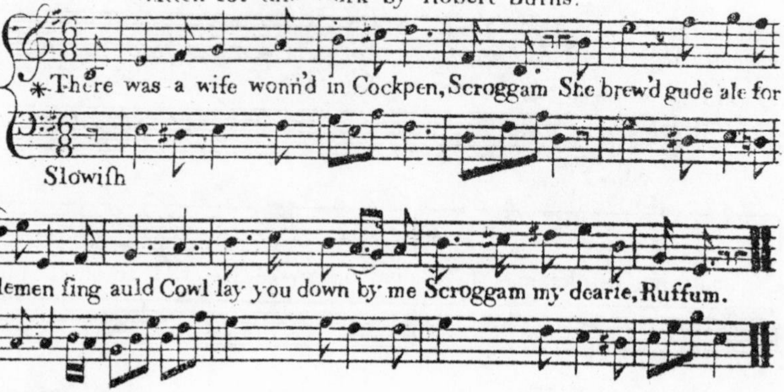
*There was a wife wonn'd in Cockpen, Scroggam She brew'd gude ale for
Slowish
gentlemen sing auld Cowl lay you down by me Scroggam my dearie, Ruffum.

The gudewife's dochter fell in a fever,
Scroggam;
The priest o' the parish fell in anither,
Sing auld Cowl, lay you down by me,
Scroggam, my Dearie, ruffum.

They laid the twa i' the bed thegither,
Scroggam,
That the heat o' the tane might cool the tither
Sing auld Cowl, lay you down by me,
Scroggam, my Dearie, ruffum. B.

## O Tell me my bonny &c.

540

O tell me my bonny young lasſie, O tell me how for to woo; O
Slowiſh
tell me my bonny ſweet laſsie, O tell me the way for to woo. O
ſay maun I rooſe your red cheeks like the morning; lips like the
roſe when it's moiſten'd wi' dew; And ſay maun I rooſe your een's pauky

Continued

ſcorning, O tell me dear laſsie the way for to woo.

O far ha'e I wander'd dear laſsie,
  To ſee thee ſail'd the ſalt ſea,
I've travel'd o'er muirlan' an' mountain,
  An' houſeleſs lain cauld on the lea;
I never ha'e try'd yet, to mak' love to ony,
  Never loe'd ony, till ance I loe'd you,
An' now we're alane in the greenwood ſae bonny,
  Now, tell me dear laſsie the way for to woo.

What care I, for your wandering, laddie,
  Or yet for your ſailing the ſea,
It was na for nought ye left Peggy,
  My tocher it brought ye to me;
An' ſay, hae ye goud for to buſk me ay gaudy,
  Ribbons an' pearlins an' breaſtknots enow,
A houſe that is canty, wi' pleniſhin' plenty,
  Without them, ye never need come for to woo.

I ha'e nae goud to buſk ye ay gaudy,
  Nor yet, buy ribbons enow,
I brag not o' houſe or o' plenty,
  But, I ha'e a heart that is true;
I came na for tocher, I ne'er heard of ony,
  Never lo'ed Peggy, nor e'er brak my vow;
I've wander'd, poor fool, for a face fauſe as bonny;
  I little thought this was the way for to woo.

Ha'e na ye rooſ'd my cheeks like the morning,
  An' rooſ'd my cherry red mow,
Ye've come o'er the Sea, Muir, and Mountain,
  What mair Johnny need ye to woo;
An' far ha'e ye wander'd I ken, my dear laddie,
  Now ye hae found me, ye've nae cauſe to rue,
Wi' health we'll ha'e plenty, I'll never gang gaudy,
  I ne'er wiſh'd for mair than a heart that is true.

She hid her fair face in his boſom,
  The tear fill'd ilk lover's ee,
An' ſabb'd by the ſide o' the burnie,
  While the mavis ſang ſweet on the tree;
He claſp'd her, he preſs'd her an' cad her his honey,
  Look'd in her face wi' a heart leel an' true,
As aften ſhe ſigh'd an' ſaid, my dear Johnny,
  Nae body need tell ye the way for to woo.

## O Mary turn awa

541

Slowish
O Mary turn a_wa that bonny face o' thine O
dinna dinna ſhaw that breaſt that never can be mine. Can
ought o' warlds gear e'er cool my boſoms care Na
na for ilka look o' thine it only feeds deſpair.

Then Mary, turn awa'
That bonny face o' thine;
O dinna, dinna ſhaw that breaſt
That never can be mine.
Wi' love's ſevereſt pangs
My heart is laiden fair,
An' o'er my breaſt the graſs maun (grow
E're I am free frae care.

Then I'll ſit down and moan,
Juſt by yon ſpreadin' tree,
An' gin a leaf fa' in my lap,
I'll ca't a word frae thee.
Syne I'll gang to the bower,
Which thou wi' roſes tied,
'Twas there by mony a bluſhing bud
I ſtrove my love to hide.

### Same Tune

WHAT ails this heart of mine?
What ails this watry ee?
What gars me ay turn cald as death,
When I tak' leave o' thee?
When thou art far awa'
Thou'lt dearer grow to me,
But change o' fouk an' change o' place,
May gar thy fancy jee.

I'll doat on ilka ſpot
Whar I ha'e been wi' thee
I'll ca' to mind ſome fond love tale
By ev'ry burn an' tree.
'Tis hope that cheers the mind,
Tho' lovers abſent be;
An' when I think I ſee thee ſtill,
I think I'm ſtill wi' thee.

## O gude ale comes &c.

Corrected by R. Burns.

542

* O gude ale comes and gude ale goes gude ale
Lively
gars me sell my hose sell my hose and pawn my shoon
gude ale keeps my heart aboon. I had sax owsen in a
pleugh They drew a' weel enough I sell'd them a' just
ane by ane gude ale keeps my heart aboon.

Gude ale hauds me bare and busy,
Gars me moop wi' the servant hizzie,
Stand i' the stool when I hae done,
Gude ale keeps my heart aboon.
O gude are comes and gude ale goes,
Gude ale gars me sell my hose,
Sell my hose, and pawn my shoon,
Gude ale keeps my heart aboon.

## Robin shure in hairst.

Chorus Written for this Work by Robert Burns.

543
*
Ro_bin shure in hairst, I shure wi' him
Brisk
Fint a heuk had I, Yet I stack by him.
Song
I gaed up to Dunse, To warp a wab o' piai__den
at his dad_dies yet, Wha met me but Ro_bin.

Was na Robin bauld,
Tho' I was a cotter,
Play'd me sic a trick
And me the Eller's dochter?
Robin shure &c.

Robin promis'd me
A' my winter vittle,
Fient haet he had but three
Goos feathers and whittle.
Robin shure &c.

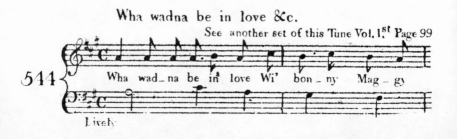

## Wha wadna be in love &c.

See another set of this Tune Vol. 1st Page 99

544
Wha wad_na be in love Wi' bon_ny Mag_gy
Lively

Continued.

Law der a pip_er met her gaun to Fife, And
spier'd what was't they ca'd her right scorn_fully she
answer'd him be_gone, you hallanshaker; Jog on your gate, you
blad_der_skate My name is Mag_gy Law_der.

Maggy, quoth he, and by my bags,
I'm fidging fain to see you;
Sit down by me, my bonny bird,
In troth I winna steer thee:
For I'm a piper to my trade,
My name is Rob the Ranter;
The lasses loup as they were daft
When I blaw up my chanter.

Piper, quoth Meg, hae you your bags,
Or is your drone in order?
If you be Rob, I've heard of you,
Live you upo' the border?
The lasses a', baith far and near,
Have heard of Rob the Ranter;
I'll shak my foot wi' right good will,
Gif you'll blaw up your chanter.

Then to his bags he flew with speed,
About the drone he twisted,
Meg up, and wallop'd o'er the green,
For brawly cou'd she frisk it.
Weel done, quoth he; Play up, quoth she:
Weel bob'd, quoth Rob the Ranter;
'Tis worth my while to play indeed,
When I hae sic a dancer.

Weel hae you play'd your part, quoth Meg.
Your cheeks are like the crimson;
There's nane in Scotland plays sae weel.
Since we lost Habby Simpson.
I've liv'd in Fife, baith maid and wife,
These ten years and a quarter;
Gin you should come to Enster fair,
Spier ye for Maggy Lawder.

# A Cogie of ale, and a pickle ait meal.

545

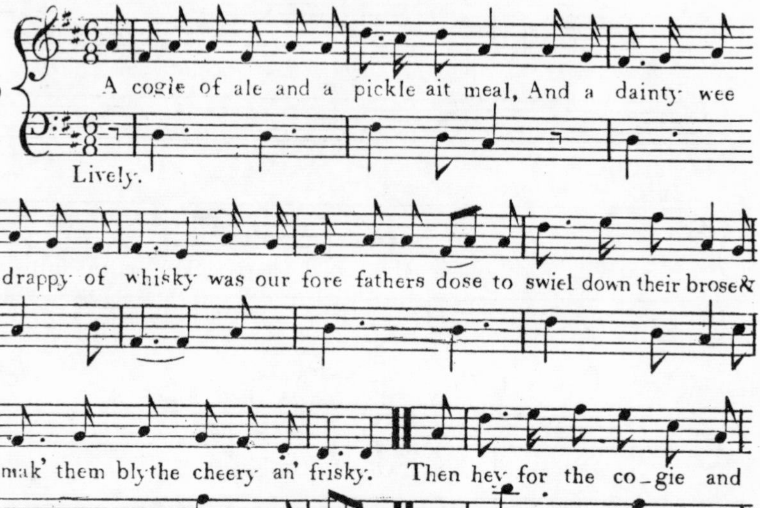
A cogie of ale and a pickle ait meal, And a dainty wee
Lively.
drappy of whisky was our fore fathers dose to swiel down their brose &
mak' them blythe cheery an' frisky. Then hey for the co_gie and
hey for the ale and hey for the whisky & hey for the meal; when mix'd a' the
gether they do unco weel, To mak' a chield cheery and brisk ay.

As I view our Scots lads, in their kilts and cockades,
A' blooming and fresh as a rose, man;
I think wi' mysel', O! the meal and the ale,
And the fruits of our Scottish kail brose, man.
Then hey for the cogie &c.

When our brave highland blades, wi' their claymores and plaids,
In the field, drive, like sheep, a' our foes, man;
Their courage and pow'r, spring frae this, to be sure,
They're the noble effects of the brose, man.
Then hey for the cogie &c.

But your spindle shank'd sparks, wha but ill set their sarks,
And your pale visag'd milksops, and beaus, man,
I think when I see them, 'twere kindness to gi'e them,
A cogie of ale and of brose, man.
Then hey for the cogie &c.

## The Dumfries Volunteers.

Written for this Work by Robert Burns.

546

Does haughty Gaul in-vasion threat, Then let the louns be-
with Spirit.
ware, Sir, There's wooden walls u-pon our seas, And Volunteers on shore, Sir.
The Nith shall rin to Corsincon, The Criffel sink in Solway, E're
Chorus.
we permit a foreign foe, On British ground to ral-ly, We'll ne'er per
mit a foreign foe, On British ground to ral-ly.

O let us not, like snarling curs,
In wrangling be divided,
Till, slap! come in an unco loun,
And wi' a rung decide it:
Be Britain still to Britain true,
Amang oursels united:
For never but by British hands
Maun British wrangs be righted.
For never but &c.

The kettle o' the Kirk and State,
Perhaps a clout may fail in't;
But deil a foreign tinkler loun
Shall ever ca' a nail in't:
Our fathers blude the kettle bought,
And wha wad dare to spoil it,
By Heavens, the sacrilegious dog
Shall fuel be to boil it!
By Heavens, &c.

The wretch that would a Tyrant own,
And the wretch, his true sworn brother,
Who would set the Mob above the throne,
May they be damn'd together.
Who will not sing, God save the king;
Shall hang as high's the steeple;
But while we sing, God save the king,
We'll ne'er forget the People.
But while we sing &c.

## He's dear dear to me &c.

547

As I was walking by yon river ſide my heart it was
Very Slow
ſair and O but I was weary I thought upon the days that are paſt and
gane for he's dear dear to me tho' he's far far frae me.

I've been in the lowlands where they ſhear the ſheep,
An' up in the highlands where they pu' the heather,
I ken a bonny ladie that lo'es me weel,
But he's far far awa' that I lo'e far better.

But I'll write a letter, an' ſend it to him,
An' tell him he's dearer to me then ony,
An' that I've ay been ſorry, ſen' he gaed awa',
Tho' he's far far away, yet he's dear dear to me.

If winter war' paſt, an' the ſimmer come in,
When daiſies an' roſes ſpring ſae freſh an' bonny,
Then I will change my ſilks for a plaiddin coat,
An' awa to the lad that is dear dear to me.

## The blue bells of Scotland.

548

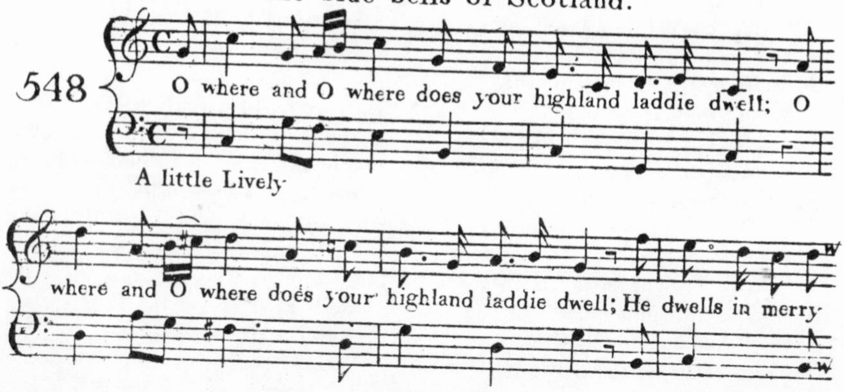
O where and O where does your highland laddie dwell; O
A little Lively
where and O where does your highland laddie dwell; He dwells in merry

## Continued.

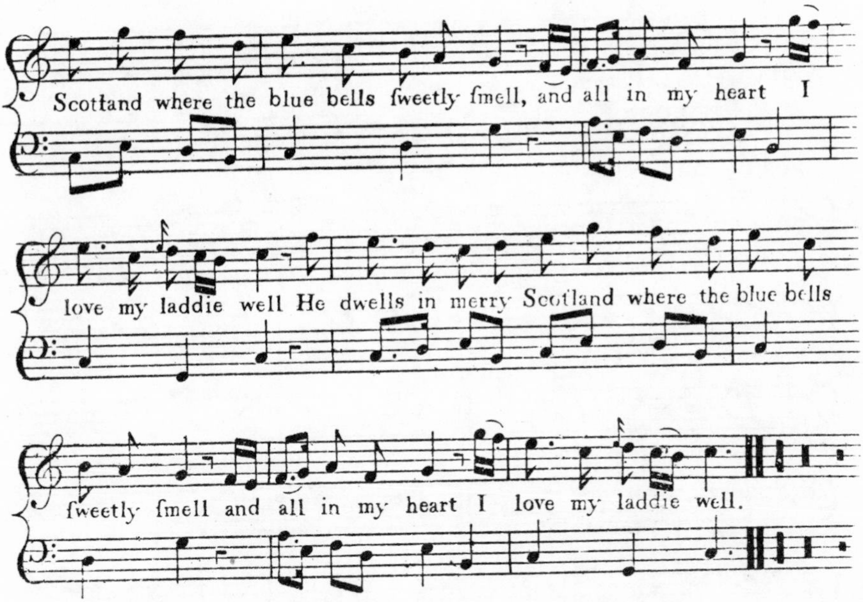
Scotland where the blue bells ſweetly ſmell, and all in my heart I
love my laddie well He dwells in merry Scotland where the blue bells
ſweetly ſmell and all in my heart I love my laddie well.

O what laſsie what does your highland laddie wear,
O what laſsie what does your highland laddie wear,
A ſcarlet coat and bonnet blue with bonny yellow hair,
And none in the world can with my love compare.

O where and O where is your highland laddie gone,
O where and O where is your highland laddie gone,
He's gone to fight for George our King, and left me all alone,
For noble and brave's my loyal highlandman.

O what laſsie what if your highland lad be ſlain,
O what laſsie what if your highland lad be ſlain
O no! true love will be his guard and bring him ſafe again,
For I never could live without my highlandman.

O when and O when will your highland lad come hame,
O when and O when will your highland lad come hame,
When e'er the war is over he'll return to me with fame,
And I'll plait a wreath of flow'rs for my lovely highlandman.

O what will you claim for your conſtancy to him,
O what will you claim for your conſtancy to him,
I'll claim a Prieſt to marry us, a Clerk to ſay Amen,
And ne'er part again from my bonny highlandman.

# Colin Clout.

549

Chanticleer, wi' noisy whistle bids the house_wife
A little Lively
rise in haste; Co_lin Clout be gins to hir_sle slaw_ly
frae his sleep_less nest. Love that raises sic a cla_mour,
driv_in' lads an' las_ses mad; Ah waes my heart had
coost his glammir o'er poor Colin luck_less lad.

Cruel Jenny, lack a daisey!
Lang had gart him greet an grane,
Colin's pate was hafflins crazy,
Jenny laugh'd at Colin's pain,
Slawly up his duds he gathers,
Slawly, slawly trudges out,
An' frae the fauld he drives his wedders
Happier far than Colin Clout.

Now the sun, rais'd frae his nappie,
Set the Orient in a low,
Drinkin, ilka glancin' drappie,
I' the field, an' a' the knowe.
Many a birdie, sweetly singin,
Flafferd briskly round about;
An mony a dainty flow'rie springin,
A' were blythe but Colin Clout.

What is this? cries Colin glow'rin',
Glaiked-like, a' round about,
Jenny, this is past endurin;
Death maun ease poor Colin Clout.
A' the night I toss an' tummle,
Never can I close an e'e
An' a' the day I grane an' grummle,
Jenny, this is a' for thee.

Ye'll hae nane but farmer Patie,
Cause the fallow's rich I trow,
Ablins, tho' he shou'd na cheat ye,
Jenny, ye'll hae cause to rue.
Auld, an' gley'd, an' crooked-backed,
Siller bought at sic a price,
Ah! Jenny, gin ye lout to tak' it,
Fo'k will say ye're no o'er nice. &c. &c.

## 'Tis nae very lang sinsyne.

550

'Tis nae very lang sinsyne, That I had a lad o' my ain, But
Lively
now he's awa to anither, And left me a' my lane. The lass he is
cour_ting has siller an' I hae nane at a'; Its nought but the
love o' the tocher That's ta'en my lad_die a_wa.

But I'm blyth, that my heart's my ain,
  And I'll keep it a' my life,
Until that I meet wi' a lad
  Wha has sense to wale a good wife.
For though I say't mysell,
  That shou'd nae say't, tis true,
The lad that gets me for a wife,
  He'll ne'er hae occasion to rue.

I gang ay fou clean and fou tosh,
  As a' the neighbours can tell;
Though I've seldom a gown on my back
  But sic as I spin mysell.
And when I am clad in my coutsey,
  I think mysell as braw
As Susie, wi' a' her pearling
  That's tane my laddie awa'.

But I wish they were buckled together,
  And may they live happy for life;
Tho' Willie does slight me, and's left me,
  The chield he deserves a good wife.

But, O. I'm blyth that I've miss'd him,
  As blyth as I weel can be;
For ane that's sae keen o' the siller
  Will never agree wi' me.

But as the truth is, I'm hearty,
  I hate to be scrimpit or scant;
The wie thing I hae, I'll mak use o't,
  And nae ane about me shall want.
For I'm a good guide o' the warld,
  I ken when to ha'd and to gie;
For whinging and cringing for siller
  Will never agree wi' me.

Contentment is better than riches,
  An' he wha has that has enough;
The master is seldom sae happy
  As Róbin that drives the plough.
But if a young lad wou'd cast up,
  To mak me his partner for life;
If the chield has the sense to be happy,
  He'll fa on his feet for a wife.

## O once I lov'd.

551
* O once I lov'd a bon_nie lass, An' aye I
Slowish
love her still an' whilst that vir_tue warms my
breast I'll love my hand_ _some Nell.

As bonnie lasses I hae seen,
And mony full as braw,
But for a modest gracefu' mein
The like I never saw.

A bonny lass I will confess,
Is pleasant to the e'e,
But without some better qualities
She's no a lass for me.

But Nelly's looks are blythe and sweet,
And what is best of a',
Her reputation is compleat,
And fair without a flaw;

She dresses ay sae clean and neat,
Both decent and genteel;
And then there's something in her gait
Gars ony dress look weel.

A gaudy dress and gentle air
May slightly touch the heart,
But its innocence and modesty
That polishes the dart.

'Tis this in Nelly pleases me,
'Tis this enchants my soul;
For absolutely in my breast
She reigns without controul.

## When I think on my lad.

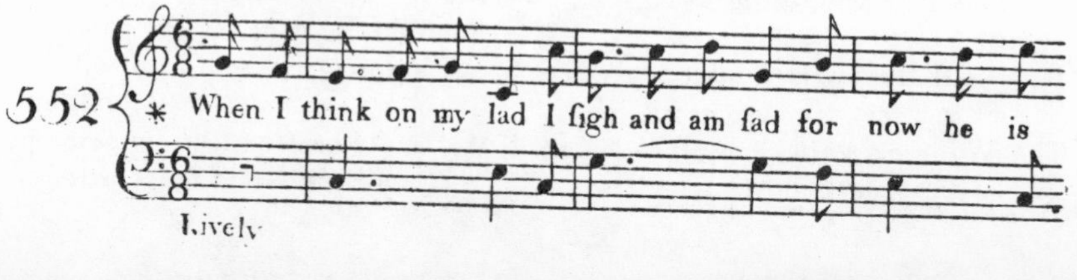
552
* When I think on my lad I sigh and am sad for now he is
Lively

Continued.

far frae me, my daddy was harſh, My minny was warſe that gart him gae
yont the ſea. Without an eſtate, That made him look blate: And
yet a brave lad is he gin ſafe he come hame, In ſpite of my
dame, He'll e_ver be wel_come to me.

Love ſpeers na advice
Of parents o'er wiſe,
That have but ae bairn like me,
That looks upon caſh,
As naething but traſh,
That ſhackles what ſhould be free.
And tho' my dear lad
Not ae penny had,
Since qualities better has he;
A' beit I'm an Heireſs,
I think it but fair is,
To love him ſince he loves me.

Then, my dear Jamie,
To thy kind Jeanie,
Haſte, haſte thee in o'er the ſea,
To her wha can find
Nae eaſe in her mind,
Without a blyth ſight of thee.

Tho' my daddy forbad,
And my minny forbad,
Forbidden I will not be;
For ſince thou alone
My favour haſt won,
Nane elſe ſhall e'er get it for me.

Yet them I'll not grieve,
Or without their leave,
Gi'e my hand as a wife to thee:
Be content with a heart,
That can never deſert,
Till they ceaſe to oppoſe or be.
My parents may prove
Yet friend to our love,
When our firm reſolves they ſee;
Then I with pleaſure
Will yield up my treaſure,
And a' that love orders to thee.

## Return hameward.

553

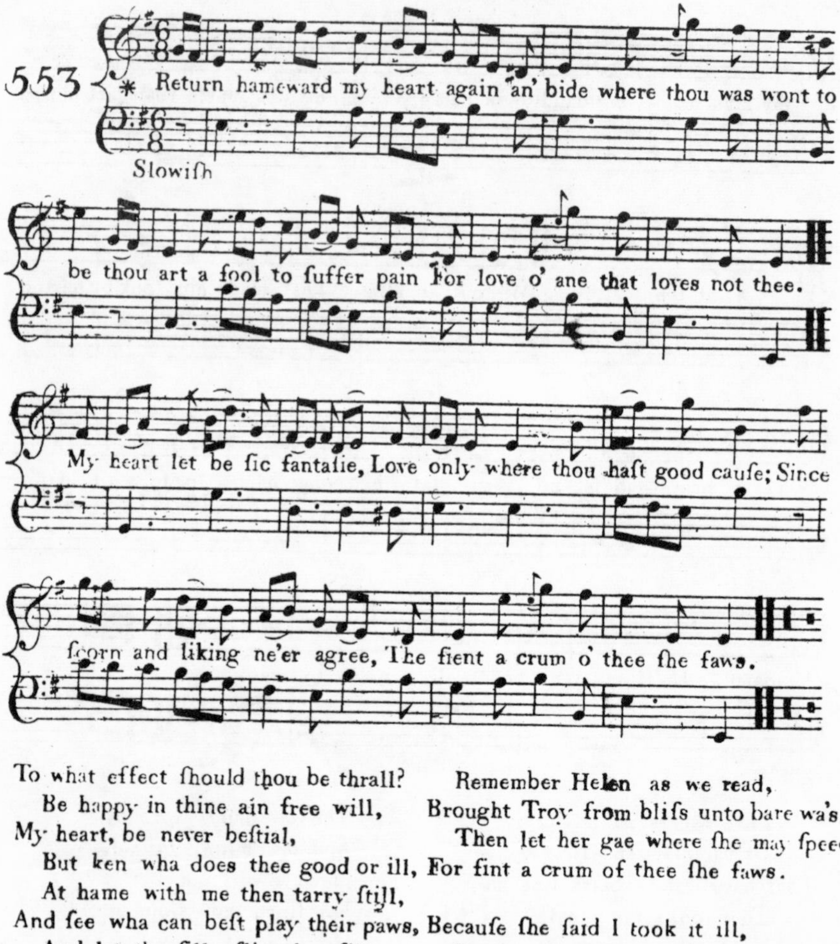
* Return hameward my heart again an' bide where thou was wont to
Slowiſh
be thou art a fool to ſuffer pain For love o' ane that loves not thee.
My heart let be ſic fantaſie, Love only where thou haſt good cauſe; Since
ſcorn and liking ne'er agree, The fient a crum o' thee ſhe faws.

To what effect ſhould thou be thrall?
Be happy in thine ain free will,
My heart, be never beſtial,
But ken wha does thee good or ill,
At hame with me then tarry ſtill,
And ſee wha can beſt play their paws,
And let the ſilly fling her fill,
For fint a crum of thee ſhe faws.

Tho' ſhe be fair I will not fenzie,
She's of a kind with mony mae;
For why they are a fellon menzie
That ſeemeth good and are not ſae.
My heart, take neither ſturt nor wae
For Meg, for Marjory, or Mauſe,
But be thou blyth, and let her gae,
For fint a crum of thee ſhe faws.

Remember, how that Medea
Wild for a ſight of Jaſon yied,
Remember how that young Creſſida
Left Troilus for Diomede;
Remember Helen as we read,
Brought Troy from bliſs unto bare wa's:
Then let her gae where ſhe may ſpeed.
For fint a crum of thee ſhe faws.

Becauſe ſhe ſaid I took it ill,
For her depart my heart was ſair,
But was beguil'd; gae where ſhe will,
Beſhrew the heart that firſt takes care.
But be thou merry late and air,
This is the final end and clauſe,
And let her feed and foully fair
For fint a crum of thee ſhe faws.

Ne'er dunt again within my breaſt,
Ne'er let her ſlights thy courage ſpill,
Nor gie a ſob altho' ſhe ſneeſt,
She's faireſt paid that get's her will
She's geck as gif I mean'd her ill,
When ſhe glaicks paughty in her braws;
Now let her ſnirt and fyke her fill,
For fint a crum of thee ſhe faws.

## My Lady's gown there's gairs upon't.

Written for this Work by Robert Burns.

Chorus
554
*
My Lady's gown there's gairs upon't And gowden flowers sae rare u_pon't; But Jen_ny's jimps and jir_kinet My Lord thinks meikle mair upon't. My Lord a hunting he is gane, But hounds or hawks wi' him are nane By Colin's, cot_tage lies his game, If Colin's Jenny be at hame.
Lively

My Lady's white, my Lady's red
And kith and kin o' Cassillis' blude,
But her tenpund lands o' tocher gude
Were a' the charms his Lordship lo'ed.
My Lady's gown &c.

Out o'er yon moor, out o'er yon moss,
Whare gor-cocks thro' the heather pass,
There wons auld Colin's bonie lass,
A lily in a wilderness.
My Lady's gown &c.

Sae sweetly move her genty limbs;
Like music-notes o' Lovers hymns:
The diamond-dew in her een sae blue
Where laughing love sae wanton swims
My Lady's gown &c.

My Lady's dink, my Lady's drest,
The flower and fancy o' the west;
But the Lassie that man loes best,
O that's the Lass to mak him blest.
My Lady's gown &c.

## May Morning.

555

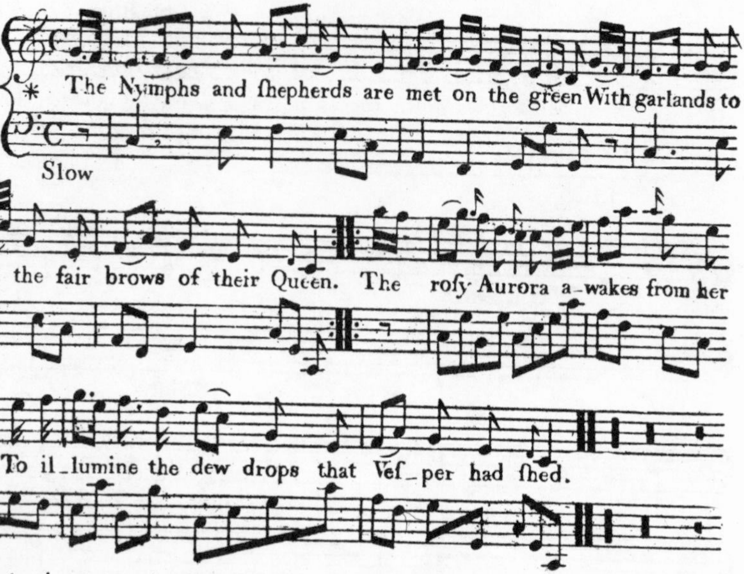
* The Nymphs and ſhepherds are met on the green With garlands to
Slow
deck the fair brows of their Queen. The roſy Aurora a-wakes from her
hed To il_lumine the dew drops that Veſ_per had ſhed.

## Dinna think bonie Laſsie I'm gaun to leave you.

556

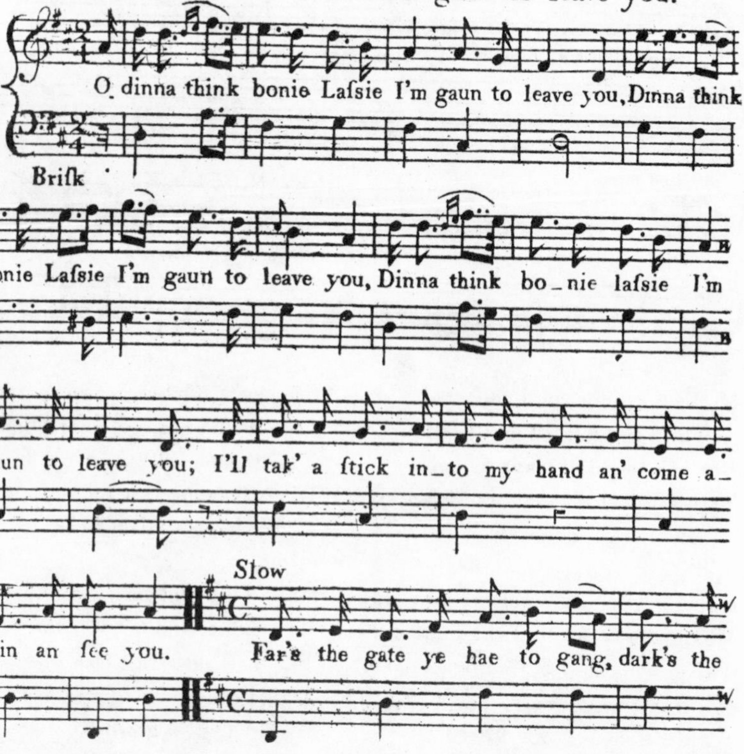
O dinna think bonie Laſsie I'm gaun to leave you, Dinna think
Briſk
-bonie Laſsie I'm gaun to leave you, Dinna think bo_nie laſsie I'm
-gaun to leave you; I'll tak' a ſtick in_to my hand an' come a_
Slow
_gain an ſee you. Far's the gate ye hae to gang, dark's the

## Continued.

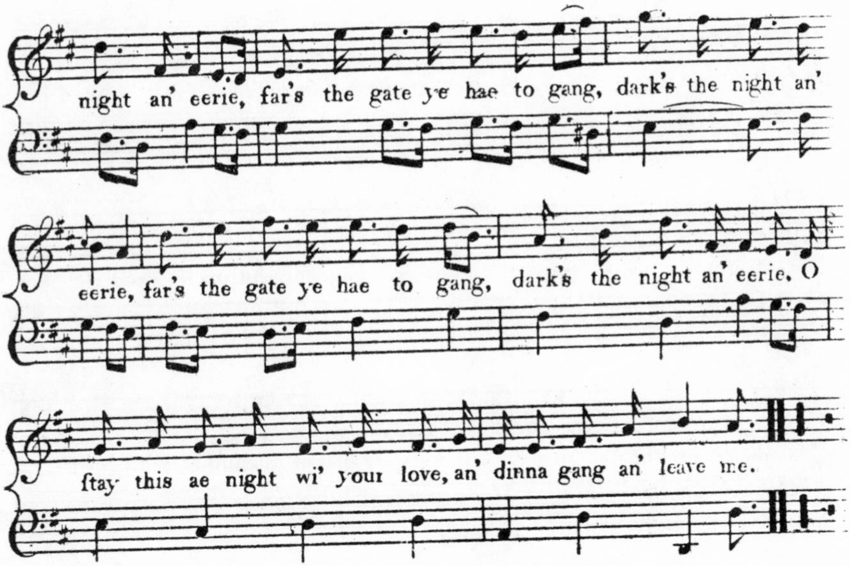
night an' eerie, far's the gate ye hae to gang, dark's the night an'
eerie, far's the gate ye hae to gang, dark's the night an' eerie. O
stay this ae night wi' your love, an' dinna gang an' leave me.

Brisk. It's but a night an' ha'f a day that I'll leave my dearie,
But a night an' ha'f a day that I'll leave my dearie,
But a night an' ha'f a day that I'll leave my dearie,
When e'er the sun gaes west the loch, I'll come again an' see thee;
Slow. Dinna gang my bonie lad, dinna gang an' leave me,
Dinna gang my bonie lad, dinna gang an' leave me,
When the lave are sound asleep I am dull an' eerie,
An' a' the lee lang night I'm sad, wi' thinkin' on my dearie.

Brisk. O Dinna think bonie lassie I'm gaun to leave you,
Dinna think bonie lassie I'm gaun to leave you,
Dinna think bonie lassie I'm gaun to leave you,
When e'er the sun gaes out o' sight I'll come again an' see you,
Slow. Waves are rising o'er the sea, winds bla loud an' fear me,
Waves are rising o'er the sea, winds bla loud an' fear me.
While the waves an' winds do roar, I am wae an' dreary,
An' gin ye loe me as ye say, ye winna gae an' leave me.

Brisk. O Never mair bonie lassie will I gang an' leave thee,
Never mair bonie lassie will I gang an' leave thee,
Never mair bonie lassie will I gang an' leave thee,
E'en let the warld gae as it will, I'll stay at hame an' cheer thee;
Slow. Frae his hand he coost the stick, I winna gang an' leave thee,
Threw his plaid into the neuk, never can I grieve thee,
Drew his boots an' flang them by, cry'd my lass be cheerie,
I'll kiss the tear frae aff thy cheek, an' never leave my dearie.

## O gin I were fairly shot o' her.

557

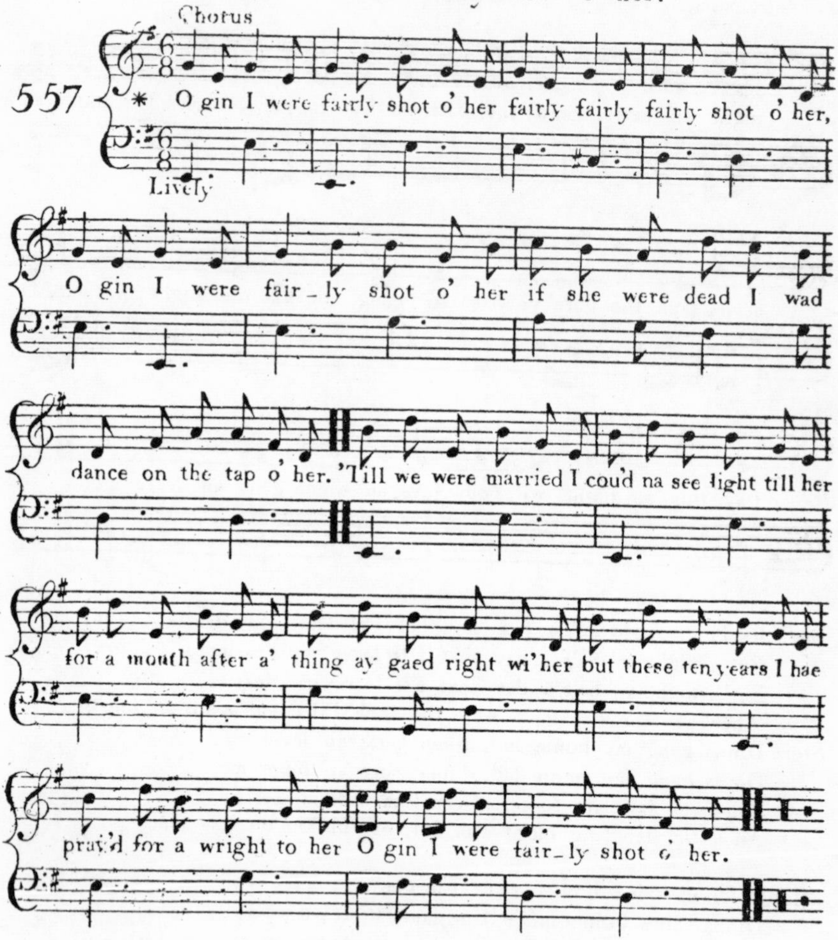
Chorus
* O gin I were fairly shot o' her fairly fairly fairly shot o' her,
Lively
O gin I were fair_ly shot o' her if she were dead I wad
dance on the tap o' her. 'Till we were married I cou'd na see light till her
for a mouth after a' thing ay gaed right wi' her but these ten years I hae
pray'd for a wright to her O gin I were fair_ly shot o' her.

Nane o' her relations or frien's cou'd stay wi' her
The neighbours and bairns are fain to fly frae her,
An' I my ain sell is forc't to gie way till her
O gin I were fairly &c.

She gangs aye sae braw, she's sae mickle pride in her
There's no a goodwife in the haill country side like her
Wi' dress an' wi' drink the d_l wadna bide wi' her
O gin I were fairly &c.

If the time wou'd but come that to the kirk gate wi' her
An' into the yerd I'd mak my sell quit o' her
I'd then be as blyth as first when I met wi' her
O gin I were fairly &c.

## Hey my kitten, my kitten.

558

* Hey! my kitten my kitten, An' hey my kitten a dearie fic a fweet
Lively
pet as this is nei_ther far nor nearie. Now we gae up up
up An' here we gang down down downy, Here we gae
backwards and forward And here round round a roundy.

Chicky, cockow, my lily cock;
See, fee, fic a downy;
Gallop a trot, trot, trot,
And hey for Dublin towny.
This pig went to the market;
Squeek moufe, moufe, moufy;
Shoe, fhoe, fhoe the wild colt,
And hear thy own dol doufy.

Where was a jewel and petty,
Where was a fugar and fpicy;
Hufh a baba in a cradle,
And we'll go abroad in a tricy,
Did a papa torment it?
Did_e vex his own baby? did_e?
Hufh a baba in a bofie;
Take ous own fucky: did_e?

Good-morrow, a pudding is broke;
Slavers a thread o' cryftal,
Now the fweet pofset comes up;
Who faid my child was pifs all?
Come water my chickens, come clock
Leave off or he'll crawl you, he'll crawl you;
Come, gie me your hand, ane I'll beat him;
Wha was it vexed my baby?

Where was a laugh and a craw;
Where was a gigling honey?
Goody, good child fhall be
But naughty child fhall get
Get ye gone, raw head and bloody bones
Here is a child that wont fear ye.
Come pifsy, pifsy, my jewel,
And ik, ik av, my deary.

## Sweetest May.

Written for this Work by Robert Burns.

559

*
Sweetest May let love inspire thee; Take a heart which he designs thee;
Slowish
As thy, constant slave regard it; for its faith and truth reward it.

Proof o' shot to Birth or Money,
Not the wealthy, but the bonie;
Not high-born, but noble-minded,
In Love's silken band can bind it.

## Argyll is my name.

560

Argyll is my name, and you may think it strange, To live at a
Lively
court, and never to change all falsehood and flattery I do dis_dain In
my secret thoughts nae guile does remain. My King and my country's foes I
have fac'd in city or battle I ne'er was disgrac'd I do ev'ry thing for my

Continued.

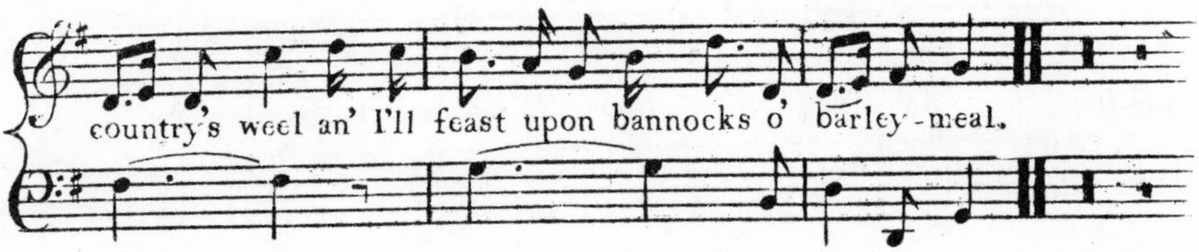
country's weel an' I'll feast upon bannocks o' barley-meal.

Adieu to the courtie of London town,
For to my ain country I will gang down;
At the sight of Kirkcaldy ance again,
I'll cock up my bonnet, and march amain.
O the muckle de'il tak a' your noise and strife,
I'm fully resolv'd for a country life,
Where a' the bra' lasses, wha kens me well,
Will feed me wi' bannocks o' barley-meal.

I'll quickly lay down my sword and my gun,
And I'll put my plaid and my bonnet on,
Wi' my plaiding stockings and leather-heel'd shoon,
They'll mak me appear a fine sprightly loon.
And when I am drest thus frae tap to tae,
Hame to my Maggie I think for to gae,
Wi' my claymore hinging down to my heel,
To whang at the bannocks o' barley meal.

I'll buy a fine present to bring to my dear,
A pair of fine garters for Maggie to wear,
And some pretty things else, I do declare,
When she gangs wi' me to Paisley fair.
And whan we are married we'll keep a cow,
My Maggie sall milk her, and I will plow:
We'll live a' the winter on beef and lang-kail,
And whang at the bannocks o' barley-meal.

If my Maggie shou'd chance to bring me a son,
He's fight for his King, as his daddy has done;
I'll send him to Flanders some breeding to learn,
Syne hame into Scotland and keep a farm.
And thus we'll live and industrious be,
And wha'll be sae great as my Maggie and me;
We'll soon grow as fat as a Norway seal,
Wi' feeding on bannocks o' barley-meal. &c. &c. &c.

## An' I'll awa to bonny Tweed-side.

561

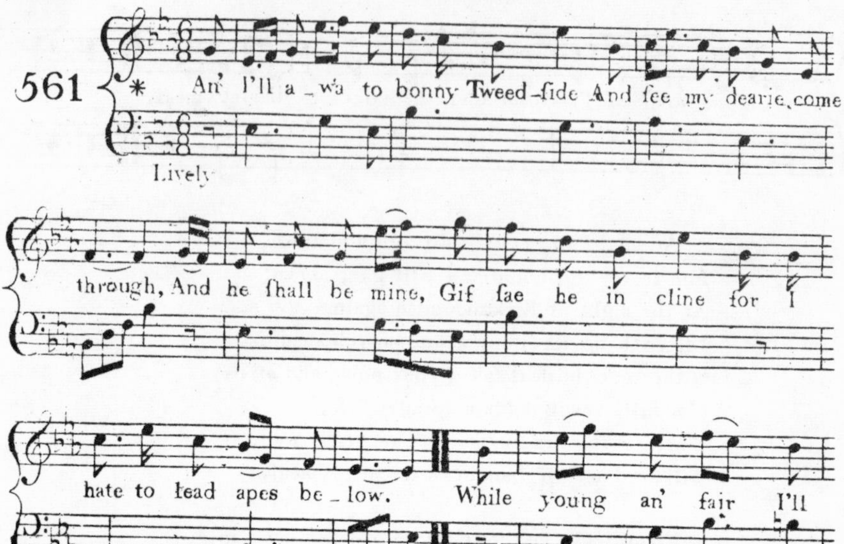
Lively
An' I'll a_wa to bonny Tweed-side And see my dearie come through, And he shall be mine, Gif sae he in cline for I hate to lead apes be_low.
While young an' fair I'll make it my care to se_cure myself in a jo; I'm no sic a fool to let my blood cool an' syne to lead apes be_low.

Few words bonny lad
Will eithly persuade,
Tho' blushing I daftly say no
Gae on with your strain
And doubt not to gain,
For I hate to lead apes below.
Unty'd to a man,
Do whate'er we can,
We never can thrive or dow.
Then I will do well,
Do better what will,
And let them lead apes below.

Our time is precious,
And gods are gracious
That beauties upon us bestow
'Tis not to be thought
We got them for nought
Or to be set up for a show.
'Tis carried by votes,
Come kilt up your coats
And let us to Edinburgh go,
Where she that's bonny
May catch a Johny,
And never lead apes below.

## Gently blaw &c.

562

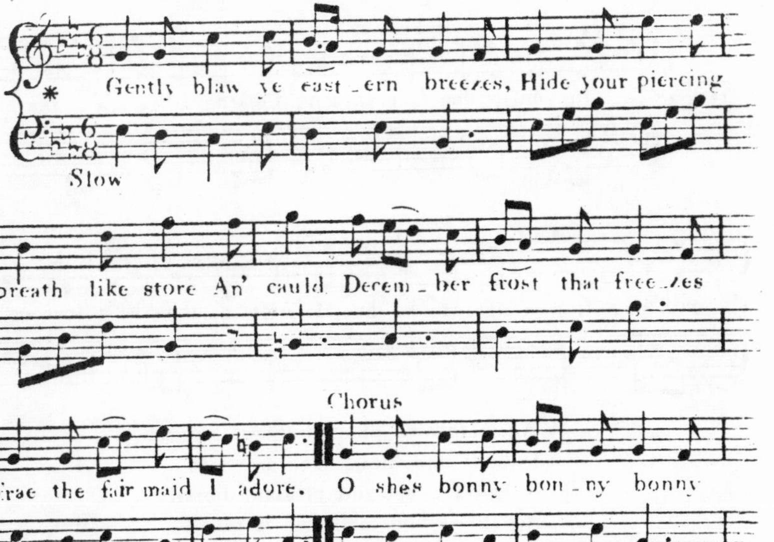
Gently blaw ye east_ern breezes, Hide your piercing
Slow
breath like store An' cauld Decem_ber frost that free_zes
Chorus
Frae the fair maid I adore. O she's bonny bon_ny bonny
O she's bon_ny and sweet to see Fair the bud an'
bonny blossom Aye the blythe blinks in her ee.

Frae winter's scoure the simmer torment
Hoary mists that point the air
Frae grief o' mind that aft does foment
Making life a dreary care
O she's bonny &c.

Red's her cheek, and sweets her feature
Glancin een like diamonds bright
Handsome shape, the choice o' nature
Wonder o' the day and night
O she's bonny &c.

For she's as the new blawn rose
That's nourish'd with the simmer's sun
Her smiles is like the sweet repose
Man seeks when his last sand is run
O she's bonny &c.

If, but this bud and bonny blossom
I could say 'twere only mine
I'd plant it deep within my bosom
An' round my heart I'd it entwine
O she's bonny &c.

## In yon garden &c.

563
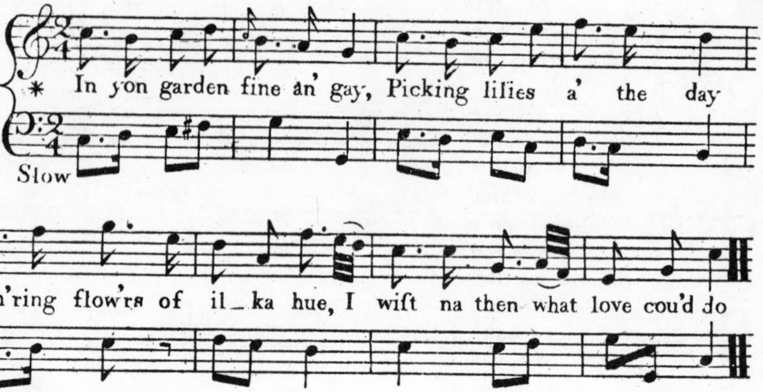
In yon garden fine an' gay, Picking lilies a' the day
Slow
gath'ring flow'rs of il_ka hue, I wiſt na then what love cou'd do

Where love is planted there it grows,
It buds and blows like any roſe
It has a ſweet and pleaſant ſmell,
No flow'r on earth can it excel.

I put my hand into the buſh,
And thought the ſweeteſt roſe to find,
But prick'd my finger to the bone,
And left the ſweeteſt roſe behind.

## The poor Pedlar.

564

There was a noble lady ſo fair looking out of her window ſo
Lively
high And there ſhe ſpy'd a poor Pedlar coming ſinging out o'er the
lee lee lee coming ſing_ing out o'er the lee.

## Continued.

She call'd upon her ſervant man,
Her ſervant that on her did wait,
"Gae open the yetts, both braid and wide,
"And let the poor pedlar in in in,
"And let the poor pedlar in.
He ſet the yetts, both braid and wide,
And let the poor pedlar in;
And then ſhe took him by the coat neuks,
And ſhe led him from room to room room room,
And ſhe led him &c.
Till he came to my lady's room,
My lady's room where ſhe lay;
"I wad gie a' my pack' he ſaid,
"For the night of a gay lady, lady;
"For the night &c.
"Wilt thou gie me my pack again,
"My pack, and my pack pinn,
"An' thou gie me my pack he ſaid,
"I'll gie thee both broach and ring, ring ring,
"I'll gie thee both &c.
"I'll no gie thee thy pack again,
"Thy pack nor thy pack pinn;
"I'll no gie thee thy pack ſhe ſaid.
"Tho' thou wad greet till thine eyes gae blin' gae blin
"Tho' thou wad &c.
Out then ſpak the noble lord,
Out of his bow'r within,
"O who is this into my houſe
"That makes ſuch a noiſe and dinn dinn dinn.
"That makes &c.
"As I came through your garden Sir,
"I pull'd ſome of your flowers;
"A box of ſpice was in my pack,
"And I borrowed a morter of yours of yours.
"And I borrowed &c.
"Gi'e the poor pedlar his pack again,
"His pack and his pack pinn,
"Keep nathing frae a poor pedlar,
"Who has a' his living to win to win.
"Who has &c.
She took the pack by the twa neuks,
And ſhe flang it out o'er the wa',
"Upo' my ſooth, quo the poor pedlar
"My pack it has gotten a fa' fa' fa'.
"My pack &c.
He took the pack upon his back,
Went ſinging out o'er the lee,
"O I ha'e gotten my pack again
"And the kiſs of a gay lady lady
"And the kiſs &c.

## You ask me charming fair.

565

* You ask me charming fair Why thus I pensive go, From
Slow
whence proceeds, my care What nourishes my woe. Why
seek'st the cause to find of ills that I en_dure Ah!
why so vainly kind un_less re_solv'd to cure.

It needs no magic art,
To know whence my alarms,
Examine your own heart,
Go read them in your charms.
Whene'er the youthful quoir,
Along the vale advance,
To raise, at your desire,
The lay, or form the dance.

Beneficent to each,
You some kind grace afford,
Gentle in deed or speech,
A smile or friendly word.
Whilst on my love you put
No value; On the same,
As if my fire was but
Some paltry village flame.

At this my colour flies,
My breast with sorrow heaves,
The pain I would disguise,
Nor man nor maid deceives.
My love stands all display'd,
Too strong for art to hide,
How soon the heart's betray'd
With such a clue to guide!

How cruel is my fate,
Affronts I could have born,
Found comfort in your hate,
Or triumph'd in your scorn.
But whilst I thus adore,
I'm driv'n to wild despair;
Indifference is more
Than raging love can bear.

# O ken ye what Meg o' the mill has gotten.

Written for this Work by Robert Burns.

566

* O ken ye what Meg o' the mill has got_ten, An
A little Lively
ken ye what Meg o' the mill has gotten; A braw new naig wi' the
tail o' a rottan, And that's what Meg o' the mill has got_ten.
O ken ye what Meg o' the mill loes dear_ly, An ken ye what
Meg o' the mill loes dearly, A dram o' gude ſtrunt in a morning
early and thats what Meg o' the mill loes dear_ly.

O ken ye how Meg o' the mill was married,
And ken ye how Meg o' the mill was married;
The Prieſt he was oxter'd, the Clerk he was carried,
And that's how Meg o' the mill was married
O ken ye how Meg o' the mill was bedded,
An ken ye how Meg o' the mill was bedded;
The groom gat ſae fu' he fell awald beſide it,
And that's how Meg o' the mill was bedded.

## How sweet is the scene.

567

* How sweet is the scene at the dawning o' morning, How
Slowish
fair il_ka object that lives in the view dame nature the valley an
hillock adorning, the primrose an' blue bells yet wet wi' the dew.
How sweet in the morning o' life is my Anna her smile like the
sunbeam that glents o'er the lee To wan_der and leave her, dear
lassie, I canna, frae love an' frae beauty I never can flee.

O lang ha'e I lo'd her an' loe her fu' dearly,
An' aft ha'e I preed o' her bonny sweet mow!
An' aft ha'e I read in her e'e blinkin' clearly,
A language that bade me be constant an' true!
Then others may doat on their fond war'ly treasure,
For pelf, silly pelf, they may brave the rude sea;
To love my sweet lassie be mine the dear pleasure
Wi' her let me live — and wi' her let me die!

## Sure my Jean.

568

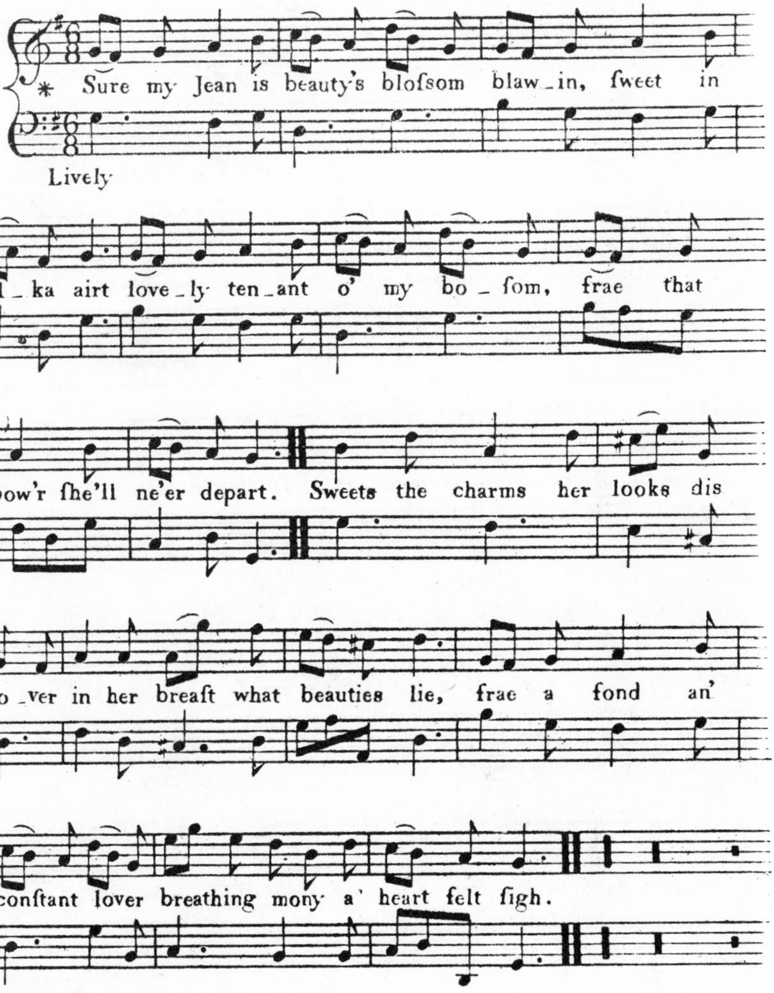
* Sure my Jean is beauty's blofsom blaw_in, fweet in
Lively
il_ka airt love_ly ten_ant o' my bo_fom, frae that
bow'r fhe'll ne'er depart. Sweets the charms her looks dis
_co_ver in her breaft what beauties lie, frae a fond an'
conftant lover breathing mony a' heart felt figh.

I ha'e feen the floweret fpringin'
Gaily on the funny lea;
I ha'e heard the mavis fingin'
Sweetly on the hawthorn tree:
But my Jeanie, peerlefs dearie.
She's the flow'er attracts mine ee;
Whan fhe tunes her voice fae cheerie,
She's the mavis dear to me.

## How ſweet this lone vale.

569
How ſweet this lone vale and how ſooth_ing to
Very Slow
feeling yon Nightingale's notes which in me_lo_dy melt ob_
_livion of woe o'er my mind gently ſtealing a pauſe from keen
anguiſh a moment is felt. The moon's yel_low light o'er the
ſtill lake is ſleeping Ah near the ſad ſpot Ma_ry ſleeps in her
tomb a_ _gain the heart ſwells, the eye flows with weeping and the
ſweets of the vale are all ſhad_ow'd with gloom.

## Jockey's ta'en the parting kiſs.

Written for this Work by Robert Burns.

570

*
Jockey's ta'en the par ting kiſs O'er the mountains
A little lively
he is gane; And with him is a' my bliſs Nought but
griefs with me remain. Spare my love ye winds that blaw,
Plaſhy fleets and beat_ing rain Spare my love thou feath'ry
ſnaw Drif_ting o'er the fro_zen plain.

When the ſhades of evening creep
  O'er the day's fair, gladſome e'e,
Sound and ſafely may he ſleep,
  Sweetly blythe his waukening be.
He will think on her he loves,
  Fondly he'll repeat her name;
For whare'er he diſtant roves
  Jockey's heart is ſtill at hame.

# What's that to you.

571
A little Lively
My Jeany and I have toil'd the live – lang ſummer day Till we were al – moſt ſpoil'd At mak – ing of the hay. Her kurchy was of hol – land clear Ty'd on her bon – ny brow; I whiſper'd ſomething in her ear But what is that to you

Her ſtockings were of Kerſy green,
As tight as ony ſilk:
O ſick a leg was never ſeen,
Her ſkin was white as milk;
Her hair was black as ane could wiſh,
And ſweet ſweet was her mou;
Oh. Jeany daintily can kiſs,
But what's that to you?

The roſe and lily baith combine
To make my Jeany fair,
There is no benniſon like mine,
I have amaiſt nae care;
Only I fear my Jeany's face
May cauſe mae men to rue,
And that may gar me ſay, Alas!
But what's that to you?

Conceal thy beauties if thou can,
Hide that ſweet face of thine,
That I may only be the man
Enjoys theſe looks divine.
O do not proſtitute, my dear,
Wonders to common view,
And I, with faithful heart, ſhall ſwear
For ever to be true.

King Solomon had wives enew,
And mony a concubine;
But I enjoy a bliſs mair true;
His joys were ſhort of mine:
And Jeany's happier than they,
She ſeldom wants her due;
All debts of love to her I'll pay,
And what's that to you?

## Little wat ye wha's coming.

572

Chorus.
Brisk
Lit _ tle wat ye wha's com _ ing little wat ye
wha's coming little wat ye wha's coming Jock and Tam and
a's com _ ing. Dun_can's com _ ing Don _ alds' com _ ing
Co _ lin's com _ ing Ron _ ald's coming Dougald's coming
Lauch _ lan's com _ ing A _ lis _ ter and a's coming.

Borland and his men's coming,
The Camerons and M^c. Leans coming,
The Gordons and M^c.Gregors coming
A' the Dunywastles' coming
Little wat ye, &c.
M^c. Gilvrey of Drumglass is coming.

Wigton's coming, Nithsdale's coming,
Carnwath's coming, Kenmure's coming,
Derwentwater and Foster's coming
Withrington and Nairn's coming
Little wat ye, &c.
Blyth Cowhill and as coming.

The Laird of M^c. Intosh is coming,
M^c. Crabie and M^c. Donald's coming,
The M^c. Kenzies and M^c.Phersons coming
A' the wild M^c. Craws' coming,
Little wat ye, &c,
Donald Gun and a's coming.

They gloom, they glowr, they look sae-big,
At ilka stroke they'll fell a Whig;
They'll fright the fuds of the Pockpuds
For mony a buttock bare's coming.
Little wat ye, &c.

# O leave novels &c.

By Burns.

573

O leave no_vels, ye Mauchline belles, Ye're ſaf_er
Lively.
at your ſpinning wheel; Such witching books, are baited hooks for rakiſh
rooks like Rob Moſsgiel. Your fine Tom Jones And
Grandiſons they make your youthful fancies reel they heat your
brains, and fire your veins and then you're prey for Rob Moſsgiel.

Beware a tongue that's ſmoothly hung;
  A heart that warmly ſeems to feel;
That feelin heart but acks a part,
  'Tis rakiſh art in Rob Moſsgiel.
The frank addreſs, the ſoft careſs,
  Are worſe than poiſoned darts of ſteel,
The frank addreſs, and politeſse,
  Are all fineſse in Rob Moſsgiel.

## O lay thy loof in mine lass.

Chorus Written for this Work by Robert Burns.

574

* O lay thy loof in mine lass, In mine lass, in mine lass, And
A little lively.
swear on thy white hand lass, That thou wilt be my ain.
Song
A slave to love's unbounded sway, He aft has wrought me meikle
wae; But now, he is my deadly fae, Un_less thou be my ain. O
Chos.
lay thy loof in mine lass, In mine lass, in mine lass, And swear on
thy white hand lass that thou wilt be my ain.

There's monie a lass has broke my rest,
That for a blink I hae lo'ed best;
But thou art queen within my breast
For ever to remain.
O lay thy loof &c.

## Saw ye the Thane &c.

575

* Saw ye the Thane o' meikle pride, Red anger in his
Slow
ee? I saw him not nor care he cry'd Red anger frights na me.
For I have stood whar honour bade, Tho' death trod on his heel; Mean
is the crest that stoops to fear, nae sic may Duncan feel.

Hark! hark! or was it but the wind,
  That through the ha' did sing;
Hark! hark! agen, a warlike sound,
  The black woods round do ring.
'Tis na for naught, bauld Duncan cry'd,
  Sic shouting on the wind.
Syne up he started frae his seat,
  A throng of spears behind.

Haste, haste, my valiant hearts, he said,
  Anes mair to follow me;
We'll meet yon shouters by the burn,
  I guess wha they may be.
But wha is he that speids sae fast,
  Frae the slaw marching thrang?
Sae frae the mirk cloud shoots a beam,
  The sky's blue face alang.

Some messenger it is, may hap,
  Then not at peace I trow.
My master, Duncan bade me rin,
  And say these words to you.
Restore again that blooming rose,
  Your rude hand pluckt awa';
Restore again his Mary fair,
  Or you shall rue his fa'.

Three strides the gallant Duncan tuk,
  He struck his forward spear:
Gae tell thy master, beardless youth,
  We are nae wont to fear.
He comes na on a wassail rout,
  Of revel, sport, and play;
Our swords gart Fame proclaim us men,
  Lang ere this ruefu' day.

The rose I pluckt o' right is mine,
  Our hearts together grew,
Like twa sweet roses on ae stak
  Frae hate to love she flew.
Swift as a winged shaft he sped;
  Bald Duncan said in jeer,
Gae tell thy master, beardless youth,
  We are nae wont to fear. &c &c &c

## Go plaintive sounds.

576

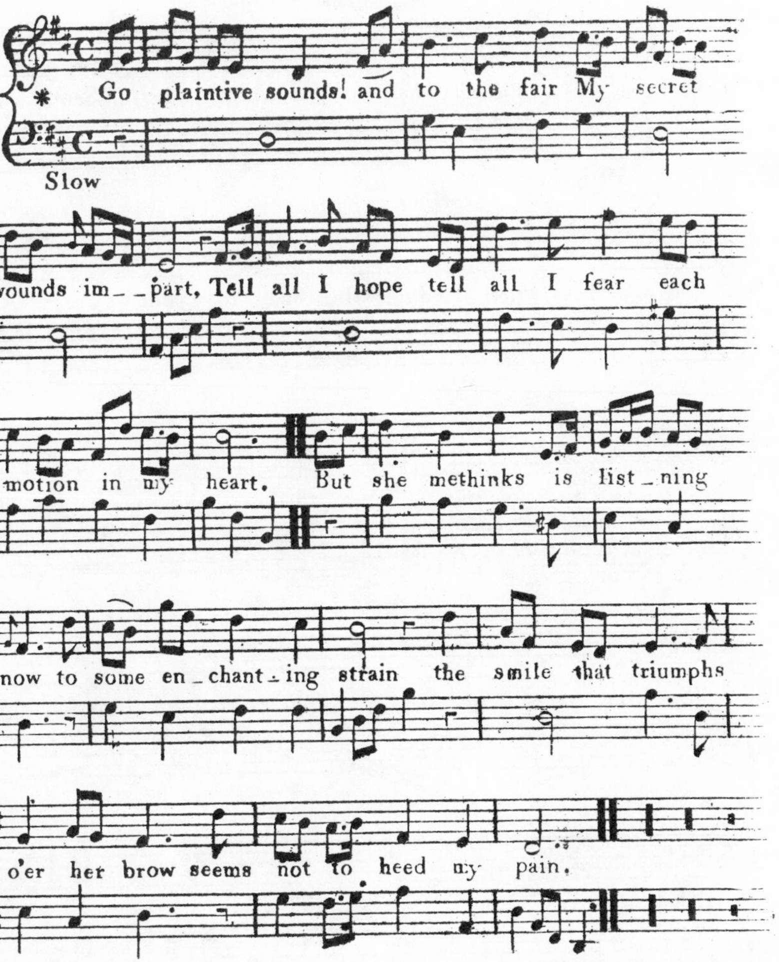
*
Go plaintive sounds! and to the fair My secret
Slow
wounds im_ _part, Tell all I hope tell all I fear each
motion in my heart. But she methinks is list_ning
now to some en_chant_ing strain the smile that triumphs
o'er her brow seems not to heed my pain.

Yes, plaintive sounds, yet, yet delay,
  Howe'er my love repine,
Let that gay minute pass away,
  The next perhaps is thine.
Yes plaintive sounds, no longer crost,
  Your griefs shall soon be o'er,
Her cheek undimpled now, has lost
  The smile it lately wore.

Yes, plaintive sounds, she now is yours,
  'Tis now your time to move;
Essay to soften all her pow'rs,
  And be that softness, love.

Cease plaintive sounds, your task is done
  That anxious tender air
Proves o'er her heart the conquest won,
  I see you melting there.

Return ye smiles return again,
  Return each sprightly grace,
I yield up to your charming reign,
  All that enchanting face.
I take no outward shew amiss,
  Rove where they will, her eyes,
Still let her smiles each shepherd bless,
  So she but hear my sighs.

# Bruce's addrefs to his Army.

By Burns.

577

"Scots wha hae 'wi' Wal_lace bled, "Scots, wham
With energy
Bruce has aften led, "Wel_come to your go_ry bed
"Or to vic_to_ry "Now's the day and now's the hour;
"See the front of bat_tle lour fee ap_proach proud
"Ed_ward's pow'r Chains and fla_ve_ry.

"Wha will be a traitor knave?
"Wha can fill a coward's grave?
"Wha fae bafe as the a flave?
"Traitor! coward! turn and flee.

"Wha for Scotland's king and law
"Freedom's fword will ftrongly draw,
"Free-man ftand, or free-man fa',
"Caledonian, on wi' me!

"By oppreſsion's woes and pains!
"By your fons in fervile chains!
"We will drain our deareft veins,
"But they fhall be – fhall be free.

"Lay the proud ufurpers low!
"Tyrants fall in every foe;
"Liberty's in every blow!
"Forward! let us do, or die!"

## Farewell ye fields &c.

578

Farewell ye fields, an' meadows green, the bleſt retreats of
Slowiſh
peace an' love Aft have I ſilent ſtol'n from hence With my young
ſwain a while to rove. Sweet was our walk, mair ſweet our
talk, amang the beauties of the ſpring, an' aft we'd lean us
on a bank to hear the feath_er'd warblers ſing.

The azure ſky the hills around,
Gave double beauty to the ſcene
The lofty ſpires of Banff in view,
On every ſide the waving grain:
The tales of love my Jamie told,
In ſuch a ſaft an' moving ſtrain,
Have ſo engag'd my tender heart,
I'm loth to leave the place again.

But if the Fates will be ſae kind,
As favour my return once more.
For to enjoy the peace o' mind,
In thoſe retreats I had before:
Now, farewell Banff! the nimble ſteeds,
Do bear me hence, I muſt away,
Yet time perhaps may bring me back,
To part nae mair from ſcenes ſo gay.

## O heard ye e'er of a silly blind Harper,

579

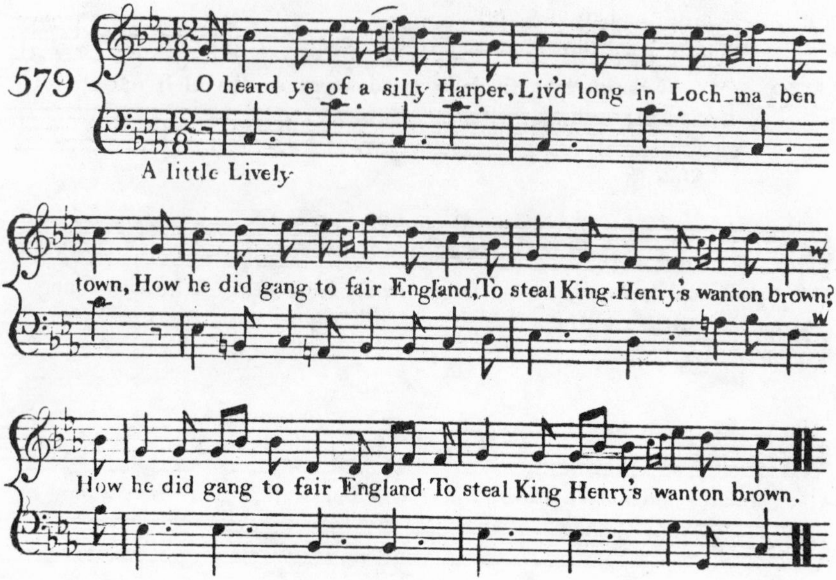
O heard ye of a silly Harper, Liv'd long in Loch_ma_ben
A little Lively
town, How he did gang to fair England, To steal King Henry's wanton brown?
How he did gang to fair England To steal King Henry's wanton brown.

But first he gaed to his gude_wife
Wi' a' the speed that he cou'd thole:
This wark, quo' he, will never work,
Without a mare that has a foal.
  This wark, &c.

Quo' she, thou has a gude grey mare,
That'll rin o'er hills baith low & hie;
Gae tak' the grey mare in thy hand,
And leave the foal at hame wi' me.
  Gae tak' &c.

And tak' a halter in thy hose,
And o' thy purpose dinna fail;
But wap it o'er the wanton's nose;
And tie her to the grey mare's tail:
  But wap, &c.

Syne ca' her out at yon back yeate,
O'er moss and muir and ilka dale,
For she'll ne'er let the wanton bite,
Till she come hame to her ain foal.
  For she'll, &c.

So he is up to England gane,
Even as fast as he can hie,
Till he came to King Henry's yeate;
And wha' was there but King Henry?
  Till he, &c.

Come in, quo' he, thou silly blind Harper;
And of thy harping let me hear.
O! by my sooth, quo' the silly blind Harper,
I'd rather hae stabling for my mare.
  O! by my, &c.

The King looks o'er his left shoulder,
And says unto his stable groom,
Gae tak the silly poor Harper's mare,
And tie her 'side my wanton brown.
  Gae tak, &c.

## Continued.

And ay he harped, and ay he carpit,
Till a' the Lords gaed through the floor,
They thought the music was sae sweet,
That they forgat the stable door.
They thought, &c.

And ay he harpit, and ay he carpit,
Till a' the nobles were sound asleep,
Than quietly he took aff his shoon,
And saftly down the stair did creep.
Than quietly &c.

Syne to the stable door he hies,
Wi' tread as light as light coud be,
And whan he open'd and gaed in,
There he fand thirty good steeds & three.
And whan &c.

He took the halter frae his hose,
And of his purpose did na' fail;
He slipt it o'er the Wanton's nose,
And tied it to his grey mare's tail.
He slipt &c.

He ca'd her out at yon back yeate,
O'er moss and muir & ilka dale,
And she loot ne'er the wanton bite,
But held her still gaun at her tail.
And she &c.

The grey mare was right swift o' fit,
And did na fail to find the way,
For she was at Lochmaben yeate,
Fu' lang three hours ere it was day.
For she &c.

When she came to the Harper's door,
There she gae mony a nicher and snear,
Rise, quo' the wife, thou lazy lass,
Let in thy master and his mare.
Rise, quo' &c.

Then up she raise, pat on her claes,
And lookit out through the lock hole
O! by my sooth then quoth the lass,
Our mare has gotten a braw big foal.
O! by my &c.

Come haud thy peace, then foolish lass,
The moon's but glancing in thy ee,
I'll wad my haill fee 'gainst a groat,
It's bigger than e'er our foal will be.
I'll wad &c.

The neighbours too that heard the noise.
Cried to the wife to put her in,
By my sooth, then quoth the wife,
She's better than ever he rade on.
By my &c

But on the morn at fair day light,
When they had ended a' their chear.
King Henry's wanton brown was stawn,
And eke the poor old Harper's mare.
King Henry's &c.

Alace! alace! says the silly blind Harper
Alace! alace! that I came here,
In Scotland I've tint a braw cowte foal,
In England they've stawn my guid grey (mare.
In Scotland &c.

Come had thy tongue, thou silly blind har (per
And of thy alacing let me be,
For thou shall get a better mare,
And weel paid shall thy cowte foal be.
For thou shall get a better mare,
And weel paid shall thy cowte foal be.

## My Nannie O

By Burns.

580

Behind yon hills where rivlets row, Are moors an' mosses
Slow
many O; The wint'ry sun the day has clos'd, An' I'll away to Nannie
O: The westlin winds blaws loud an' shrill, The night's baith mirk an'
rainy O; I'll get my plaid an out I'll steal, An' o'er the hill to Nannie O, To
Nannie O to Nannie O; I'll get my plaid an out I'll steal, An' o'er the hill to Nannie O.

My Nannie's charming, sweet, and young,
Nae artfu' wiles to win ye O;
May ill befa' the flattering tongue,
That wad beguile my Nannie O:
Her face is fair, her heart is true,
As spotless as she's bonnie O;
The op'ning gowan wat wi' dew,
Nae purer is than Nannie O.

A country lad is my degree,
And few there be that ken me O;
But what care I how few they be,
I'm welcome ay to Nannie O:

My riches a's my penny fee,
And I maun guide it cannie O;
But warld's gear ne'er troubles me,
My thoughts are a' my Nannie O

Our auld guidman delights to view,
His sheep an' kye thrive bonnie O;
But I'm as blythe that hauds his pleugh
An' has nae care but Nannie O;
Come well, come woe, I care na by,
I'll tak what Heav'n will send me O;
Nae ither care in life have I,
But live and love my Nannie O

## As I lay on my bed on a night.

581

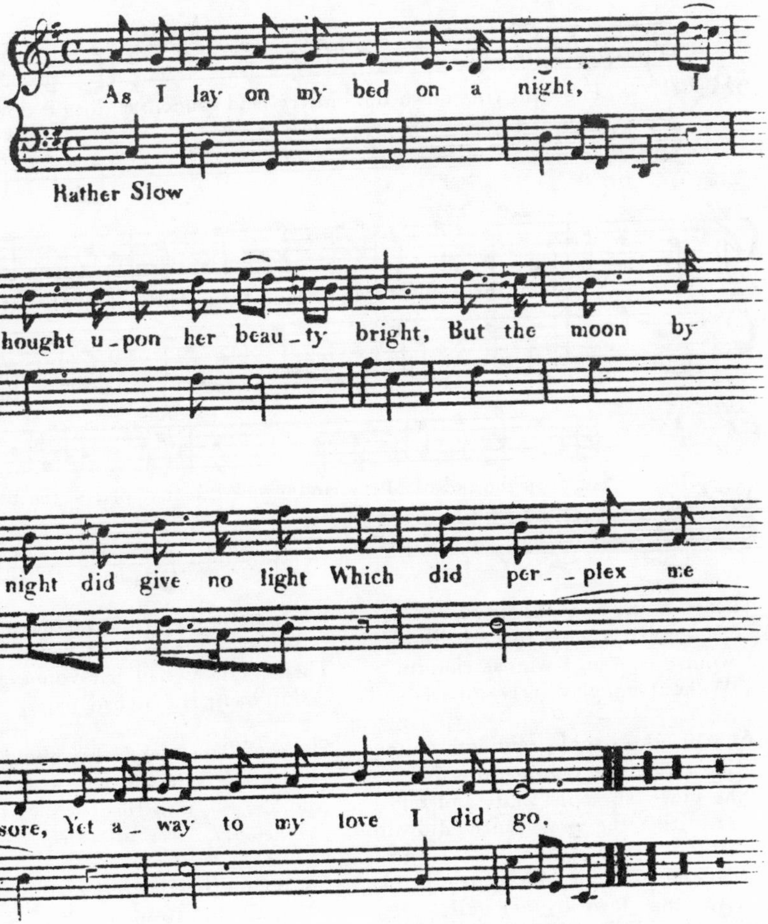
As I lay on my bed on a night, I
Rather Slow
thought u_pon her beau_ty bright, But the moon by
night did give no light Which did per_-plex me
sore, Yet a_way to my love I did go.

Then under her window I came,
I gently call'd her by her name,
Then up she rose, put on her clothes,
And whisper'd to me slow,
Saying, go from my window, Love, do.

My father and my mother are asleep,
And if they chance to hear you speak,
There will be nocht but great abuse.
Wi' many a bitter blow,
And it's go from my window, Love, do.

☆ ☆ ☆ ☆ ☆ ☆ ☆ ☆ ☆ ☆ ☆ ☆ ☆ ☆ ☆ ☆

## The rain rins down &c.

582

Slow
The rain rins down thro' Mirry-land toune, Sae does it down the
Pa: Sae does the lads of Mirry-land town, When they play at the
ba. Sae does the lads of Mirry-land town When they play at the ba.


Then out and cam the Jew's dochter,
Said, will ye com in and dine!
I winnae cum in, I winnae cum in,
Without my play feres nine.

She pow'd an apple reid and white.
To intice the young thing in:
She pow'd an apple white and reid,
And that the sweet bairn did win.

And she has taine out a little pen-knife,
And low down by her gair,
She has twin'd the young thing o' his life,
A word he ne'er spake mair.

And out and cam the thick thick bluid,
And out and cam the thin;
And out and cam the bonny herts bluid;
Thair was nae life left in.

She laid him on a dressing borde,
And drest him like a swine,
And laughing said, gae now and play
With your sweet play-feres nine.

She row'd him in a cake of lead,
Bade him ly still and sleep.
She cast him in a deep draw-well,
Was fifty fathom deep.

When bells wer rung, and mass was sung
And every lady went hame:
Than ilk lady had her young son,
But Lady Helen had nane.

She row'd her mantil her about,
And sair sair gan she weep:
And she ran into the Jews castle,
When they wer all asleep.

My bonny Sir Hew, my pretty Sir Hew,
I pray thee to me speak:
"O lady rinn to the deep draw-well
"Gin ye your son wad seek."

Lady Helen ran to the deep draw well,
And knelt upon her knee,
My bonny Sir Hew, an ye be here,
I pray thee speak to me.

The lead is wondrous heavy, mither,
The well is wondrous deep,
A keen pen-knife sticks in my hert,
A word I downae speak.

Gae hame, gae hame, my mother dear,
Fetch me my winding-sheet,
And at the back o' Mirry-land toune,
Its there we twa sall meet.

☆ ☆ ☆ ☆ ☆ ☆

# Cauld is the e'enin blast.

Written for this Work By Robert Burns.

583

Cauld is the e'en _ in blast O' Boras o'er the
A little Lively
pool, And daw _ in it is dreary, When birks are bare at Yule O
cauld blaws the e'en _ in blast When bitter bites the frost. And
in the mirk and dreary drift The hills and glens are lost,
Ne'er sae murky blew the night That drifted o'er the hill, But
bonie Peg a Ram _ sey Gat grist _ to her mill.

# O turn away those cruel eyes.

584
O turn a_way those cru_el eyes, The stars of my un_
A little Lively
do_ing Or death, in such a bright dis_guise, May
tempt a se_cond woo_ing. Pun_ish their blind_ly
impious pride, Who dare contemn thy glo_-ry; It was my
fall that de_i_fy'd Thy name and seal'd thy sto_-ry.

Yet no new sufferings can prepare
A higher praise to crown thee;
Tho' my first death proclaim thee fair,
My second will dethrone thee.
Lovers will doubt thou canst entice
No other for thy fuel;
And if thou burn'st one victim twice,
Think thee both poor and cruel.

## O Mary ye's be clad in silk.

585

O Ma_ry ye's be clad in silk, And dia_monds
Slow
in your hair, Gin ye'll con_sent to be my bride Nor
think on Ar_thur mair. Oh wha wad wear a silken gown, Wi'
tears blind_ _ing their ee, Be_ _fore I'll break my
true love's heart, I'll lay me down and die.

For I have pledg'd my virgin troth,
  Brave Arthur's fate to share,
And he has gi'en to me his heart
  Wi' a' its virtues rare.
The mind whase every wish is pure,
  Far dearer is to me,
And e'er I'm forced to break my faith
  I'll lay me down and die.

So trust me when I swear to thee,
  By a' that is on high,
Though ye had a' this warld's gear,
  My heart ye could na buy;
For langest life can ne'er repay,
  The love he bears to me,
And e'er I'm forc'd to break my troth,
  I'll lay me down and die.

## There was a bonie lass.

By R. Burns.

586

There was a bonie lass, and a bonie, bonie lass, And she
Rather Slow
lo'ed her bonie lad_die dear; Till wars loud a_larms tore her
lad_die frae her arms, Wi' mo_nie a sigh and a tear
O_ver sea, o ver shore, where the can_nons loud_ly roar; He
still was a strang_er to fear: And nocht could him quail, or his
bosom assail, But the bo_ nie lass he lo'ed sae dear.

## No Churchman am I,

By R. Burns.

587

No Churchman am I for to rail and to write, No statesman nor soldier to
Lively

Continued.

plot or to fight, No sly man of business contriving a snare, For a big belly'd
bottle's the whole of my care. The Peer I don't envy I give him his bow I
scorn not the peasant tho' ever so low, But a club of good fel_lows like
those that are here And a bottle like this, are my glory and care

Here passes the Squire on his brother _ his _horse;
There Centum per Centum, the Cit with his purse;
But see you the Crown how it waves in the air,
There a big_belly'd bottle still eases my care
The wife of my bosom, alas! she did die;
For sweet consolation to church I did fly;
I found that old Solomon proved it fair,
That a big belly'd bottle's a cure for all care.

I once was persuaded a venture to make,
A letter inform'd me that all was to wreck,
But the pursy old landlord just waddled up stairs,
With a glorious bottle that ended my cares.
'Life's cares they are comforts ☆'__a maxim laid down
By the Bard, what d'ye call him, that wore the black gown;
And faith I agree with th' old prig to a hair;
For a big-belly'd bottle's a heav'n of eare.

A Stanza added in a Mason Lodge:

Then fill up a bumper and make it o'erflow,
And honours Masonic prepare for to throw;
May every true brother of th' Compass and Square
Have a big belly'd bottle when harass'd with care.

☆ Young's Night Thoughts.

## The Highlander's lament

588

A Soldier for gallant atchievements renown'd, Revolv'd in des
Very Slow
pair the campaigns of his youth; Then beating his bosom & sigh_ing pro_
_found, That malice itself might have melted to ruth. Are these he exclaim'd the re_
sults of my toil, In want & obscurity thus to retire? For this did compassion re_
strain me from spoil, When earth was all carnage and heaven was on fire?

☆ ☆ ☆ ☆ ☆

The sun's bright effulgence, the fragrance of air
The vari'd horizon henceforth I abhore,
Give me death the sole boon of a wretch in despair,
Which fortune can offer or nature implore.
To madness impell'd by his griefs as he spoke,
And darting around him a look of disdain,
Down headlong he leapt from a heaven towring rock,
And sleeps where the wretched forbear to complain

Supposed to have been written in the year 1746

## There's news lasses news

Written for this Work by Robert Burns.

589

There's news lasses news, Gud news I've to tell, There's a
A little lively.
Chorus
boat_fu' o' lads Come to our town to sell. The
wean wants a cradle, An' the cradle wants a cod, An' I'll
no gang to my bed Un_til I get a nod.

Father, quo' she, Mither, quo' she
Do what ye can,
I'll no gang to my bed
Till I get a man.
The wean &c.

I hae as gude a craft rig
As made o' yird and stane;
And waly fa' the ley_crap
For I maun till'd again.
The wean &c.

## Hard is the fate of him who loves.

590

Hard is the fate of him who loves, Yet dares not tell his
Slow
trembling pain, But to the sympa_thetic groves, But to the lonely
list'_ning plain. Oh, when she bless_es next your shade, Oh,
when her foot_steps next are seen, In flow' ry tracts a
_long the mead, In fresh_er maz_es o'er the green.

Ye gentle spirits of the vale,
To whom the tears of love are dear,
From dying lilies waft a gale,
And sigh my sorrows in her ear.
O, tell her what she cannot blame,
Tho' fear my tongue must ever bind;
Oh, tell her, that my virtuous flame
Is a her spotless soul refin'd.

Not her own guardian angel eyes
With chaster tenderness his care,
Not purer her own wishes rise,
Not holier her own sighs in pray'r.
But if, at first, her virgin fear
Should start at love's suspected name,
With that of friendship soothe her ear;
True love and friendship are the same.

## Ye Muses nine, O lend your aid.

See P. 1st Vol. 1st

591

Ye Mus_es nine, O lend your aid, In_spire a ten_der
Rather Slow
bash_ful maid That's late_ly yield ed up her heart, A conquest
to love's pow'rful dart. And now would fain at_tempt to sing, The
prais_es of my High_land King, And now would fain at
_tempt to sing, The praises of my Highland King.

Jamie, the pride of all the green,
Is just my age, e'en gay fifteen:
When first I saw him, 'twas the day,
That ushers in the sprightly May;
When first I felt love's pow'rful sting,
And sigh'd for my dear Highland King.

With him for beauty, shape, and air,
No other shepherd can compare;
Good reture, honesty, and truth,
Adorn the dear, the matchless youth;
And grace, more than I can sing,
Bedeck my charming Highland King.

Would once the dearest boy but say,
'Tis you I love; come come away,
Unto the kirk, my love, let's hy;
Oh me in rapture, I'd comply!
And I should then have cause to sing
The praises of my Highland King.

## Nelly's Dream.

592
Bright the moon a_boon yon mountain, Upwards tow'ring
Slow
shed her light, Nothing heard but fal_ling waters, Thro' the
shades of si_lent night. Nel_ly on her couch re_clin_ing
fet_ter'd in the arms of sleep whilst in dreams the wand'ring
Fan_cy sighs for William on the deep.

Loud she hears the tempest howling,
High she sees the billows roll,
Lightnings flash and thunders roaring,
Spreading terror to each Pole.
On the sea-beach this beholding.
Tremblingdreads her William, lost,
Yes, she cries he comes I see him,
O how pale! tis William's Ghost.

Sighs and tears, and wild distraction,
Rend the maiden's tender breast,
William! why my William shun me,
O my heart is sore opprest.
Oft you swore you lov'd me dearly,
How have I your favour lost
Bear me to him rolling billows
Let me clasp my William's Ghost.

Nelly's mind thus wildly raving,
Deeply drown'd in sleep the while,
William in the harbour landing,
Went to meet his Nelly's smile,
At her window gently calling,
Wake my love, 'tis day almost,
Yes, she cry'd I'll come to thee,
Yes, I'll follow William's Ghost.

Clear at length the sun was shining,
Sleep forsook her death-like throne,
Nelly started from her slumbring,
Glad her dream and night was gone.
Fair and spotless as the lily,
Laden with the morning dew,
Nelly ran to meet her William
With a heart both kind and true.

# O that I had ne'er been Married.

Corrected by R. Burns.

593

O that I had ne'er been married; I wad ne_ver
A little Lively
had nae care, Now I've got_ten wife and bairns An'
they cry crow_die ever mair. Ance crow_die twice crowdie
Three times crow_die in a day; Gin ye crow_die
o_ny mair Ye'll crow_die a' my meal a_way.

Added by BURNS.

Waefu' Want and Hunger fley me,
Glowrin by the hallan en';
Sair I fecht them at the door,
But ay I'm eerie they come ben.
Ance crowdie &c.

## O gin my love were yon red rose.

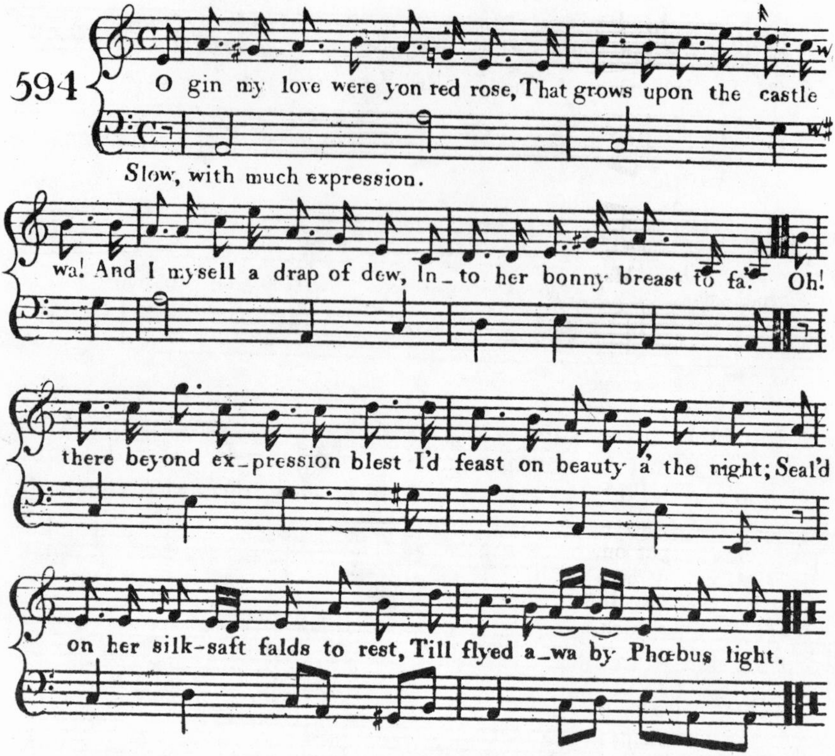
594
O gin my love were yon red rose, That grows upon the castle
Slow, with much expression.
wa! And I mysell a drap of dew, In_to her bonny breast to fa'. Oh!
there beyond ex_pression blest I'd feast on beauty a' the night; Seal'd
on her silk-saft falds to rest, Till flyed a_wa by Phœbus light.

## Nae luck about the house when our goodwife's awa.

595
You sing of your good_man frae hame, ✡ But whiles they're
Lively
best a_wa', For tho' the good_wife stay at hame, John
does not toil for a' There was nae luck a_bout my house An'

✡ See Vol. 1st Pag 44.

Continued.

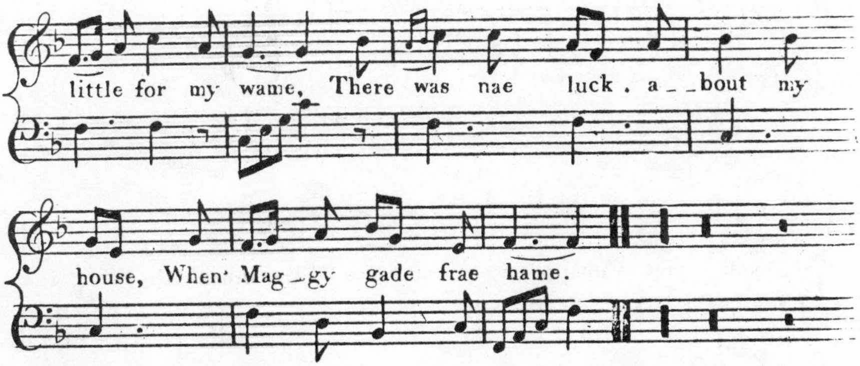
little for my wame, There was nae luck . a_ _bout my
house, When Mag_gy gade frae hame.

For first the bairns raise frae their bed,
And for a piece did ca',
Then how could I attend my work,
Who had to answer a'
There was nae luck,&c.

Their hands and faces was to wash,
And coaties to put on,
When every dud lay here and there,
Which vexed honest John.
There was nae luck,&c.

He made the pottage wanting salt,
The kail sing'd in the pot,
The cutties lay under his feet,
And cogs they seem'd to rot.
There was nae luck,&c.

The hen and birds went to the fields,
The glaid she whipt up twa,
The cow wanting her chaff and stra',
Stood routing thro' the wa'.
There was nae luck,&c.

The bairns fought upon the floor,
And on the fire did fa';
Which vex'd the heart o' honest John,
When Maggy was awa'.
There was nae luck,&c.

With bitten fingers and cutted thumbs,
And scriechs which pierc'd the skies,
Which drove his patience to an end,
Wish'd death to close their eyes.
There was nae luck,&c.

Then went to please them with a scon,
And so he burnt it black,
Ran to the well with twa new cans,
But none of them came back.
There was nae luck,&c.

The hens went to the neighbour's house,
And there they laid their eggs,
When simple John reprov'd them for't,
They broke poor chuckie's legs:
There was nae luck,&c.

He little thought of Maggy's toil,
As she was by the fire,
But when he got a trial o't,
He soon began to tire.
There was nae luck,&c.

First when he got the task in hand,
He thought all would go right,
But O he little wages had,
On Saturday at night.
There was nae luck,&c.

He had no gain from wheel or reel,
Nor yarn had he to sell,
He wish'd for Maggy hame again,
Being out of money and meal.
There was nae luck,&c.

The deil gade o'er Jock Wabster,
His loss he could not tell.
But when he wanted Maggy's help,
He did nae good himsell.
There was nae luck,&c.

Another want I do not name,
A' night he got no ease,
But tumbl'd grumbl'd in his bed,
A fighting wi' the flaes.
There was nae luck,&c.

Wishing for Maggy's muckle hips,
Whereon the flaes might feast,
And for to be goodwife again,
He swore it was nae jest.
There was nae luck,&c.

## Liv'd ance twa lovers in yon dale.

596

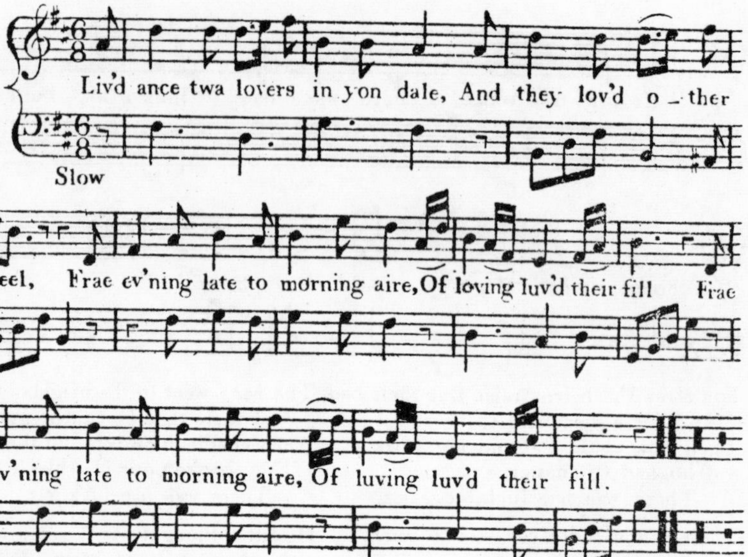
Liv'd ance twa lovers in yon dale, And they lov'd o - ther
Slow
weel, Frae ev'ning late to morning aire, Of loving luv'd their fill Frae
ev'ning late to morning aire, Of luving luv'd their fill.

"Now, Willie, gif you luve me weel,
As sae it seems to me,
Gar build, gar build a bonny ship,
Gar build it speedilie.

And we will sail the sea sae green,
Unto some far countrie,
Or we'll sail to some bonie isle
Stands lanely midst the sea."

But lang or ere the ship was built,
Or deck'd, or rigged out,
Came sick a pain in Annet's back,
That down she cou'd na lout.

"Now, Willie, gif ye luve me weel,
As sae it seems to me,
O haste, haste, bring me to my bow'r,
And my bow'r maidens three."

He's tane her in his arms twa,
And kiss'd her cheek and chin;
He's brocht her to her ain sweet bow'r,
But na bow'r maid was in.

"Now, leave my bower, Willie, she said,
Now leave me to my lane;
Was neverman in a lady's bower
When she was travelling."

He's stepped three steps down the stair,
Upon the marble stane:
Sae loud's he heard his young son's greet,
But and his lady's mane!

"Now come, now come, Willie, she said,
Tak your young son frae me,
And hie him to your mother's bower
With speed and privacie."

He's taen his young son in his arms,
He's kiss'd him cheek and chin,
He's hied him to his mother's bower
By the ae light of the moon.

And with him came the bold Baron,
And he spake up wi' pride,
"Gar seek, gar seek the bower maidens,
Gar busk, gar busk the bride.

"My maidens, easy with my back,
And easy with my side.
O set my saddle saft, Willie,
I am a tender bride".

# O Mally's meek, Mally's sweet.

Written for this Work by Robert Burns.

597

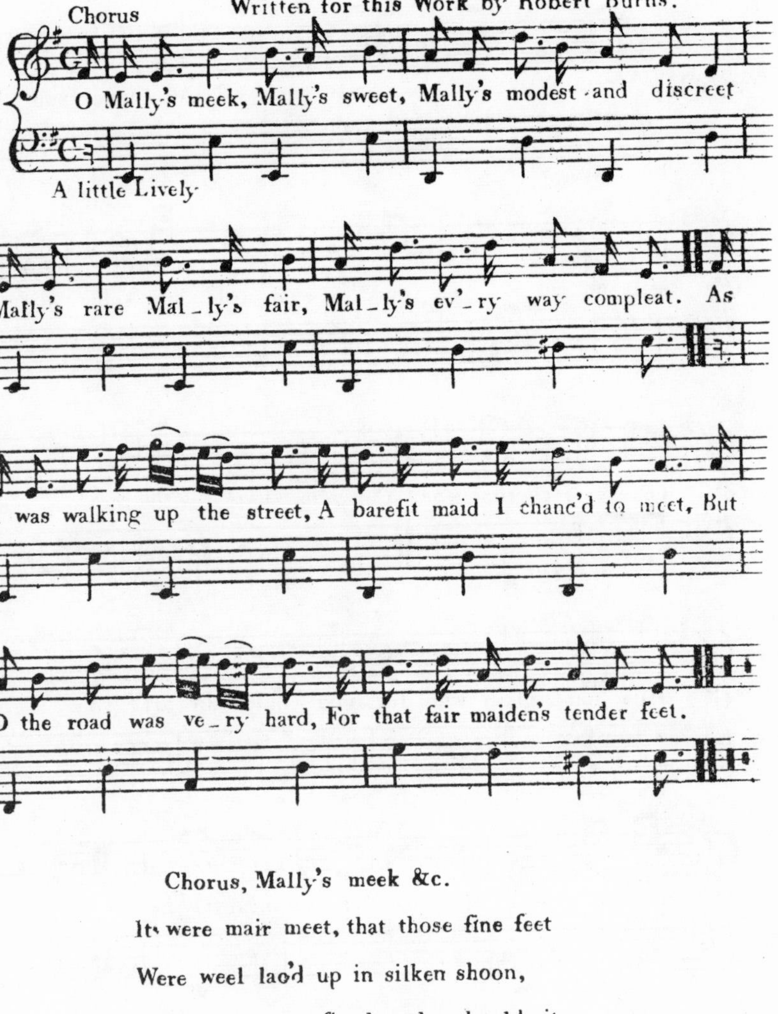
Chorus
O Mally's meek, Mally's sweet, Mally's modest and discreet
A little Lively
Mally's rare Mal_ly's fair, Mal_ly's ev'_ry way compleat. As
I was walking up the street, A barefit maid I chanc'd to meet, But
O the road was ve_ry hard, For that fair maiden's tender feet.

Chorus, Mally's meek &c.

It were mair meet, that those fine feet
Were weel lac'd up in silken shoon,
And twere more fit that she should sit,
Within yon chariot gilt aboon.

Chorus, Mally's meek &c.

Her yellow hair, beyond compare,
Comes trinkling down her swan white neck,
And her two eyes like stars in skies,
Would keep a sinking ship frae wreck.

# Tell me Jessy tell me why

598
*
Slow
Tell me Jessy tell me why My fond suit you still de_ny Is your bo som cold as snow did you ne_ver feel for woe. Can you hear with_out a sigh Him com_plain who for you could die, If you e_ver shed a tear Hear me Jes_sy hear O hear.

Life to me is not more dear,
Than the hour brings Jessy here,
Death so much I do not fear
As the parting moment near.
Summer smiles is not so sweet,
As the bloom upon your cheek,
Nor the chrystal dew so clear,
As your eyes to me appear.

These are part of Jessy's charms
Which the bosom ever warms
But the charms by which I'm stung,
Comes, O Jessy, from thy tongue.
Jessy be no longer coy,
Let me taste a lover's joy,
With your hand remove the dart
And heal the wound that's in my heart.

## I care na for your een sae blue.

599

*
I care na for your een sae blue, Un_less your heart to
Slow
me is true, Nor yet that dim_pled cheek o' thine, Till
ev'_ry smile ye hae be mine. D'ye think I'll roose your shape an'
Air, Or ca' you bo_nie sweet an' fair Un less ye can to
me impart, A look which say ye hae my heart.

I care na for your witching tongue,
Which pleases a' an' pierces some,
Until I hear that tongue declare
Nane but mysel your heart shall share
An' gin that saft an' melting ee,
Doth beam on me an' only me
My fate is seal'd, then I am thine
An' let me die when I repine.

## Good night and joy be wi' you a'.

600

The night is my departing night, The morn's the day I maun a_
A little lively
_wa, There's no a friend or fae o' mine, But wishes that I were awa. What
I hae done for lack o' wit I never never can re_ca'. I trust ye're
a my friends as yet, Gude night and joy be wi' you a'.

By Burns.

ADIEU! a heart-warm, fond adieu!
Dear brothers of the mystic tye!
Ye favour'd, ye enlighten'd Few,
Companions of my social joy!
Tho' I to foreign lands must hie,
Pursuing Fortun's slidd'ry ba',
With melting heart, and brimful eye,
I'll mind you still, tho' far awa'.

Oft have I met your social Band,
And spent the chearful, festive night,
Oft, honour'd with supreme command,
Presided o'er the Sons of light:
And by that Hieroglyphic bright,
Which none but Craftsmen ever saw!
Strong Mem'ry on my heart shall write
Those happy scenes when far awa'!

May Freedom, Harmony, and Love.
Unite you in the grand Design,
Beneath th' Omniscient Eye above,
The glorious Architect Divine!
That you may keep th' unerring line,
Still rising by the plummet's law,
Till Order bright completely shine,
Shall be my pray'r when far awa'.

And You, farewell! whose merits claim,
Justly that highest badge to wear!
Heav'n bless your honour'd, noble Name,
To Masonry and Scotia dear!
A last request permit me here,
When yearly ye assemble a',
One round, I ask it with a tear;
To him, the Bard that's far awa'.



FINIS.